Prentice Hall

HEALTH
Choosing Wellness

Prentice Hall

HEALTH
Choosing Wellness

Prentice Hall · Needham, Massachusetts · Englewood Cliffs, New Jersey

Program Consultants

Roger Wayne Seehafer

Chair, Health Promotion and Education
School of Humanities, Social Science and Education
Purdue University
West Lafayette, IN

Carol Bershad

Health Consultant
Former Director
Learning for Life Project
Boston, MA

Deborah S. Haber

Health Education, Teacher/Consultant
Framingham, MA

Grateful acknowledgment is made to the following publishers for permission to reprint:

p. 81 *Viviene: The Life and Suicide of an Adolescent Girl*, p. 63, by John E. Mack and Holly Hickler. Copyright © 1981 by David Loomis and Paulette Loomis by permission of Little, Brown and Company.

continued on page 655.

ISBN 0-13-384785-3

1 2 3 4 5 6 7 8 9   97 96 95 94 93 92 91 90 89

A Simon & Schuster Company

Staff Credits

Editorial Department:	Robert J. Hope
	Lois Arnold
	Thomas Frado
	Natania Mlawer
Product Manager:	Paul P. Scopa
Production Editor:	Patricia Carda
Design Direction:	L. Christopher Valente
Design Production:	Shay J. Mayer
Production/Manufacturing:	Roger Powers

Outside Credits

Project Editor:	Marita A. Sullivan
Contributing Writers:	Dotty Burstein
	Ann Collins
	Deborah Osnowitz
	Lynn Robbins
	Kathleen Sterling
Art Editor:	Carol H. Rose
Artists:	Leon Bishop
	Edwin Huff
	Lane Gregory
	Boston Graphics, Incorporated.
Design Production Assistants:	Caroline Bowden
	Katherine S. Diamond
	Michael A. Granger
	Helen Cusack Maxwell
Cover Design:	Martucci Studio
Photo Research:	Pembroke Herbert/Picture Research Consultants

Consulting Authors

Eva E. Conrad, Ph.D.
Associate Professor,
Department of Psychology
San Bernardino Valley College
San Bernardino, CA

Nancy DiMella
Drug Alcohol Education
    Specialist
Newton Public Schools
Newton, MA

David F. Duncan
Professor of Health Education
Coordinator of the Community
    Health Program
Southern Illinois University at
    Carbondale
Carbondale, IL

Joseph Peter Felice
Retired Health Teacher
Lockport Senior High School
Health Education Department
Lockport, NY

Jay Alan Fishman, M.D.
Assistant in Medicine,
Massachusetts General
    Hospital
Instructor in Medicine,
Harvard Medical School
Boston, MA

Norman Eburne
Associate Professor of Health
    Education
Western Oregon State College
Monmouth, OR

Seymour J. Friedland, Ph.D.
Clinical Adolescent
    Psychologist
Psychological Resources
    Associates
Arlington, MA

Wendy Harrison, Ed.D.
Director of Market Research/
    Wellness Consultant
Brookshire Group
Bel Air, MD

Kathleen H. Hester, M.S., R.D., L.D.
Principal, Kitty Hester &
    Associates
Consultants in Nutrition and
    Food Marketing
Houston, TX

Margaret M. Smith, Ed.D.
Associate Professor of Health
    Education
Oregon State University
Corvallis, OR

Thomas E. Gwin
Biology Teacher
Newton North High School
Newton, MA

Herrick Hawkins, Ed.D.
Health Educator
Sharon Public Schools
Sharon, MA

Kenneth L. Packer
Regional AIDS Education
    Coordinator
Curriculum Research
    Department
Board of Cooperative
    Educational Services
Yorktown Heights, NY

Carol Stone, Ph.D.
Science and Health Education
    Writer
Alameda, CA

Michael R. Weil
Associate Professor
University of Wisconsin—Eau
    Claire
Biology Department
Eau Claire, WI

Kenneth A. Zeno
Health Educator
Needham Public Schools
Needham, MA

Content Consultants

**Mental Health
and Social Health**

Lyn Lawrance
Assistant Professor
University of North Carolina-
    Greensboro
Public Health Education
Greensboro, NC

**Physical Fitness, Food,
and Nutrition**

Christopher L. Melby
Associate Professor of
    Community Health
Purdue University
Physical Education, Health,
    and Recreation Studies
West Lafayette, IN

**Human Sexuality
and Reproduction**

Marlene K. Tappe
Assistant Professor of Health
    Education
Purdue University
Physical Education, Health,
    and Recreation Studies
West Lafayette, IN

v

Content Consultants

Childhood Development
Susan R. James RN, MSM
Health Writer
East Sandwich, MA

Diseases and Disorders
Gerald C. Hyner, Ph.D.
Associate Professor and
  Chairman, Program in
  Health Promotion
Purdue University
Physical Education, Health,
  and Recreation Studies
West Lafayette, IN

Aids
Emily Rhinehart RN, CIC
Infection Control
  Epidemiologist
Children's Hospital
Infectious Diseases
Boston, MA

Drugs, Alcohol, and Tobacco
Robert Anastas
Executive Director
STUDENTS AGAINST
  DRIVING DRUNK
Marlboro, MA

Consumer, Public, and Environmental Health
Richard St. Pierre
Chair, Health Education
Pennsylvania State University
University Park, PA

Safety and First Aid
David L. Bever, Ph.D.
Associate Professor of Health
  Education
George Mason University
Health, Sport, and Leisure
  Studies
Fairfax, VA

Teacher Reviewers

Laura E. Williams
Health Educator
Sheffield High School
Memphis, TN

Patricia Hunt Obley
Director, Physical Education
  and Health
Kansas City Public Schools
Kansas City, KS

Gene P. Butler
Secondary Health Curriculum
  Consultant
Clark County School District
Department of Curriculum
  and Instruction
Las Vegas, NV

Pattie Jo Tower
Science Teacher
Casa Grande High School
Petaluma, CA

Linda Harrill Rudisill
Teacher, Department
  Chairman
Health Education
York Chester Jr. High School
Gastonia, NC

Nanette H. Franck
Health and Physical Education
  Specialist
Jefferson County Public
  Schools
Department of Curriculum
  and Instruction
Louisville, KY

Dr. Arthur E. Ware
Administrative Assistant
Physical Education, Health,
  and Athletics
Edmonds School District
Lynnwood, WA

Ollie Josephine Tipton
Health and Physical Education
  Teacher
Hume-Fogg Academic High
  School
Nashville, TN

James Patrick Shanafelt
Health Consultant
Boise Independent School
  District
Health Education Department
Boise, ID

John J. Grant, Jr.
Health Education Supervisor
  and Consultant
Somerset School Department
Somerset, MA

Robert Frye
Health Education Consultant
Apex, NC

Contents

UNIT·1

Mental Health   20

UNIT · 2

Social Health   92

UNIT · 3

Physical Well-Being   142

U N I T · 4

The Human Life Cycle 268

U N I T · 5

Diseases and Disorders   366

U N I T · 6

Drugs, Alcohol, and Tobacco   434

U N I T · 7

Health and
Society   512

U N I T · 8

Safety and First Aid   572

Features

Features

Health Frontiers

Decide

Friend to Friend

Health Careers

Charts and Tables

Charts and Tables

1

As you read, think about

▶ what is meant by the terms *health* and *wellness*.
▶ how your behavior affects your level of wellness.
▶ how you can start to improve your health now.

Choosing Wellness

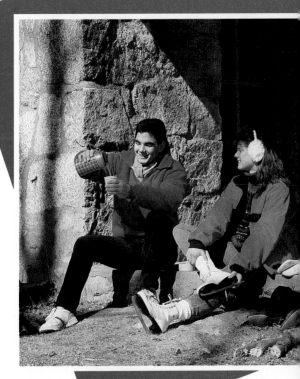

Y ou and your friend swoop and glide over the lake like two brightly colored birds. The air is clean and cold, and the ice glistens white against the blue of the sky and the dark green of the pines. The blades of your skates sparkle as you cut a graceful pattern on the glassy surface of the ice. The feeling of all your muscles working together as you gather speed is exhilarating. Your cheeks are tingling with the cold and the excitement. Your whole body is alive with energy and good health.

Everyone wants to feel good and to have special moments like these. The choices you make every day contribute to your ability to enjoy life to its fullest. In this chapter, you'll find out how you can choose and maintain the particular life style that suits you—a life style that will keep you feeling fit, energetic, and happy.

**The choices you make every day affect
your health now and in the future.**

1

1. WHAT ARE HEALTH AND WELLNESS?

What is health? How can I tell if I am healthy? Can I control my own health? How can I influence my future health? You may have just begun to ask yourself questions like these. At one time you might have said that a healthy person is anyone who does not have a cold or some other illness. Now that you are older, you may feel that this definition does not include all the things that cause you to feel well or to be healthy.

Aspects of Health

The term *health* has come to have a wider meaning than it used to. It no longer means just the absence of illness. **Health** is now used—and will be used in this book—to refer to the well-being of your body, your mind, and your relationships with other people. These types of well-being are called physical health, mental health, and social health. The concept of health that includes all three of these aspects is called **wellness.**

When you are physically healthy, you are able to carry out everyday tasks without becoming overly tired. You have enough energy to enjoy leisure activities and to meet emergencies. If you are mentally healthy, you like yourself for your achievements, and you learn from your mistakes. You can cope with the demands of life and adjust to new situations. When you have healthy social relationships, you get along well with others. You have friends, and you are capable of loving relationships. You respect the rights of others, and you know how to give and accept help.

It is easy to see how the three aspects of wellness are related. When you are ill or facing many problems and pressures, your relationships with your friends and family may suffer. When you are coming down with the flu, for example, you may get upset if you are asked to do the dishes or take out the garbage. If you are worried about an exam in a difficult subject, you may get a headache or stomachache. If you are lonely and have few friends, you probably do not feel good about yourself. You may even feel tired or overeat because of your unhappiness.

This view of wellness as a combination of physical, mental, and social well-being is also known as a **holistic** (hoh **lis** tik) concept of health. Holistic means whole, and here it refers to the connections among these three aspects of health as they affect the whole person. People with a holistic view of wellness are aware of and work to improve all three aspects of their health. They regard wellness as an important **goal,** the result they want to achieve through their actions.

Check Your Wellness

Your level of wellness is high if you can answer yes to the following questions.

1. Do you eat a well-balanced diet and avoid foods high in fat, salt, and sugar?
2. Do you participate in vigorous exercise at least three times a week?
3. Is your weight within the normal range for your age, height, and sex?
4. Do you feel good about yourself?
5. Do you set aside time each day to relax?
6. Do you avoid drugs, alcohol, and tobacco?
7. Do you get about eight hours of restful sleep each night?
8. Do you have close relatives and friends you can talk to?
9. Can you express your feelings in healthful ways?
10. Do you use a seat belt and avoid driving with a person who is using drugs or alcohol?
11. Do you try to lessen your exposure to air, water, and noise pollution?
12. Are your decisions based on your own values and goals, rather than those of others?

Another way to express the holistic concept of wellness is with the term **quality of life.** Quality of life refers to how satisfying and rewarding your life is. Recently, this term has received more attention in our society. One reason for this increasing emphasis can be found in the length and conditions of life that people have now come to expect. Look at Figure 1-2. You can see that since 1900, the life expectancy of Americans has increased by about 27 years. For much of the history of the world, just staying alive and active until age 47 was quite an accomplishment. This is still true in some parts of the world today. You can imagine that people living in areas of drought and food shortages are not concerned about what we call quality of life. They are too busy just trying to stay alive. In this country and other countries, however, many people are concerned about how they will feel and what they can accomplish and enjoy during these added years of life expectancy. These people are concerned not only about feeling good in the present but also about planning for a lifetime of wellness.

What Determines Health and Wellness

What are some of the factors that influence your wellness and life expectancy? Can you control or influence any of these factors?

To answer these questions, consider another set of statistics comparing 1900 to the present. The three leading causes of death in 1900 were not the same as the leading causes of death today. The leading causes of death then were diseases that could be passed from one person to another,

Figure 1-2. Americans live longer today than ever before.

Life Expectancy

Year	Expected Life Span (years)
1985	74.7
1980	73.7
1960	69.7
1940	62.9
1920	54.1
1900	47

Source: Statistical Abstract of the United States, 1987

Figure 1-3. Today, many of the leading causes of death are influenced by life-style choices.

Leading Causes of Death

1900	Today
1. Pneumonia and influenza	1. Heart disease
2. Tuberculosis	2. Cancer
3. Diseases of the stomach and intestines	3. Stroke
4. Heart disease	4. Accidents
5. Stroke	5. Lung disease
6. Kidney disease	6. Pneumonia and influenza
7. Accidents	7. Diabetes mellitus
8. Cancer	8. Suicide
9. Childhood diseases	9. Liver disease
10. Diphtheria	10. Atherosclerosis

Although heredity affects health, life-style choices are often more important in determining overall wellness.

as shown in Figure 1-3. In contrast, today's leading causes of death are diseases that are strongly influenced by your individual **life style,** the way you choose to live your life.

As you will see, the way you choose to live your life strongly influences the quality of your life, both now and in the future. Of course, some other factors also influence your health and wellness. These include heredity, environment, and culture, but even these factors are affected to some extent by your life-style decisions.

HEREDITY   To some extent, **heredity,** all the traits that are passed on biologically from parent to child, determines a person's level of wellness. These traits include hair color, eye color, height, build, and many other characteristics. Heredity also influences the soundness of your body, your reactions to stressful situations, and the aging process.

As you probably know, some disabilities, diseases, and tendencies toward certain illnesses are inherited. Although inherited disabilities put some limits on an individual's level of wellness, there are still many things a person can do to reach his or her **optimum (ahp** tuh mum) **health,** the highest level of wellness possible. Many disabled people are energetic and productive and enjoy a high quality of life in spite of their disabilities.

Overcoming a disability is an extreme example of using mental, social, and physical resources to make up for a limitation. There are also less dramatic examples. For example, some people inherit a tendency toward high blood pressure, a condition that can contribute to heart disease and shorten life. If they are aware of their condition and know how to cope with it, they can make diet and other life-style changes to control their blood pressure. Their actions allow them to lead long and healthy lives in spite of this inherited tendency.

Except in a small number of cases, heredity does not prevent a person from enjoying a healthy life. For most people, the life-style choices they make every day are far more important than heredity in maintaining, harming, or improving their wellness.

PHYSICAL ENVIRONMENT   Your **environment** is all your surroundings and the influences they have on you. To be healthy, everyone needs a healthful **physical environment,** or physical surroundings. You know that climate, extreme heat or cold, and extremely dry or damp air can affect your wellness. It is also true that air pollution, water pollution, radiation, and even loud noise can injure your health. If you are aware of environmental hazards, you can take steps to protect yourself. You can avoid swimming in polluted water, wear a sunscreen for protection against the sun's rays, and always keep your radio's volume at less-than-harmful levels.

You can also take steps to make your environment healthier. Everyone should be aware of the dangers of a polluted environment and help to limit or decrease pollution. That includes disposing of waste materials correctly, bicycling or walking short distances instead of driving, and recycling paper goods, cans, and bottles. Some teenagers are part of environmental watch groups that keep track of air and water cleanliness in their communities.

Your physical environment includes the environment indoors as well as outdoors. Your home, school, and workplace are part of your physical environment. Cigarette smoking in public places and disease-causing organisms in restaurant food are some indoor hazards of the physical environment. Your own knowledge and behavior can help make your physical environment safer. How could you and your friends contribute to improving the environment of your school cafeteria or a local park?

SOCIAL ENVIRONMENT   Your environment is made up of more than your physical surroundings. The people around you—your family, friends, and other people you spend time with—make up another part of your environment, your **social environment.**

When you were a child, your parents were the major part of your social environment. They taught you to speak and to communicate in other ways. They strongly influenced your feelings about yourself and your ideas of how to get along with other people. In addition, they probably taught you health habits that are so basic you do not even think about them anymore. Washing your hands before eating or fixing a meal, for example, may have become routine, but now you understand that these habits help to prevent the spread of germs.

HEALTH FRONTIERS

Mind Over Illness?

Do emotions and thoughts play a role in helping the body ward off disease? The new field of psychoneuroimmunology (PNI) suggests they might.

PNI researchers are now exploring the two-way connection between the brain and the immune system, the body's defense against disease. The brain's network of nerves releases many chemicals, some of which depend on mood. These chemicals bind directly to the disease-fighting cells of the immune system and influence how the cells behave. Immune cells are more active when a person's mood is good than when he or she is depressed.

The immune cells send chemical messages back to the brain. These chemicals affect sleep, body temperature, heart rate, and mood.

PNI supports common beliefs. A person with a positive attitude combats disease better than someone who has "lost the will to live." Good health and a positive outlook tend to reinforce each other. While wellness may not be "all in your mind," PNI has found that there is a close connection.

What role does mood play in fighting disease?

As you have grown older, your social environment has expanded to include your neighbors and schoolmates. Your teachers, relatives, friends, and those involved in the community activities you participate in are an important part of your social environment.

You have probably heard a lot of talk about peer pressure. Traditionally, the word *peers* has meant equals, those people who are in the same situation as you. Today, it is often used to mean your friends, or a larger group of acquaintances your own age. The friends you select from among your acquaintances can have an important effect on your level of wellness. Friends who practice unhealthful behaviors can put a lot of pressure on you to do the same. It is sometimes difficult to stand up to that kind of pressure. Selecting friends who choose healthful habits and life styles makes it easier for you to choose wellness.

CULTURE Your social environment is only one part of your culture. **Culture** is all the ideas, customs, and ways of living that characterize a particular group of people. That group may be a nation, a region of a country, or an ethnic group. Culture includes accents and food preferences, attitudes and manners.

Sometimes you are not aware of the characteristics of your own culture until you come in contact with another culture. You probably do not think you have an accent until you visit a part of the country where people speak differently. In some cultures, it is rude to take off your shoes when

Your friends, or peers, have an important effect on your wellness.

Figure 1-4. Do your friends help you to make healthful decisions? ▶

▲ **Figure 1-5. The culture in which you live can affect your health in many ways.**

visiting someone else's house; in other cultures it is rude not to. In some cultures, people eat little or no meat; in others, meat is central to the diet. This is just one example of how cultural differences can affect your health. Can you think of other examples?

Sometimes, you may get "mixed messages" from your culture. For example, our culture emphasizes the value of health and fitness. At the same time, it suggests that unhealthful behaviors, such as smoking and drinking, are fun and part of a healthful life style. You have probably seen advertisements with young, healthy-looking people trying to promote products that are not really good for your health. Because your culture offers you so many choices, you must be informed about what promotes health and what does not. This way you will be able to make your own choices without being influenced by misleading messages.

O—┳ The culture in which you live affects the healthful choices you make.

Section Review

1. What are the three aspects of wellness?
2. What is a holistic view of health?
3. How are the three leading causes of death today different from those of 1900?
4. What factors determine your health? Which of these factors can you control?

What Do You Think?

5. What are two ways you could improve your physical health? Your mental health? Your social health?

2. YOU AND YOUR HEALTH

If there were just a few painless habits you could choose to practice that would lead to a long and healthy life, of course you would practice them. Even if there were no absolute guarantee of good health, just a greater probability of it, the choice would still be worthwhile.

Such a choice does not come from a fairy-tale land of magic potions that protects the user from disaster. It is a real choice you can make in your daily life. One way to judge the changes in your health that your daily life-style choices can make—for the better as well as for the worse—is to use the Illness-Wellness continuum.

The Illness-Wellness Continuum

Remember the last time you were coming down with the flu? You could feel it beginning, perhaps with a runny nose or general tiredness. Then, your symptoms became worse and your energy level dropped lower. You might have run a fever and had to stay in bed. After several days, your fever broke, you felt more energetic, and your cough no longer kept you awake at night. You might have been a bit tired and sniffly still, but you were feeling better. Finally, you felt great again. You moved from having the sniffles to walking around with a cold to lying in bed with a fever and cough to being up and around with a few symptoms to regaining wellness. You can think of the sequence you followed—from wellness to illness and back again—as a **continuum** (kun **tin** yoo um), a progression in either direction from one stage (sniffles) to another (walking around with a cold) to another, and so on.

Continuums can represent other health-related changes in your life. How would you use a continuum to express changes you might experience when you start (or stop) an exercise program? How could a continuum show the changes brought on by your moving away from friends to a new school or by failing to make the swim team?

Your overall wellness also can be illustrated on a continuum. This sliding scale is called the **Illness-Wellness continuum.** Look at Figure 1-7. Notice that on the Illness-Wellness continuum, you can move in either direction. As you move in one direction, you move toward illness; as you move the other way, you approach wellness. You can see also that there is a midpoint on the continuum. At this neutral point, a person is not sick but is not enjoying the full benefits of optimum health, either.

At one time, as you learned earlier, many people in this country were satisfied just to be at the neutral point of health. Then, people were much more concerned about avoiding illness than about improving the quality of their lives. Today,

▲
Figure 1-6. Eating nutritiously is one way to improve the quality of your life.

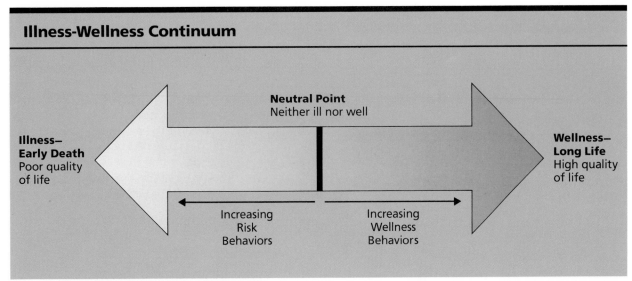

Illness-Wellness Continuum

Neutral Point
Neither ill nor well

**Illness—
Early Death**
Poor quality
of life

**Wellness—
Long Life**
High quality
of life

Increasing
Risk
Behaviors

Increasing
Wellness
Behaviors

Source: Adapted from Travis and Ryan, *The Wellness Workbook*, 1981

achieving a higher level of wellness and a better quality of life is possible for many of the people in this country. More than ever before, people today control where on the Illness-Wellness continuum they fall.

Risk Behaviors

Look again at the Illness-Wellness continuum in Figure 1-7. You can see that a **risk behavior,** or an action that increases the chances of a harmful outcome, moves you toward the illness-early death end of the continuum. You are probably aware of many risks to your health and do your best to avoid them. For example, you know it is dangerous to run across a four-lane highway. You also know that wearing a seat belt in a car will reduce your risk of injury in case of accident, but do you always remember to use one? If you do not, you are taking a risk that moves you toward the illness-early death end of the continuum. Perhaps thinking about your behavior in these terms will change your mind about some of the unnecessary risks you take.

Most activities have varying degrees of risk. For example, if you exercise vigorously without doing warm-ups first, you risk pulling a muscle. If you ride a motorcycle without a helmet, you risk serious injury and death.

Sometimes, risks are worth taking if there is a benefit greater than the possible harm. Skiing, for example, involves some risk of injury, but many people decide that this enjoyable and healthful activity is worth the risk. They also may realize that equipment, instruction, fitness, and attitude can lessen their risks while skiing. It is always worthwhile to think carefully about any activities that involve risks *before* you do them.

Figure 1-7. Where along the Illness-Wellness continuum would you place yourself? How could you move closer to wellness?

Risk behaviors increase the chances of illness and early death.

Figure 1-8. Every activity involves a degree of risk. How could these people lessen their risks?

A risk factor that does not pose an immediate threat to your health may have a long-term effect.

Not all risk behaviors involve immediate threats to your physical safety. Eating an unbalanced diet is a risk behavior. As you may know, the typical fast-food meal contains a great deal of salt, fat, and sugar. Eating a meal like this too frequently may cause you to put on too much weight. Living on a diet of fast food may lead to more serious, long-term health problems, such as cancer and heart disease. How far along the Illness-Wellness continuum do you think one fast-food meal per week would move you? What about two meals per day? You will learn more about the effects of dietary risk factors in Chapters 8 and 9.

Another set of risks to your wellness involves mental and social health. Keeping anger or other strong emotions "bottled up" inside can risk both your mental and social well-being. It is much better for your health to express your feelings by talking with someone you trust. Your relationships with others will also benefit. Strong negative feelings, when not communicated, can harm a relationship, causing resentment, jealousy, and arguments. You will learn more about the healthy expression of emotions in Chapter 2 and about communication skills in Chapter 5.

Moving Along the Continuum

To achieve a better quality of life, you need to know about, choose, and practice behaviors that promote wellness. You also should be aware of your own particular conditions and needs. Awareness is the first step toward making healthful choices and decisions. The second step is acquiring the knowledge you need to promote your own wellness. Some of this knowledge is general information, such as the benefits of regular exercise, and some knowledge may relate to your particular circumstances, such as the proper diet for gaining weight. You also need to be able to distinguish between risk behaviors, which lead away from wellness, and healthful behaviors, which lead toward wellness. The last step is applying your awareness and knowledge by making healthful choices and then taking action on those choices.

The remainder of this chapter, and the chapters that follow, will show you how to gain an awareness of your own health, how to acquire and evaluate health-related knowledge, and how to decide which behaviors best promote your health. Finally, you will learn how to turn your decisions into a healthful life style.

AWARENESS How do you become aware of your own level of wellness? In some cases, you know when you have a health problem. You know when your ankle hurts or when you have a sunburn. You are probably aware that some symptoms require medical attention and some do not.

Other medical problems do not show up so readily. You should have regular check-ups to detect early signs of illness you might not be aware of. At these check-ups, you will probably discuss your life style, including what you eat, how much you sleep, how much exercise you do, and whether or not you smoke. Together, you and your doctor can determine if you are at risk for certain health problems because of your life-style choices.

You may even discuss some of your feelings with your doctor. If you are depressed, for example, it is worthwhile to discover why. Feeling "low" all the time can be the cause or the result of a physical problem. If you are unhappy because of something that cannot be changed, such as the death of a loved one, the support of friends or professionals may help you to understand and accept your feelings.

Learning what questions to ask of your doctor and of yourself is an important step toward health self-awareness. The Check Your Wellness inventory at the beginning of this chapter should give you a good start. How well did you do on the inventory? What other questions might you ask yourself about your health? What questions might you ask your doctor or other health professional?

KNOWLEDGE Knowledge about health is growing every day. New discoveries and research studies appear in the news all the time. Some of this knowledge—about the dangers of overexposure to sunlight, for example—is important to everyone. Some, such as the development of new medications, is useful to the professionals who prescribe them. Other information, such as research on the harmful effects

▲
Figure 1-9. Are you aware of how your behaviors affect your health?

O━╦

Together, you and your doctor can evaluate how your life-style choices affect your health.

of a particular fad diet, is important to people who may try it. You need to be able to sort out the knowledge that might apply to your life.

Some sources of health information are more reliable than others. Which is a better source of knowledge, an advertisement for a quick weight-loss diet or a study of weight loss in a scholarly journal? While the answer to that question is obvious, the value of other sources of information may not be as easy to determine.

This book gives you a good foundation of health-related knowledge. It also suggests how you can evaluate other health information you receive. It is up to you to stay informed about things that affect your wellness. The process of updating your knowledge is one you will need to continue throughout your life.

BEHAVIOR CHOICES Even with awareness and knowledge, it is not always easy to decide on the best course of action. In the earlier discussion of risks, the action of running across a highway presents a clear risk, but the skiing example is more complicated. Many behaviors have both positive and negative results, and you must choose between them. Suppose you were an inexperienced skier invited to ski a run known for its difficulty. Your best friend, a good skier, could not go on the trip if you did not go. Add some more complications, such as bad weather, or an upcoming exam for which you need to study, or alcohol being consumed in the car. Real life is full of such complications. How would you decide what to do?

Awareness of your own skiing ability is essential in this example. Knowledge of the dangers of driving or skiing in bad weather is also important, but even more important is knowledge about the extreme risk of drinking and driving. But, what about your friend or your exam? Here you must consider your **values,** the things most important to you. You value friendship, but you also value your own and your friend's safety. You value doing well in school, and so do your parents. Your decisions not only affect you, they affect other people, their health, and their values.

The DECIDE process described in the Health Skills on page 16 provides a step-by-step procedure that can help to make hard decisions easier. Look at the DECIDE process and review the steps. How could you apply these steps to the skiing example?

SKILLS What would you think of a baseball team that spent all its time thinking and learning about the game but never played? Do you think that the team would win many games without practice? Of course not. Many people think that knowing about healthful behavior is enough to guarantee good health. This is not true. Like the baseball players,

Updating your knowledge of things that affect your wellness is a lifelong responsibility.

Figure 1-10. The only way to master a skill is through practice.

you have to practice. To have good health, you must apply the healthful decisions you have made.

One quality a successful baseball player needs is skill. Awareness of natural talent, knowledge of the game, and a good choice of bat are not much good without the skill to hit a curve ball or lay down a bunt. How do baseball players develop new skills? They usually begin by observing and analyzing their current behavior. Next, they make changes. Then, there is practice and more practice.

Just like the baseball player who worked to change his or her swing, you may have some habits you wish to change. A **habit** is a pattern of behavior that has become automatic and is hard to break. It is possible, however, to break old habits by learning new skills. With practice, your new skills will become just as natural as the old habits had been. The Health Skills in this book will help you to develop the skills you need to put decisions for wellness into action.

To put your decisions into action, you must have the skills necessary to do so.

Section Review

1. What is the Illness-Wellness continuum?
2. What is a risk behavior? Give an example of an immediate risk and a long-term risk.
3. What steps should a person take to move toward the wellness side of the Illness-Wellness continuum?

What Do You Think?

4. Where do you think you are on the Illness-Wellness continuum? List five behaviors that you currently practice that influence your level of wellness.

Leading Causes of Death Among Teenagers

1. Accidents
2. Suicide
3. Homicide
4. Cancer
5. Heart disease
6. Birth defects
7. Stroke
8. Pneumonia and influenza
9. Lung disease
10. Diabetes mellitus

▲
Figure 1-11. Risk behaviors account for the majority of teenage deaths.

3. TAKING CONTROL OF YOUR HEALTH

Now is the time for you to start taking control of your own health. In the last few years, as you have become more physically and emotionally mature, you have also become more independent. You have begun to make many of the decisions that used to be made for you by your parents and other adults. How many of your own food choices do you now make, for example? Who decides how much exercise you should do? Who chooses your friends? Who decides what you do with your friends? More and more, the answer is *you*.

Accepting Responsibility

Now that you have so much control over your own life, you also need to accept responsibility for it. Begin by learning the answers to these two questions: What are the leading causes of death among teenagers today? What are the risk behaviors associated with these deaths?

In Figure 1-11, you can see that the three most common causes of teenage death are not illness. Would you be surprised to learn that there is a risk behavior common to all three? That risk behavior is substance abuse, the use of alcohol or drugs. Most fatal accidents, for example, involve cars, and nearly half of all car accidents involve alcohol or drugs. Many suicides, too, are related to substance abuse. Homicide also is often tied to drugs and alcohol. The im-

Figure 1-12. Drinking and driving is a ▶ risk that is never worth taking.

paired judgment of people under the influence of drugs or alcohol can lead to violent behavior.

Some other risk behaviors also contribute to the rate of death among teenagers. These include: taking chances for the fun of it; being unwilling or unable to talk about problems or to ask for help; and accepting a known risk just to be one of the crowd. You will learn more about each of these risk behaviors throughout this book.

Some of these risk behaviors contribute to another set of health threats to teenagers: unwanted pregnancy and sexually transmitted diseases. All of these problems have a major impact on physical, mental, and social health. They affect not only the quality of your life but that of others.

Making responsible decisions about relationships of all kinds, including sexual ones, is an important sign of maturity. It shows that you are beginning to take control of your own health. Thinking about the possible effects of your actions before you take them may be difficult, but it is an important thing to do.

Looking Ahead

Considering the long-term effects of your behavior is another sign of maturity. Earlier in this chapter, you looked at the statistics on life expectancy and causes of death for adults today. The decisions you make and the behaviors you practice now are already influencing the length and quality of life you can expect in the future.

The most common killers of adults today are health conditions that can be strongly influenced by life style. Life-style choices include diet, exercise, and the use of tobacco, alcohol, and other drugs. Your current and future health depend largely on the decisions you are starting to make now. Learning to make decisions for wellness and to practice healthful behaviors is a wise investment that you can make in yourself and your future. It is an investment that pays the highest reward—the reward of good health.

▲
Figure 1-13. Responsible decision-making means thinking about all the possible consequences of your actions.

○━┳

Considering the long-term effects of your behavior is a sign of maturity.

Section Review

1. What are the three most common causes of teenage death today?
2. What kind of accidents kill the most teenagers?
3. What risk behavior is often associated with the three leading causes of teenage death?

What Do You Think?
4. What life-style changes could you make now to improve your future quality of life?

Making a Decision

Suppose you had to make this decision: You've just found the perfect after-school job. It's near home, it's fun to do, and it will pay for the bicycle you need for your bicycling trip next summer. Then you make the basketball team that you've tried out for three times. Unfortunately, the team practices during the same hours as your job. How should you choose between the team and the job?

Although many of your choices are not this complicated, you sometimes face even harder decisions. They require much thought and soul-searching because they can make important differences in your life. Do you sometimes "hide from" tough choices because they make you feel anxious? Do you ever rush headlong into decisions without really thinking them through? There is a process, called DECIDE, that makes decision-making easier. This process is simple to remember because each letter in the word DECIDE stands for a step in the process.

D E C I D E

1. Define the Problem

Look carefully at the decision you are facing, and state the issue clearly. Is it important and complex enough to warrant using DECIDE? Some choices are too easy. You already know what to do. Others don't really make much difference, a flip of a coin would do.

2. Explore the Alternatives

Make a list of all possible alternatives for solving your problem. Be sure to include "doing nothing" if it is appropriate. If you need more information to fully understand some alternatives, do the research now. You may find some choices unrealistic; do not include them.

3. Consider the Consequences

One by one, think through what might happen with each alternative. List both positive and negative results. Consider what probably would happen, not what you hope would happen. Ask yourself: How risky is each alternative? What are its chances of success? How

5. List three possible health hazards in the physical environment. Explain how you can protect yourself from them.

6. Define peer pressure and explain how it can affect your health.

7. Use a continuum to illustrate a health-related change in your life.

8. List three risk behaviors that can be fatal.

9. Briefly describe a situation in which a risk is worth taking and explain why.

10. What are two ways to become aware of your own level of wellness?

11. What are two good sources of knowledge about health?

12. Explain how values can affect a health-related decision.

What Do You Think?

1. Describe a problem you recently had to face. Then explain how your physical, mental, and social well-being played a part in reacting to the problem and in resolving it.

2. In spite of all the knowledge available about the health risks of smoking, many teenagers still smoke. Why do you think this is so? What argument against smoking do you think would be the most effective for teens?

3. Compare a TV, magazine, or newspaper ad promoting a healthful behavior with one for an unhealthful activity. How do the ads try to influence your behavior?

4. Some people say that teenagers do not take the dangers of risk behaviors seriously. They behave as though they think that harm only comes to other people. Do you think this is true or not? Give three examples to support your opinion.

5. Give some thought to the term *quality of life*. What five elements do you think are most important to your quality of life? Why?

What Would You Do?

1. You have a friend who lives on junk food and smokes cigarettes. He says he knows these behaviors are not harming him because he feels fine. What would you tell him?

2. You are not getting along with your friends or family. Often, you want to be alone. Should you seek help? From whom? Explain.

3. All your friends are drinking a diet supplement instead of eating regular meals. When you ask about the diet, they give you the brochure that came with supplement. How would you make a well-informed decision about this diet?

4. You are happy with your current state of wellness, but you want to be healthy in the future, too. What actions can you take now to promote your future well-being?

5. You have diabetes, a condition that limits the amount of sugar your body can process. You need to restrict your diet and check your blood-sugar levels. How can you achieve optimum wellness?

For Further Study

1. Find out what is meant by the term *preventive medicine*. How does preventive medicine lead to optimum health?

2. Research the disease tuberculosis. Find out the cause of the disease and what environmental and social conditions led to its being a "killer disease" in 1900. Then, explain why tuberculosis of the lungs, or consumption, is no longer a major threat in this country.

3. Look in the library for reliable sources of information about health; ask a librarian for help, if necessary. Select three sources and explain why they are reliable.

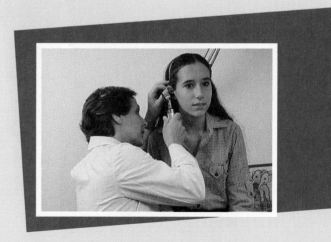

Yeah, it's a little strange doing that breathing and stuff before a test, but it's worth it. An exam is tough enough without having a bad case of nerves, too.

2

As you read, think about

▶ the ways in which your personality contributes to your mental health.

▶ how personality is formed.

▶ why it is important to learn to express your emotions in healthful ways.

Your Personality

Your party guests will be arriving shortly. You check the table again to be sure everything is in order. You rearrange the fruit bowl, and count the dishes for the third time. You've been looking forward to your party for weeks, but now you're feeling nervous. You take a look at yourself in the mirror and try out your best party smile. You step back and . . . there goes the doorbell!

Everyone is a bit nervous before a party, although most people aren't likely to admit it. Everyone feels shy and unsure sometimes. These are normal feelings that you cannot get rid of entirely. However, you can learn how to keep them in perspective and how to deal with them positively. In this chapter, you'll learn about ways to build your self-image so that you'll feel better about yourself. You'll also learn how to improve the way you reveal your personality to others.

You express your unique personality in everything you do.

1. PERSONALITY AND MENTAL HEALTH

Think about a party you have been to recently. Remember the different ways people were acting. One person may have been the "life of the party." Perhaps some others enjoyed dancing, while yet another group of people held a quiet conversation. There might have been another person sitting quietly on the couch, watching the dancing and appearing not to have a care in the world.

Did you ever wonder why people act so differently in the same situation? It is because each person has a unique personality. An individual's **personality** consists of the traits that make him or her different from everyone else. These traits include behaviors, attitudes, feelings, and ways of thinking that are characteristic of an individual in a given situation. For example, when you are introduced to a new group of people, you may be characteristically outgoing or you may be shy. At school you may be the first to raise your hand, or you may be daydreaming. You may cry frequently or hardly ever. These traits are all part of your personality.

Describing Personality

How do you describe someone's personality? Here is how four teenagers described their own personalities:

Yoon: I have a lot of energy and make friends easily. I love sports and am very competitive. But if things don't go my way, I get extremely upset and even throw tantrums.

Richard: School doesn't interest me all that much, but I study enough to get by. Sometimes I just don't feel like talking to people and prefer to be by myself. I like to stick to doing the things that I am used to.

Cory: I'm usually in a pretty good mood. Things just don't bother me the way they do some people. If a problem comes up, I can usually figure out how to solve it.

Sally: People call me the class clown. Sometimes I like to liven things up with jokes. There are a few subjects in school that really interest me, so I devote a lot of time to them. After school I enjoy spending time with my friends.

In describing their personalities, these teenagers chose the behaviors, feelings, and thoughts that best defined the way they are. How would you describe your own personality? Think about the things you like to do and how you

Figure 2-1. Your personality causes you to think and act in a way that is all your own.

normally act. Do you tend to be friendly and outgoing? This is called being an **extrovert** (**ek** struh vurt). Are you an **introvert** (**in** truh vurt), someone who is less outgoing and whose thoughts are directed inward? Are you moody or even-tempered? Driven or relaxed? Would you say you are **assertive** (uh **sur** tiv), able to stand up for yourself and express your feelings in a nonthreatening way? Perhaps you are more **passive,** holding back your thoughts and feelings and yielding to others, or **aggressive,** communicating your ideas and feelings in a forceful or threatening way. Are you satisfied with the way you are? Are there any characteristics of your personality that you would like to change?

Behaviors, attitudes, and feelings are signs of a person's mental health.

The Healthy Personality

Look back at the descriptions of Yoon, Richard, Cory, and Sally. Which of these teenagers would you say has a healthy personality? Which would you consider an un-healthy personality? Why?

When **psychologists** (sy **kahl** uh jists), people who study the human mind and behavior, are asked to describe char-acteristics of a healthy personality, they often speak of mental health. **Mental health** is the state of being comfortable with yourself, with others, and with your surroundings. People who are mentally healthy are also:

- realistic about their strengths and weaknesses.
- able to take on the responsibilities of daily living.
- caring toward themselves and others.
- able to handle disappointments and learn from them.
- able to feel enjoyment and a sense of achievement.

Figure 2-2. Being happy and relaxed ▶
with yourself is a sign of mental
health.

Psychologists like to think of mental health as a continuum much like the Illness-Wellness continuum you read
about in Chapter 1. Individuals can move toward the wellness end of the mental health continuum by developing the
characteristics listed above. Psychologists have found some
personality traits are often associated with mental health.
Mentally healthy people tend to be friendly, optimistic, and
loving. They are also able to be assertive, laugh at themselves, try new experiences, and strive to do the best they
can. What other personality traits do you think are important
for mental health?

How Is Personality Formed?

Some personality traits appear to be inborn. They are
acquired by **heredity,** the transmission of traits biologically
from parent to offspring, just as hair color and eye color are.
Other personality traits are shaped by a person's **environment** (en **vy** run ment), the physical and social conditions
surrounding a person. Most personality traits, however, are
believed to be influenced by a combination of heredity and
environment.

HEREDITY   Personality traits apparent shortly after birth
are thought to be inborn. In fact, even before birth, some
aspects of personality are evident. For example, some babies
kick and move around a lot inside their mothers, while others
are relatively calm.

After birth, individual differences become more apparent. Some babies are calm and cheerful; others tend to cry a
lot. Some babies hate new surroundings; others seem to

Some personality traits are acquired
through heredity.

thrive on a change of scene. These differences indicate that each person is born with definite personality traits. Psychologists are not sure how these early personality traits affect one's personality later in life.

Scientists believe a person's basic intellect may also be inherited. It is also thought that talents, such as musical or artistic abilities, may be at least partly inherited.

ENVIRONMENT Although some early personality differences persist into adulthood, most are modified by a person's environment. Your friends, family members, home, school, and even the climate that you live in affect your personality.

Experiences during childhood strongly influence the development of a healthy personality. A baby who is lovingly cared for learns to trust and love others. Children learn about feelings, attitudes, and appropriate ways of behaving from the people close to them. This process is called **socialization** (soh shul ih **zay** shun). As children develop, they copy the behavior of others. This is called **modeling.** For example, a child may learn acceptable table manners by watching his or her parents' behavior at the table. Children also learn through **conditioning,** or being rewarded for desirable behaviors and punished for undesirable behaviors. A child who is repeatedly praised for trying to do new things for himself or herself is very likely to grow up self-reliant and willing to try new experiences.

Beginning with childhood and extending throughout the teenage years, friends, school, and community become increasingly important influences on personality. American teenagers spend more than half their time with other teens. These friends, who are about the same age and share similar

Environmental experiences have a strong influence on personality development.

◀ **Figure 2-3. A child's personality is shaped by inherited traits as well as love and care from family members.**

Being a member of a healthy peer group can have a positive influence on personality development.

interests, are known as a **peer group.** By being part of a group, you learn how to get along with others. A peer group also gives you a chance to learn about yourself and to make decisions and to do things without your parents. Being a part of a healthy peer group is likely to have a positive influence on your personality.

By young adulthood, your personality traits are fairly well established. This does not mean you cannot work to change personality traits with which you are dissatisfied. In fact, recognizing weaknesses and working to improve them is a sign of mental health. At the same time, it is important to recognize your strengths and achievements.

Your Self-Concept

If you were to ask a psychologist what the most important influence on mental health is, the answer would be self-concept. Your **self-concept,** the physical and mental picture you have of yourself and your place in the world, includes all of the beliefs that you have about yourself. People with a positive self-concept feel good about themselves and have a realistic view of their strengths and weaknesses. They maintain a positive attitude even when they fail at a task and they take the opportunity to learn about themselves.

Health careers

An art therapist can help people feel good about themselves and their abilities.

Sometimes an effective way to help people understand themselves and their problems is through creative expression. Art, dance, and music therapists combine their artistic talents with therapy programs to help improve a person's self-concept.

An **art therapist** may teach people to paint or create things with their hands. A **dance therapist** may teach a person how to move in a graceful manner. A **music therapist** may teach a person to play a musical instrument or sing.

Art, dance, and music therapists work with a wide range of people from the mentally ill to the physically handicapped. They may also provide instruction and therapy for children at summer camps or they may work with the elderly in nursing homes.

For these careers, you need a bachelor's degree in psychology or in art, dance, or music therapy. You also need a solid background in either art, dance, or music.

They show that they value themselves by taking care of their health and appearance and by forming close friendships.

Your self-concept begins to form when you are young. It depends on the responses of others to your behavior and appearance. Young children need support and encouragement from family members to develop a positive self-concept and to become confident individuals. As you grow older, teachers, friends, and other people, as well as events in your life, influence your self-concept. If you do well in school or excel at a sport, your achievements and the encouragement you receive can influence your self-concept in a positive way. Think about the people and events that influenced your self-concept. How have these events helped you form a realistic picture of yourself?

You may realize that you are not always the same person in different situations. You behave differently in public than in private. For example, your **public self,** the way you want others to see you, may be cheery and outgoing, while your **private self,** the real you or the way you are when you are alone, may often feel shy and insecure. Although it is normal to have these two "selves," it is best when your public self and private self blend into one. People with a positive self-concept are not afraid to reveal their true nature. It is not easy to let others see your faults. By revealing your weaknesses as well as your strengths, you let others know that you feel good about yourself and about them.

It may be difficult to improve your self-concept, but it can be done. It is a good idea to take an inventory of your strengths and weaknesses. Learn to focus on your strengths and build on the things you do well. Select friends who will give you support and encouragement to do what you do best. Focus on activities in which you can excel, but accept the fact you will not excel in everything. When you do experience defeat or discouragement, avoid dwelling on it. Try to learn something positive from the experience and then move on to something else.

▲
Figure 2-4. Feeling good about yourself is the most important influence on your mental health.

Section Review

1. Define the term personality.
2. Give five characteristics of mental health.
3. How does a person's environment influence his or her personality?

What Do You Think?
4. Your best friend is struggling to overcome a negative self-concept. She or he asks you for help. What could you say or do to help?

2. THEORIES OF PERSONALITY

Although your personality grows and changes, some traits remain with you throughout life.

People's personalities change as they grow and are exposed to new ideas, attitudes, and behaviors. Still, some basic personality traits stay the same throughout a person's life. Think back to when you were seven or eight. How has your personality changed since then? In what ways has it remained the same?

Psychologists have tried to explain how and why the human personality develops. These explanations are called theories. A **theory** (**thee** uh ree) is an organized set of ideas used to explain something. Three important theories of personality will be described in this section.

Freud

In the late 1800s, an Austrian physician named Sigmund Freud became interested in mental illness. From his work with the mentally ill, he concluded that each individual's personality is made up of three parts: the id, the ego, and the superego. The **id** consists of biological urges, such as hunger, thirst, and seeking physical pleasure. The **ego** is the thoughtful, decision-making part of the personality. For example, if the id urged you to eat, the ego would help you find food. The **superego** is the knowledge of right and wrong, or what you might refer to as your conscience. For example, the superego would direct you not to steal the food that your id urges you to find.

According to Freud, people's minds operate at two levels of thought: **conscious** (**kahn** shus) **thought** and **unconscious thought.** Conscious thoughts are those of which a person is aware. Unconscious thoughts are those of which a person is not aware. A forgotten childhood event is an example of an unconscious thought.

Freud believed that people often push unpleasant or frightening thoughts into their unconscious. These unconscious thoughts influence the individual's personality, even though he or she may not be aware of their effects. For example, a child who was unloved by a parent might, as an adult, be constantly searching for the approval of people in authority, people such as teachers or bosses. Such a person might seem overly obedient and anxious to please others.

To Freud's way of thinking, adult personalities are shaped mainly by early childhood experiences and conflicts. These memories are stored in the unconscious. Freud believed that by undergoing **psychoanalysis** (sy koh uh **nal** uh sis), a form of therapy that involves unlocking these memories and bringing them into the conscious mind, the painful memories can be eased and the inner conflicts resolved.

Figure 2-5. According to Sigmund Freud, childhood experiences strongly influence personality.

Erikson

One follower of Freud, Erik Erikson, devised an eight-stage theory of personality development covering a person's entire life span. Unlike Freud, Erikson believes that an individual's personality continues to be influenced by experiences beyond the childhood years. According to Erikson, people continue to develop socially and psychologically up until their death. Each phase of life has its own particular problems or crises to overcome. If each crisis is worked out in a satisfactory way, it has a positive effect on personality development. If, however, the problem or crisis is not worked out in a satisfactory way, it has a negative effect on personality development.

Figure 2-6 outlines Erikson's theory of personality development. As you can see, you already have faced four of Erikson's eight conflicts. The first conflict, that of trust versus

Figure 2-6. In which of Erikson's stages is identity established? Independence?

▼

Erikson's Eight Stages of Development

Age	Stage	Important Event
birth to 18 months	**Trust versus Mistrust** If cared for and loved, infant gains trust, views world as safe place. Otherwise, mistrust and fear develop in infant.	Feeding
18 months to 3 years	**Autonomy versus Shame/Doubt** Child learns bodily control—walking, talking, elimination. With encouragement, child gains confidence. Otherwise, inadequacy and doubt.	Toilet Training
3 to 6 years	**Initiative versus Guilt** Child takes charge more, sense of right and wrong, play-acting. Self-worth grows, if encouraged. Low self-esteem and guilt if scolded.	Independence
7 to 12 years	**Industry versus Inferiority** Child accomplishes tasks and attempts new things. If encouraged, feels competent. If not praised, may feel like a failure.	School
13 to 19 years	**Identity versus Role Confusion** Teen seeks sense of self. Raises questions about sex, religion, role. If not resolved, confusion results.	Adolescence
Young Adulthood (20–40)	**Intimacy versus Isolation** Young adult develops close bonds with others, shares self. Otherwise suffers loneliness.	Love Relationships
Middle Adulthood (41–64)	**Generativity versus Stagnation** Adult finds self-worth helping younger people. If self-absorbed, person lacks true satisfaction.	Parenting
Late Adulthood (65–death)	**Ego Integrity versus Despair** Older adult reflects on and accepts the life lived. Otherwise, approaches death with regret.	Reflections on Life

mistrust, occurs during the first year of life. A young child who is cared for and loved learns to trust. The trusting child is likely to develop a secure personality.

The second conflict, that of self-control and independence versus lack of self-control and dependence, occurs during the second and third years of life. This is the time when children gain control over their own bodies. Children who are encouraged to gain control over themselves tend to develop independent, confident personalities.

The third stage involves acquiring self-confidence. Between the ages of three and six, children begin to explore who they are through fantasy play and imitating the behavior of others. They also develop a sense of right and wrong. Children who are encouraged to initiate activities on their own and to create fantasies tend to develop a sense of self-worth.

The fourth stage lasts until the teenage years; children learn how to accomplish real tasks. They learn how to help around the home, how to succeed at school, and how to get along with others. These skills make children feel competent. Without them, the child may feel like a failure.

The fifth stage is the one you are going through right now. Teenagers are concerned mainly with finding out who they are and what they want to do with their lives. Erikson calls this the search for **identity.** Some teenagers resolve their identity crises by trying new experiences and thinking and behaving in ways that are different from family teachings. Other teenagers focus on shaping their identities to go along with standards set by their family or community. Often, the search for identity extends beyond the teenage years.

Look again at Figure 2-6. What is the next stage that you will be going through, according to Erikson? What crisis will you need to resolve during that stage?

Figure 2-7. Learning about the things you value will help you establish your identity.

Maslow

An American psychologist named Abraham Maslow theorized that everyone has a basic drive to achieve their fullest potential. Maslow gave a name to the process by which each person strives to be all that she or he can be: **self-actualization.** To define the characteristics of a self-actualized person, Maslow studied people who, in his view, had attained self-actualization. These people included Abraham Lincoln, Thomas Jefferson, Eleanor Roosevelt, and many others. Based on these studies, Maslow arrived at the following list of ideal personality traits:

- realistic
- accepting
- spontaneous
- problem-centered
- independent, self-sufficient
- appreciative of life
- spiritual or mystical
- concerned about humankind
- capable of loving others
- fair, unprejudiced
- creative
- hardworking
- not afraid to be different

Maslow found that few people ever reached their full potential. He developed a theory to explain why. Maslow suggested that before people could achieve self-actualization, they had basic needs that had to be met. Maslow put these needs in an ascending order, called **Maslow's hierarchy of needs.** Notice the hierarchy, shown in Figure 2-8, is a pyramid, with self-actualization at the top. At the base is what Maslow considered to be a person's most urgent needs: physical needs of the body. These include getting enough sleep, exercising, and satisfying hunger and thirst. If these basic needs are not met a person has little or no energy to pursue higher needs.

Look again at Figure 2-8; the next need is for safety. This includes the needs for adequate shelter, adequate income, and protection from danger. Once the need for safety is met, a person has the energy to pursue the next level of Maslow's hierarchy: social needs.

Once social needs are met, people can direct their energies toward the need for **self-esteem.** Self-esteem refers to how much one likes oneself and feels good about oneself. To gain self-esteem, people need to experience competence and independence. In other words, you need to know what you do well and you need the opportunity to accomplish things for yourself. Achieving success will give you a sense of self-esteem and will gain you the respect of others.

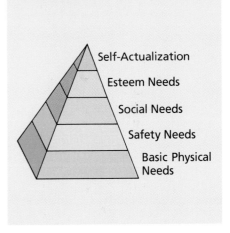

Maslow's Hierarchy of Needs

Self-Actualization
Esteem Needs
Social Needs
Safety Needs
Basic Physical Needs

Figure 2-8. Maslow showed how people progress from basic to higher needs. Which needs must be satisfied to gain self-esteem?

Figure 2-9. Martin Luther King is an example of a self-actualized person.

Once you have achieved self-esteem, you can then go on to be creative, accepting, caring, unprejudiced, and to achieve all the other qualities of a self-actualized person. On the other hand, if you have low self-esteem, then you are not likely to reach your full potential.

Maslow's hierarchy provides a framework for thinking about human needs. It is possible to meet some of your basic needs only partially and still strive to meet higher needs. For example, many great artists, such as Mozart and van Gogh, were extremely creative although some of their basic needs were not met. Nevertheless, a well-fed person with adequate shelter is more likely to be friendly, have higher self-esteem, and perform tasks better than someone who lacks adequate food and shelter.

Section Review

1. What is psychoanalysis?
2. What is one major difference between Freud's view of personality development and Erikson's view?
3. According to Erikson, what three conflicts must adults resolve?
4. What are some of the characteristics of someone who has achieved self-actualization?

What Do You Think?
5. Think about one aspect of your personality that you would like to change. How could you work either to change this trait or to develop a more positive view of the trait and use it to your advantage?

3. EXPRESSING EMOTIONS

Read the following four descriptions and identify what each teenager might be feeling in the situation described:

Patty just received a call from Bob, who invited her to go with him to the spring dance. This is just what Patty had been hoping for; she cannot wait to tell her best friend.

Clayton has flunked math and science. He dreads telling his parents about it. Worse still, he knows that he will have to give up being on the football team until he brings his grades in those subjects up to at least a C.

Linda is going to try out for the lead in the class play. She has already memorized her lines but is certain that she will forget them at the audition. Every time she thinks about getting on stage her heart beats faster, and she feels as if she were going to faint.

Peter's dad has lost his job. Money is tight at home. Peter wants to help, but he has not been able to find an after-school job. Yesterday he spotted a twenty-dollar bill in his friend Bill's locker. When Bill looked away, Peter grabbed the money and stuffed it into his pocket.

Common Emotions

You and your classmates may disagree about exactly what Patty, Clayton, Linda, or Peter are feeling. However, everyone probably would agree that each is experiencing some kind of **emotion,** or feeling. Psychologists define an emotion as a reaction to a situation that involves a person's mind, body, and ways of behaving. The ability to recognize and appropriately express emotions is an important part of a healthy personality.

LOVE Many people think of love primarily as a romantic involvement between two people. While this certainly is a kind of love, there are many other types of love. Love of self is the basis for all other kinds of love. A person who feels self-love has the capacity for loving others. Love may be directed toward friends. Loving friendships are characterized by mutual respect and caring. The love between two married people includes a caring commitment to support and respect each other and act in responsible ways. Love within a family involves expressions of affection and concern. These expressions include caring enough to set or adhere to limits and to enforce or obey rules of behavior.

Feelings are brought on by the situations you face.

Figure 2-10. You can express love by showing affection and concern for others.
▼

Figure 2-11. Anger can be either a constructive or destructive emotion.

Figure 2-12. Fear causes your body to prepare for action.

You can also feel love toward places and things. You may love your country. You may feel love and concern for your fellow human beings. Love is perhaps one of the most positive emotions of which people are capable. The capacity to give and receive love is essential to mental health.

ANGER It is normal to feel angry sometimes. What are some situations in which you have felt angry? How did you express your angry feelings?

Anger can be either helpful or harmful. Anger can be a strong motivating force; it may provide you with the energy necessary to try to change things. Consider the case of Clayton, the teenager who flunked math and science. Clayton's first reaction to his poor grades might be anger toward his teachers. After thinking about his situation, however, Clayton may realize that he has to change his own behavior. He may have to give up some after-school activities and spend more time studying. Anger can also be a destructive emotion. Suppose Clayton continued to direct his anger at his teacher or turned his anger upon himself. He might give up on his schoolwork altogether or become aggressive or even violent. These reactions would tend to worsen the situation instead of improve it.

What is the best way to deal with anger? First, it is important that you do not deny your feelings or try to ignore them. Second, find a healthful way of expressing your anger. For example, find a physical outlet such as jogging or hitting a punching bag. Third, after you have calmed down, think about exactly what made you angry. Writing down what happened or talking it over with a friend can help. Fourth, consider what constructive action you can take to improve a situation that makes you angry or to prevent another angry episode from occurring.

FEAR Everyone is afraid of something: a figure in the dark, spiders, or horror films. Fear can be a helpful emotion; it can cause you to run from life-threatening situations, such as a fire or a dangerous person. When you feel fear, your heart races, and your breathing quickens. You are prepared to fight or flee the situation if necessary. Do you know people who enjoy scary films or frightening amusement park rides? These people like to feel the reaction brought on by fear.

Fear can also be a harmful emotion. A person who is afraid of something may choose to avoid the fearful situation rather than to confront it. Fear can lead to physical problems. You have probably experienced indigestion, loss of sleep, or headaches when you were afraid of something. Over a long period, fears can lead to physical damage.

Admitting that you are afraid and talking about it with someone often make a fear more manageable. Sometimes it helps to picture your worst fears. For example, Linda, who was nervous about auditioning for the school play, handled her fear by talking with her mother. Her mother asked Linda to project the worst thing that could happen. Linda said that she was terrified that she would forget her lines and everyone would laugh at her. To give Linda more confidence in herself, Linda's family acted as an audience for several nights. Although Linda was nervous the day of her audition, she got the part.

GUILT   You feel guilty when you think you have done something wrong. Guilt can be a helpful emotion; it can stop you from doing something you know is wrong, or it can make you take action to correct something you've done. Feeling too much guilt, however, can make you doubt yourself and your actions.

The best way to deal with feelings of guilt is to correct the situation if possible and to talk about your feelings. Peter, the boy who stole money from his friend Bill, felt both anger and guilt. He was angry because his father was out of work. He felt guilty because he stole Bill's money. Peter tried to justify taking the money, but he knew what he did was wrong. After a sleepless night, Peter decided to tell Bill about what he had done. Bill was understanding but said that he needed the money back. Together, the two boys worked out a plan by which Peter could pay back the money.

HAPPINESS   Like love, happiness is a strong, positive emotion. Think about a recent time when you felt happy. Were you happy about something you accomplished? Or was your happiness a result of a pleasant surprise? People feel happy for many different reasons and sometimes for no particular reason at all. It is a normal response to pleasant events in one's life.

When a person feels happy, he or she also feels satisfied with life. Feeling happy makes you feel good about yourself. What makes you feel happy? Take some time to make a list of the things you enjoy. Then, try to "build" these happy times into your daily life. If you enjoy skating with your friends, for example, make a date with your friends to go skating. If you like to read books, set aside some time each day for reading. The good feelings will stay with you for the rest of the day.

SADNESS   Sadness is a feeling of sorrow or grief that can be a normal response to life events, such as a day when nothing seems to go right, a poor grade in school or some other failure, or the death of a loved one. If you feel sad for too long, however, you may become depressed. **Depression** is an emotional state in which you feel hopeless and worthless. People who remain in a depressed state for a long time may require the help of a psychologist.

▲
Figure 2-13. Happiness is a positive emotion that helps you enjoy life.

Figure 2-14. Feeling sad is a normal response when you are faced with a disappointing event.
▼

SAD Patients See the Light

Do you suffer from the "winter blahs" as the days get shorter? Some people are not only sad in winter, they *have* SAD, seasonal affective disorder.

SAD, researchers have discovered, is a deficiency disorder. Just as scurvy is caused by a lack of vitamin C, so some people get SAD from a lack of a full range of light, which is not typically found indoors. As the supply of natural light decreases, those with SAD begin to show signs of depression. Unlike depressed people, who have trouble sleeping and eating, SAD patients act more like hibernating animals. They sleep excessively (up to 18 hours a day), crave starchy foods, and gain weight.

Treatment for SAD sufferers involves phototherapy, exposure to a full range of bright lights for two hours a day. For 80 percent of SAD sufferers, the light treatment seems to lower the level of certain substances in the body, which relieves the symptoms of SAD.

Researchers suggest two simple cures for normal "winter blahs"—taking a walk outdoors during daylight and increasing the light level in your home.

Phototherapy relieves SAD.

If you are sad about the death of a loved one, you will probably experience a period of deep sorrow known as **grief.** Often, one's first reaction is to feel numb and deny the death. Then you may feel angry toward the person who has died. You may feel the person has abandoned you. You also may feel guilty about your angry feelings, because you know that the person could not help dying. Finally, you may feel depressed. All these feelings are normal reactions to the death of someone you love.

What can you do to overcome feelings of sadness? It is important to admit the emotion and to share your feelings with a close relative or friend. If you are sad about a failure, it might also help to make a list of your accomplishments or do something nice for yourself. If you are grieving, allow yourself to cry and to feel all of the emotions the loss brings on. It is important not to withdraw from other people or isolate yourself. If you do, the feeling can become overwhelming and may interfere with your ability to cope with everyday events.

Coping with Your Emotions

Sometimes emotions can become too much to handle. In such cases, people may use coping strategies consciously or unconsciously. A **coping strategy** is a way of dealing with an unbearable feeling or situation. Freud referred to coping strategies as **defense mechanisms** because they are the ways people defend themselves against negative emotions.

To some extent, coping strategies can protect you from painful situations. When you use a coping strategy, you temporarily put off dealing with a problem and the emotions it causes. You experience a feeling of temporary relief, which allows you to think through the problem with a clear mind. When overused, however, coping strategies can stunt emotional growth. If you become too dependent on coping strategies, you may not learn to express your true feelings. By using coping strategies to avoid problems, you may not develop the skills that are important for mental health.

Figure 2-15 describes some common coping strategies. A few will be discussed here to illustrate how they relate to your emotions. More will be said about coping strategies in the next chapter, which deals with stress.

DENIAL Refusing to recognize an emotion or problem is called **denial.** For example, suppose Clayton, the teenager who failed math and science, tried to hide his failure by "forgetting" to tell his parents of his poor grades. By doing this, he has not only hidden the truth from his parents but from himself as well. By denying the situation, Clayton put off dealing with it until the initial pain has lessened. He might then be better able to deal constructively with his failure. He may be able to come up with a plan for studying harder, perhaps even asking his parents for help. If, however, Clayton continued to use denial to ignore his problem, he would not take action to correct the situation. This would be a negative use of the coping strategy.

Sometimes denial can allow a person to escape from an extremely painful experience, such as the death of a loved one. In this situation, denial may be a necessary step in the person's recovery process. At some point, however, the grieving individual has to allow him- or herself to feel the pain and accept the loss.

DISPLACEMENT   Sue is furious with her boyfriend because he is, once again, late for their date. Sue may vent her anger in different ways: she can punch a pillow, or she can scream at her little sister, even though her sister has done

Figure 2-15. Which strategy have you used to cope with strong emotions?

Common Coping Strategies

Compensation: making up for weaknesses in one area by excelling in another area

You do poorly in school so you make up for it by becoming the lead saxophone player in the school orchestra and starting up your own jazz band.

Daydreaming: creating made-up situations in your mind and indulging in periods of fantasy to escape unpleasant events

You wish that you did well at sports. You imagine scoring the winning basket in your school's most important basketball game.

Denial: refusing to recognize the existence of an emotion or problem

Your parents are getting divorced, but you act as though nothing is wrong. When concerned friends ask how you feel about it, you laugh and tell them it does not bother you.

Displacement: transferring emotions from the original source to another

You are arguing with a friend and slam the door to your locker.

Identification: assuming the qualities of a person you admire

You admire your older brother so much that you begin to talk and act like him.

Projection: putting your own faults onto another person

At your after-school job you do not complete your tasks. When you get fired, you blame your boss, saying she was too lazy to explain the tasks to you.

Rationalization: making excuses for actions or feelings

You work in a convenience store on weekends. When no one is watching, you take some candy and magazines. You figure it's a large store and they can afford it.

Reaction Formation: behaving in a way opposite to the way you're feeling

You feel guilty smoking a cigarette. You cover up your feelings by bragging to friends about your smoking.

Regression: returning to immature behavior to express emotions

You are mad at your brother for using your bicycle. You scream at him and your parents and run into your room and slam the door.

Sublimation: channelling energy into an acceptable goal rather than an unacceptable one

You always seem to argue with people. You join the debate team at school.

nothing wrong. Have you ever taken out the anger you feel toward one person on someone or something else? If so, you have used the coping strategy known as **displacement,** the transferring of an emotion from the source to another person or object.

Although venting your emotions on an object is better than taking them out on an innocent person, it is best to discuss your feelings with the person who caused them. Displacement can be useful because it allows you time to calm down before you confront the problem. In Sue's case, if she is angry because her boyfriend is always late, she should tell him how she feels. Together, they can work out a solution to the problem. If Sue does not confront the situation, she has used displacement to avoid the problem.

RATIONALIZATION When a person makes excuses for his or her actions or feelings, it is called **rationalization.** Usually people use rationalization to avoid risking their self-concept or feeling guilty. For example, Denise wanted to ask William out to a movie. She was nervous because she did not know whether William would accept her invitation. Denise convinced herself that she had too much homework to do to go to a movie. By rationalizing, Denise was able to avoid a possible rejection by William. If Denise admits her fears, she may be able to convince herself not to let them stand in her way. If, however, Denise continues to make excuses to herself, she may miss out on an important opportunity for growth. When rationalization is overused, a person does not learn how to deal with problems effectively.

REGRESSION Exhibiting emotional behavior that is characteristic of young children is called **regression.** You can see a lot of regression during a traffic jam at rush hour: adults leaning on their horns or screaming at the top of their lungs. For the most part, regression is not a constructive coping strategy because it does not solve the problem at hand. Instead, the childish behavior that indicates regression often makes a situation worse.

In most cases of regression, it is better to find another way of expressing frustration or anger. If you feel a tantrum coming on, take an emotional break by calling a friend, taking a walk, or by counting to ten before you react to the problem. The break will allow you to think more clearly about the situation and about a mature solution.

OTHER COPING STRATEGIES Some other coping strategies that people use to deal with their emotions include **compensation, daydreaming, identification, projection, reaction formation,** and **sublimation.** Look over the definitions and examples of these coping strategies in Figure 2-15. Can you think of times when you used each of these coping

Figure 2-16. Behavior like this does little to solve the problem.
▼

Figure 2-17. A trusted friend or relative can help you to cope with difficult emotions.

strategies? Did you use the coping strategy in a positive or negative way? How could you have turned a negative use into a positive one?

Learning to express your emotions in positive ways is not an easy skill to master. Most people need help dealing with their emotions from time to time. Strong emotions can interfere with your ability to concentrate on or think clearly about a situation. If you find that your emotions are preventing you from participating in your normal activities, it may be time to ask for help. Try talking to a trusted friend or family member about your problem. Sometimes, just talking about your feelings will help you see things more clearly. Other times, mental health counselors may be available to help you learn how to cope with life situations.

When coping strategies stop you from facing a problem, they are not effective.

Section Review

1. How do psychologists define emotion?
2. Name five common emotions.
3. Give an example of a coping strategy.
4. Why should you avoid using coping strategies too frequently?

What Do You Think?
5. Describe a situation in which you or a friend expressed an emotion in an unhealthful way. How could the emotion have been expressed in a healthful way?

Expressing Feelings in a Positive Way

Matthew had been dating Joan for a year, and he thought things were great between them. Joan felt differently. She wanted to start dating other boys. Matthew was so stunned he couldn't even describe his feelings.

How would you react if you were in Matthew's situation? Yell? Cry? Pound a pillow? Act as if you didn't care? Pick a fight with your little sister? Talk to Joan? All of these behaviors are possible responses to strong feelings. They are ways of trying to cope with emotions that can seem overwhelming. While you cannot control what you feel, you can control what you do, or your behavior.

Some responses to strong feelings improve the situation or at least make you feel better. Others can make a bad situation worse. The following guidelines will help you learn to express your feelings constructively.

1. Accept Your Feelings

Strong emotions, even unpleasant ones, are normal. Denying them will not make them go away, and it may cause them to erupt later in destructive behaviors. It is important to identify and accept your feelings; then you can start to work on expressing them constructively.

2. Inventory Your Current Behavior

Everyone experiences emotions, such as love, fear, sadness, and anger. Are you aware of how you usually react to these feelings? On index cards, inventory your recent responses to each of these emotions. Briefly describe

Anger

1. My sister wore my blouse. I yelled at her. She yelled back. Mom got mad. I was frustrated.

2. Argued with Dad about the car. Went for a bike ride. Cooled off. Then talked to Dad. Felt better.

when and how you expressed each feeling in the recent past and how the situation was resolved. Circle those responses that led to a positive outcome.

3. Seek Constructive Alternatives

Your inventory will show what has worked well for you in the past. Here are some other tips to help you deal with your emotions in a positive way:

Communicate your feelings: Find someone trusted to talk to or "a shoulder to cry on." Don't lash out and hurt people's feelings; that just adds to your—and their—problems. Try not to withdraw from those who care about you. They can be a big help if you let them.

Let off steam: Do something you enjoy that requires physical or creative energy. Run or do some other physical activity; paint or play an instrument. Even taking a walk to clear your head can help. Smashing things does *not* help. While you may feel better for a moment, you will have to deal with the damage later.

Confront the cause of the feeling: Once you have calmed down, talk to the person who caused the emotion. Make clear how you feel *without* blaming the other person. You may find it was all a misunderstanding or that the person is now sorry. Even if the situation cannot be reversed by clearing the air, you may feel ready to move on.

Avoid "drowning your sorrows": Do not turn to destructive behaviors as a smokescreen. Although overeating or not

Remaining friends after a breakup is difficult. How can expressing emotions help?

eating, drinking, smoking, doing drugs, or taking extreme physical risks may help you forget your problems for a moment, they can do damage that lasts a lifetime.

4. Evaluate Your Progress

If the way you currently express your emotions works, keep it up. If not, try to stop and think a moment before you act. Recall your own positive experiences (from your inventories) and the tips above. Consider the consequences of possible responses.

At first it may take a lot of self-control to change your responses to strong emotions, but the more you practice constructive behaviors, the more automatic they will become. If, however, persistence doesn't help, or if you often feel overwhelmed by your emotions, it is time to ask a trusted adult for some help.

APPLY THE SKILL

1. Review Matthew's situation. What do you think his feelings were? List two positive and two negative ways he could have expressed those emotions. For each, what might the results have been?

2. Make a response inventory for fear, love, sadness, and anger. Write each emotion at the top of an index card. Briefly describe three times in the recent past when you have experienced that feeling, how you expressed it, and the outcome. What responses worked best for you? Worst? Why?

3. Look over your inventories. Make a new card for the emotion that gave you the most trouble. For a week, record each time you express that emotion. Make a real effort to improve your responses. If your progress is not satisfactory to you, consider asking someone for help.

2 | Chapter Review

Chapter Summary

- An individual's personality consists of all the traits that make the person unique.
- People with good mental health are comfortable with themselves and the world around them, realistic about their strengths and weaknesses, and able to handle the responsibilities of daily living.
- Some personality traits are thought to be inherited, while others are shaped by a person's environment. Most traits are influenced by both heredity and environment.
- Self-concept, the view a person has of him- or herself, is the most important influence on mental health. Self-concept is mostly influenced by people and events in an individual's early years.
- Freud believed that personality is shaped by early childhood experiences and conflicts that the individual may not even remember. Through psychoanalysis, the person can become aware of these experiences and resolve the conflicts.
- Erikson developed an eight-stage theory of personality development. Each stage is characterized by different crises.
- Maslow theorized that every individual has a basic drive to live up to his or her potential and achieve self-actualization. Most people, however, are not able to satisfy that drive because other more basic needs have not been met.
- The ability to recognize and appropriately express emotions, such as love, anger, fear, guilt, happiness, and sadness is an important component of mental health.
- Coping strategies are ways of temporarily dealing with overwhelming feelings or situations. When coping strategies are overused, a person may not learn to solve problems or express his or her true feelings.

Vocabulary Review

Listed below are some of the important terms in this chapter. Choose the term that best matches the phrase in the exercise that follows.

conscious thought	extrovert	personality	self-concept
coping strategy	id	psychoanalysis	self-esteem
denial	identity	rationalization	superego
displacement	introvert	regression	unconscious thought
ego	Maslow's hierarchy	self-actualization	
emotion	of needs		

1. all the traits that make each person different from everyone else

2. the part of an individual's personality that distinguishes between right and wrong

3. a thought of which a person is not aware, but which affects a person's behavior

4. the mental and physical picture one has of oneself

5. an ordering of a person's needs from most basic to self-fulfillment

6. reaching one's full potential

7. the degree to which one likes oneself or feels good about oneself

8. a reaction to a situation or event that involves a person's mind, body, and ways of behaving

9. transferring an emotion, such as anger, to an innocent person or object

10. a conscious or unconscious way of dealing with a strong feeling or difficult situation

What Have You Learned?

1. Describe a mentally healthy person.
2. Explain how heredity and environment interact to shape personality.
3. Why are peer groups an important influence on a teenager's personality?
4. What factors affect self-concept?
5. What did Freud believe to be the most important influence on personality?
6. Compare and contrast the personality theories of Freud, Erikson, and Maslow.
7. According to Erikson, what crisis must teenagers resolve?
8. Explain why love is such a positive and important emotion.
9. How can guilt and fear be positive emotions? How can they be negative emotions?
10. Describe some of the emotions that a person who has experienced the death of a loved one might be feeling.
11. How can frequent, long-term use of coping strategies be harmful?
12. Give an example, other than the ones discussed in the text, of how a coping strategy can be beneficial.

What Do You Think?

1. How do you think emotions add to the enjoyment of life?
2. Which do you think has the most impact on personality: heredity or environment? Explain your answer.
3. Why is a loving home so important to the development of a healthy personality?
4. Explain how school affects self-concept.
5. Describe a person you know who you would say has achieved self-actualization.

What Would You Do?

1. You are feeling angry because your friend broke one of your favorite records and refuses to pay for it. What would you do to work out your anger in a healthful way?
2. Imagine you have been grounded for poor grades. Your parents say you cannot go out with your friends until you bring your grades up to a C average. How would you feel and what would a healthful response be?
3. If a good friend moved far away, what would you do to ease your sadness?
4. Describe what you are doing or hope to do to resolve your identity crisis. How will these actions help you develop a secure identity?
5. Imagine that every time you fail at something, you rationalize your failure. How might this behavior be harmful? Think of a way that the habit of rationalizing could be broken.

For Further Study

1. A Swiss psychologist named Jean Piaget (1896–1980) developed a theory accounting for how intellectual abilities develop in children. Research Piaget's theory of cognitive development. Explain his theory in a written report.
2. At the library, find out the name of one person Maslow considered to have achieved self-actualization. Write a report describing the person's positive, healthful personality traits. Do you agree that this person achieved self-actualization?
3. Interview five teenagers to find out how they are resolving their identity crises. Discuss the results with your class. With the help of your classmates develop a list of healthful ways to resolve an identity crisis.

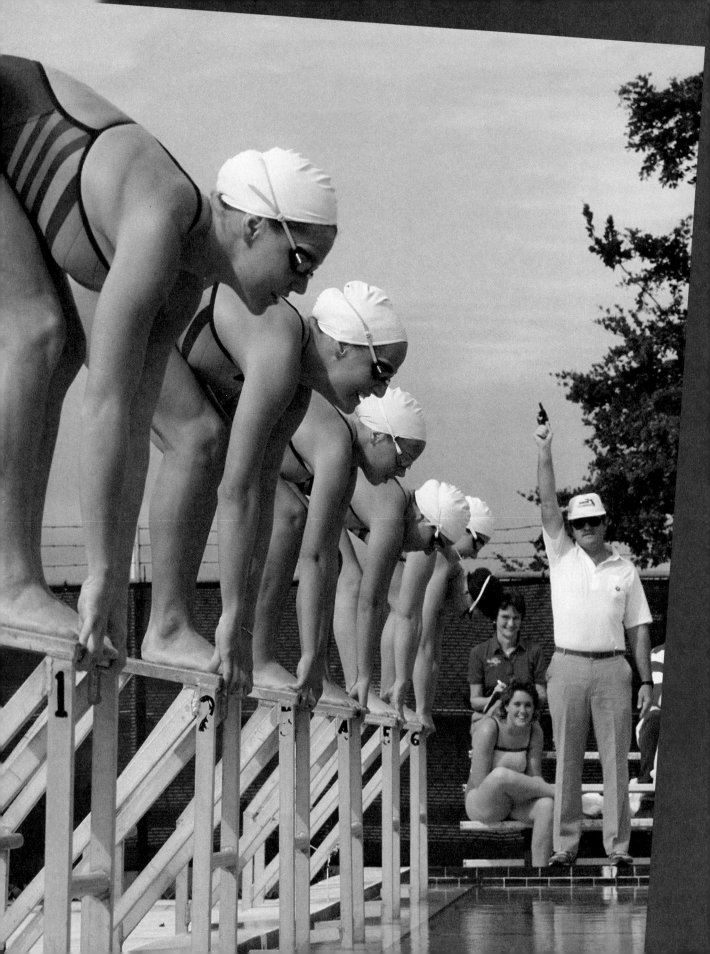

3

As you read, think about

▶ what stress is and how you react to stressors in your life.

▶ how your body responds to stressful situations.

▶ how your personality and coping strategies affect the way you experience stress.

▶ how you can manage stress in a healthful way.

Managing Stress

Y ou crouch on the starting platform, gripping the edge with your fingertips. Every muscle in your body is tense as you wait to dive into the pool. All your physical and mental energy will be channeled into this race. You listen for the starting gun.

But what if the gun never sounds? What happens to the energy and tension stored in your body? How does it get released?

There are many occasions when you are prepared to take action and can't. Sometimes, it's because you are worried or excited too far in advance. Sometimes, it's because you don't know what action to take. There are some things you cannot change no matter what you do.

The result of situations like these is stress. The stresses of living, growing, and changing are part of your everyday life. In this chapter, you will learn about stress and how it affects you. You will also learn how to cope with stress and how to redirect it in positive ways.

You can use stress to channel your energies in positive ways.

47

1. WHAT IS STRESS?

Stress is a reaction of the body and mind to something in everyday life. You experience stress when situations, events, or people make demands on your body and mind. These demands are often part of your daily routine. The sound of an alarm clock, for example, can cause stress. When you hear the alarm, you know that you must open your eyes, sit up, and start the day. Your body and mind react to the ringing alarm, and you experience stress.

Many situations, events, and people can cause stress. The cause is not always obvious, but all stress is caused by something in your life. The causes of stress are called **stressors.** The alarm that wakes you is one example of a stressor. Other stressors in your life may be upcoming tests or games or arguments with friends. These stressors make demands on your body and mind and cause you to react. Can you think of other stressors that you experience daily?

What's Good About Stress?

Stress is a necessary part of living. Without stressors and the demands they make, you might not face many of the challenges that lead you to accomplish things. Think about a recent accomplishment—perhaps you defeated a tough opponent in tennis. You may remember the feeling of stress you experienced. Do you think that you performed well as a result of the stress? Although people speak of stress as a negative experience, stress can be a positive experience.

Stress that produces positive effects is called **eustress** (**yoo** stres). Not all stress is eustress. The positive or negative effect that a stressor has on you is often the result of your ability to manage, or cope with, the stress it produces. As you know, coping strategies help you manage your difficult emotions. Coping strategies also help you manage stress.

When coping strategies are constructive, they are healthy. When they are unconstructive, they are unhealthy. Suppose you must take a major test next week, and you feel you must do well on it. In the week before the test, there are many ways you can cope with the stress it causes. Constructive coping strategies might include setting aside time to study each day, asking a friend to review with you, or asking the teacher for help. Unconstructive coping strategies might include ignoring the test until the day before or complaining to the teacher after the test that it was too hard.

Constructive coping strategies are skills that help you solve a problem. They last a short time and are appropriate for the situation. No matter what coping strategy you use, once the stressor has occurred, you have solved the problem. You will be healthier, however, if you learn skills that make a stress a positive experience whenever possible.

What's Bad About Stress?

People who complain about being under too much stress are usually talking about **distress,** or negative stress. Distress can be caused by unconstructive coping strategies, by too many stressors at one time, or by situations or events that are distressful. These situations or events are often unhappy but unavoidable. For example, the death of someone you love always causes distress. Although you learn to cope with the loss, the experience is still a negative one.

Figure 3-1 lists some significant stressors for high-school students. Many of these stressors are changes in one's family or school life. These changes threaten a person's sense of security or self-concept. Not all of the changes are distressful. Each change is measured in ''life-change units'' and given a score. The number of life-change units you accumulate during a year is one way to measure the amount of stress you experience. Even if the changes are for the better, many changes in a short time can cause distress.

Distress in everyday life is often caused by too many stressors at one time, such as too many things to do in the

Figure 3-1. Add the number of life-change units for each event you experienced last year. If your score is less than 150, you have experienced little stress; between 150 and 300, you have experienced moderate life change; over 300, your life has changed greatly.

▼

Ranking of Stressors by High-School Students

Life Event	Life-Change Units	Life Event	Life-Change Units
Getting married	101	Being suspended from school	50
Being pregnant and unwed	92	Having a newborn brother or sister	50
Experiencing the death of a parent	87	Having more arguments with parents	47
Acquiring a visible deformity	81	Having an outstanding personal achievement	46
Going through a parent's divorce	77	Observing an increase in the number of arguments between parents	46
Becoming an unwed father	77	Having a parent lose his or her job	46
Becoming involved with drugs or alcohol	76	Experiencing a change in parents' financial status	45
Having a parent jailed for a year or more	75	Being accepted at the college of your choice	43
Going through parents' separation	69	Being a senior in high school	42
Experiencing the death of a brother or sister	68	Experiencing serious illness of a brother or sister	41
Experiencing a change in acceptance by peers	67	Experiencing father's increased absence from home due to change in his occupation	38
Having an unwed, pregnant teenage sister	64	Experiencing departure from home of a brother or sister	37
Discovering that you are an adopted child	64	Experiencing the death of a grandparent	36
Having a parent remarry	63	Having a third adult added to the family	34
Experiencing the death of a close friend	62	Becoming a full-fledged member of a religion	31
Having a visible congenital deformity	62	Observing a decrease in the number of arguments between parents	27
Having a serious illness requiring hospitalization	58	Having fewer arguments with parents	26
Moving to a new school district	56	Having mother begin to work outside the home	26
Failing a grade in school	56		
Not making an extracurricular activity	55		
Experiencing the serious illness of a parent	55		
Breaking up with a boyfriend or girlfriend	53		
Having a parent go to jail for 30 days or less	53		
Beginning to date	51		

Figure 3-2. Stressful situations make demands that you cope with in either a positive or negative way.

time available. For example, Sandra is a good student, but she is taking advanced courses. This year, she is also on the field hockey team and has the lead in the class play. Each day after school, she attends either rehearsals or field hockey practice. She has little time in the evenings for homework and studying. Sandra has coped with the stress by completing her assignments on weekends. This weekend, however, she has promised to help with the housework. With the time she has left, she will have to choose between doing her school work and visiting her friends.

If Sandra's problem continues, she may experience other stressors. She may begin to sleep or exercise less than she should. Her grades may suffer. These problems also can become stressors and lead to feelings of helplessness, anger, or fear. Sandra will then have to cope with her emotions and the stressors. The result can become a complicated series of problems that interfere with her health.

Section Review

1. What is stress?
2. What is a stressor? Give some examples of stressors from your own life.
3. What is a coping strategy?
4. How can stress be good or bad?

What Do You Think?

5. From the list in Figure 3-1, choose the stressor that you feel would cause you the most distress. Which one would cause the most eustress?

2. HOW STRESS AFFECTS YOUR BODY

When you encounter a stressor, physical changes take place in your body. These changes allow you to react quickly and to use your body's resources to cope with the stressor. The changes that occur can be either helpful or harmful. Their effect depends on your response, the length of time they last, and the coping strategies you use.

Stages of Stress

As your body copes with stress, it must adapt, or adjust, to the stressor and the changes it causes. This process of adapting, called the **general adaptation syndrome,** occurs in three stages. The three stages—the alarm stage, the resistance stage, and the exhaustion stage—can happen quickly, or they can happen slowly. Your body's responses as you go through these stages depend on the stressor and the way in which you deal with it.

Imagine that you are walking through a forest. Just as you are enjoying the sights, sounds, and smells of the forest, a huge black bear appears in front of you. How would your body react?

ALARM STAGE As soon as you become aware of something you consider dangerous, such as the bear, you enter the first stage of stress, the **alarm stage.** Your body releases a substance known as **adrenaline** into your bloodstream, which gives you a burst of energy and causes many other changes in your body. Your heart begins to beat faster, increasing the flow of blood to your muscles. Your breathing quickens, providing more oxygen for your body's activities. Your muscles tighten, making you ready to run. Less blood flows to your stomach and digestive system, so your arms and legs can have all the blood they need. Your pupils widen, allowing more light into your eyes. A lump develops in your throat as your throat muscles contract to help open the airways to your lungs and make breathing easier.

These changes take only a few seconds, but once they have taken place, your body is ready to react. You can react in one of two ways: you can stand and fight, or you can run away. This reaction is called the **fight or flight response** because the changes prepare you to either "fight" the stressor or take "flight" and escape.

Scientists believe that these reactions were essential for primitive people who had to survive wild animals and other dangers. The same reactions still occur to some degree with any stressor. When faced with a challenge, such as a difficult test or a theatrical performance, your body reacts with some

The body adapts to stress in three stages: the alarm stage, the resistance stage, and the exhaustion stage.

Figure 3-3. When faced with a danger, you enter the alarm stage, much like this cat does.

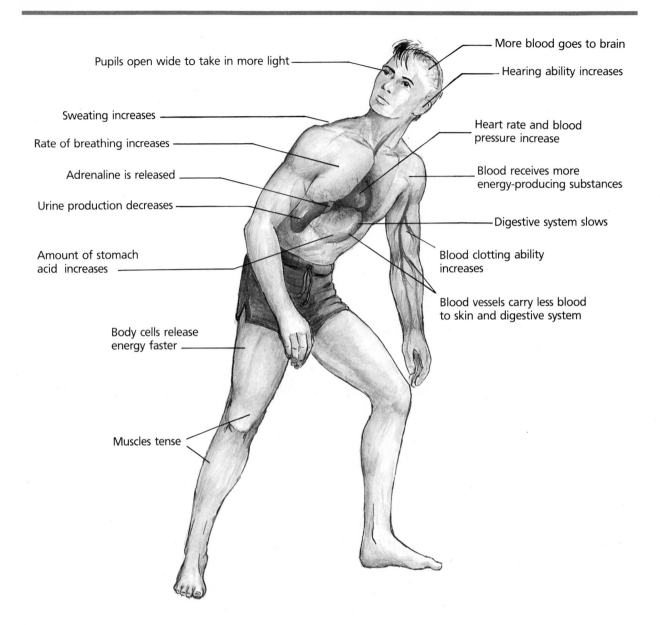

Pupils open wide to take in more light

More blood goes to brain

Hearing ability increases

Sweating increases

Rate of breathing increases

Adrenaline is released

Urine production decreases

Amount of stomach acid increases

Heart rate and blood pressure increase

Blood receives more energy-producing substances

Digestive system slows

Blood clotting ability increases

Blood vessels carry less blood to skin and digestive system

Body cells release energy faster

Muscles tense

Figure 3-4. When you encounter a stressor, your body and mind prepare you to fight or take flight.

of the same physical changes. These physical changes, which are shown in Figure 3-4, make it possible for you to choose between "fight" and "flight."

As your body responds to the stressor, your mind also reacts. During the alarm stage, you become more alert. You take in information and concentrate better. You also experience a greater level of anxiety, which can lead to either constructive or unconstructive coping strategies.

For example, Bill, who had a major part in a class play, reacted with fear and anxiety on the opening night of the play. By concentrating on his role and ignoring the audience, he did well and did not forget his lines. In other words, Bill used the energy that the fight or flight response gave him to concentrate on his role. At the play's second performance, Bill did not cope constructively. He watched the audience and allowed the lump in his throat to keep him from delivering his lines clearly. His muddled lines caused him even more anxiety, and he forgot some of them altogether.

RESISTANCE STAGE The **resistance stage** is the second stage of the general adaptation syndrome. During this stage, the body tries to recover from the alarm of the first stage. The heart and breathing slow down. Pupils return to their normal size. Muscles relax. Blood returns to the stomach and digestive system. This normal, balanced state is called **homeostasis** (home ee o **stay** sis). When your body is in homeostasis, its internal functions stay the same, even when the external environment changes. You then have the energy to do the things you usually do.

If coping strategies are constructive and last a short time, the stress response ends at this stage. The body has resisted the stressor effectively and can regain homeostasis. When Bill coped constructively with the anxiety of opening night, his body was able to regain homeostasis soon after the curtain went down.

When Bill did not cope constructively, he experienced further distress, and his body did not return to homeostasis quickly. He continued to feel anxious for several days. His distress and unconstructive coping kept both his mind and his body from functioning well. He felt tired, irritable, and unable to face new stressors.

EXHAUSTION STAGE Imagine that Bill used unconstructive coping strategies to deal with other stressors in his life. He ignored his homework assignments. When his grades began to drop, he blamed his teachers and classmates for his problems. He withdrew from friends and school activities. As his distress became overwhelming, he began to feel exhausted and ill.

If Bill's coping strategies continue to be extremely unconstructive, Bill may enter the **exhaustion stage,** the third stage of the general adaptation syndrome. The exhaustion stage does not occur with each stress response. If it did, your body would wear out. Exhaustion occurs only if distress continues for a long time—usually weeks, months, or even years. People often enter the exhaustion stage when they experience stress that is beyond their control—such as a divorce or other serious family problems. In the exhaustion stage, you become less able to resist new stressors, and your body has more difficulty returning to homeostasis. As your body's balance remains disturbed, making judgments, interacting with people, and maintaining your health become more difficult. In extreme cases, the exhaustion stage can lead to unhealthy behavior, serious illness, or even death.

▲
Figure 3-5. When you cope negatively with stress, your body does not regain homeostasis quickly.

⊶🔑

The exhaustion stage can occur when distress continues and feels uncontrollable.

HEALTH FRONTIERS

Understanding Headaches

What gives you a headache? Anxiety over an upcoming test? Skipping meals? Eating a particular food? Bright lights? These and other stresses of daily life can lead to headaches. Until now, millions of headache sufferers have relied on painkillers to relieve their headaches.

Recently, scientists have begun looking at the chemical and electrical changes that occur in the brain during a headache. They have found that the level of neurotransmitters, the chemical messengers of the brain, often falls just before a headache starts. The brain's electrical activity also dulls, limiting blood flow throughout the brain.

Knowing this, doctors can now deal more directly with headaches. For people who suffer from severe daily headaches, doctors now prescribe drugs that restore the chemical balance of the brain and improve blood flow. Other headache sufferers are taught how to use biofeedback and relaxation techniques to reduce the pain.

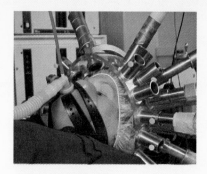

Now research offers help to the headache sufferer.

To remain healthy, your body needs to regain homeostasis soon after experiencing stress. To help your body do this, you need to learn constructive coping strategies.

Stress and Illness

Once you understand the fight or flight response, you can identify some of your own physical responses to stress. Muscle tension, "butterflies" in your stomach, flushing of your face, and a pounding in your head can all be **symptoms,** or evidence, of stress. Physical symptoms such as indigestion, skin rashes, backaches, or headaches can be caused by prolonged stress. These symptoms are sometimes called **psychosomatic** (sy kuh soh **mat** ik) **symptoms.** *Psycho* means "of the mind," and *somatic* means "of the body"; psychosomatic symptoms therefore are evidence of the ways in which the mind affects the body.

By itself, stress does not usually cause serious illness. Most of us experience physical symptoms from time to time but regain homeostasis rather quickly. Severe or prolonged distress, however, can affect your health. It can lower your body's resistance to illness, and it can make some diseases more serious and harder to control.

LOWERED RESISTANCE Normally, the body protects itself from disease through the **immune** (ih **myoon) system.** The immune system protects the body through a complicated process involving a number of specialized body cells. When you speak of "fighting off" the flu or a cold, it is the immune system that does the fighting. When your immune system functions well, you are able to resist some illnesses, even when you are exposed to them.

Scientific research has shown that prolonged stress or distress can keep the immune system from functioning well. If your immune system is not working well, you may have minor illnesses, like colds and flu, more often. You may also be more likely to develop a serious illness. Scientists have found that many infections and even certain kinds of **cancer,** the uncontrolled growth of cells, are more common among people who experience prolonged stress or distress. Although stress is not the major cause of these diseases, it can be one of many causes that combined lead to illness.

Stress-Related Illnesses

The changes that occur in the body because of stress can lead to illness. For example, for some people, the experience of stress increases the amount of acid in the stomach until they develop ulcers. **Ulcers** are open sores in the lining of the stomach, caused by too much acid. The increased acid then keeps the ulcer from healing. Additional stress—perhaps just the stress of worrying about the ulcer—can make the ulcer worse.

Some diseases become worse during stressful experiences. People with **asthma** (**az** muh), a type of lung disease, may react to stress with an asthmatic attack. During an asthmatic attack, the person has trouble breathing and gasps for air. Although these symptoms usually can be controlled with medication, people with asthma need to recognize their bodies' reactions to stressors so that they can manage serious asthmatic attacks.

Another disease that causes problems for people under stress is **diabetes** (dy uh **bee** tis). Diabetes is a disease in which the body has difficulty maintaining a balanced amount of sugar in the blood. Because sugar is a source of energy for the body, unexpected changes in energy levels can cause problems with a diabetic person's sugar balance. Diabetic people often need to take medication or control their diets so that their bodies regain homeostasis. Because stress changes the body's energy level, recognizing and coping with stress are especially important for people with diabetes.

Stress can even contribute to diseases that take years to appear. Heart disease, for example, can be caused partly by stress. Stress raises a person's blood pressure. **High blood pressure** occurs when the blood pushes hard against the blood vessels as it flows through them. Over time, high blood pressure can contribute to heart attacks. Coping constructively with stress is one way to help control high blood pressure and lower the risk of heart attacks.

Stress also contributes to accidents and injuries. People who are tired, distracted, or careless are more likely to injure themselves and others. When stress affects your ability to concentrate or to think clearly, you need to be especially careful. Recognizing stress allows you to take extra care.

▲

Figure 3-6. It is important not to let stress take your mind off what you are concentrating on.

Section Review

1. Name and describe the stages of the general adaptation syndrome.
2. What is the fight or flight response?
3. Name some ways stress is related to illness.
4. What are some illnesses that are caused partly or made harder to control by stress?

What Do You Think?
5. Choose a major stressor that you think you may encounter in the near future. How would you cope with the stressor? Trace how your body and mind would react as you progress through the stages of stress.

Common Emotions and Behaviors Associated with Stress

Anger
Anxiety
Boredom
Depression
Fear
Feeling bothered
Forgetfulness
Frustration
Hurrying
Indecisiveness
Irritability
Lack of motivation
Laughter
Loss of appetite
Nail biting
Nervousness
Overeating
Overcritical thoughts and
   actions
Poor attention span
Tears
Teeth grinding
Upset
Withdrawal

▲

Figure 3-7. Which of these common reactions have you experienced during stressful situations?

3. STRESS AND BEHAVIOR

While stress, both eustress and distress, is a normal part of life, your response to stressors and the ways in which they affect you is unique. No two people experience stress in the same way. Each person reacts to events, situations, and people with a different personality and with his or her own series of coping strategies. Figure 3-7 lists some common feelings and behaviors that people experience when under stress. As you can see from the list, there is a wide range of emotions and behaviors associated with stress. Which of these reactions do you experience? Do your friends and family members react to stress in a similar or a different manner?

Personality

As you learned in Chapter 2, your personality affects the way you see the world and the way you interact with those around you. One theory on personality claims that there are two basic personality types: type A and type B. This theory was first proposed by a group of researchers who were studying heart disease and its possible causes. The researchers discovered that personality was one important factor in an individual's reaction to stress.

People with **type A personalities** frequently create some of their own stressors. These people tend to be rushed, trying to accomplish as much as possible in the shortest time possible. Type A personalities tend to be competitive. They want to succeed and will drive themselves hard to accomplish their goals. They also have high standards for themselves. If they fail to meet these standards, they can become angry and frustrated. Type A personalities may experience stressors as challenges, but they can easily experience distress.

Figure 3-8. The success-driven go-getter and the calm, unhurried person are two basic personality types.

▶

Type B personalities are less competitive and less rushed. They are calmer and less concerned about accomplishment. Type B personalities are less likely to experience distress if they do not meet high standards for success. They also are less likely to develop stress-related symptoms and illnesses. Some type B personalities, however, have difficulty facing challenges. They may cope with stressors by ignoring them. Doing this, they may miss opportunities for learning and achievement. They may be bored and unable to set goals. These problems can create another kind of distress in which the person needs to learn to recognize stressors and react.

In reality, few people are entirely type A or type B personalities, most people are a combination of both types. The difference between the types, however, can be useful in thinking about stress and the ways in which you cope with it.

Coping Strategies

Everyone uses a variety of coping strategies to react to the stressors in their lives. The coping strategies you choose depend on your age and experience. Babies, for example, have no experience with coping and can only cry when faced with a stressor. As you grow older, you learn new coping strategies, and experience shows you which ones are most constructive.

The coping strategies you use are linked to your self-concept, personality, and emotions. As shown in Chapter 2, part of staying healthy is learning to recognize and express your emotions. Emotions are often stressors, because they challenge your body to react. It is not surprising, then, that many of the same coping strategies you use to express emotions, you also use when you deal with stress.

The following section describes some coping strategies that are used by high-school students and adults. Remember that these are only a few of the ways in which you may cope with stress. Remember, too, that a coping strategy is constructive if it is appropriate to the situation and if it is a short-term method for dealing with a problem.

DENIAL Denial is a way of ignoring a stressor by acting as if it did not exist. Denial can be constructive when you are coping with many stressors at one time. For example, suppose that you had to take four final exams in three days. At first, you might feel overwhelmed, frustrated, and almost ready to give up. As you begin to cope with the stress, however, you might try ignoring, or denying, all but one of the exams at any one time. In this way, you could concentrate on one exam at a time without worrying about all four at once. This coping strategy may work because it lasts only a short time and helps you to meet the challenge of taking all four tests.

Type A and B personalities experience stressful challenges differently.

Denial is used to block a stressor out of your mind.

Of course, you also can use denial unconstructively. Suppose you denied all four exams and did not study at all. When faced with taking each exam, you would probably enter the alarm stage. Because you would not be ready to meet the challenge, you would have trouble coping with the stressor, and your body would not regain homeostasis quickly.

SUBLIMATION   Sublimation is a way of shifting your attention and energy from a stressor to something else in your life. Sublimation gives you an appropriate way to express emotions that are stressful. David, for example, was angry when his parents refused to let him go to an evening party. After a few angry words, he spent the afternoon playing football with his friends. By evening he was too tired to go to the party, and his anger was over. He had released his anger and the stress he experienced by coping constructively.

Physical activity, playing football, shooting baskets, taking walks, can be a constructive form of sublimation. It can also be unconstructive. If David had coped with his anger by breaking windows, his use of sublimation would have been unconstructive. His behavior would have become an additional stressor, and he probably would have remained angry.

DAYDREAMING   Most people use daydreaming once in a while as a way of escaping stressors for a short time. Daydreaming can be constructive if it helps you concentrate on a goal or feel less anxious about a stressor. For example, Emily was worried about her gymnastics competition and found concentrating on her routine difficult. That afternoon, before she was scheduled to perform, she began daydreaming, imagining that she had won first place. To her surprise, she performed better than ever, winning second place.

A constructive coping strategy is both appropriate to the situation and a short-term method for dealing with it.

Figure 3-9. Daydreaming can take your mind off stress and can help you to cope with it better.

In this instance, Emily's daydreaming was constructive. It lasted only a short time, took her mind off the stress, and thus helped her to accomplish her goal. Daydreaming, of course, can also be unconstructive. If Emily had daydreamed during class, for example, or if her daydreaming had kept her from performing other activities, she would have coped unconstructively with the stress she experienced.

HUMOR   Humor can be an effective way to deal with some stressful situations. If you have ever laughed at yourself after doing something that was not really funny, such as slipping on a wet floor or saying something embarrassing in front of a group of people, you may have realized your laughter helped to relieve the feeling of stress the event caused. Humor can be a constructive coping strategy because it allows you to deal with a stressor and quickly reestablish homeostasis. Humor can also be an unconstructive way of handling stress. If a person uses laughter to cover up his or her true reactions to a stressor, or if a person laughs inappropriately at a serious situation, the coping strategy may be unhealthy.

Learning how to use coping strategies in constructive ways is important.

Section Review

1. What is the difference between a type A personality and a type B personality?
2. How do you know whether or not a coping strategy is constructive?
3. How are denial, humor, and daydreaming used to cope with stress?

What Do You Think?
4. Review the list of coping strategies in Figure 2-15 on page 39. Do you use different coping strategies to cope with stress than you did five years ago? Explain.

4. MANAGING STRESS

Because stress affects your health in many ways, stress management is essential to staying healthy. In a sense, everything you do to maintain your health is a way to manage stress. Eating right, exercising regularly, expressing your feelings, managing your time well, developing hobbies, participating in a variety of activities, saying no to drugs and alcohol—these are all ways in which a healthy person manages stress.

You will learn more about these skills in later chapters. Here, you will learn about some methods that help to counteract the negative effects of stress.

Relaxation

Many special methods can help you achieve **relaxation,** a state in which your body and mind are resting. When you are relaxed, you may be awake and alert, but you are not responding actively to stressors.

Taking a hot shower or bath, stretching, or having someone massage your neck can help relax tense muscles. Stretching the muscles in your neck, shoulders, and upper back is an especially useful way to relax because these muscles often become tense when you sit for long periods.

One method for relaxing tense muscles is called **progressive relaxation.** It is a technique in which you relax by concentrating on each group of muscles in your body, one at a time. Progressive relaxation is described in the Health Skills on page 64.

Deep breathing is a good way to manage short-term stress when you can't take time for progressive relaxation. When you breathe deep, you take in as much air as you can,

Figure 3-11. Relaxing alone can help you to handle stress more effectively.

Simple Relaxation Exercises

Turn your head slowly to the left and then to the right. Return to normal position.

Roll shoulders forward and backward. Then raise both shoulders toward ears and drop them down as far as possible. Keeping your head straight slowly touch your left shoulder to your left ear. Then touch your right shoulder to your right ear. Relax.

Place your right hand on your left shoulder. With your left hand, grab your right arm above the elbow. Pull to the left while looking over your right shoulder. Hold, breathe deeply and release. Repeat with other side.

Figure 3-12. These relaxation exercises help to ease tension in the muscles of the back and neck.

making sure that your abdomen as well as your chest expands. By breathing this way, you take in more oxygen, which helps your body to function better. Deep breathing helps you relax muscles throughout your body. It is also useful with other relaxation methods.

Creative Visualization

Another method of stress management is called **creative visualization** (vizh oo ul y **zay** shun). It is a way of using your imagination to cope with stressors. When you visualize, you imagine that the stressor is an object that you can see, or sometimes hear, and you act on the stressor by doing something to what you have imagined.

Suppose, for example, that you come home from school feeling overwhelmed with work and worries. You might try imagining that each of your problems is a piece of clothing. You might imagine that you are picking each piece of clothing off the floor and hanging it in your closet. As you visualize your closet filling with clothes, you can feel your problems disappearing.

When you first begin to use creative visualization, you will find that your problems constantly reenter your mind. Creative visualization, like most methods of stress management, requires practice.

The ability to visualize stressors can lead to greater control over them.

Biofeedback

Biofeedback is a special method of stress management in which you learn to control some of your physical functions by recognizing your body's signals. To learn biofeedback, you use special equipment that allows you to know what is happening in your body. A trained health professional usually teaches this method.

The health professional might, for example, attach a special device to the muscles in your back. The instrument will let you know when you begin to tense these muscles. By paying attention to your thoughts as your muscles become tense, you can learn to control the tensing of the muscles by changing your thoughts.

With training and practice, people can master biofeedback. Many do not need special equipment to visualize and control their tension. Biofeedback has been useful for people who have stress-related symptoms or illnesses such as headaches, high blood pressure, or asthma.

Getting Help When You Need It

Learning ways to manage stress is important, but most people need extra help at some time. Another skill that keeps you healthy is recognizing when the stresses in your life are becoming overwhelming. At these times, you may want to find someone to help you with your problems. For many people, changes in their lives create special problems for a while. Because high school is a time of many changes, high-school students often find themselves in need of help.

Biofeedback assists in managing stress by allowing you to control physical functions.

Friend to Friend

George:
I'm so worried about this big paper due next week, I don't even know where to begin.

Larry:
I know what you mean. I feel like that at times, too.

George:
Well, what helps you when you feel that way?

Sometimes, all you need is someone to talk to. Sharing your problems can help you see them more clearly. Just describing your concerns to someone else often helps you to understand them better.

Many people are willing to talk if you take the time to ask. Friends, parents, teachers, school counselors, school nurses, and clergy are usually available for support. If you have a specific question and do not know whom to ask, any of these people can refer you to someone who can answer your question and address your concerns.

At some time in your life, you may want or need some kind of long-term counseling. There are many specialists available to help people who need special attention. Some specialists are trained to treat mental illnesses, which you will learn about in Chapter 4. Others are trained to help you identify stressors and learn constructive coping strategies.

Stress can be overwhelming. When this occurs, talk with someone you trust.

Section Review

1. What is relaxation? Name and describe three relaxation techniques.
2. Explain how the process of creative visualization can help you manage stress.
3. What is biofeedback?

What Do You Think?
4. Suppose, after a particularly stressful day, you find yourself unable to fall asleep. How would you relax?

Larry:
When I have a big project to do, I think of all the steps I have to follow to get it done. Then, I make a list of all the steps and figure out how long each step will take me.

George:
That sounds like a good approach. Do you think you can help me plan the steps involved in doing this paper?

Larry:
Sure. Why don't we meet in the library after school and talk about it then?

A Relaxation Technique

It is nine o'clock at night, and Pam is busy studying for the three exams she has this week. Although she has a lot of work ahead of her, Pam feels calm and relaxed. Her mind is alert and focused on her studies.

How does Pam stay in control while faced with this workload? She uses progressive relaxation to help her relax. Pam has found that this 15-minute technique relieves fatigue, reduces anxiety, and helps her feel more alert.

During progressive relaxation, you focus on relaxing each part of your body, from your head down to your toes. This helps you release any tension that has been building up in your body.

The technique of progressive relaxation is outlined below. You will discover that the more you practice the technique, the better you become at managing stress.

1. Getting Ready

- Find a quiet environment where there will be few distractions. Choose a comfortable position, either sitting or lying down. Make sure that your arms and legs are uncrossed.
- Close your eyes and take several deep breaths. Consciously relax your body, releasing tension each time you exhale. Try to imagine that you are in a peaceful environment, for example, by a mountain stream or in a beautiful meadow.

2. Relaxing Your Muscles

Begin with your forehead and work your way down to your toes. Tighten each muscle group and hold for 10 seconds,

then relax and go to the next muscle group. Try the following sequence:

- **Forehead:** Wrinkle your forehead—try to make your eyebrows touch your hairline.
- **Eyes:** Close your eyes as tightly as you can.
- **Mouth:** Form a frown with the corners of your mouth.
- **Shoulders:** Raise your shoulders up to your ears.
- **Upper arms:** Bend your elbows and tense your upper arms.
- **Hands and forearms:** Tightly clench your fists.
- **Back:** Gently arch your back.
- **Stomach:** Tighten your stomach muscles.
- **Hips:** Tighten your hip and buttock muscles.
- **Thighs:** Squeeze your legs together.
- **Feet:** Bend your ankles back toward your body.
- **Toes:** Curl your toes under as tightly as you can.
- **Whole body:** Tense all the muscles in your whole body. Relax, breathe deeply, and release any remaining tension in your muscles. Stay still and just enjoy the feeling of deep relaxation for a few moments.

3. The Final Step

Now you are ready to come out of your deeply relaxed state.

- Count backwards from ten while you gradually start moving your toes, fingers, and limbs.
- Open your eyes and stand up slowly. Your whole body should feel rested and alert.

Practicing some form of relaxation regularly makes it easier to cope with stress.

APPLY THE SKILL

1. Choose a time when you are feeling tense or tired and try the progressive relaxation method. Find a quiet spot and spend about 15 or 20 minutes doing the exercise.

Before you begin, write down how you feel and what is on your mind. After you finish, write down how you felt during and after the exercise.

2. Teach the progressive relaxation technique to a friend or relative. After they have tried it, discuss with them their reactions to and feelings about the technique. What other techniques have they used to handle the stress in their lives? How does this technique compare to those?

3. For a quick relaxation technique, simply tense the muscles in your whole body, as in the last part of step 2. Hold for 10 seconds and release. Repeat three times. Try this technique when you feel stress during the day, such as before an exam or competition. Did the technique help you to relax? List some other times during a typical day that this technique might be helpful.

4. For one week, practice the progressive relaxation technique twice a day. Try to set aside some time each morning and evening to do the exercise. Each time, record how you felt before, during, and after doing the exercise.

3 ▌Chapter Review

Chapter Summary

- Stress is a reaction of the mind and body to a stressor—a situation, event, or person—that makes a demand on the individual.
- Stress can be positive or negative. Positive stress is eustress; negative stress is distress.
- People manage stress with coping strategies.
- A number of life changes over a short time can lead to distress.
- People undergo a three-stage reaction to stress, called the general adaptation syndrome. The stages of the syndrome are alarm, resistance, and exhaustion.
- During the alarm stage, the body prepares itself to deal with the stressor. This is known as the fight or flight response. During resistance, the body tries to regain homeostasis. If the body remains under stress, it enters the exhaustion stage.
- Stress can lower the body's resistance to illness and make some diseases worse.

- Personality affects the response to stressors. Type A personalities view stressors as challenges but may experience distress. Type B personalities tend to ignore stressors and may miss opportunities.
- The coping strategies used to handle stress can be either constructive or unconstructive. Constructive coping strategies last a short time and are appropriate to the situation.
- Common coping strategies include denial, sublimation, daydreaming, and humor.
- Most of the skills used to maintain health are also ways to manage stress.
- Methods for managing stress include relaxation, creative visualization, and biofeedback.
- Many people need help in managing stress from time to time. Many sources of help, including friends, family members, teachers, clergy, school counselors, and other specialists, can help people deal with stress.

Vocabulary Review

Listed below are some of the important terms in this chapter. Choose the term that best matches the phrase in the exercise that follows.

adrenaline
alarm stage
biofeedback
creative visualization
distress
eustress

exhaustion stage
fight or flight response
general adaptation
   syndrome
high blood pressure
homeostasis

psychosomatic
   symptoms
relaxation
resistance stage
stress

stressor
symptoms
type A personality
type B personality
ulcer

1. stress that produces positive effects
2. reaction of the body and mind to something in everyday life
3. series of stages by which the body reacts to a stressor
4. ways in which the mind affects the body
5. state in which the body's internal functions remain balanced, even when the external environment changes

6. personality that is competitive, driven to achieve, and likely to create stressors
7. the state in which the mind and body are at rest
8. method of using the imagination to cope with stressors
9. open sore in the lining of the stomach
10. substance that produces a burst of energy in the body

What Have You Learned?

1. What is stress? What is a stressor?
2. Explain how eustress and distress differ.
3. What are coping strategies?
4. What happens to your body during the fight or flight response?
5. How can you use the physical changes of the fight or flight response to help you cope with stress?
6. Describe the general adaptation syndrome.
7. Why does the body need to regain homeostasis after facing a stressor?
8. In what ways can stress lead to illness?
9. How does your personality affect your experience of stress?
10. What is the difference between a constructive and unconstructive coping strategy?
11. Why is good stress management healthy?
12. Describe some relaxation techniques.

What Do You Think?

1. Name three things your school could do to help reduce student stress.
2. Many people who experience serious distress do not seek help. Why is this so?
3. What might life be like if there were no stress at all?
4. Why do you think distress is linked to changes in a person's life?
5. How would the fight or flight response help you if you were in a car accident?
6. What special stress management methods would be most useful to you? Why?

What Would You Do?

1. Last year you found that you experienced a lot of distress at exam time. Imagine that in four weeks, it will be exam time again. What could you do to cope better with the stress?
2. Your best friend is complaining of stiff, cramped muscles. The problem has become worse since her parents separated. How would you help her?
3. You have decided to run for class president and must make a speech in front of the student body. What can you do to help yourself perform better during your speech?
4. You have a friend who is involved in so many activities that he no longer has time for you. Lately, he complains that he "can't think straight anymore." What advice would you give him?
5. You become overwhelmed during a test and have difficulty concentrating. What can you do to help yourself regain control?
6. Review Figure 3-1 and determine how much life changes might be affecting the level of stress you are now experiencing. If your stress is high, how might you reduce it?

For Further Study

1. Keep a stress journal for one week. During the week, note the stressors you face, the ways in which your mind and body react to these stressors, and the coping strategies you use. At the end of the week, determine whether your coping strategies were constructive or unconstructive. Consider other coping strategies that you might have used.
2. At the library, find out more about the work of Hans Selye, the scientist who first identified the general adaptation syndrome. What else did he say about stress in our lives? What other research did he do?

**4**

As you read, think about

▶ what mental disorders are and what may cause them.

▶ how mental disorders are recognized and classified.

▶ how to recognize signs of suicide and how to help prevent it.

▶ how mental disorders can be prevented and treated.

Understanding Mental Disorders

When you begin your sculpture, you don't fully concentrate on what you are doing. You're feeling anxious and depressed, and your thoughts are on your troubles. As your fingers knead the clay, you find you are focusing on the form you are shaping, and you realize that you are feeling a little better.

Expressing your feelings through some art form or by talking with another person often can relieve feelings of depression. Sometimes, however, emotions can get out of control. Then, special help is needed. In this chapter, you will learn about various mental disorders, how they develop, and what can be done to control them. You'll also find out about the services that are available for help in times of emotional crisis.

Everyone is depressed now and then. Having an outlet helps when you feel "down."

1. WHAT ARE MENTAL DISORDERS?

When are some types of behavior considered normal and appropriate? Why are some types of behavior considered abnormal and inappropriate? As you read about the teenagers described below, would you say they were displaying healthy or unhealthy behavior?

In the last six months, Linda has become more and more concerned about germs. She washes her hands at least 100 times a day, scrubs the doorknobs in her house, and insists that her knives, forks, and spoons should be boiled before she uses them.

Bob is an avid skateboarder. Since his parents' divorce, he has used his skateboard in increasingly dangerous situations. Now, he regularly dodges cars and trucks as he skateboards across a four-lane highway near school.

Pat is five feet six inches tall and weighs 97 pounds. For the past year, she has been on a strict diet of cottage cheese, lettuce, and water. She still considers herself heavy and wants to lose five pounds.

Willy enjoys collecting pictures and descriptions of past wars. Outside of school, he spends all of his spare time in his room organizing his collection. He has no time for friends or social activities.

Recognizing Mental Disorders

Most mental health specialists would agree that each of these teenagers shows signs of a mental disorder. A **mental disorder** is an illness that affects the mind and prevents a person from being productive, adjusting to life situations, and getting along with others. Most mental disorders are characterized by abnormal thoughts, feelings, or behaviors that make people uncomfortable with themselves or at odds with others. **Abnormal** means that a person behaves, feels, or thinks in a way that is highly unusual and inappropriate in a given situation. Washing your hands before eating is considered normal behavior. Washing your hands 100 times a day like Linda is considered abnormal. When a mental disorder is present, its signs usually occur frequently and over a long period of time.

Labeling a person as mentally ill is difficult. It involves making a judgment. Unlike a cold or the flu, the signs of mental disorders are not always easy to identify. For example, it is sometimes hard to tell if someone is seriously depressed or just appropriately sad.

Check Your Wellness

How much do you know about mental disorders? To test your knowledge, decide whether each of the statements below is true or false.

1. Some physical diseases, such as brain tumors, may lead to mental disorders.
2. If feelings of depression are long-lasting and interfere with everyday activities, a person should seek professional help.
3. Some mental disorders, such as clinical depression, tend to run in families.
4. Eating disorders, such as anorexia nervosa and bulimia, are really mental disorders.
5. Many suicide victims talk about committing suicide before they actually do it.
6. Some warning signs of mental illness are: sudden personality change, inability to concentrate, risky behaviors, and persistent feelings of hopelessness.
7. Help for mental problems is available from many sources, including school counselors, hotlines, crisis centers, clergy, local hospitals, and mental health clinics.

Since each person exists as part of a particular society and culture, each person's notion of mental illness is shaped by his or her culture, as well as his or her family and community experiences. **Culture** is the ideas, customs, expectations, and ways of living that characterize a particular group of people. A behavior or way of thinking that might be considered normal in our culture may be considered abnormal in another culture. Look at Figure 4-1. Would these behaviors be considered abnormal in another culture? Are they considered normal in our culture?

You may be surprised to find that not everyone in your class agrees on what is normal or abnormal behavior. Mental health specialists also do not always agree. For this reason, mental health specialists meet every so often to discuss mental disorders. They define and describe mental disorders and group them according to similar symptoms, which are the signs or evidence of an illness.

Over the years, the descriptions and classifications of mental disorders have changed. Today, over 230 types of mental disorders are recognized. Although many experts agree on the kinds of mental disorders, there are still many different opinions about the causes.

Causes of Mental Disorders

Some mental disorders have been traced to physical causes. When the cause of a mental disorder is physical, the mental disorder is classified as an **organic disorder.** The type of brain damage caused by the misuse of alcohol or drugs, such as cocaine, is an example of an organic disorder. The mental confusion and loss of brain function that can occur if an individual has a growth, or tumor, in the brain is another example. This condition is known as **dementia** (dih **men** shuh). There are other diseases that also lead to dementia.

Mental disorders not due to alcohol, drugs, or disease are called **functional** (**fung** shuh nul) **disorders.** These disorders can be caused by personal experiences, such as painful childhood experiences or a series of stressful events. These experiences are known as **environmental factors.**

The exact cause of many mental disorders is not understood. Sometimes, there are a combination of factors involved. These factors can include inborn causes, early experiences, and current causes.

INBORN CAUSES Some mental disorders may be inherited, or passed on to an individual before birth, like other physical characteristics, such as eye color and body type. Sometimes, an individual may inherit a tendency toward a disorder. The disorder may only become apparent when it is set off by an environmental factor, such as repeated physical abuse or a series of difficult events.

Figure 4-1. Some unusual behaviors may be considered normal in our culture.

Figure 4-2. Positive parent-child interactions affect a child's personality. ▶

Mental disorders may be due to inherited, physical, or environmental factors such as stressful experiences.

EARLY EXPERIENCES Other mental disorders may be the result of unresolved conflicts. As you may recall from Chapter 2, Sigmund Freud, the founder of psychoanalysis, believed that these unresolved conflicts often involve childhood or early life experiences. Today, psychoanalysts help people to connect the symptoms of mental disorders with difficult early experiences and unresolved inner conflicts.

CURRENT CAUSES Some mental health specialists think that current environmental influences are more important than early childhood experiences in explaining a mental disorder. They consider the significant people in the individual's life, as well as the individual. When treating an individual, these mental health specialists often include persons, such as the patient's family, who are important to the patient.

Section Review

1. What is a mental disorder?
2. Why is it sometimes difficult for someone to recognize a mental disorder?
3. What is the difference between organic disorders and functional disorders?
4. Give four examples of various possible causes of mental disorders.

What Do You Think?
5. Why do you think that some people seek a doctor's help for a physical disease, such as flu, but hesitate to seek professional help for a mental disorder?

2. KINDS OF MENTAL DISORDERS

Every mental disorder has many different symptoms, depending upon the individual. For this reason, it is difficult to describe in detail specific mental disorders. A **case history,** a brief description of someone who suffers from a disorder, is often used to give a general picture of the disorder. A case history focuses on only a few symptoms of a disorder, but these symptoms are usually the ones most frequently experienced. You should remember when you read a case history that only a trained, experienced mental health professional can diagnose a mental disorder.

There usually is more than one way to treat a mental disorder. The particular **therapy,** or treatment technique, chosen depends upon the individual and the training of the **therapist,** the mental health professional. More will be said about the different types of therapies in the last section of this chapter.

Anxiety Disorders

Have you ever been afraid of a situation, person, or object that you knew could not really harm you? Have you been fearful without knowing why? If so, you have experienced **anxiety** (ang **zy** ih tee). Anxiety is fear that does not have an identifiable source or fear caused by a danger that no longer exists. Severe anxiety can cause people to flee from situations or objects that cannot really harm them.

> **Case History:** Martin was going on a job interview. As he walked toward the elevator, he began to feel dizzy and nauseous. His heart began to pound, and he had trouble catching his breath. He knew he could not face getting into the elevator so he climbed three flights of stairs to get to his interview on time.

Everyone experiences some anxiety at one time or another. For example, you may feel anxious before a final exam, a big date, or tryouts for the basketball team. These feelings are normal and usually short-lived. When anxiety persists and interferes with normal, everyday functioning, however, it may be a sign of an **anxiety disorder.**

PHOBIC DISORDERS When anxiety is related to a specific situation or object, it is called a **phobia** (**foh** bee uh). One of the most common phobias is **agoraphobia** (ag uh ruh **foh** bee uh), the fear of going out alone. People with agoraphobia are often too frightened to leave their own homes. Figure 4-3 lists some common types of phobias.

Common Phobias

Acrophobia
A fear of high places
Agoraphobia
A fear of going out alone
Ailurophobia
A fear of cats
Algophobia
A fear of pain
Astraphobia
A fear of lightning and thunder
Claustrophobia
A fear of small, closed-in places
Cynophobia
A fear of dogs
Hydrophobia
A fear of water
Monophobia
A fear of being alone
Mysophobia
A fear of dirt and germs
Nyctophobia
A fear of darkness
Ophidiophobia
A fear of snakes
Pyrophobia
A fear of fire
Thanatophobia
A fear of death and dying
Xenophobia
A fear of strangers and the unknown
Zoophobia
A fear of animals

Figure 4-3. Which phobias might interfere with normal, everyday activities?

Figure 4-4. People with claustro- ▶
phobia might feel uneasy in a
large crowd.

When Martin, the person in the case history, sought help in handling his severe anxiety, he was diagnosed as having **claustrophobia** (klaw struh **foh** bee uh). Claustrophobia is the fear of small, closed places. Martin overcame his fear through **psychotherapy** (sy koh **thehr** uh pee). Psychotherapy is conversation with a trained therapist who helps an individual understand and overcome the cause of a mental problem. In Martin's case, the therapist discovered that as a small child, Martin had fallen into a well and had been trapped for several hours. The terror Martin had felt during this experience was the source of his anxiety. Once Martin was able to understand the roots of his anxiety and that the danger he associated with closed places no longer existed, he was able to overcome his fear.

GENERAL ANXIETY AND PANIC DISORDERS
When a person is anxious and cannot specify a cause for the anxiety, it is called a **general anxiety disorder.** When attacks of extreme anxiety come and go for no apparent reason, it is called a **panic disorder.** A person with a panic disorder can be anywhere when he or she suddenly starts to feel panicky or extremely anxious.

OBSESSIVE-COMPULSIVE DISORDER   Sometimes, people respond to anxiety by letting an idea or thought take over their mind. An idea or thought that takes over the mind and cannot be forgotten is called an **obsession** (uhb **sesh** un). A person with an obsession that leads to a **compulsion** (kum **puhl** shun), an unreasonable need to behave in a certain way, has an **obsessive-compulsive disorder.**

Obsessive-compulsive disorders lead to an uncontrollable need to think or act in a certain way.

Remember the case history of Linda at the beginning of this chapter? Linda suffers from an obsessive-compulsive disorder. Because of some deep-seated anxiety, she is obsessed with catching germs. This causes her to behave in a compulsive way: washing her hands constantly, scrubbing doorknobs, and boiling knives, spoons, and forks.

Affective Disorders

When the moods or emotions a person feels become extreme and interfere with the person's daily life, it is known as an **affective disorder.**

Case History: Ever since Jason's girlfriend broke up with him, he has been feeling sad and hopeless. Jason used to love playing in the school band, but now he has decided to quit playing the drums altogether. He is having trouble sleeping and feels tired all the time. His grades have fallen from a B average to a D average.

Everyone feels depressed now and then. It is normal to feel depressed if you experience an important loss or a failure in your life. For example, you would expect to feel depressed if you just broke up with someone you loved, if you had recently moved to a new school, or if you didn't make a team you tried for. Usually, however, the feeling of depression lifts after a few days or weeks, and you get on with your life. In Jason's case, however, his feelings of hopelessness and depression are taking over his life, leaving him unable to cope with everyday activities.

CLINICAL DEPRESSION When a person is overwhelmed by sad feelings for months and stops being able to carry out everyday activities, it is called **clinical depression.** Clinical depression can be caused by a stressor, or it can be a symptom of another disease, such as alcoholism. Depression also tends to run in families. Negative attitudes learned early in life may also contribute to clinical depression.

Many people receive treatment for depression outside of a hospital or clinic. If a depressed person becomes extremely withdrawn, dangerous, or suicidal, it may be necessary for the person to enter a hospital for treatment.

Some of the early signs of clinical depression are listed in Figure 4-5. Some teenagers who develop clinical depression lose interest in most of their usual activities and become withdrawn like Jason. Other teenagers may become overly active or put themselves in risky situations like Bob, whom you read about at the start of this chapter. Anyone who has the symptoms of clinical depression should seek help from a parent, teacher, guidance counselor, physician, or another health-care professional.

Signs of Clinical Depression

A person probably is suffering from clinical depression if the person feels sad and hopeless and has at least four of the following symptoms nearly every day for at least two weeks:

1. Change in appetite: either poor appetite with significant weight loss or increased appetite with significant weight gain
2. Change in sleep patterns: either difficulty sleeping or sleeping too much
3. Change in activity level: either increased physical activity or slowed down levels of activity
4. Loss of interest or pleasure in usual activities
5. Loss of energy, feeling tired all the time
6. Feelings of worthlessness; excessive or inappropriate guilty feelings
7. Difficulty thinking or concentrating
8. Recurrent thoughts of death and suicide

Figure 4-5. What would you do if a friend showed signs of clinical depression?

Manic Depression: An Inherited Defect?

Recent studies suggest that some forms of manic depression may be inherited through the body's chromosomes. Scientists studying three Amish families in Pennsylvania recently linked manic depression to a defect on the tip of chromosome 11. A similar study of non-Amish families in the United States found no evidence of this defect. Since there are many manic depressives who are not Amish, this finding supports the theory that manic depression may be the result of two defects.

A study of five families in Israel suggests that manic depression is also linked to a defect on the X chromosome. Scientists think that this defect, which has not been identified yet, may be responsible for one-third of all cases of manic depression.

Once these chromosome defects are identified, researchers will be able to study individuals who have inherited one or more of them. These studies could lead to an understanding of the factors that cause the disease.

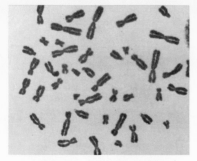

Can chromosomes carry defects leading to manic depression?

With help, clinical depression can be eased and will usually go away. With help, individuals suffering from clinical depression can learn new strategies for coping with problems. Jason and Bob found the help they needed through group therapy. **Group therapy** involves talking with others who share the same problems as you. A therapist usually leads the group. Group members give each other emotional support and work together to develop better coping strategies and a more positive outlook on life.

MANIC-DEPRESSIVE DISORDER   Normally, people have moods that shift from happy and lively to sad and somewhat disinterested, depending on what is happening in their lives. People who suffer from a **manic-depressive disorder** shift from one emotional extreme to another for no apparent reason. During a manic episode, manic depressives usually become overly excited and restless. They may talk so rapidly that you cannot follow what they are trying to say. They may have difficulty concentrating for long on any one thing. They frequently show poor judgment. They may overspend during a shopping spree, for example, or they may drive recklessly. These manic episodes alternate with periods of deep depression. In between these periods of extreme moods, manic depressives may behave normally.

Manic depression can be treated with a combination of psychotherapy and drug therapy. **Drug therapy** is the use of special medications to relieve some or all of the symptoms of a mental disorder. Often, people with mild cases of manic depression receive treatment outside of a hospital. People with more severe cases may need to be hospitalized so that they can undergo treatment.

Eating Disorders

Perhaps you recognized the symptoms of an eating disorder when you read the case history of Pat at the beginning of this chapter. An estimated 4 percent of the teenaged girls in this country suffer from an eating disorder called **anorexia nervosa** (an uh **rek** see uh nur **voh** suh). Anorexia nervosa is a refusal to eat normally or to retain food in the body. The main symptom is an extreme loss of body weight. A person suffering from anorexia nervosa can starve to death.

Because of her extreme weight loss, Pat was hospitalized. After her weight and eating habits were stabilized, she received psychotherapy along with the members of her family. With prompt attention from a mental health professional and cooperation from the patient and family members, anorexia nervosa can be treated successfully.

Another eating disorder found among teenaged girls is **bulimia** (boo **lim** ee uh). Individuals go on eating binges followed by purging, or getting rid of the food they have eaten. Often bulimics get rid of the food they have eaten through self-induced vomiting. Aside from mental problems, bulimics may also have some serious physical problems, including damaged kidneys, teeth, gums, stomach, and heart. As with anorexia nervosa, persons suffering from bulimia require the assistance of a mental health professional as soon as possible.

Somatoform Disorders

A mental disorder in which a person complains of physical symptoms, such as pain, but there is no underlying physical cause for the symptoms is known as **somatoform** (soh **mat** uh form) **disorder.**

Case History: Juanita is convinced that she is about to become seriously ill. Each morning she takes her temperature. After school she reads popular health magazines for the symptoms of major illnesses. At least once a week, she goes to the school nurse's office complaining of chest pains, headaches, or stomachaches. She blames her poor performance in school on her poor health. The school nurse and the school physician tell Juanita that there is nothing wrong with her physically, but Juanita does not believe them.

Juanita is suffering from a somatoform disorder commonly known as **hypochondria** (hy puh **kahn** dree uh). Sometimes, the underlying cause of hypochondria is anxiety or depression. In Juanita's case, the cause was anxiety. Juanita was extremely anxious about doing well in school because her older brother and sister had both excelled in school. Juanita was helped through psychotherapy.

Many people confuse somatoform disorders such as hypochondria with the stress-related symptoms and illnesses discussed in Chapter 3. Stress-related conditions are characterized by real physical damage to the body. With somatoform disorders, a person complains of disease symptoms, but no physical damage can be found.

Personality Disorders

Every person has a different way of dealing with life situations. You may like to have every minute of your day carefully planned, or you may love to do things on the spur of the moment. You may be neat, or you may be messy. You may crave time to yourself, or you may always like being with others. As you learned in Chapter 2, these long-lasting patterns of behavior are formed during your childhood. They are a part of the normal range of traits that, together, make up your personality.

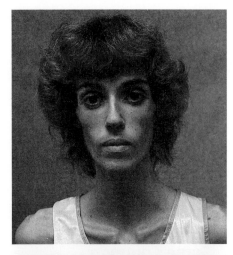

Figure 4-6. Through psychotherapy and strong family support, this young woman overcame anorexia nervosa.

Figure 4-7. Most people can get along with people with different personalities.

Some Common Personality Disorders

- **Antisocial:** Disregard for rights of others; inability to hold a job or stay in school; impulsive with no regard for the consequences. Early signs frequently include lying, stealing, and fighting.
- **Dependent:** Allows and seeks others to assume responsibility for actions; lacks self-confidence; cannot function independently; usually gives in to wishes of others.
- **Histrionic:** Overly dramatic; needs to always be the center of attention; seeks excitement; overreacts.
- **Narcissistic:** Exaggerated sense of self-importance; has fantasies of unlimited success; usually needs constant attention and admiration.
- **Paranoid:** Suspicious for no reason; envies and mistrusts others; overly sensitive; limited emotional reactions; rarely seeks help.

Figure 4-8. People with personality disorders are often unaware that a problem exists.

A **personality disorder** is characterized by behavior that is inflexible and interferes with a person's pursuit of a happy, healthy life. Because personality traits usually are deeply entrenched by young adulthood, these disorders often require long-term treatment. Figure 4-8 lists a number of personality disorders in addition to the ones described below.

COMPULSIVE PERSONALITY DISORDER Following a set routine can be helpful, but some people carry this activity to an extreme. It is the focus of their lives.

> **Case History:** Alex is obsessed with doing everything on a set schedule. For example, every morning he follows an unvarying routine of exercises, followed by tidying up his room. Alex becomes extremely agitated if his routine is interrupted for any reason.

Alex is showing the symptoms of a **compulsive personality disorder,** which is characterized by the compulsion to do things in a set way over and over again. People with this disorder need to have a set routine for everything they do.

PASSIVE-AGGRESSIVE PERSONALITY DISORDER Persons with **passive-aggressive personality disorders** depend on others to direct them. At the same time, they resent being told what to do. Unable to express their anger openly, they vent it indirectly.

> **Case History:** LeRoy hates his after-school job. Every day he arrives late and leaves early. His boss criticizes him for doing his work slowly and sloppily. Half the time, LeRoy "forgets" to do what his boss has told him.

LeRoy shows many of the signs of a passive-aggressive personality: chronic lateness, forgetfulness, slowness, and sloppiness. He expresses his resentment indirectly, through his failure to be reliable.

OPPOSITIONAL DISORDER Some mental health specialists think that a passive-aggressive personality disorder has its roots in a childhood disorder called an **oppositional** (ahp uh **zish** uh nul) **disorder.** An oppositional disorder is characterized by behavior that causes constant conflict with others. For example, a child or a teenager with an oppositional disorder is often stubborn, may frequently disregard the rights of others, has outbursts of temper, and argues constantly with other people.

SCHIZOID PERSONALITY DISORDER People who are totally withdrawn from others, that is, who show no warm feelings toward other people, may suffer from a **schizoid** (**skit** soyd) **personality disorder.** They often avoid contact with others. Any criticism of their behavior tends to make them withdraw further. Willy, the boy in the case history at the beginning of this chapter, shows some of the symptoms of a schizoid personality disorder.

DISSOCIATIVE DISORDERS Suppose you read a newspaper article that began "Joan Smith was found wandering the streets of a major city in winter. She was wearing summer clothing and did not know who she was." What would you think? A **dissociative disorder** is a mental disorder in which persons become disconnected from, or dissociated from, their former identity. Joan shows signs of **amnesia** (am **nee** zhuh), the sudden loss of memory. Amnesia may be brought on by a severe **trauma** (**trow** muh), a painful physical or emotional experience. For example, a person who witnesses the death of a loved one may develop amnesia. Amnesia may last a short time or for the rest of a person's life.

Another dissociative disorder is called **multiple personality disorder.** People with this disorder change between two or more separate personalities. Usually, they are not aware of the different personalities coexisting within their minds. They are also unable to control or predict their changes in personality. Although in real life multiple personality disorder is extremely rare, you may know about it from some popular books or movies.

SCHIZOPHRENIA Severe mental disorders characterized by unpredictable disturbances in thinking, mood, awareness, and behavior are known as **schizophrenia** (skit suh **free** nee uh). Schizophrenia means "split mind." People with this mental disorder have minds that are "split off" from reality.

▲
Figure 4-9. The movie *Sybil* portrayed a woman suffering from multiple personality disorder.

Figure 4-10. These self-portraits, done by a schizophrenic, reflect the artist's mental state before (left) and after (right) receiving treatment.

Schizophrenics withdraw into a world of make-believe as their minds "split," or become detached, from reality.

Schizophrenics are rarely harmful to others. At times they may appear to be normal. As the disease progresses, schizophrenics become more and more withdrawn and seem to lack emotion.

Schizophrenic disorders that are characterized by the false belief that others are trying to harm or influence a person are known as **paranoid** (**par** uh noyd) **schizophrenic disorders.** People with paranoid schizophrenic disorders may believe that they are being controlled by aliens or that there is a worldwide plot against them.

Figure 4-10 shows drawings done by a teenager who is schizophrenic. The drawing on the left shows a state of mental confusion. The drawing on the right shows that, with successful treatment, the artist's mental state has improved.

The treatment for schizophrenia varies. In many cases, drug therapy has helped. Drug therapy may be used alone or in combination with other kinds of therapies.

Section Review

1. What is a phobic disorder and how can it be treated?
2. How can you tell if a person is appropriately depressed or clinically depressed?
3. What is a somatoform disorder? How does it differ from a psychosomatic illness?
4. What are the symptoms of schizophrenia?

What Do You Think?
5. How would you react if you found out that a friend was taking medication regularly for a mental disorder?

3. SUICIDE

It takes tolerance
Not to give in to death,
To resist the temptation
How easy just to die.
To keep on living an empty life
Takes patience from an empty person.

A teenager named Vivienne wrote this poem. She committed suicide when she was fourteen. From this poem, would you have realized Vivienne was thinking of suicide?

Suicide affects all kinds of people: young, old, bright, average, handsome, homely, rich, poor, female, male. In this country, it is one of the leading causes of death among teenagers. In fact, in the last 25 years, the number of suicides has tripled among young people between the ages of 15 and 24.

The Warning Signs

Suicides can be prevented if people know how to recognize and help potential victims. How much do you know about the problem of suicide? Figure 4-11 presents some of the myths and facts about suicide. Severe depression may

Figure 4-11. Why is it important to reveal a friend's "secret" about suicide?

▼

Myths and Facts About Suicide

1. **Myth:** People who talk about suicide seldom actually attempt suicide.
   Fact: Suicide victims often talk about committing suicide before they actually do it.
2. **Myth:** If you dare a suicidal person to go ahead and do it, the person is not likely to attempt suicide.
   Fact: Daring a suicidal person to go ahead and attempt suicide may only confirm in that person's mind that nobody really cares and may strengthen the person's resolve to commit suicide.
3. **Myth:** Suicidal persons are always tired, sad, and inactive.
   Fact: Some suicidal persons, teenagers in particular, may suddenly become overly active and aggressive before attempting to take their own lives.
4. **Myth:** If a suicidal person confides in you and makes you promise not to tell anyone of his or her plans to commit suicide, you should keep the secret no matter what.
   Fact: By sharing the secret with a parent, teacher, or other responsible adult, you may save the suicidal person's life.
5. **Myth:** If a depressed, suicidal person suddenly seems better, you do not need to worry.
   Fact: A suicidal person's sudden shift in mood from depressed to happy may indicate that he or she has resolved to commit suicide and needs help.
6. **Myth:** If people try to take their own lives and do not succeed, they usually will not try to do it again.
   Fact: Suicide victims often have a history of several attempts on their own lives.
7. **Myth:** If people have a history of suicide in their families, they are unlikely to attempt suicide because they know how much pain it can cause to others.
   Fact: People may become suicidal because of a loss of a family member or they may feel that the tendency to commit suicide runs in their family and there is nothing they can do about their own suicidal feelings.
8. **Myth:** Suicide attempts should be kept secret because the information could ruin a suicidal person's future life.
   Fact: The suicidal person may have no future unless professional help is sought.

Earlier suicide attempts or radical changes in behavior are warning signs that a person may be planning suicide.

cause a person to give up. Anyone who is suffering from a major depression should be watched carefully.

Of course, any previous attempt at suicide is a signal that a person needs help, but there are other, less obvious signals. Radical changes in a person's personality often are a sign of possible danger. An outgoing person suddenly withdraws from people, for example, or a shy, retiring person suddenly becomes aggressive, irritable, or overly active. These people may be showing signs of severe depression and could be thinking about suicide.

Sometimes, a person's actions are a warning sign. If a person stops doing things that he or she enjoys and gives away favorite belongings, the person may be in need of help. Another sign, which is especially common among severely depressed teenagers, is a sudden increase in risk-taking behavior and accidents. Bob's case history at the start of this chapter is a good example of this type of behavior. Bob was risking his life every time he skateboarded across the highway near his school. Bob's depression led him almost to the edge of suicide.

Sometimes a major trauma may bring a person to the brink of suicide. Moving to a new place, losing a boyfriend or girlfriend, getting a serious illness, having a family member or friend die, or going through a family divorce, all can lead to depression and, sometimes, suicide.

Sometimes a suicide or an attempted suicide triggers a particularly tragic form of suicide known as cluster suicide.

Friend to Friend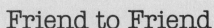

Laura:
I'm really worried about Joan. She seems so depressed lately. She acts like a zombie.

Carla:
I'm worried too. On Tuesday, she didn't show up at the movies as we planned. She didn't even apologize to me. She didn't seem to care. It's just not like her.

Laura:
I can't believe it. And, yesterday, when I stopped by her house to see why she missed school, she asked me if I would take Pappy.

Carla:
She wanted you to take Pappy? But, she adores that dog. It just doesn't make sense.

Cluster suicides, which are frequently associated with teenagers, occur when several people in the same school or social group attempt to kill themselves within a short period of time. To prevent cluster suicides, all the people in the school or social group where a suicide or an attempted suicide has occurred should receive counseling.

Suicide signals can be deceptive.

The warning signs of suicide can be deceptive. If a person you know has been severely depressed and suddenly becomes happy and carefree, you may conclude that the problem has passed. This is not necessarily so. A sudden change from depressed to happy may mean that the person has resolved to end his or her life. The person feels happy because the decision is made.

Suicidal behavior is a cry for help in dealing with problems that seem impossible. Showing your care and concern is only the first step in getting help for the person.

Prevention

If people act promptly to get professional help, often suicides can be prevented. Figure 4-12 offers some of the "do's" and "don't's" for dealing with people who are potential suicide victims.

Suicidal teenagers often feel that they have looked to others for support and have received no response. It is vital for friends and relatives to respond with concern and interest. If you believe that a friend is thinking of suicide, or if

Laura:
Remember that program on suicide last month? The speaker said that one of the warning signs of suicide is when a person gives away her favorite possessions. I think Joan may be in serious trouble.

Carla:
I think you're right. What should we do?

Laura:
We've got to talk to someone. This is no time to keep things to ourselves. Let's go talk to Mr. McCarthy, my counselor. He'll know what to do.

How to Help a Suicidal Person

Do	Don't
Trust your feelings if you believe the person may be suicidal.	Dare the suicidal person to go ahead and make the suicide attempt.
Take seriously a suicidal person's threats.	Judge the suicidal person.
Tell the suicidal person how concerned you are and how much you care about him or her.	Analyze the suicidal person's motives.
Listen carefully to the suicidal person.	Argue or try to convince the suicidal person of reasons why he or she should not attempt suicide.
Talk calmly with the suicidal person.	Keep the suicidal person's self-destructive thoughts or actions a secret.
Find professional help for the suicidal person.	
Stay with the suicidal person until help arrives.	Leave a suicidal person alone with no help.

Figure 4-12. What is the most important thing that a friend can do to help a suicidal person?

you become aware of a suicide pact among a group of teenagers, you should report it immediately to an adult, such as a parent, teacher, or physician. Sometimes, a friend may make you promise not to tell anyone about a plan to commit suicide. Whether or not your friend realizes it, by confiding in you, your friend is asking for help. To help your friend, you must break the promise and notify an adult that your friend is in danger.

Suicide is not a reasonable or useful solution to a problem. Suicidal people usually want to get rid of their pain or sense of helplessness, not their lives. You can help by listening to and providing support for friends or family members who are feeling depressed, hopeless, or overwhelmed by stress. When the support you offer is backed by professional intervention, a life may be saved.

In most communities, crisis centers and suicide prevention hotlines provide support for suicidal and depressed people. Some communities have hotlines that are staffed by specially trained, concerned teenagers who help depressed teenagers. The telephone number of the crisis centers and hotlines in your area can be obtained by calling the information operator in your area.

Figure 4-13. If you are depressed, instead of being alone it is better to talk to people you trust.

Section Review

1. What are four warning signs of suicide?
2. Is it "true" that a person who talks about committing suicide never does? Explain.
3. What should you do if someone is suicidal?
4. How can cluster suicides be prevented?

What Do You Think?

5. Why do you think cluster suicides occur most frequently among teenagers?

4. TREATING MENTAL DISORDERS

Can mental disorders be prevented? To some extent, they can be. The surest way to prevent mental disorders is to work constantly to improve your mental health. Here are a few ways that you can promote your own mental health.

- Express your feelings to others.
- Set realistic goals for yourself.
- Recognize your strengths as well as your weaknesses.
- Accept your shortcomings.
- Show respect for yourself and others.
- Keep a list of things you enjoy and things you do well.
- Maintain friendships.
- Reward yourself when you achieve a goal, such as maintaining your proper weight or exercising daily.
- Take good care of yourself by getting enough rest and eating a healthful diet.
- Practice behaving in an independent, responsible way.
- Handle problems as they come up.
- Try to do your best but do not expect to be perfect.
- Be honest with yourself and others.
- Avoid alcohol and drugs.
- Keep disappointments in perspective.
- Seek the help of a physician or mental health professional if you think you need it.

Are there other ways to promote your mental health?

When to Seek Help

About one out of every five adults in this country is likely to suffer from a mental disorder at some time during his or her life. The first step toward recovery is recognizing the need for help. Do not ignore the warning signs of mental illness. Some of these warning signs include:

- a sudden, radical change in personality
- self-destructive actions: overeating, undereating, alcohol or drug abuse, and risky behaviors
- violent, uncontrollable shifts in mood
- persistent feelings of worthlessness or hopelessness
- deepening sadness that interferes with functioning
- sleep disturbances
- inability to concentrate on anything
- trouble getting along with others
- paralyzing attacks of fear or anger
- frequent illness without a physical cause
- obsessive thoughts or compulsive actions
- delusions or hallucinations

▲
Figure 4-14. Social workers, occupational therapists, and hotline counselors are specially trained to help people with problems.

Where to Find Help

In most communities, it is not difficult to find help. Often, a parent, teacher, school counselor, physician, or religious leader can tell you about local mental health professionals. Information on support groups for the families of the mentally ill can be obtained by calling or writing the National Alliance for the Mentally Ill in Arlington, Virginia.

In many communities, local hospitals have mental health centers. Other communities have special mental health centers or clinics. The Family Service Association of America also has agencies throughout the country that offer counseling and mental health education programs. Some communities have drop-in centers for teenagers. The counselors in these centers provide teenagers with help and guidance.

Types of Help

There are many types of mental health professionals. These are people who are specially trained to recognize and treat mental disorders. The type of treatment they offer depends upon their training.

PSYCHIATRISTS Doctors who specialize in the treatment of mental disorders are called **psychiatrists** (sy **ky** uh trist). Psychiatrists are M.D.s (doctors of medicine) with advanced training in the treatment of mental illnesses. They are trained to look for physical, as well as nonphysical, reasons for mental illnesses. They not only talk with the patients, and often the patient's family, to identify symptoms of a mental disorder but also examine the patient for signs of a physical cause of the illness. After diagnosing a disorder, a psychiatrist may treat the disorder in a variety of ways. Because psychiatrists are medical doctors, they can prescribe medications. Another approach is the use of psychotherapy. Frequently, psychiatrists use a combination of drug therapy and psychotherapy. If a psychiatrist suspects that a patient's symptoms may have an organic cause, he or she may recommend testing by a **neurologist** (nu **rahl** uh jist). A neurologist is a physician who specializes in detecting and treating organic disorders of the brain and nervous system.

PSYCHOLOGISTS   The study of the mind and behavior is called psychology. A psychologist is someone who has earned an academic degree in psychology. Psychologists are not medical doctors, but they usually have a master's degree or a Ph.D. in psychology or a related field.

Clinical psychologists are mental health professionals who specialize in recognizing and treating abnormal behavior. In addition to a Ph.D. degree in psychology, they usually have at least two years of practical training in a psychiatric hospital. Because they are not medical doctors, clinical psychologists cannot prescribe medications.

Psychologists often work with psychiatrists. A psychologist may help a psychiatrist diagnose a mental disorder or give tests to determine the psychological condition of a patient. Others also treat patients with psychotherapy.

SOCIAL WORKERS   Social workers usually complete four years of college and two years of study in a school of social work. **Psychiatric social workers** specialize in helping the mentally ill and their families accept and adjust to mental illness. Most psychiatric social workers work in hospitals, mental health clinics, or family service agencies.

OTHER MENTAL HEALTH SPECIALISTS   There are many other people who help people with mental disorders. **Psychiatric nurses** work in hospitals, mental health facilities, or in private practice and specialize in the care and treatment of the mentally ill. **Occupational therapists** help the mentally ill become productive members of society by teaching them practical skills. **Pastoral counselors** are members of the religious community who have had practical training in counseling people with mental and social problems.

Some mental health counselors work with specific problems or specific groups. Substance abuse counselors, for example, work with people who have drug or alcohol problems. School adjustment counselors work with students who are having problems in school. Youth counselors work with teenagers who are having problems.

Whatever the problem, there are people to help you. Parents are a good place to start. Although it may be difficult, try to share your problems with a parent, guardian, or other responsible adult. Facing up to a problem and talking about it are the first steps to overcoming it.

Psychiatrists and psychologists are mental health specialists who diagnose and treat mental disorders.

Kinds of Treatments

After a mental disorder has been diagnosed, it may be treated in a number of ways. These ways include drug therapy, psychotherapy, and hospitalization. Often, a combination of treatments is used.

DRUG THERAPY Many mental disorders, such as anxiety disorders, affective disorders, and schizophrenia, can be treated effectively through medication. Although the medications may not cure the mental disorder, they do relieve the symptoms, which allows many patients to function normally again. Unfortunately, some people experience negative side effects from the drugs and can also develop a dependency on the medication.

PSYCHOTHERAPY Depending on their training and experience, psychotherapists can use a variety of methods in treating mental disorders. A few examples are analytic, behavioral, cognitive, and client-centered therapies. Along with any of these therapies, therapists also may use family therapy, group therapy, role-playing, and, for younger patients, play therapy.

Analytic psychotherapy is based on the idea that mental disorders are the result of unresolved inner conflicts. Freudian psychoanalysis is an example of an analytic approach.

Behavioral therapies try to relieve the symptoms of a mental disorder by helping people alter their behavior. One way this is accomplished is by rewarding healthful behaviors while ignoring or mildly punishing unhealthful behaviors.

Cognitive therapies involve changing a patient's attitudes or ways of looking at the world. For example, a depressed patient might be asked to keep a daily record of things that make the patient feel happy, hopeful, or worthwhile. This record helps the patient to develop a more positive outlook on life.

In client-centered therapy, the patient, or client, sets the pace and the goals for therapy. The therapist shares his or her personal experiences with the client and provides a supportive environment for the client to figure out ways of solving his or her own problems.

While using these therapies, mental health professionals may encourage their patients to act out problem situations or new behaviors. Sometimes this may be done through role-playing. For example, if a person has difficulty saying no to friends, the therapist may take on the role of a demanding friend. The person can use this nonthreatening situation to practice how he or she would say no to the friend. For young patients, play therapy may be used. Children undergoing play therapy use toys, such as dolls, to act out problem situations or to try out solutions to problems.

Figure 4-15. Family therapy can be an effective means of solving some mental problems.

HOSPITALIZATION People with mental disorders who need constant attention or who are in danger of harming themselves are usually hospitalized. During the time that they are in a hospital, they may be given drug therapy, psychotherapy, or both. In some cases of severe depression, where other treatments are not effective, the patient may be given **electroconvulsive therapy,** or **ECT.** ECT involves passing an electric current through the brain for a fraction of a second. Although it is not yet understood why, ECT has been found to relieve symptoms of severe depression.

During hospitalization, the hospital staff work with patients to prepare them for the time when they are able to leave the hospital. Occupational therapists teach patients practical skills, which will help them manage on their own outside of the hospital. After the patient leaves the hospital, psychiatric social workers provide continued support to help the patient readjust to everyday life.

Some people with mental disorders may be treated in a hospital where they are helped to adjust to normal, everyday life.

Section Review

1. What is the best way to prevent mental disorders?
2. What are four warning signs of mental illness?
3. Name three types of mental health professionals and describe their training.
4. Describe three treatments for mental disorders.

What Do You Think?
5. Suppose that a friend of yours has been acting strangely for the past six months. You think that your friend may need help. What would you do?

4 | Chapter Review

Chapter Summary

- Mental disorders are illnesses that affect the mind. They prevent a person from being productive, adjusting to life situations, and getting along with others.
- Mental disorders may be caused by organic (physical) factors, functional (environmental) factors, or a combination of both.
- In anxiety disorders, a person's fears interfere with normal, everyday functioning. Phobias are fears that are related to specific objects or situations.
- Affective disorders, such as clinical depression, result when moods or negative emotions persist over time and interfere with normal activities.
- Eating disorders, such as anorexia nervosa and bulimia, are mental disorders found mainly in teenage girls. With these disorders, prompt professional help is crucial for effective treatment.

- In somatoform disorders, a person complains of physical symptoms, although there is no underlying physical cause.
- When an individual's personality traits prevent him or her from functioning normally and interacting with others, he or she may have a personality disorder.
- In dissociative disorders and schizophrenia, a person loses touch with reality and with his or her identity.
- Suicide frequently can be prevented if people recognize the problem and know how to help potential victims.
- Mental health professionals, such as psychiatrists, clinical psychologists, and psychiatric social workers, are trained to recognize and treat mental disorders.
- Mental disorders can be treated with drug therapy, psychotherapy, role-playing, group therapy, play therapy, and hospitalization.

Vocabulary Review

Listed below are some of the important terms in this chapter. Choose the term that best matches the phrase in the exercise that follows.

affective disorder
anorexia nervosa
anxiety disorder
bulimia
clinical depression

clinical psychologists
dissociative disorder
drug therapy
functional disorders
manic-depressive
 disorder

mental disorder
obsessive-compulsive
 disorder
organic disorder
personality disorder
phobia

psychiatric social
 workers
psychiatrists
psychotherapy
schizophrenia
somatoform disorder

1. mental disorder marked by mood swings
2. a mental disorder with a physical cause
3. anxiety about a specific situation or object
4. doctors who specialize in the diagnosis and treatment of mental disorders
5. severe mental disorders characterized by unpredictable disturbances in thinking, mood, awareness, and behavior
6. a mental disorder marked by a person forgetting or changing his or her identity

7. interactions between a trained therapist and a patient, which help the patient identify and overcome mental problems
8. a mental disorder in which a person is overwhelmed by sad feelings
9. a mental disorder characterized by severe weight loss due to a refusal to eat
10. a mental disorder in which patients suffer from symptoms, such as pain, that have no underlying physical cause

What Have You Learned?

1. Define *mental disorder*. Give one example.
2. What are some causes of organic disorders?
3. Give an example of how a mental disorder might be caused by an environmental factor.
4. Explain how an anxiety disorder might be treated by a mental health professional.
5. How are anorexia nervosa and bulimia similar? How do they differ?
6. Distinguish between compulsive, passive-aggressive, and schizoid personality disorders.

7. Why is schizophrenia one of the most severe of the mental disorders? What is an effective treatment for schizophrenia?
8. Why is depression linked to suicide?
9. List four common myths and then four facts about suicide.
10. How can you promote your mental health?
11. Which mental health specialist is qualified to give drug therapy? Which mental disorders are generally treated with drugs?

What Do You Think?

1. In some states, the mentally ill have been released from institutions. Some now live on the streets, where they receive little or no help. What, if anything, should be done about these mentally ill, homeless people?
2. People recovering from mental disorders sometimes live in "halfway houses" where they get treatment and readjust to life. Many neighborhoods object to having halfway houses. How do you feel about it?

3. Families of the mentally ill frequently need support and counseling. Why do you think this is so? Do you think it is a good idea for families to seek help? Why or why not?
4. A child's family experiences influence his or her mental health. Give four examples of a healthy parent-child interaction.
5. Why do you think that eating disorders are classified as mental disorders? Do you agree with this classification? Why or why not?

What Would You Do?

1. A friend of yours has dieted her weight down to 75 pounds from 120 pounds. You are very concerned about your friend's health. What would you do?
2. Your parents are getting a divorce, and you are having trouble sleeping, eating, and concentrating on your schoolwork. What steps could you take to help yourself?

3. Every time you have a big exam coming up, you feel really anxious. What could you do to help ease your anxiety?
4. You feel down in the dumps sometimes, but you always snap out of it quickly. Should you seek help? Why or why not?
5. List five ways in which you can improve your mental health.

For Further Study

1. Using your phone book, look up mental health facilities. Call five facilities to find out what services they provide. List the facilities, their phone numbers, and services.
2. Some veterans of the Vietnam War suffer from post-traumatic stress syndrome. Use your library to find out about this mental disorder and how it is treated. Do people other than veterans suffer from this disorder? If so, why?
3. Research the drug lithium. What mental disorder is it used to treat? How does it work? How effective is this drug?

Yeah, talking is the key. When I can get my brother to listen to me we do all right.

U N I T

2

Social Health

5

Developing Relationships

6

Marriage and Family

5

As you read, think about
▶ why relationships are important to your health.
▶ how communication skills affect relationships.
▶ how you can develop close, lasting friendships.
▶ why emotional intimacy is important in close relationships.

Developing Relationships

 ou and your friend are almost finished painting this part of the mural. You ask her to hand you the bucket of yellow paint. But, before you get a firm grip on the handle, she lets go. The paint bucket crashes to the ground and spills.

You open your mouth to shout at her for causing the accident, but then you have second thoughts. "Accidents happen!" you say. She gives you one of her big smiles, and you both get to work cleaning up the mess. You're still friends.

Getting along with people isn't always easy. In this chapter, you'll find out about the various ways people relate to each other—at home, at school, at work, and within their communities. You'll also learn about the different kinds of communication that help shape relationships. Finally, you'll look at the various types of relationships that are especially important during the teen years.

Coping with the ups and downs of friendship helps you learn about yourself and others.

1. YOU IN YOUR RELATIONSHIPS

Do you have a close friend whom you have known since early childhood? If so, as preschoolers you may have spent hours together building whole cities with wooden blocks. Later, you may have discussed sports or favorite television programs. Now, as teenagers, you talk about problems you face at home or at school and give each other advice and encouragement. This bond that you and your friend have established over the years is one kind of relationship. A **relationship** is an association that develops between people who share similar interests or goals and exchange information, feelings, or ideas over a period of time.

How Relationships Develop

Relationships often begin by chance—you happen to meet the person who lives in the apartment across the hall from you, who sits in the desk next to you at school, or who works as your lab partner in a science class. The person across the hall from you may have lived there for the past five years but still be only an **acquaintance** (uh **kwayn** tuns), a person you are familiar with but not close to. On the other hand, the lab partner you have known only a few months may have already become a close friend.

What determines whether a relationship will remain casual or become a close, lasting friendship? Social scientists have found that most people form close relationships with others who are like themselves in some important ways. It is reassuring to discover that another person agrees with you or has similar goals and interests. You and your lab partner, for example, may begin the relationship by sharing the goal of completing an experiment and writing up the lab report. As you work together, you may discover that you two also have similar interests. You may both enjoy backpacking and listening to jazz music. The person across the hall may be about your parents' age and enjoy classical music. Although you may exchange greetings, your relationship remains casual because you have little in common.

Common interests and goals are not the only reasons why people form close relationships. Some studies have suggested that people may get along better with other people whose personalities complement their own. In other words, a friend may have some positive qualities that you lack, and you may have some positive qualities that your friend lacks. Your lab partner, for example, may take risks: she may like trying new ways of setting up experiments. You, who are more cautious and well-organized, may admire her adventurous qualities. She may value your organizational ability

Check Your Wellness

Are the relationships you have with others healthful and satisfying? See if you can answer yes to the following questions.

1. Are you friendly with a variety of people, including boys and girls?
2. Do you have close friends with whom you feel you can be yourself?
3. Are you able to show your friends that you care about them? Can your friends show caring toward you?
4. Can you work out problems that arise between you and your friends?
5. Are you able to express your feelings without feeling anxious or hurting others?
6. Can you carry on conversations with people you would like to get to know?
7. Do you stick to your limits for expressing affection on dates? Do you respect the limits set by others?

and your attention to detail. The two of you may get along well with each other because you respect and admire each other's abilities.

For a relationship to be healthy, it must change as the individuals involved in the relationship change. Perhaps you have noticed some changes taking place in your present relationships with close friends. You may be able to argue with a friend now and then and not feel it is the end of the relationship. In fact, you may feel better about each other after an argument than before. You may have discovered that you can go for days or even weeks without seeing a friend and still feel close. These are some of the signs of healthy, growing relationships.

You and your parents probably are adjusting to a new relationship. The new relationship that you are establishing may be based more on shared responsibility and decision-making than it was before. As with all types of change, changes in a relationship sometimes create tension. By working together to resolve the problems and conflicts that are bound to arise, a relationship, and the individuals involved in it, can grow.

The Importance of Relationships

Although you may like to be alone at times, relationships with others are important to your health. As you read in Chapter 1, your social health affects your overall wellness and your position on the Illness-Wellness continuum. Healthy relationships fulfill important emotional and physical needs throughout your lifetime. In fact, the need for relationships runs so deep that some social scientists believe it is as basic as your need for food and sleep.

If people are deprived of human company for too long, they may become depressed, lose interest in eating and caring for themselves, and even die. For our ancestors, groups provided protection from the dangers they faced every day. Today, the family and social groups within which a person lives are important for other reasons. Family groups, for example, usually provide love and guidance. Social groups provide a sense of belonging and independence. Often, you learn more about yourself and what you believe when you are a member of a group. It is within the family group, for example, that young children first begin to develop their physical and mental skills and begin to form their opinions about themselves. The family also teaches young children social skills, such as how to cooperate with others and how to behave in different situations, which allow them to get along in other social groups.

Most teenagers consider it important to be part of one or more groups outside their families. These groups may include school groups, religious groups, sports teams, social

▲
Figure 5-1. Relationships fulfill many needs during your lifetime.

▲
Figure 5-2. Being part of a group provides a sense of belonging and builds confidence and self-esteem.

Most teenagers need the support and comfort that close friends provide.

clubs, political groups, or hobby clubs. The support of a group of people you trust helps to build your confidence and **self-esteem,** feeling good about yourself and being proud of who you are.

When you are part of a group, many of the things you do become more fun. All kinds of activities, like studying for a test, going to a show, or roller skating, can be more enjoyable when you do them with others. Something that might seem silly doing alone, like dressing up in a costume, can be fun to do with friends.

Right now, some of your most important relationships may be with a small group of close friends. Close friends can give each other confidence and bring out the best in one another. When you are feeling sad or discouraged, it is reassuring to have a friend who will listen to you and help you through the hard time.

Section Review

1. Identify two things that people look for in friends.
2. What tends to cause stress in relationships between teenagers and their parents?
3. Why is being part of a group or groups especially important during the teenage years?

What Do You Think?

4. Think about an important relationship in your life. How has this relationship had a positive influence on your overall wellness?

2. COMMUNICATION IN RELATIONSHIPS

When you laugh at someone's joke, hug your younger sister or brother, listen to a friend's problems, ask for advice, or write a letter, you are communicating. **Communication** is the process of sharing information, thoughts, ideas, or feelings. It happens whenever you use words, sounds, gestures, or body movements to interact with other people.

You communicate for many reasons: to make plans, to get your point of view across, to receive comfort, or to share good times with other people. Learning to communicate effectively can help you make friends and get along with other people. It can help to ease tensions between you and your parents and create a trusting atmosphere in which each of you respects the other's opinions.

Levels of Communication

When you chat with a stranger at the bus stop, you may talk about the weather, the local political campaign, or the bus schedule. As the examples in Figure 5-3 show, this type of casual or trivial conversation is called **small talk.**

Now suppose that you happen to see the same person a few days later. You continue your chat about the campaign. This time, you say how interested you are in politics and reveal that you are delivering campaign fliers in your neighborhood. You discover that the person you are speaking to supports the same candidate and lives in your neighborhood. At this point, you introduce yourselves and say that you hope you will see the person at the next political rally, which will be held in the high school. You discover that you both attend the same school.

Your relationship has now moved from that of stranger to acquaintance, and the level of your communication has changed as well. You and your new acquaintance are no longer engaging in small talk; you have begun to share ideas. When you see each other again, you may continue to talk about the campaign and what you expect the candidate to do for the community. As the conversation continues, it may shift from talking about the campaign to talking about yourselves. When people express personal feelings and reveal information about themselves, the communication is called **self-disclosure.** Some examples are given in Figure 5-3.

Although most relationships do not develop as smoothly as the one described here, this one may show the connection between the closeness of a relationship and the level of communication. Social scientists have found, for example, that college roommates tend to make few self-disclosures early in the semester. As the relationship becomes closer and more

Levels of Communication
1. **Small talk**   "I heard it's going to rain today."   "That's a nice hat you're wearing."   "Who won the game last night?"
2. **Sharing ideas**   "Why don't we try doing it this way?"   "I think they should ban smoking here. What do you think?"   "Which college do you think is best for studying philosophy?"
3. **Self-disclosure**   "I'm so nervous about the try-outs."   "I'm having trouble getting along with my mom."   "I don't think I'm ready for a serious relationship."

Figure 5-3. Close relationships are formed by advancing from one level of communication to the next.

trusting during the semester, the level and number of self-disclosures increases.

Sometimes a person may offer personal information or "secrets" too early in a relationship. When this happens, the other person may feel threatened and withdraw, at least temporarily. Farther along in the relationship, however, offering privileged information frequently gains the other person's liking or acceptance.

Style in Communication

Communication is more than just speaking words; you communicate in your own personal style. **Style** is your delivery, or the attitude you express as you speak, listen, and respond. Your style is a combination of behaviors. Each behavior helps to determine the kinds and quality of relationships you have with friends, parents, siblings, teachers, and others.

Body language is a way of communicating information, mood, or attitude through body movements, posture, gestures, and facial expressions. Body language can send a message along with spoken words, or it can send a silent message of its own. For example, some people slouch to show that they are at ease; others stand tall to show that they are confident.

Experts in **kinesics** (kih **nee** siks), the science of body language, say that most body language is learned behavior.

Your style of communication is revealed in the way you speak, listen, and respond.

Figure 5-4. Communication is more than spoken words. Are you aware the messages sent by your body language?

By observing others, children learn early in life that a kiss is a gesture of affection, a wave signals a greeting or a departure, and a scowl shows anger.

You may find it interesting to observe your own and others' body language. You may find, for example, that you use body language to hide feelings of anxiety when you speak before a group. Perhaps you smile and stand in a way that makes you appear more relaxed. Or, you may see your brother, head lowered, shoulders slumped, moving heavily across the soccer field after his team's defeat. Your brother's posture and body movements convey his disappointment without his saying a word.

Eye contact, or meeting someone's gaze, is another way to communicate. Teachers may use eye contact to establish a kind of connection with their students. Eye contact can help teachers to know whether students are listening or whether they understand what is being taught. As you talk with a friend, eye contact and little noises, such as "uh-huh" and "yeah," let each of you know that the other is listening. Failure to make eye contact with a person, on the other hand, may be interpreted as shyness, shame, indifference, or even sneakiness.

A range of emotions can be implied through eye movements. Happiness can show in eyes that "dance" or sparkle. Disgust can be displayed in rolling eyes or anger in glaring eyes. Even eyebrows can convey a variety of messages. They may shoot up when you question what someone has said, or they may move closer together when you hear something that you find disturbing or hurtful.

Did you know that a statement can have different meaning depending on how you say it? Suppose, for example, that you use low tones or even whisper as you tell someone, "Leave the package on the desk." This may imply that you want to be secretive. If you "bark" the same sentence in quick, sharp tones, it may be interpreted as an impatient or angry order. The difference is in your **tone of voice,** or how something is said. Tone of voice can be loud and demanding, soft and understanding, or cool and indifferent.

Communicating Effectively

The best way to get your point across is to send a clearly stated message. If you do that, there is little question about what you really mean. But, it is not always easy to send a clear signal. In fact, communicating effectively is an acquired skill, much like learning to ride a bicycle. When you first started to ride a bicycle, you probably hesitated and fell. The more you practiced, however, the less you needed to think about what you were doing and the better cyclist you became. Your skill at riding eventually became second nature, and once learned, you will never forget it.

Helping the Handicapped to Speak

For some people, physical handicaps make communication with others difficult. But, with the help of recent technology, this situation is changing.

A new computer system, called an Assistive Communication Device (ACD), is a welcome development for people who are not able to speak. ACDs enable a handicapped person to "speak" using the voice generated by a speech synthesizer that is part of the system.

The design of an ACD depends on the needs of the person using it. Some ACDs are equipped with a typical keyboard. The computer simply speaks the words typed in. Other ACDs have keyboards with pictures instead of letters. This simplifies typing since each picture substitutes for an entire word. These systems are best for people who have limited use of their hands.

Despite the power and complexity of a typical ACD, many are lap-sized and portable. ACD users can now take their own "speech" wherever they go.

An ACD allows a speech-impaired person to speak.

▲ **Figure 5-5. Crying at a happy event, such as a graduation, may send a mixed message.**

○━┱

Listening is one of the most useful communication skills you can learn.

MIXED MESSAGES   As with bicycling, part of learning how to communicate effectively is knowing what *not* to do as well as what to do. In communication, it is important to avoid giving mixed messages. A **mixed message** occurs when one part of a message contradicts another. Parents, for example, may tell their daughter that she is too young to be wearing eyeshadow and blush. Later in the conversation, they may say, "Can't you act more grown up? You're not a child anymore, you know."

Mixed messages also are sent when the spoken words clearly differ from the message conveyed through body language or tone of voice. For example, if someone warns you about the dangers of smoking but lights up a cigarette while talking, you will be confused about the message. Although people often do not realize it, their actions may speak louder than their words.

"I" MESSAGES   One of the most important steps in learning to communicate effectively is to take responsibility for your own feelings. Feelings can be difficult to communicate, especially feelings of anger or frustration. Think about the last time you were angry with someone. How did you let the person know you were upset?

In order to express your feelings accurately, you may want to practice using "I" messages. An **"I" message** is a statement of your feelings and expectations that does not blame or judge the other person. Suppose you are upset with a friend who forgot to call you. When you speak to your friend the next day, you shout, "Can't you remember anything?" The question could put your friend on the defensive and cause a serious disagreement. Instead, it would be better to focus on how the situation made you feel. By saying something like "I'm upset because we didn't talk on the phone last night," you open the lines of communication between you and your friend.

ACTIVE LISTENING   Learning to listen is one of the most useful communication skills you can acquire. Although it is not a difficult skill to learn, it does require a lot of effort because listening is more than just hearing words.

Active listening is focusing your full attention on what the other person is saying and, at the same time, letting that person know you understand and care. Active listening is truly active. The listener makes the speaker feel comfortable about opening up and expressing personal feelings. The Health Skills feature on page 114 explains how you can become a more effective listener.

ASSERTIVENESS   How do you express your opinions and feelings when they differ from another person's opinions? Are you **passive,** holding back your true feelings and

Assertive, Passive, and Aggressive Communication

Assertive Behaviors	Passive Behaviors	Aggressive Behaviors
Using "I" messages to explain your feelings	Hoping the other person will guess your feelings	Using "you" messages to blame the other person
Actively listening to the person	Always listening, rarely talking	Interrupting the other person; being sarcastic
Trying to understand the person's feelings	Denying your own feelings; making excuses	Making fun of the other person's feelings; using name-calling
Expressing appreciation; being respectful	Criticizing yourself; always apologizing	Criticizing the other person; never giving a compliment
Seeking a compromise that does not go against either of your values	Always giving in to the person	Always wanting your own way
Speaking clearly and confidently; making eye contact; appearing interested	Mumbling; looking away; fidgeting nervously	Yelling or refusing to talk; pointing your finger; glaring; using physical force

going along with the other person? Are you **aggressive**? That is, do you communicate your opinions and feelings in a way that may seem threatening or disrespectful to other people? When you are **assertive** (uh **sur** tiv), you express your true feelings in a way that does not threaten the other person or make you feel anxious.

People who are assertive tend to have healthier, more satisfying relationships than those who are either passive or aggressive. This is because assertive behavior communicates respect both for yourself and for the other person. What do you think passive behavior communicates? What does aggressive behavior communicate?

Figure 5-6 compares assertive communication behaviors to passive and aggressive behaviors. Like all skills, assertiveness can only be mastered with practice.

▲
Figure 5-6. Which of the assertive communication behaviors do you need to work at?

⌐○━┳

Assertive behavior communicates respect for yourself and for others.

Section Review

1. Why is communication important?
2. Describe three levels of communication.
3. Name and describe the three components of style in communication.
4. Describe two ways to communicate your thoughts and feelings effectively.

What Do You Think?
5. How can knowing yourself better help you to communicate more effectively?

3. FRIENDSHIPS

Friendship is a give-and-take relationship based on mutual trust, acceptance, and common interests or values. People look to friends for honest reactions, for encouragement during bad times, and for understanding if they make mistakes. Friends offer a sense of belonging and a handy way to remember an important fact: there are other people who understand and care about you.

Friendships give you an opportunity to develop and use communication skills. Friendships allows you to try out a variety of roles: leader, helper, advice-seeker, or supporter. Experimenting with roles can help you learn about yourself and how you relate to others. This knowledge will be important throughout your adult life—as you enter the work world, marry, start a family, and participate in community groups and decisions.

Types of Friendships

Friendships range from the casual acquaintances you greet in the halls at school to the friends who share your most intimate thoughts and most of your free time. Between these two extremes are many other categories.

Casual friendships are ones that often do not go beyond the sharing of ideas. Some casual friendships are friendships of convenience. You and a neighbor may mow lawns together or go sledding after a snowstorm. Even though you have little in common, you get together occasionally because you can amuse each other when there is no one else around.

You may be involved in some other casual friendships. When you and a classmate are assigned to the same project or to seats next to each other, a classroom friendship may begin. Common-interest friendships are based on mutual interests or hobbies. You may, for example, meet a person who, like you, does volunteer work at the local hospital or enjoys hiking just as much as you do. These friendships that develop may remain casual, or they may lead to deeper, more long-lasting friendships.

What makes the handful of people you think of as close friends different from those in the other categories of friendships? A close friend is a person you feel you can be yourself with, a person who can be honest with you but is not out to put you down or hurt your feelings. In a close relationship, each of you is able to overlook at least some of the other's shortcomings. A close friend is generally reliable: your friend is there to support you during the hard times as well as to share with you during the good times.

During adolescence, it is common for young people to develop close friendships. These friendships offer a way to pull away from the family. By forming close friendships, ado-

▲
Figure 5-7. Close friendship may develop between casual friends who share similar interests.

lescents can feel part of a small group, much as they did within the family, but still act independently.

Although some friendships are casual, and others are important enough to last a lifetime, each is valuable for different reasons. Short-term, casual friendships offer the chance to have fun, to try new things, and to learn to be comfortable with many different people. Emotional support, self-disclosure, and the opportunity to see yourself as others see you are all possible in a close friendship.

Friendships with the Opposite Sex

When you were younger, you probably formed friendships with children of your own sex. This is because traditionally boys and girls have been socialized differently, or taught different types of behaviors. Boys, for example, often were encouraged to be competitive. As a result, young boys tended to form casual friendships with groups of boys with whom they could compete in sports or other activities. Girls, on the other hand, were taught to nurture, or care for, others. They tended to form close one-to-one relationships with other girls.

The behaviors and attitudes a person has because they are socially accepted as either masculine or feminine are called **sex roles.** Today, sex roles are less rigid than in the past. Many people now participate in activities and behave in ways that traditionally were reserved for members of the other sex. These people recognize that each person has a range of characteristics that cannot be labeled either masculine or feminine. In choosing friends, they look for people of either sex with interests and goals similar to their own. With less rigid sex roles, both males and females learn to express a variety of emotions including tenderness, compassion, or whatever a situation calls for. Opposite-sex friendships develop more frequently today than in the past. Friendships between males and females can be satisfying and close but not involve romance. These friendships help you to feel comfortable with members of the opposite sex and allow you to develop fully as a person. Some opposite-sex friendships may develop into romantic relationships as they progress. Many others simply remain friendships.

Forming and Maintaining Friendships

How would you describe your friendship pattern? Do you like having many friends or do you prefer just a few close friends? Are your friendships long-lasting or more short-term? No matter what your pattern is, developing a friendship is always a two-step process: making a friend and keeping a friend.

▲
Figure 5-8. Because sex roles are not as rigid today, it is common for friendships to develop between boys and girls.

MAKING FRIENDS Whatever your friendship pattern, it is likely that forming friendships with other teenagers is important to you. All you need to do is get started. But how? What do you look for in friends? Certainly, you may be attracted to people who are popular, good-looking, fun to be with, and witty. But outward appearances may not tell the whole story. You want friends who are trustworthy and loyal. A true friend would not cheat you or talk negatively about you to others.

Look for people with whom you are compatible. **Compatibility,** the ability to exist in harmony, makes it possible for friends to have occasional disagreements and still get along well together. Of course, it is difficult to judge whether you will get along with someone before you know the person. With experience, you will become a better judge of the types of people with whom you are most compatible.

It is also a good idea to look for friends who are sensitive to another person's hurts, losses, or failures and who will lend support for future success. A caring friend might say, "I know how much it hurt you when the debate team didn't accept you, but I hope you'll try again." Or, "I know how hard this assignment is. Maybe we can work on it together." Words like these show **empathy** (**em** puh thee), an ability to understand how another person feels.

Once you have identified a person who has qualities that are particularly important to you, how do you approach him or her? Asking for the person's telephone number and following up with a call is one way to begin. Being sincerely complimentary about something—"You were terrific in last night's game"—is another way to open up the lines of communication. Sometimes, simply letting someone know directly that you want to be friends is the best approach. Figure 5-9 gives some additional suggestions for making new

A good friend should be able to understand how the other person feels.

Figure 5-9. Which of these tips could help you to make new friends?
▼

Making New Friends		
To Meet New People	**To Start a Conversation**	**To Keep Up a Conversation**
■ Go up to someone new and introduce yourself.	■ Choose someone who is not in a rush and looks friendly.	■ Use active listening techniques.
■ Ask your friends to introduce you to someone you'd like to meet.	■ Compliment the person and follow with a question.	■ Ask questions that require more than a yes or no answer.
■ Join a new club or team; do volunteer work in your community.	■ Introduce yourself and talk about something that you like to do.	■ Mention things you both have in common.
■ Go to museums, libraries, sporting events, or parties.	■ Ask the person about things he or she likes to do.	■ Talk about something you've done that you think would interest the other person.

friends. The most important thing to remember is to be yourself. Putting on an act to win a friend will only make both of you feel uncomfortable.

KEEPING FRIENDS   Forming friendships is only half the story. Maintaining them is just as important and sometimes far more difficult. Lasting friendships are built on sharing: sharing experiences, feelings, responsibility. For a friendship to grow, friends must spend time together. It is the quality of time, rather than the quantity of time, that is most important to a relationship. Friends do not need to see each other every day, or even every week, in order for them to build a lasting friendship.

Friendships also grow when friends are able to understand and trust each other. Understanding and trust develop from self-disclosure, that is, talking honestly about yourself, your feelings, and your needs. Both friends must also take equal responsibility for a relationship. You may be involved in a friendship in which one of you is always the "giver" and the other the "taker." Givers may feel that they are always helping their friends but getting little in return; takers may feel as if their friends do not trust them enough to ask for help. Relationships like these are not satisfying for either

| **D**efine problem | **E**xplore alternatives | **C**onsider consequences | **I**dentify values | **D**ecide and act | **E**valuate results |

SHOULD YOU TELL A FRIEND THAT YOU ARE ANGRY?

You and Cal have been friends for years, so it's hard to believe he didn't invite you to his party. All the other kids in your old group are going. That's how you found out about it: Ted asked you for a ride. Cal's also invited some people you don't know well but would like to meet. Maybe he doesn't think you're good enough for this crowd.

You're angry and hurt. It might feel good to tell Cal off, but what about your friendship? There are still three days left before the party, and Cal sits next to you in homeroom.

1. Use the DECIDE process on page 16 to decide what you would do in this situation. Explain your reasons for making this decision.

2. How might this situation become more difficult if you choose not to talk to Cal before the party?

What should you do when a good friend hurts your feelings?

▲
Figure 5-10. When jealousy arises, friends need to discuss the problem and work things out.

person and usually do not last long. For a friendship to last, both people must learn to be the "giver" sometimes and the "taker" other times.

In all friendships, even strong ones, problems arise and must be dealt with. Jealousy, for example, can cause problems in any friendship. A person may be jealous of a friend's accomplishments, appearance, possessions, or something else. Sometimes, jealousy results when a friend wants to branch out of one group or best-friend relationship and develop other close relationships. This can represent a threat to the existing group or friendship and can cause feelings of anxiety about being left out.

When jealous feelings arise, it is important to use your communication skills to discuss the problem. First, get your feelings out in the open. It is best to do this in person, but if this is too difficult, you can write a letter explaining your feelings. Be sure to listen to your friend's point of view and try to understand his or her feelings.

It also may be helpful to discuss what each of you expects and needs from your friendship. It may be that your expectations are different from your friend's or that they changed without your being aware of it. Perhaps you wanted someone to confide in, or you hoped the friendship would make you more popular at school. Thinking about and discussing these things helps you to gain a better understanding of friendship and of ways to work things out.

Occasionally, a friend may act cruelly toward you. You may have done something that angered your friend, or your friend may be facing problems at home, school, or elsewhere. Unfortunately, sometimes people transfer the pain or anxiety they are feeling onto their close friends. If you are the victim of a friend's cruelty, you should confront your friend to find out what the real problem is. By confronting your friend, you communicate that you are not willing to be mistreated, and you also show your concern and desire to work things out.

Section Review

1. Why do you need friendship?
2. Why are close and casual friendships important for personal growth?
3. How have changes in traditional sex roles affected friendship patterns?
4. Describe two qualities that are desirable in friends.

What Do You Think?

5. What do you see as the most important problem that can arise within a friendship? How would you handle this problem?

4. INTIMATE RELATIONSHIPS

Developing as a person means developing also as a sexual being. As teenagers become aware of their sexuality, some tough questions arise: How can I show physical affection without it leading to sex? Are my sexual feelings normal? Are my partner and I emotionally ready right now for a sexual relationship?

There are no easy answers for these questions. The values you learn from your family, religious teachings, personal experiences, and friends influence your thinking about questions involving physical intimacy. The important thing is that you think about these questions, gather as much information as you can, and then make decisions that feel comfortable and right for you.

Physical Attraction

The teenage years are a time when most young people experience intense feelings of attraction. Perhaps you have had a crush on a rock star or a teacher. You may have spent a great deal of time daydreaming about him or her. This feeling of intense, sometimes overwhelming, interest in another person is called an **infatuation.** From these normal, healthy feelings of infatuation you have as a teenager, you develop the ability to form strong attachments as an adult.

During the teenage years, most people develop an attraction to members of the other sex. Being sexually attracted to people of the other sex is called **heterosexuality** (het uh roh **sek** shoo al ih tee). Some people are sexually attracted to people of their own sex, which is known as **homosexuality** (hoh mo **sek** shoo al ih tee). Homosexuality is still not well understood. Some teenagers who have close, caring relationships with members of their own sex wonder if they are homosexual. Close, caring friendships between members of the same sex do not indicate sexual preference. Homosexuality also is not determined by your physical appearance, style of dress, hobbies, or interests.

Homosexuals have sometimes been the target of unflattering jokes, discrimination, and even violence. With education, it is possible that more people may accept the fact that sexual preference does not determine honesty, loyalty, caring, or other valuable qualities.

Dating

While some teenagers have begun to date by high school, others do not start dating until later. Dating is a way for a teenager to get to know a person to whom he or she is

▲
Figure 5-11. Questions about intimacy and sexuality may arise during the teenage years.

attracted. Dating often grows out of group activities that include both boys and girls. A group of you may enjoy skating together on a Saturday afternoon, for example, or going to school sports events and meeting for pizza afterward.

During mixed-group activities you may discover that you especially enjoy being with a certain friend of the other sex. You may enjoy being with someone who shares your interests or has a similar sense of humor. You may also be physically attracted to this person. It is natural and healthy to feel physical attraction and to want to get to know the person better. This may lead to dating, either in a group or by yourselves.

Dating gives you an opportunity to learn about members of the other sex. It may help you develop communication skills and to learn how the other person views the sex roles that he or she learned as a child. You may even discover what qualities you want in the person you choose to marry.

Dating practices vary with individuals and according to family guidelines. Although it has been traditional for males to initiate dates, today many young women make arrangements for dates, provide transportation, and pay their share of expenses.

At first, most teenagers date in a random, casual way. They may not focus on one special person or stick to a pattern of dating every Friday or Saturday night. After a few dates, however, some couples decide to go steady, that is, to form a relationship in which it is understood that the partners will

O═══╍

Dating provides an opportunity to learn more about yourself and the other person.

Figure 5-12. A mixed-group date is a good way to get to know members of the opposite sex.

see each other regularly. Some couples go steady because it is a form of security: each is guaranteed a date whenever the need arises. For some couples, going steady also can be a time of **courtship,** a period that often leads to engagement and then marriage.

Having a "steady" does give you a chance to know the other person well, but dating on a steady basis also has some drawbacks. By dating the same person, you limit your chances of meeting other people with whom you might like to develop long-term relationships. You may also feel pressured to make decisions about physical intimacy before you are ready. If conflicts arise and the relationship does not work out, it is sometimes difficult to break up with a steady boyfriend or girlfriend.

Although going steady provides a sense of security, it also limits your chances of meeting other people.

Teenage Pregnancy

It is normal to have sexual feelings for someone to whom you are physically attracted. It is also normal to be confused and unsure of how to handle these feelings. Most teenagers try to think ahead and to set limits for expressing their sexual feelings on dates. By setting limits before a situation arises, it is easier to stick to the standards you set.

Unfortunately, some teenagers do not always think through the possible consequences of sexual behavior. One serious consequence is teenage pregnancy. In this country, at least 1 million girls between the ages of 15 and 19 become

◀ **Figure 5-13. Teenage pregnancy is one of the most serious problems facing our country today.**

pregnant each year. About 40,000 pregnant teenagers are under the age of 15. In fact, the pregnancy rate for teenagers aged 14 and younger has been increasing at an alarming rate.

Teenage pregnancy is a serious health problem. Babies born to young mothers are often smaller and less healthy than those born to older women. Teenage mothers themselves are more likely to have health problems during pregnancy than older women. This is because pregnant teenagers do not always eat well or get adequate medical care during pregnancy, especially in the early months.

Aside from the health problems, how does having a baby affect the lives of a teenage couple? Teenage parents often report feeling trapped and overwhelmed by the responsibilities of parenthood. Many teenage mothers drop out of school. Some fathers do not help support or care for the child; others drop out of school and work at jobs that pay much less than what a high-school graduate can earn. As a result, many teenage parents never complete their educations, often live in poverty, and must depend on public assistance programs for survival.

Although many young people are aware of the health, economic, and social problems teenage parents face, they often do not believe pregnancy can happen to them. Few teenagers want to become pregnant. Statistics have shown, however, that one in six teenagers who engage in intimate sexual contact become pregnant. Sexual intimacy is a high-risk behavior for anyone who is not ready to accept the lifelong responsibility of children.

Figure 5-14. Over time, couples can develop strong emotional bonds.

▼

Emotional Intimacy

In a public television program that dealt with adolescent sexual feelings, one young man who had been going steady for two years noted that he and his partner had decided that their relationship came before sex. "We're not ready for sexual intimacy, but we share lots of other intimate experiences," he said.

Perhaps you are wondering how two people can share intimate experiences without being sexually active. You may be surprised to discover that you and your partner are sharing intimate experiences when you trust each other with personal feelings or fantasies that you have not told to anyone else. You may exchange "inside" jokes or have pet names for each other that other people are unaware of. You may study together or practice lines for your school play and find that you are not embarrassed even when you make mistakes. You may enjoy hobbies or sporting events together and frequently feel like best friends.

When young couples share experiences like these and can express how they feel about each other without physical intimacy, they are giving their relationship a chance to mature through emotional intimacy. **Emotional intimacy** is a kind of communication that involves sharing innermost feelings and being supportive. Trust is absolutely necessary for this sort of intimacy. When people are emotionally intimate, each trusts the other to listen and accept what is being said without making judgments.

Sometimes, however, sexual feelings become so strong and confusing that it can be hard to resist experimenting. Part of experimenting in anything you do is making mistakes. Usually, mistakes make little difference in the long term, and you learn from them. Mistakes in sex, however, can be serious, especially if they result in pregnancy, sexually transmitted disease, or low self-esteem. If you are sexually active or are considering sexual activity, ask yourself whether or not you are prepared to cope with the kinds of problems, regrets, and disappointments that are listed in the chart in Figure 5-15.

Contrary to what you may think, not every teenager is sexually experienced. Often those who talk the loudest do the least. They may be exaggerating or even fantasizing about their sex lives. Today millions of young people under the age of eighteen are choosing to postpone sexual activity for a variety of good reasons. After all, saying "no" is the best method of birth control there is.

If you happen to be sexually active now and believe that building a relationship around emotional intimacy makes more sense, you and your partner can change. If your partner tries to make you feel guilty about abandoning the sexual aspects of your relationship, then he or she is not interested in respecting your feelings or getting to know you more deeply. Rather than stay in an unhealthy relationship, try to meet people who understand the importance of dealing responsibly with sexual feelings and maintaining constructive, emotionally close relationships.

How Sexual Intimacy May Leave You Feeling
■ **Guilty** for going against your values
■ **Disappointed** that sex fails to measure up to your expectations
■ **Hurt** that partner seems more interested in physical gratification than emotional closeness
■ **Anxious** about pregnancy and sexually transmitted disease
■ **Fearful** that parents will find out

Figure 5-15. Sexual intimacy without a close emotional relationship can have unwanted results.

Section Review

1. How does dating usually begin?
2. What are the benefits of having a steady boyfriend or girlfriend? What are the drawbacks?
3. In what ways does having a baby change the lives of teenage parents?
4. How can partners maintain emotional intimacy without physical intimacy?

What Do You Think?

5. How will your relationships with the opposite sex help you to determine the qualities that are important in a marriage partner?

Being an Effective Listener

Tom's friend Meg ran up to him in the hall between classes and grabbed his arm. She looked very upset.

"I *really* need to talk," Meg whispered. "Can you come over after school? You won't believe what happened!"

Meg has done this before, and Tom is always willing to listen. Once Meg starts to explain what's bothering her, though, she gets embarrassed and stops talking. Sometimes she even gets mad at Tom. He knows that talking things over would help Meg a lot, and he worries that he's not a good enough listener. What can he do?

The guidelines that follow give concrete suggestions for being an effective listener. They can help you translate your good intentions into real help for a friend.

1. Start with Passive Listening

When you're listening, you can show that you're paying attention and interested without actually speaking in return. Passive listening techniques include making eye contact, nodding your head, leaning forward, and letting your facial expression reflect your response. Short, encouraging verbal responses such as "uh-huh" and "oh?" are also part of passive listening.

2. Emphasize Active Listening

Passive listening does not always indicate that you fully understand what the other person is saying. To show acceptance, respect, sympathy, and encouragement, be an active listener.

- Use verbal responses, such as "I see," "I know what you mean," "Then what happened?" or "Really?" and "That's wonderful!" or "How terrible!"
- Comment directly on what the other person is saying or restate the speaker's ideas in

your own words. Resist telling the person what to do. Instead, assure the speaker that you are understanding—not judging—what is being said. This can encourage the person to explore unexpressed feelings. Listen for the emotions behind the words. Phrase your responses so they communicate: "This is what I understand your ideas and feelings to be. Am I correct?"

Try these strategies:

Restating: *"Do you mean . . .?"*

Comparing: *"Was it like . . .?"*
Encouraging unexpressed feelings: *"I guess you felt . . ."*
Encouraging more information: *"Tell me more about . . ."*

3. Use Door Openers

Many people find it difficult to express their feelings. They need direct encouragement, or door openers, to continue speaking. You may also use door openers at the start of a conversation in order to help a speaker begin.

Try these door openers:

"Do you want to talk about it?"
"You seem upset about . . ."
"Why does that bother you?"

4. Be Natural

The guidelines above indicate types of responses. Exactly what you say will depend on you and the person you're listening to. Being an effective listener means responding "from the heart," not "by the book." You are the best judge of what words to use when a friend needs a good listener.

Effective listening shows the speaker that you care.

APPLY THE SKILL

1. Review Tom's situation. What do you think he might have been doing to make Meg embarrassed, frustrated, or angry? Explain. How might he improve his listening skills?

2. Imagine that a friend has just said the statements below to you. How would you communicate that you have heard what is being said and that you understand and accept the friend?

(a) *"My math teacher gives too much homework. I can never get it all done. I don't even know where to begin."*

(b) *"I don't want to talk about it. You wouldn't understand anyway. No one understands—especially my parents!"*

(c) *"Don't tell anyone, but I think I'm in love!"*

Now imagine that these conversations are taking place on the telephone instead of in person. In what way would you change your responses? Why would you change them?

3. Observe two people in conversation in such places as the cafeteria, on line at the movies, or at your own dinner table. Pay attention to signs of effective listening. Jot down examples of passive and active listening techniques. Also list negative listening practices. How successful was the conversation. Why?

4. Ask one person to tell you about his or her day. As the person speaks, practice effective listening. Then ask the speaker if he or she noticed any difference in the way you listened. Did you notice any improvement in your listening techniques? Explain. Was this conversation more or less successful than others you've had with this person? Explain.

5 | Chapter Review

Chapter Summary

- Relationships develop over time when people who share similar interests or goals exchange ideas, thoughts, and feelings.
- Being part of a group may provide a sense of belonging, an opportunity to learn social skills, an awareness that you are not so different from others, and a way to have fun.
- Friendships provide an opportunity to try out a variety of roles, to build self-esteem, to see yourself as others see you, and to develop and use communication skills.
- Communication is important to relationships. In a close friendship, both friends must be able to disclose personal information, to actively listen, and to take responsibility for their own feelings.
- Male and female friendship patterns have differed because of the different ways boys and girls were socialized. As sex roles become less rigid, more boys and girls will form close, nonromantic friendships.

- Some desirable qualities in friends are honesty, loyalty, trustworthiness, compatibility, and empathy. In trying to make a new friend, be sincere and act natural.
- To keep a friend, it is important to share experiences, feelings, and responsibilities, and to work out any problems that arise.
- Dating provides an opportunity to understand the other sex, develop communication skills, and learn what you want in a mate.
- Going steady guarantees a certain kind of security and offers a chance to know another person well. It also may mean limiting your chances of meeting other people, conflicts over physical intimacy, and difficulties if the relationship ends.
- When teenagers begin to date, they must make difficult decisions about their sexuality. Millions of teenagers maintain emotionally intimate relationships while postponing sexual activity.

Vocabulary Review

Listed below are some of the important terms in this chapter. Choose the term that best matches the phrase in the exercise that follows.

acquaintance
active listening
assertive
body language
communication

compatibility
emotional intimacy
empathy
eye contact
friendship

heterosexuality
homosexuality
"I" message
mixed message
passive

relationship
self-esteem
self-disclosure
sex roles
small talk

1. process of sharing information, thoughts, ideas, or feelings

2. the ability to exist in harmony with another person

3. one part of a message contradicts another

4. the sexual attraction to people of one's own sex

5. revealing information about yourself

6. expressing one's true feelings in a way that does not threaten others

7. communicating mood or attitude through body movements, gestures, posture, and facial expression

8. a give-and-take relationship based on mutual trust, acceptance, and common interests or values

9. the ability to understand how someone else feels

10. behaviors and attitudes that are accepted as either masculine or feminine

What Have You Learned?

1. Describe what happens when people are deprived of human company for too long.
2. How do families help children acquire the skills that allow them to interact with others?
3. Give an example of how a person might send a mixed message.
4. Of what value is eye contact? How does tone of voice give meaning to what you say?
5. What is active listening? Why is it important in relationships?
6. Give examples of passive, aggressive, and assertive communication behaviors.

7. Describe the benefits that close friends can provide. How is a close friend different from other kinds of friends?
8. Why are friendships between members of the opposite sex more common today?
9. How can a lack of self-disclosure make it difficult to form a lasting friendship?
10. Why are communication skills important when problems arise within a friendship?
11. Why do some couples go steady?
12. How can emotional intimacy strengthen an intimate relationship between teens?

What Do You Think?

1. How might communication skills help improve your relationships with others?
2. What are some common barriers to good communication between adults and teens?
3. Why do you think that some people find it difficult to make or to keep friends?

4. Do you think that mixed-group activities are important in the process of developing relationships with the other sex? Explain.
5. What do you think can be done to control the number of teenage pregnancies? Provide at least three suggestions.

What Would You Do?

1. You are visiting another country and are unable to speak the language. How can you communicate your needs?
2. You know that one of your friends is shy and probably has low self-esteem. How could you help your friend?
3. You are at a party where you know only two people. How would you get acquainted with other people?

4. Imagine that you are part of a close-knit group of friends at school. Members of your group sometimes tease a classmate who is mentally disabled. You think this behavior is not right. How would you handle the situation?
5. Imagine that you are a parent of a teenager who has begun to date. What advice would you give your child about physical and emotional intimacy?

For Further Study

1. Watch a half-hour television program with the sound off. Jot down various types of body language that you observe along with the messages they conveyed. Were you able to interpret the story or the situation? Describe what you think the program was about.
2. From an advice column in a newspaper or magazine, select two letters about problems in teenage relationships. Without reading the advice, write your own response to the problems. Then, compare your response to the advice offered in the column. Bring the letters into class for further discussion.

6

As you read, think about

▶ what factors contribute to a successful marriage.

▶ why family forms differ and how family members share in household responsibilities.

▶ how stressful situations affect families.

▶ why communication and problem-solving skills are important to families.

Marriage and Family

Y ou haven't been on a family outing for a while. Everyone is so busy that it's been hard to find a time when you can all relax together. Now the day of the family picnic has arrived, and you're in luck: There's not a cloud in the sky, and only the gentlest breeze ripples through the meadow grass. You helped your mom make her special sandwiches, and your dad created one of his famous salads and a surprise dessert. Even your little sister helped. You're ready to "get to know each other" again.

Contact and communication are important in every family, large or small. In this chapter, you'll learn about many different kinds of families. You'll also learn about the different roles you play in your current family and roles you may play in the future. You'll see how parents and children cope with the daily stresses of family life and with the more serious problems that can occur in all families.

Sometimes, people take family for granted. Doing things together can enrich family relationships.

119

1. THINKING ABOUT MARRIAGE

Ninety-five percent of all Americans marry at some time during their lives. Therefore, it is highly likely that you will marry someday. Marriage is probably one of the most important commitments you will make. It affects you, your partner, your family, your friends, your acquaintances, and future generations.

What are your expectations about marriage? Do you hope to fulfill personal needs, including love, companionship, and emotional support? Do you anticipate contributing to your partner's well-being? Do you plan to have children?

Why People Marry

People marry for a variety of reasons. Some people marry because they desire another person's love and companionship. Others marry for financial or social reasons. Some couples marry with a view to starting a family of their own. Some marry simply because it is expected.

You probably feel, as most people do, that successful marriages are based on love. But what is love? Often, young people mistake sexual attraction or short-lived infatuation for love. Real love is part of a long-lasting relationship in which people really know, like, and accept each other as they are. People who are truly in love appreciate the things they like about each other and accept the things they dislike. When you love someone, his or her well-being becomes as important to you as your own.

Successful Marriages

Although love is a basic element in a successful marriage, it is not the only one. Some of the important factors to consider when thinking about marriage are listed in Figure 6-1. It is important for you and your partner to be compatible, or able to exist in harmony with each other. Do you have similar interests and educational backgrounds? Do you share the same religious beliefs, ethnic heritage, and cultural values? Studies show that compatibility and shared interests and backgrounds increase the likelihood of a successful marriage. People who are quite different from each other, however, also can have successful marriages.

One of the most important characteristics of a good marriage is a couple's commitment to one another. **Commitment** is the determination to develop a fulfilling relationship. A fulfilling relationship usually means that you can share thoughts and feelings, have fun together, develop mutual respect, satisfy sexual needs, and gain emotional security.

Characteristics of a Successful Marriage

- compatibility
- love
- friendship
- similar interests, backgrounds, goals
- strong commitment to each other and to the marriage
- ability to communicate
- shared responsibilities
- physical attraction
- mutual concern and respect
- ability to compromise

Figure 6-1. Which factors do you think are most important in a marriage?

Researchers have found that in successful marriages, spouses work at being a couple by setting aside time and energy for each other.

People usually set goals for what they want out of life and marriage. Your marriage is more likely to succeed if you and your partner talk about your goals. These goals may include buying a home, getting further education, pursuing a career, or having children.

Sometimes spouses have conflicting goals. A wife, for example, may want to pursue a career before having children, but her husband may not want to wait for children. A conflict may develop over whether money should be spent or saved for future needs. Communication helps couples resolve conflicts and determine mutual goals.

Many happily married couples use the types of communication skills you read about in Chapter 5. Imagine, for example, that you are married and are having a conflict with your partner over a visit to your in-laws. You do not want to visit your partner's parents every weekend even though you enjoy their company and know your partner looks forward to the weekly visits. How will you discuss this without hurting your partner's feelings? For effective communication, you could begin with an "I" message: "I enjoy seeing your parents, and I know you certainly do, but I have other interests too. . . ."

Some conflicts may require **compromise** (**kahm** pruh myz). Compromise is the willingness of each person to give up something in order to reach agreement. Suppose, for example, a husband wants to use the couple's savings for a new car while his wife wants to buy new living room furniture. The couple might compromise by agreeing to buy a used car, which costs less money. This would leave enough money to buy a few pieces of furniture as well.

Communication and compromise help couples adjust to each other's needs and wants.

Chapter 6 Marriage and Family **121**

▲
Figure 6-2. Today, most married couples share responsibilities both inside and outside the home.

○━━
Determining how household responsibilities will be shared is one of the most difficult adjustments in marriage.

Stresses in Marriage

Every marriage involves some type of adjustment. As you saw in the examples, communication and compromise help partners to adjust to each other's needs and wants. The changes in attitudes, expectations, life patterns, and goals that these adjustments may require can produce stress.

One of the most difficult adjustments in marriage can be determining **marital** (**ma** rih tul) **roles.** Marital roles are the responsibilities accepted by each spouse. Not long ago, most Americans accepted traditional marital roles: a husband earned money and a wife took care of the home and children. Some people still follow this pattern, but in most marriages today, both husband and wife work outside the home and often share housework and child care.

Some couples decide at the beginning of their marriage how each one will contribute financially and who will do certain household tasks. Who should do the cooking? Who will work in the yard? If partners are willing to compromise and accept tasks that fit their own abilities, interests, and schedules, they usually can develop a comfortable give-and-take relationship.

Couples must also determine how to manage the family income. Each partner in a marriage may have a different idea or attitude about earning, spending, and managing money. Imagine, for example, that your spouse wants to spend any extra income on things such as restaurant dinners and vacations. You may be more cautious and insist on putting some of the earnings into savings. You may disagree about whether one or both of you should manage the income. If

partners cannot agree on money matters, there is likely to be conflict and stress. To resolve differences over finances, they may try communicating their ideas and compromising on their wants.

Marriages can become strained when unexpected problems arise. Perhaps the major wage earner loses his or her job. A partner may become seriously ill or abuse alcohol or other drugs. There may be an unplanned pregnancy.

Handling crises is never easy. Effective communication can be an important tool in helping you get through a crisis. Sometimes you may need to seek help from community agencies that provide financial or counseling services. Turning to family and friends for emotional support is another way to get through the hard times.

Unexpected problems such as job loss, illness, or substance abuse can add stress to a marriage.

Teens and Marriage

When teenagers marry, they often face more stress than do those who marry later. The strains of adjusting to a new relationship, earning a living, and completing an education can feel overwhelming. If they have children, a young couple may also have difficulty adjusting to the emotional and financial responsibilities of parenthood.

Many married teenagers drop out of school. Without a high-school diploma, they may find only low-paying jobs. Sometimes, even if both partners work, they have difficulty earning enough money for rent and food. In these cases, teenage couples may end up living with parents or other relatives. Such an arrangement can limit a couple's oppor-

Figure 6-4. Teenagers who marry face many obstacles. Partners must be emotionally mature and committed to the marriage.

tunities to get to know each other, to make decisions, and to develop as partners in marriage.

Another difficulty for married teenagers involves changes in their friendships. Unmarried friends may not have the same interests and goals as a married couple, especially if the couple has a baby. A married couple may be concerned about stretching a small income to cover expenses, while single friends may be more concerned about having attractive clothes and getting good grades in school.

It is difficult to know when you are 17 or 18 just how you will feel and what will be important to you when you are 25 or 30. People change a great deal during their teenage years and early twenties. For this reason, many teenagers choose to wait before making a long-term commitment. They want to find out more about themselves, to meet people, and to have other experiences. In spite of all the obstacles, some teenage marriages are successful. Teenage partners must be willing to put in the effort needed to make their marriage work. They need to learn to communicate, to compromise, and to develop the qualities that will enable them to have a fulfilling relationship.

Most teenagers choose to wait before making a long-term commitment to marriage.

Section Review

1. What percentage of Americans marry?
2. List five of the factors that can contribute to a successful marriage.
3. List three stresses that may challenge any marriage.
4. What obstacles might married teenagers face?

What Do You Think?
5. If you were married, which goals would you find it most difficult to compromise on? Why?

2. BECOMING FAMILY

American families differ in size and form, but all have common functions or purposes. How is your family or living situation similar to those of your friends? How does it differ? What functions do you think a family has?

Family Forms

One basic family form is the **nuclear** (**noo** klee ur) family, which consists of only parents and their child or children. Often, the nuclear family is part of an **extended family,** or a network of close relatives. Your extended family might include your aunts, uncles, cousins, and grandparents. Sometimes members of the extended family live in the same household as the nuclear family. Today, most nuclear families live separately from their extended family. Still, it is common for several generations of a family to gather for holidays, reunions, weddings, and other special occasions.

In addition to the traditional nuclear family, a variety of other family forms exist. Many childless couples consider themselves a family. Groups of unrelated people who support and share with each other also may consider themselves a family. **Foster parents,** who provide affection and temporary homes for children whose biological parents are unable to care for them, often think of themselves and their foster children as families.

A nuclear family is made up of two parents and their children.

Figure 6-5. The traditional nuclear family and the single-parent family are two common family forms.
▼

Over half of the children born during the 1980s will live, at least for a time, in single-parent families. A single-parent family is a family in which only one parent lives with the child or children. **Single-parent** families are most often the result of **divorce,** a legal agreement to end a marriage. Other single-parent families form when parents decide to live apart or when one parent dies. Mothers head about 90 percent of single-parent families. In some cases, however, divorced parents have joint custody of the children. **Joint custody** means that parents equally share responsibility for all aspects of their children's lives: living quarters, physical care, financial support, and emotional and social well-being.

When single parents remarry, they form a blended family. A **blended family** consists of a biological parent, a stepparent (a parent related by marriage) and the children of one or both parents. Today, more than 7 million children under the age of 18 live in blended families.

When blended families form, the usual problems of families may become more complex. Children may feel that a stepparent is an intruder and not really part of the family. Stepchildren also may feel that they must choose between their stepparent and their biological parent who lives in a separate household. Sometimes stepbrothers and stepsisters have to adjust to new ways of relating to each other.

Successful blended families say that it is important to make adjustments slowly and to be flexible. Members of blended families adjust through compromise and communication. They do not try to blot out old memories and relationships. They talk about the traditions and activities that made children feel comfortable and cared for in their original family, and they try to incorporate these traditions and activities into the new family.

Responsibilities Within the Family

Whatever the family structure, members have to share responsibilities to ensure that the family will function effectively. Some responsibilities belong mainly to adult family members, some belong to the children, and some are shared by the whole family.

ADULTS' RESPONSIBILITIES In our society, heads of families are expected to provide for their children's basic needs. These needs include food, clothing, shelter, education, and love. Responsible heads of families care for their children when they are sick. If all adult family members work outside the home, they must arrange for a safe, caring environment for their children during work hours.

In families that fulfill the emotional needs of a child, children develop feelings of being loved and accepted, and they gain a sense of security. They also develop self-esteem if their abilities are recognized, their accomplishments praised, and their strengths encouraged.

Another basic responsibility of heads of families is the **socialization** (soh shul ih **zay** shun) of children, or teaching children behavior that is acceptable to the family and to society. Through socialization, children learn to respect the rights of others and to give and receive love. They also absorb their family's values and learn how to relate to others.

Fulfilling social needs also means learning to obey rules. Adult family members are responsible for setting rules that help to maintain order within the family and help members to live peacefully and safely in society. Figure 6-6 lists some typical rules that parents may set for their children.

CHILDREN'S RESPONSIBILITIES The responsibilities of children grow as children become older and more able. As a child, you were responsible for dressing yourself, tidying up your room, and doing your homework. Today, you may have other responsibilities as well, such as doing household chores, caring for younger brothers and sisters, or even adding to the family income with earnings from a part-time job. You are also responsible for following family rules and for showing respect for all family members.

Nearly all young people rebel against some of the rules set by their parents. When this happens, conflicts arise, and family members need to discuss their problems in a calm and respectful manner. If each member recognizes the need for rules and limits that are satisfactory to all, it will be easier to work together to resolve the conflict.

SHARED RESPONSIBILITIES In some families, both adults and children may share in the responsibility of caring for physically or mentally handicapped family members. In other families, everyone helps meet the needs of elderly members who may no longer be able to care for themselves.

Typical Household Rules

1. You must be home by 10 p.m. on weekdays and by midnight on weekends.
2. No watching television before homework is done.
3. You must keep your room clean, take out the trash, and help with the dishes.
4. No friends in the house when we are not home without first checking with us.

▲
Figure 6-6. How would you negotiate to change one or more of these rules?

It is important for each family member to understand the need for rules and limits.

Section Review

1. What is the traditional family form?
2. Describe three nontraditional family forms that are common today.
3. Why is it important for heads of families to meet their responsibilities?
4. What are three major responsibilities that children have in a family?

What Do You Think?
5. How do you think your family's rules are helping you prepare for independent living?

Figure 6-7. When parents divorce, children need to deal with their anger and sadness.

3. FAMILY STRESS

If you watch weekly television programs that depict family life, you may observe that most stressful situations seem to be handled quickly and easily. Within a half hour, a television family may have worked out a way to overcome some kind of crisis.

In real life, stressful situations usually are not so easily resolved. Divorce, abuse of alcohol and drugs, and family violence are some of the major causes of family stress. For a family to remain healthy, these problems must be talked about and dealt with.

Separation and Divorce

Conflict and tension occur as a normal part of living together. When a husband and wife cannot resolve their difficulties, however, they may try a period of **separation,** an arrangement in which spouses live apart and try to work out their problems. A separation is often painful for children in the family. They may feel helpless because they are unable to solve their parents' problems. They may think that the separation is their fault. Children need to be reassured that they are not to blame for their parents' problems.

If a couple is not able to work out differences, a separation may lead to divorce. For many, divorce is a devastating experience. Often, people who divorce believe that they are failures and suffer from grief and loss. Children may feel resentment, guilt, anger, sadness, shame, or embarrassment over their parents' divorce.

When parents divorce, it often helps to concentrate on various parts of your own life, such as school, friends, and activities that you enjoy. If you are feeling depressed, talk with a teacher, guidance counselor, or a member of the clergy. It also may help to learn how others have handled a family breakup. Many books and articles explain how families deal with divorce. In some schools, teenagers have formed groups in which they can talk about problems such as divorce and share ways of handling the problems. Sometimes, talking with a friend or relative who has been through a similar experience can help.

Alcohol and Drug Abuse

Some adults have serious problems. If they happen to be members of your family, their problems affect you, too. If you are afraid to go home or bring friends to your house because an adult in your home might be drinking or using drugs, you have a problem.

In most communities, there are groups such as Al-Anon and Alateen to help with problems related to someone else's

If an adult family member has a serious problem, the problem also affects you.

◄ **Figure 6-8. Alateen is one group that helps teenagers cope with an alcoholic family member.**

drinking or drug use. **Al-Anon** is an organization that helps people cope with an alcoholic family member. **Alateen** provides help for teenagers who have an alcoholic in the family. These groups hold meetings that are open to anyone who wants to share experiences about living with an alcoholic. You can find the telephone numbers of these organizations in your local telephone book. To find out about groups that help family members of drug abusers, look under "Drug Abuse" in your local telephone book.

Family Violence

The problems associated with family violence are potentially the most disturbing and destructive in our society. People who resort to family violence often feel hopeless. They may believe they have no constructive way of dealing with their problems. In other cases, abusive adults may view their children or other family members as possessions rather than as people, and they may use physical or emotional abuse to keep control.

○—⚷

Family violence, even when it does not cause physical damage, causes emotional damage.

PHYSICAL ABUSE If punishment, even when it is given for something a child or other family member did wrong, leaves a mark that can be seen the next day, it is considered **physical abuse.** This could be a bruise, a scratch, or a welt, even a small one. Victims of physical abuse may be afraid to go home, or they may feel it is hopeless to try to avoid punishment. Victims can be children, spouses, or elderly relatives. Even when children are not themselves physically damaged, they are emotionally damaged by family violence.

Figure 6-9. Women who are victims of physical abuse can find shelter and companionship in a home for battered women.

Many victims of abuse are afraid that if they tell someone, their family will be destroyed. Other victims believe that they somehow deserve the batterings they receive. They worry that if they let someone know what is going on they will be told it is their own fault. As a result, the self-esteem of victims drops. Regardless of fears or feelings of guilt, it is far more damaging to keep silent than to seek help.

A good place to seek help is the telephone book. There should be a listing for Parents Anonymous, a self-help group for parents who abuse their children. Hotline numbers for battered women or elders are often listed as well. If children cannot find an appropriate group to call, they should talk with a teacher, a counselor, a trusted relative, a physician, or a member of the clergy. Speaking up about physical abuse is the first step toward putting an end to an intolerable, potentially dangerous situation. Victims are not responsible for abusive behavior, nor can they cure it by themselves.

Victims of abuse are not responsible for the abusive behavior. They need to seek help to put an end to it.

SEXUAL ABUSE All children want to be hugged and cuddled and made to feel that they have a special relationship with their parents and other caring adults. Some adults, however, respond sexually to the affection or innocence of children. Adults who respond in this way are committing an act of sexual abuse. **Sexual abuse** is a criminal offense in which a child or an adolescent is used for sexual activity. Sexual abuse ranges from touching in inappropriate places to unwanted sexy kisses to sexual relations. Even a single instance of sexual abuse can have a devastating effect on a child. It may be more difficult for the child to trust others and to develop caring relationships later in life. For example, a sexually abused teenager may be uncomfortable with dating. A young adult who was sexually abused may have difficulty making a commitment to a long-term relationship, such as marriage.

Sexual relations between family members other than husband and wife is called **incest.** Incest may not necessarily be a violent attack like rape. Instead, it may involve persuasion in which a victim is pressured to do something sexual through bribes or threats. Often the incest can go on for years. The person initiating the act is unwilling or unable to take responsibility for stopping it. The victim, through guilt and shame, assumes all the responsibility or blame in his or her own mind.

Victims of any type of sexual abuse should seek the help of a trusted adult, such as a teacher, school counselor, physician, relative, or member of the clergy. Victims also can find help by calling the Child Abuse Hotline, which is listed in the phone book. Seeking help can be extremely difficult. Victims risk angering, hurting, or betraying the family member who abused them. Sometimes other relatives may not want to believe what is going on and may accuse the victim of lying. Victims need to know they have the right not to be touched sexually by anyone. Victims also need to know that it is far more dangerous to believe the threats of the abuser than to report the abuser.

Victims of sexual abuse should seek the help of a trusted adult.

EMOTIONAL ABUSE "You rotten, no-good little punk, you never do anything right." "I wish that you had never been born." "If you don't straighten out, I'm going to throw you out of the house for good." A child who is constantly exposed to negative statements like these is likely to suffer from emotional abuse. **Emotional abuse**, nonphysical mistreatment, can destroy a person's sense of worth.

Emotional abuse may take several different forms. Verbal abuse consists of any words or remarks that destroy a person's self-esteem. If a child is often called a stupid, clumsy brat, he or she comes to believe it must be true. The use of threats, such as that a child will be locked out or put up for adoption, will destroy a child's self-worth. The child has no way of contradicting such crushing words or threats. When parents' attitudes are tense, hostile, or threatening most of the time, children do not receive the warmth and security they need to feel wanted and loved.

Emotional neglect occurs when parents fail to give their child love and emotional support. Although nothing harmful may be done or said to victims of emotional neglect, they suffer from the feeling that they do not belong. They also do not receive the emotional support necessary for the development of a healthy personality.

Even though most emotional abuse is invisible, it leaves victims feeling inadequate, helpless, or worthless. Children who are being emotionally abused need to seek help as much as physically or sexually abused children. Emotionally abused children should talk with a trusted adult or call the Child Abuse Hotline.

Figure 6-10. Emotional abuse, although it leaves no physical scars, can destroy a child's self-worth.

Computer Aging of Missing Children

A child is missing—a desperate search begins. Recent photos are distributed in the immediate neighborhood—later, nationwide. As time passes, the photo becomes outdated. The child, now older, no longer looks like the photo.

Updated pictures of missing children—predictions of how they would look today—would help police locate these youngsters. Such updated pictures can now be made.

Artists team up with computers to produce "aged" photographs of missing children. A camera scans the child's photo and translates it into an image on the computer screen. Working from pictures of the child's brothers and sisters and of the parents when they were younger, the artist-computer team reshapes the image on the screen to look older.

Once the computer prints out the updated picture, police can distribute it with the original photograph. Computer aging adds one more tool to the search for missing children.

The computer-updated photo (left) helped find this missing boy (shown at right after he was found).

▲

Figure 6-11. Runaways can get a free bus ride home.

Runaways

Thousands of the nation's young people are runaways. Some leave home because of sexual or emotional abuse or other violence in their families. Others run away because of emotional problems or school failure. Some turn to crime, including prostitution, as a way to support themselves.

Many communities have shelters for homeless youth and hotlines for runaways. Law enforcement agencies in cooperation with bus companies conduct programs that offer free transportation to runaways who want to return home. Through these efforts, some runaways return home or get the help they need from health-care professionals.

If you are a runaway or are thinking of running away, you owe yourself a call to your local runaway hotline. Call the operator or look up "Runaway" in your phone book. The counselors can advise you about where to stay and how to get help for family or other problems.

Section Review

1. How might a divorce affect children?
2. Where can teenagers turn for help in dealing with a family member's drinking problem?
3. Describe three kinds of family violence.
4. Why should emotional abuse not be ignored?

What Do You Think?
5. How do you think young people who experience divorce can help each other cope with a family breakup?

4. KEEPING THE FAMILY HEALTHY

What factors or characteristics determine whether or not a family is healthy? Members of healthy families say that commitment and communication top the list. It is also important for members to cooperate with one another, share responsibilities, spend time together, and respect and appreciate each other. Within a healthy family, members should be able to compromise.

Skills to Solve Family Problems

Healthy families develop skills to work through problems. Members learn how to resolve conflicts, express emotions, and use decision-making techniques.

RESOLVING CONFLICTS Have you ever argued with your parents over who is responsible for certain household chores? What do you do when your parents dislike one of your friends? Do your parents complain that you spend too much money?

Your family can resolve conflicts without shouting matches. Communication skills are the keys to conflict resolution. Saying what you mean, listening to others, observing the silent messages of body language, and offering feedback are important elements in communication. Family members have to work at developing these skills.

Healthy families develop skills to resolve problems, express emotions, and communicate openly.

◀ **Figure 6-12. Enjoying activities together is essential to family health and happiness.**

In many conflict situations, family members struggle for power. Teenagers want control over their lives and decisions, while parents want family life to function in ways they believe are best. When trying to resolve conflicts, you need to find time to talk openly, honestly, and lovingly, that is, with the idea of learning from one another.

Resolving conflicts in a constructive way also means trying to determine what each person hopes to achieve. The Health Skills on page 138 teaches a method for resolving conflicts in a way that benefits both people.

EXPRESSING EMOTIONS Learning to express emotions constructively is part of effective communication and problem-solving. While everyone needs to express anger at times, angry outbursts that are verbal attacks on another person usually worsen problems and block communication. Sometimes, it is better to say "I get upset when people criticize me" than to angrily accuse someone with "All you ever do is criticize me!"

Family members can help each other solve problems if they also express appreciation and show respect for one another's ideas. Being able to say "I love you" is another important aspect of overcoming family difficulties. If family members understand that problem-solving is a loving process, not a time to judge and place blame, solutions may be more easily and quickly achieved.

USING DECISION-MAKING SKILLS Families that are successful in resolving conflicts and finding solutions to problems frequently use decision-making skills. These skills involve choosing between alternatives. For example, suppose

It is important for families to discuss problems in a loving and caring way.

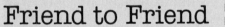

Friend to Friend

Andy:
Last night I asked my father if I could use the car and he just blew up at me.

Michael:
Why do you think he was so angry?

Andy:
Who knows? Sometimes I can't figure him out. You used to fight a lot with your dad, but you seem to get along OK now. What helped you?

you want to go the movies Saturday night, but you promised your parents weeks ago that you would babysit your younger brother. What can you do?

By sitting down with your parents and going through the decision-making process together, you may be able to arrive at a solution that is mutually agreeable. Perhaps you can find another babysitter, or perhaps you can take your brother to the movies with you. By agreeing on a solution, you can avoid an argument and show that you are a mature and responsible person.

Family decision-making can be a difficult process to follow. Each person may have different needs or opinions. Some may find it difficult to communicate their opinions in a respectful way. Sometimes, family members or people outside the family may disrupt the decision-making process. In these cases, families may decide to seek outside help to solve their problems.

Teenagers and their parents can use the decision-making process to reach agreeable solutions.

Help for the Family

Where can families go for help in solving problems? Many families depend on relatives to help them resolve their difficulties. Other families call on trusted friends for help and support. Sometimes families seek advice from clergy or health professionals. If family members have no immediate source of help in a time of crisis, they may use a crisis hotline, or contact a crisis center. People who respond to hotline calls or work in crisis centers may serve as sympathetic listeners, or they may refer people to support groups, family service agencies, or family therapists.

Michael:
We're getting along better since we had a family talk. One of the points my dad made was that I often asked him for things when he was tired or in the middle of doing something. So now I pick my times more carefully, and he pays more attention to what I'm saying.

Andy:
I guess I did ask for the car as soon as my dad walked in the door from work. Next time, I'll try to be more aware of my timing and my dad's feelings.

SUPPORT GROUPS Hundreds of thousands of support groups have been set up across the nation. A **support group** is a network of people who help each other cope with a particular problem. Group members learn from one another rather than from a group leader. They learn how to express their emotions in a positive way and how to deal effectively with their problems. One well-known support group is Alcoholics Anonymous, which holds meetings in communities across the country for those who abuse alcohol.

Other support groups help people cope with divorce, death, family violence, gambling, teenage delinquency, and serious illness.

FAMILY AGENCIES In many communities, families can get help with problems through a variety of public and private service agencies. Local family service association agencies offer such services as counseling, education about family life and teen parenting, and pregnancy services. Mental health agencies help meet the needs of the emotionally disturbed and mentally ill. Child welfare agencies offer protective services for children, ranging from organizing foster care to dealing with abuse and neglect. Other agencies help families with financial aid, food, housing, employment, medical care, and other basic needs.

FAMILY THERAPY Some family agencies provide counseling or therapy for troubled families or refer families to outside therapists. Therapists work with family members to find better ways to solve problems. Family therapists usually encourage all family members to participate in order to resolve conflicts and to learn to get along better.

Figure 6-13. Learning to express love toward family members can help strengthen family ties. ▶

Making the Most of Family Time

- Develop family traditions—celebrate holidays, birthdays and other occasions in special ways; set aside time for regular family events.
- Make mealtimes special—try to eat together and share your day's events.
- Hold a family meeting—allow family members to discuss any important issues or problems, suggest some improvements, and make plans to do things together.
- Show caring—do a special household chore as a pleasant surprise; give a backrub; write a note of appreciation; call a family member on the phone just to chat; give a sincere compliment.

Source: YMCA of Metropolitan Los Angeles, 1979

The Healthy Family

During the latter part of the 1980s, several major magazines polled thousands of families. These polls indicated that most Americans are satisfied with the way their families are functioning. Although many teenagers go through periods of insecurity and times when everything they do seems to drive their families crazy, these times are balanced by other times when teens feel loved and accepted.

The key to family health and happiness is to make the most of the time that families spend together. Many family members take their time together for granted. Figure 6-13 lists some simple ways that families can strengthen their relationships and improve the quality of their shared time.

Maintaining family traditions and ties is an important characteristic of healthy families. When extended family members gather during holidays, birthdays, or other occasions, they often share a sense of belonging and security. When there are problems, extended family members can help each other with understanding, advice, or encouragement.

Maintaining family traditions and ties is important for family health and happiness.

Section Review

1. List three characteristics of healthy families.
2. What are three skills families can learn to help solve their problems?
3. Why are the steps in decision-making sometimes hard for families to follow?
4. Where can families go for help with their problems?

What Do You Think?
5. If you were a parent of a teenager, how would you handle conflicts that arise between you?

Using Win-Win Negotiation

Dad, there's no good reason why I can't stay out late on weekends. I'm tired of being treated like a baby!

You're only fifteen, Rosa. You can't just come and go as you please. Midnight is late enough.

Rosa and her father have been having this "discussion" for weeks. They just go around and around, getting more and more annoyed and stubborn. Conflicts like this also occur between friends, neighbors, and nations. Often at the heart of a disagreement is a breakdown in communication. When communication is poor, conflict can tear a relationship apart. But with good communication, conflict can lead to greater understanding and growth.

The following steps can help you to turn a no-win situation into one where everyone comes out a winner.

1. Describe the Problem

When you find yourself in a conflict situation, take the time to really understand the problem. Write out answers to the following questions:

- What do you believe is happening in the situation?
- How does it make you feel?
- What don't you like about the situation?
- What do you want out of the situation?

Dad makes me come in so early. It makes me angry that he doesn't trust me, but I hate fighting with him. I'd like to have more freedom and to get along with him.

Rosa's not old enough to stay out late. I worry about her safety. I don't want to fight with her, but I don't want her to get hurt.

2. Explore the Other Point of View

Now describe the problem as you think the other person sees it. What do you think are the other person's beliefs, feelings, and interests?

Dad probably thinks he's protecting me. He worries when I'm out late, but he wants to get along with me and keep me out of trouble.

Rosa probably thinks I don't trust her. She's angry because she can't spend enough time with her friends. She wants me to trust her.

Obviously, it is best if both the people involved in an argument go through the steps of Win-Win Negotiation. Suggest and explain the process to the other person. Ask the other person to go through steps 1 and 2 on his or her own. If the person is not willing to try the process, you can still go through the steps yourself. Your willingness to see the other person's point of view may help the situation.

Win-Win Negotiation can help resolve important conflicts.

3. Share and Discuss

Use the following guidelines to share your understanding of the situation with the other person involved in it.

- Actively listen to the other person and acknowledge that you understand his or her view. Understanding is *not* the same as agreeing with the other person.
- Talk about and acknowledge each other's feelings. Unexpressed feelings often get in the way of resolving conflicts. Listen quietly without interrupting.
- Attack the problem, not the person. Seek solutions, and do not blame.
- Look for shared goals. Avoid taking specific positions at first.
- Focus on what you want to happen in the future. Look forward, not back.

Dad, I understand that you worry when . . .

Rosa, I realize that time with your friends is important . . .

4. Invent Solutions

Brainstorm a list of solutions that meet at least some of the needs of both of you. Invent solutions first; you can judge them later.

Dad, what if I call you if I'm out after 11 p.m. and have late hours twice a month?

Why don't you invite your friends to our house, Rosa?

5. Agree on a Solution

From your list, select the one solution that best meets the most important interests of both of you. The two of you must agree on the solution.

So, Dad, I'll call you at 11 p.m. to let you know where I am and when I will be home.

OK, Rosa. That way I won't have to worry about where you are and whether you're all right.

APPLY THE SKILL

1. Jack and Sam are having a disagreement. In writing, describe their problem and use the Win-Win method to resolve it.

Sam: How could you go to a baseball game tonight, Jack? You promised to help me study for tomorrow's math test!
Jack: How could you expect me to turn down free tickets to the most important game of the season?

2. List five areas in which you or people your age may conflict with friends, family members, teachers, or others.

3. Think of a conflict you are now (or recently have been) involved in. Ask the other person to work through the Win-Win method with you. Then evaluate how successful the process was in resolving the conflict.

6 | Chapter Review

Chapter Summary

- Ninety-five percent of all Americans marry. Marriage is a lifelong commitment.
- Love, compatibility, an ability to compromise, and a commitment to the marriage are some of the factors that contribute to having a successful marriage.
- Changing marital roles, disagreements over money matters, and unexpected problems, such as illness and job loss, can create stress in a marriage.
- When teenagers marry, they often face more problems than do older couples. Teenage couples may not be financially or emotionally ready for marriage or parenthood.
- Today, people live in a wide variety of family forms, including nuclear families, foster families, single-parent families, and blended families.
- All families have similar functions and responsibilities.
- Parents are responsible for meeting children's basic physical and emotional needs, socializing children, and setting rules. As children grow, they gain new responsibilities, such as taking care of themselves, helping with household tasks, and caring for less able members of their household.
- Divorce requires major adjustments for all members of the family. Children may feel guilty, angry, and embarrassed about divorce. It is important that they discuss their feelings with others.
- Acts of violence in families include physical abuse, sexual abuse, and emotional abuse. Drug and alcohol abuse also contribute to family problems. Many organizations exist to help family members deal with these types of problems.
- Family members can learn skills to improve communication, express their emotions, and solve family problems. Families may seek help with problems through support groups, family agencies, or family therapy.
- Healthy families maintain family traditions and ties. Family members share time together and enjoy each other's company.

Vocabulary Review

Listed below are some of the important terms in this chapter. Choose the term that best matches each phrase in the exercise that follows.

Alateen	divorce	incest	separation
Al-Anon	emotional abuse	joint custody	sexual abuse
blended family	emotional neglect	marital roles	single-parent family
commitment	extended family	nuclear family	socialization
compromise	foster parents	physical abuse	support group

1. responsibilities accepted by each partner in marriage

2. skill that requires each partner to give up something in order to reach agreement

3. an organization that helps teenagers cope with an alcoholic family member

4. parents and their child or children

5. teaching children acceptable behavior

6. legal agreement to end a marriage

7. stepparents and their children and stepchildren

8. network of close relatives

9. sexual interaction between any family members except husband and wife

10. determination to develop a fulfilling relationship

What Have You Learned?

1. Describe the components of real love. How is real love different from infatuation?
2. How might today's marital roles differ from traditional roles in marriage?
3. How can teen marriages be successful?
4. What can you do if you are having trouble feeling comfortable in your blended family?
5. Why is it important that children be socialized?
6. List and describe five basic functions of the family.
7. List three stressful situations that affect some families.
8. What should a child abuse victim do?
9. How is witnessing family violence damaging to children?
10. How might support groups help children of divorce?
11. What kinds of communication skills can family members use to resolve conflicts?
12. How might using a hotline help a family member in a time of crisis?

What Do You Think?

1. What do you think are the two most important factors in a marriage? Why?
2. What factors do you think are important for determining marital roles?
3. How do you think education can help teenagers succeed in marriage?
4. What kinds of family rules for teenagers do you think are fair and reasonable? Unfair and unreasonable?
5. Why do you think it is sometimes difficult for family members to communicate with one another?

What Would You Do?

1. Your friends, a teenage couple who have dated for two years, plan to marry. Would you encourage or discourage them? Why?
2. You would like to develop better communication with the other members of your family. How would you go about achieving this goal?
3. Your friend has confided that she is being sexually abused by her stepfather. How can you help her?
4. Several classmates want to start a support group for teens who have to cope with divorce or separation. They have asked you for advice on what to discuss at the first meeting. What would you tell them?
5. You suspect that your friend's mother has an alcohol problem although your friend has never said anything about it. What could you do to help your friend?

For Further Study

1. Create a bulletin board display entitled "Strong Families." Illustrate with family snapshots, magazine photos, and posters. Prepare and display lists of resources on parenting, communication, conflict resolution, and other topics related to healthy families.
2. Research and report on the types of agencies in your community that provide help for troubled families. List the services each provides and explain how people can make their first contacts with the agencies.
3. Interview some teenagers and some married adults to find out what qualities they think are important in a spouse. How do the teenager's responses compare to those of the adults?

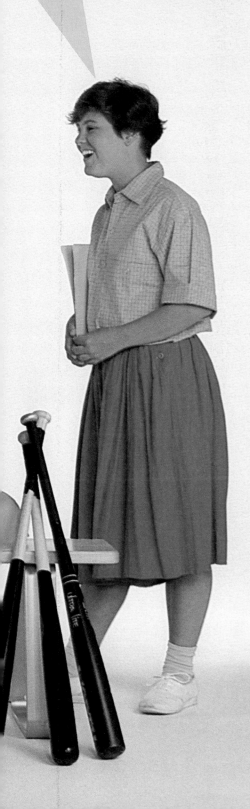

Now, that's something really new!

U N I T

3

Physical Well-Being

7

As you read, think about

▶ how your skin functions and how you can keep it healthy.

▶ how you can protect your eyes.

▶ how your ears function and what you can do to protect them.

▶ what you should do to maintain the health of your teeth and gums.

Personal Care

Y ou have just skied a difficult slope, and you stop to catch your breath. Your senses are alive. The sky is deep blue, and the snow is a brilliant white. You hear the snow crunching beneath your skis and hear the shouts of the other skiers near you. You feel a crisp breeze and the gentle warmth of the sun on your skin.

Below you is the ski lodge. There you can warm your hands around a mug of hot soup as you enjoy its hearty flavor, and you can choose an ''oldie'' on the huge, antique juke box. As much as you love skiing, the music, warmth, and soup at the lodge are tempting you now.

Imagine how different these experiences and others would be if you couldn't see, hear, or feel the things around you. In this chapter, you will learn how your eyes, ears, and skin connect you to your surroundings. You will also learn why proper care of these important organs, as well as of your hair, nails, and teeth, will help you to look and to feel your best.

Looking your best makes you feel good and shows that you care about your health.

Check Your Wellness

How many personal care behaviors do you practice? See how many of these questions you can answer yes to.

1. Are you careful not to overexpose your skin to the sun?
2. Do you bathe or shower daily?
3. Do you comb or brush your hair frequently and wash it with a mild shampoo?
4. Are your fingernails and toenails clean and neatly clipped?
5. Have you had your eyes examined within the last year?
6. Do you avoid putting objects, such as cotton-tipped swabs, in your ears?
7. Do you minimize your exposure to loud noises, including music, whenever possible?
8. Do you brush your teeth after breakfast and dinner?
9. Do you floss your teeth daily?

1. YOUR SKIN, HAIR, AND NAILS

Having healthy skin, hair, and nails is a part of looking and feeling your best. After all, these are the first things people see when they look at you. Learning how to take care of your skin, hair, and nails will help you to look and feel your best.

Your Skin

Like every other part of your body, your skin is made of cells. A **cell** is the smallest living unit of the body. Your body is made up of billions of cells that can only be seen through a microscope. These billions of cells are divided into hundreds of types. Cells of the same type that are connected and function together form **tissue**. Within your body, tissues are organized into structures called organs. An **organ**, for example, the skin, is a structure that performs one or more specific functions in the body. Your skin is the largest organ of your body.

SKIN STRUCTURE   Skin is made up of two main layers and a third layer that holds the skin in place. These layers are illustrated in Figure 7-1. The outermost layer—the layer you see when you look at someone—is the **epidermis** (ep uh

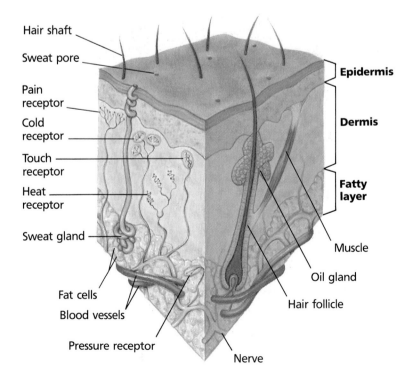

Figure 7-1. The skin has a complex structure. In what layer of the skin are the oil glands?

dur mis). It forms a barrier between the organs within your body and your environment, including any germs in your environment. Just below the skin's surface is a layer of the epidermis that continually produces new skin cells. These cells are nourished by the blood vessels that run through the skin. As cells are produced here, older cells are constantly pushed to the skin's surface. Since there are no blood vessels at the surface, the cells are deprived of nourishment and die. As more new cells are pushed to the surface, the dead cells already there are shed.

Within the epidermis are special cells that produce a brown substance known as **melanin** (**mel** uh nin). Melanin is a major factor in determining the color of your skin. Sunlight can stimulate the melanin-producing cells to produce more melanin, which causes the skin to darken, or tan. A person or animal lacking cells that produce melanin is known as an **albino** (al **by** noh).

Within the epidermis are structures known as pores. A **pore** is the opening of a narrow channel, or duct, that leads to a gland. A gland may be a cell, a group of cells, or an organ that produces and releases one or more substances. A sweat gland, for example, produces sweat, or perspiration, which flows out through the pores on the skin's surface. Sweat absorbs heat and evaporates from your skin, which helps to cool your body. Another type of gland, called an oil gland, produces oil that helps to waterproof the skin. These glands are found in the inner layer of the skin, the **dermis** (**dur** mis). The dermis, which is usually much thicker than the epidermis, is tough and elastic. It contains muscle fibers, blood vessels, and nerves. The blood vessels bring nutrients to the skin, and carry away waste products. When your temperature rises, blood flow through the skin increases, which allows more heat from your blood to escape into the environment. When you are cold, blood flow through the skin decreases, which means less heat is lost through your skin. The nerves in the dermis help you to sense your environment. They tell you whether something is hot or cold or rough or smooth. They also transmit messages of pain that warn you of possible danger or injury.

Beneath the dermis is a tough layer of connective tissue that holds the skin in place. This tissue has a layer of fat that varies in thickness, depending on the area of the body. The fat tissue in this layer acts as insulation, preventing excessive heat loss.

The three layers that make up your skin help to prevent injury to the other tissues and organs of your body and help your body to maintain a constant temperature. Finally, these layers preserve the environment that your cells need to survive. Body fluids surround and bathe all of the cells in your body. Without this watery environment, your cells could not function. Without skin, your body fluids would evaporate.

▲ **Figure 7-2. Skin color is determined by a substance in the skin known as melanin.**

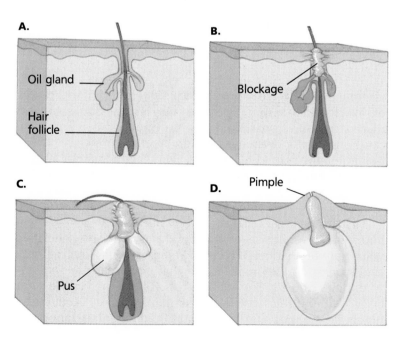

SKIN PROBLEMS Because your skin is exposed to the environment, it faces many hazards. Freezing temperatures can damage your skin, especially on your toes, fingers, ears, and nose. Exposure to the sun can lead to sunburn and skin cancer. If you cut or scrape your skin, germs, or **bacteria** (bak **teer** ee uh), can enter the body. Burns damage the skin and reduce the protection it offers to other tissues and organs. You will learn how to care for frostbite, cuts, and burns in Chapter 26.

One of the most common skin problems you may face as an adolescent is **acne** (**ak** nee), a condition in which the oil glands become irritated, infected, and swollen. Acne frequently develops during adolescence when the oil glands in your skin begin to grow larger and produce excess oil. When excess oil combines with the dead skin cells of the epidermis and plugs pores exposed to the air, a "blackhead" forms. "Whiteheads" are blocked pores that are not exposed to the air because of overlying epidermis. Blackheads and whiteheads are two kinds of blemishes. As Figure 7-3 illustrates, bacteria can infect a plugged pore, resulting in a pimple.

You may have heard that oily food, chocolate, and cola drinks cause acne. Doctors now feel that acne may not be directly affected by a diet containing these foods. Research has shown, however, that a balanced diet, a lack of stress, and proper sleep contribute to a healthy skin, free of acne.

The best defense against acne is clean skin. If your skin is oily, you should wash it with mild soap two or three times a day. More frequent washings only stimulate your oil glands to produce more oil. Products that contain **benzoyl peroxide** (**ben** zo ihl pur **ox** ide), a chemical that dries out pimples and

Acne is caused by blocked pores.

A.
Oil gland
Hair follicle

B.
Blockage

C.
Pus

D.
Pimple

Figure 7-3. A pimple forms when ▶
bacteria infect a plugged pore.

kills bacteria, can help mild cases of acne. Because your fingers and nails can carry bacteria, you do not want to scratch or squeeze pimples, blackheads, or whiteheads. A **dermatologist**, a doctor who handles skin disorders, should treat severe cases of acne to avoid complications.

Another skin disorder is **dermatitis** (dur muh **ty** tis) in which an area of skin may become red, swollen, hot, and itchy. Sometimes, the area blisters and oozes. Any substance, for example, chemicals, soaps, or even plants, such as poison ivy, that irritates the skin can cause dermatitis. Sometimes, certain medicines and foods also cause skin problems. In most cases, dermatitis can be cured with a medication applied to the skin. You can prevent dermatitis from recurring if you can identify and avoid the substances that irritate your skin.

Several common skin problems are caused by viruses. A virus is a simple kind of germ that causes an infection or disease. One type of virus, called **herpes** (**hur** peez) **simplex I**, causes clusters of watery blisters, or cold sores, around the mouth. Cold sores often heal in 7 to 10 days. Warts, growths on the skin, frequently the hands and feet, also are caused by viruses. Warts can grow deep into the skin and should be removed only by a dermatologist.

There are some skin infections that are caused by a fungus. A fungus is a simple organism, such as a yeast or mold, that grows into the tissue of another organism. Infections caused by a fungus usually occur in warm and moist areas of the skin. Athlete's foot is a common fungal infection that causes burning, itching, cracking, and peeling of the skin on the bottom of the foot and between the toes. To prevent athlete's foot, keep your feet dry and try wearing cotton socks and shoes made of leather instead of plastic. Because fungal infections are often hard to cure with over-the-counter medicines, you may want to see a dermatologist if you develop an infection.

Skin cancer is a serious skin disease. A **cancer** is an area of uncontrolled cell growth that invades the surrounding tissue and destroys it. There are at least three types of skin cancer. The most serious form of skin cancer usually starts with a mole, or brown spot, that suddenly increases in size and becomes blue-black. Because almost all skin cancers are caused by overexposure to the sun's ultraviolet rays, you should protect your skin when in the sun. Sunscreens, substances that block the ultraviolet rays of the sun, are numbered with a sun protection factor (SPF) from 1 to 29. The higher the SPF of a sunscreen, the more protection it provides. To protect your skin, you should apply sunscreen with an SPF of 5 or higher before going into the sun. Reapply it frequently while you are in the sun, especially if you have been swimming or sweating. You will learn more about skin cancer in Chapter 18.

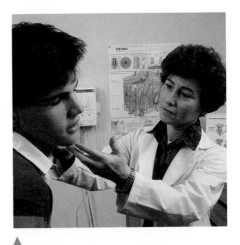

▲
Figure 7-4. A dermatologist specializes in the care and treatment of skin disorders.

Figure 7–5. You can enjoy the sun and still avoid overexposure.

SKIN CARE Usually, your skin only needs basic care to stay healthy. Basic skin care includes keeping it clean, protecting it from extremes in heat and cold, and preventing infection in cuts and scrapes. A balanced diet, regular exercise, and sleep are also essential for healthy skin.

To clean your skin you need to wash away dirt, body oil, perspiration, and cosmetics every day. The best substance to wash with is soap. Although manufacturers may claim that the perfumes, deodorants, lotions, extra fats, and vitamins added to their products improve them, the fact is any soap will get you clean. Deodorants do help to destroy the bacteria that cause odors, but deodorants and perfumes also can irritate the skin and cause a rash. Soaps with lotions added to them do not effectively moisturize the skin. The best way to moisturize dry skin is to apply a body lotion after washing and while your skin is still moist. The lotion will help your skin retain its natural moisture.

Although sunbathing is relaxing, and the sun helps your body to make vitamin D, as you know, prolonged exposure to the sun can lead to sunburn and skin cancer. While a tan may help you to avoid sunburn, it also causes the skin to become wrinkled and leathery. Sunlamps and tanning booths can cause the same damage to the skin as the sun. With these tanning devices, severe sunburn or eye damage can occur in just minutes.

Your Hair

Like your skin, hair helps to insulate your body from the cold in winter and the heat in summer. Eyelashes and the hair in your nostrils and ears help to keep dust and dirt out of your eyes, nose, and ears. Eyebrows help to keep sweat from running into your eyes. The hair on your arms and legs helps you sense when something, such as an insect, is on or close to your skin.

HAIR STRUCTURE Your hair is part of your skin. Hairs are formed in the dermis layer of the skin. Each hair develops in a narrow cavity called a **hair follicle**. The hair that you see, like the surface of your skin, is made of dead cells. This is why it does not hurt you when your hair is cut. The living part of the hair, or the root, is found at the base of the follicle. As cells are added to the root, the hair is pushed out of the follicle, or grows. Each hair follicle is connected to an oil gland. Oil moves up the hair follicle to the surface of the skin to help keep your hair and skin supple. This oil also helps to "waterproof" your skin and hair.

A tiny muscle that contracts when you are cold or frightened is also attached to each hair follicle. When these muscles contract, they cause your hairs to "stand on end," producing goose bumps.

The color of your hair and whether it is curly or straight depends on several different factors. The amount of colored substance and the number and size of air spaces in each hair affect your hair color. The shape of each hair determines if it is curly or straight.

HAIR PROBLEMS   Some people are bothered by unwanted hair on the face or body. There are several ways it can be removed, at least temporarily. The easiest way is shaving, but some people pluck unwanted hairs out one by one. This can be painful and may lead to infection. Another method uses a cream or lotion that dissolves hair, which then can be washed away. If the unwanted hair is dark, it may be enough to use a special bleaching product that lightens hair.

Head lice are another common hair problem. Head lice are small insects that live on the scalp and lay their eggs on hair. There are several special shampoos available to kill lice. After shampooing, a fine-toothed comb should be used to remove the eggs, or nits, from the hair. Not sharing combs and brushes with others is the best way to avoid head lice.

Some hair problems, for example, dandruff, are really scalp problems. Dandruff occurs when dry flakes of skin from the scalp come off as the hair is combed or brushed. Dandruff shampoos can help to control the problem, if regular hair care does not help.

HAIR CARE   Attractive hair is clean hair. Frequent, gentle brushing helps to remove dirt and makes your hair shine. Shampooing washes away built-up oil and keeps your hair clean and fresh-smelling. When used correctly, products that straighten, wave, or curl your hair will not damage it.

Head lice and dandruff are problems that can be treated with special shampoos.

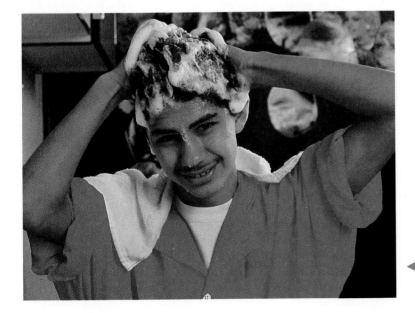

◀ **Figure 7-6. Shampooing is an important part of keeping your hair healthy and attractive.**

Your Nails

Fingernails and toenails, like your hair, are outgrowths of the skin that protect the sensitive upper surfaces of the tips of your fingers and toes. With these surfaces protected, the fingers become more useful in grasping objects and in prodding and scratching. Toenails, covering the tips of the toes, protect the toes when you walk or run.

NAIL STRUCTURE Like your hair, your fingernails and toenails are produced by special skin cells. As the cells in your nails age, they die and are pushed to the skin surface by new cells. In fact, most of the tissue of a nail consists of dead cells. If you have ever looked closely at your nails, you know they are colorless, although they appear to have the color of the skin under the nails.

NAIL PROBLEMS Growth, brittleness, and white spots are common nail problems. The rate of nail growth varies from person to person. No specific food, mineral, or vitamin will make your nails grow faster—not even gelatin. If your hands are in water frequently, your nails may become brittle. Wearing rubber gloves when you are washing dishes will help to protect your nails from becoming brittle. White spots on nails are the result of minor injuries. The spots will vanish as the nail grows.

Although most of these nail problems are not a sign of illness, your nails can be an indicator of your health. Any dramatic changes in their texture, shape, color, or growth rate may be a signal to seek medical advice.

NAIL CARE Clean, well-cared-for nails add to your appearance. A fingernail brush, used regularly, will keep the area under your nails clean. Clip or file your fingernails and toenails so that their edges are smooth and cannot catch on your clothes or scratch your skin. To prevent ingrown toenails, clip toenails straight across. An ingrown toenail results when the edges of the nail grow into the skin on each side of the nail. If not treated properly, ingrown nails can become infected and cause serious problems.

▲
Figure 7–7. Regular use of fingernail clippers improves your appearance.

Section Review

1. Name the two main layers of your skin.
2. What are two functions of the skin?
3. What is a hair follicle?
4. What functions do your nails serve?

What Do You Think?

5. What would you do to improve your skin?

2. YOUR EYES

Much of the information you gather about your environment reaches your brain through your eyes. They are your windows to the world.

Because your eyes come into contact with your environment, they need protection. As you know, your eyelashes and eyebrows keep dust, dirt, and sweat out of your eyes. The bones around your eyes protect your eyes on the sides, top, bottom, and back. Your eyelids also prevent foreign objects from entering your eyes. When anything, even a gentle puff of air, touches your eyes, your eyelids close. Even your tears help to protect your eyes. The fluids produced by your **tear glands,** which are located above each eye, keep your eyes moist. Tears wash away foreign particles that can injure the eyes and contain a substance that kills bacteria. This substance helps to protect your eyes from infection.

Your eyes have some protection from sweat, dirt, dust, and bacteria.

Eye Structure

You can think of your eyes as having three layers. As you see in Figure 7-8, the outside layer, which is white, is the **sclera** (**skleer** uh), commonly called the white of the eye. Muscles attached to the sclera allow the eye to move within its socket. At the back of the sclera is an opening for the **optic nerve**, the nerve that transmits visual information to the brain. The front of the sclera curves outward to form the transparent **cornea** (**kor** nee uh). Because the cornea is transparent, it permits light to enter the eyes. A thin, moist membrane, called the **conjunctiva** (kahn jungk **ty** vuh), covers the front part of the sclera and the inside of the eyelid.

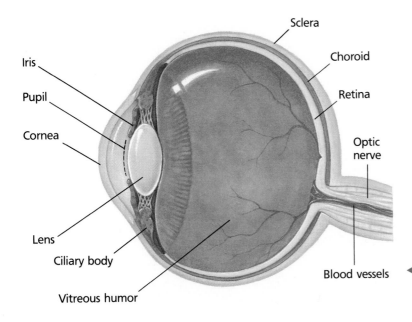

◀ **Figure 7-8. Structures in the front of the eye focus light to the back of the eye. Where is the cornea?**

A dark colored membrane, called the **choroid** (**kor** oyd), makes up most of the middle layer of the eye. The choroid, which is filled with blood vessels, lies just inside the sclera and ends at the front of the eye in two specialized structures. One of these structures is the **iris**. The iris is a colored disk with an opening in its center. This opening is the **pupil**. The color of the iris determines the color of your eyes. The size of the pupil determines how much light enters the eye from the cornea. In bright light, muscle fibers in the iris contract, causing the pupil to narrow and let in less light. In dim light, the muscle fibers relax, and the pupil becomes larger, letting in more light.

The second structure, formed from the choroid and illustrated in Figure 7-8, is the **ciliary** (**sil** ee ehr ee) **body**. This structure produces a watery fluid that fills the front chamber of the eye between the cornea and the lens. The **lens**, which lies just behind the iris, is a transparent structure that focuses light on the inner, back side of the eye. Small muscles in the ciliary body contract or relax to change the shape of the lens. Changes in the shape of the lens enable you to focus on objects at different distances from you.

Behind the lens is the large central chamber of the eye. This chamber is filled with a clear, jellylike substance, the **vitreous** (**vit** ree us) **humor**, which gives the eye its shape.

The innermost layer of the eye consists of a thin, delicate membrane known as the **retina** (**ret** un uh). The retina is the light-sensing part of the eye. It consists of thousands of special light-receptor, or light-receiving, cells and nerve cells. As you can see in Figure 7-9, there are two kinds of light-receptor cells—rod-shaped cells, called rods, and cone-shaped cells, called cones. The rods only respond to dim light and allow you to see black, white, and gray. The cones are

The size of the pupil determines how much light enters your eyes.

Figure 7-9. Rods and cones are the two types of light-receptor cells in the human eye.

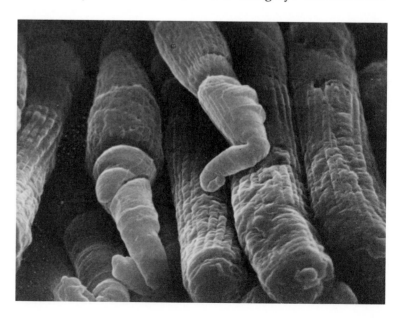

only stimulated by bright light and enable you to see color. There are three types of cones. There is one type for the color blue; one type for green; and one type for red. When at least two types of cones are stimulated at the same time, you see other colors. The rods and cones convert images focused on the retina to nerve signals, which are transmitted to the brain by the optic nerve.

How Vision Occurs

If you look at Figure 7-8 again, you will notice that light passes through the cornea, the lens, and the vitreous humor before reaching the retina. Because of their curved shapes, the cornea and the lens focus the light on the retina. The light-receptor cells in the retina then convert the light images to signals that travel through the optic nerve to the brain, where they are interpreted.

When you look at an object, you usually can see its height, its width, its depth, and how near to, or far from, you it is. This ability to see things three dimensionally is called **stereoscopic** (stehr ee uh **skahp** ik) **vision**. Because your eyes are spaced apart, each eye receives an image that is slightly different from the image received by the other eye. When these two images are combined in the brain, stereoscopic vision results.

Have you ever noticed that you can see things to either side of what you are looking at? The ability to see things off to the side of what you are looking at is called **peripheral** (puh **rif** ur ul) **vision**. Peripheral vision allows you to avoid hazards that are not directly in your line of sight. It gives you a wide field of view—the area you see at any one instant.

Eye Problems

Many people have vision problems caused by the inability to focus light correctly. People who can see objects that are near to them clearly but cannot clearly see objects that are far away suffer from **nearsightedness**. Nearsightedness is caused by an eyeball that is too long. As you can see in Figure 7-10, when the eyeball is too long, light rays are brought into focus in front of the retina, rather than on it.

Look again at Figure 7-10. The opposite of nearsightedness is **farsightedness**. A person who is farsighted can see objects that are far away clearly but cannot see objects nearby. Farsightedness is caused by an eyeball that is too short, which causes light rays to be focused behind the retina.

When the curvature of the cornea or the lens is uneven, light rays entering the eye cannot be focused at a single point on the retina. This causes **astigmatism** (uh **stig** muh tiz um), or blurred vision. Eyeglasses or contact lenses can correct nearsightedness, farsightedness, and astigmatism.

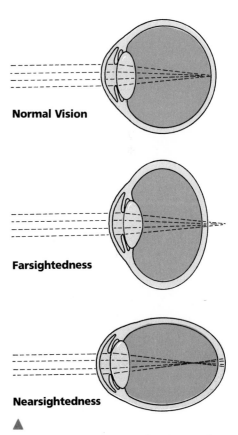

Normal Vision

Farsightedness

Nearsightedness

▲

Figure 7-10. How does the shape of the eyeball affect vision?

Injuries to the eye or the optic nerve, infections of the eye, pressure on the optic nerve, or a cloudy lens can cause blindness, the inability to see anything. Pressure buildup within the eye, known as **glaucoma** (glau **koh** muh), and the clouding of the eye's lens, which is known as a **cataract** (**kat** uh rakt), frequently occur in older adults. Blindness also may be the result of factors that interfere with the development of the lens before birth.

A hard blow to the eye or to the head may cause the retina to become detached from the choroid. This condition, known as a detached retina, can cause blindness if the choroid and the retina are not surgically reattached.

The inability to distinguish one or more colors is called **color blindness**. Color blindness is a vision problem that is usually passed on from a parent to a child. A person who is color blind was born without one or more sets of cones or with one or more sets of weak cones, which makes it difficult or impossible for the individual to see certain colors.

A lack of the light-sensitive substance produced by the rod and cone cells causes **night blindness**, the inability to see well in dim light. Night blindness can be inherited, or it can be caused by a lack of vitamin A. Sometimes, night blindness can be an early sign of other eye diseases that involve the retina.

When the blood vessels of the conjunctiva become swollen, the white of the eye may appear red, or bloodshot. Dust, chlorine, and smoke can irritate the conjunctiva, causing bloodshot eyes.

When the conjunctiva becomes inflamed due to infection, it is known as **conjunctivitis** (kun jungk tuh **vy** tis), or pinkeye, the inflammation of the conjunctiva. It is usually caused by bacteria or a virus in the conjunctiva. The white of the eye becomes red, itches, and may ooze a yellowish fluid. Conjunctivitis should be treated with medicated eyedrops, prescribed by a doctor.

Sometimes the pore of an oil gland for an eyelash becomes infected. The infected pore becomes red, and a painful swelling known as a **sty** forms. A sty can be treated easily by an eye doctor.

Eye Care

There are many things you can do to protect your eyes and keep them healthy. If you work with dangerous substances that could splash into your eyes, or if you work around machinery, you should wear protective glasses or goggles. If you play a sport, such as racketball or lacrosse, in which you could be hit in the eye by a ball or some other fast-moving object, you should also wear protective glasses or goggles. Wearing swimming goggles when you swim will protect your eyes from chlorine and other substances that

Eye infections, injuries, clouding of the lens, or pressure on the optic nerve can cause blindness.

Shield your eyes from harmful chemicals, moving objects, or harsh light.

▲
Figure 7–11. Protective goggles or glasses can protect your eyes from injury and infections.

can irritate them. Goggles will also give you better under-water vision. Another way to protect your eyes is to avoid looking directly into the sun or any bright light. Hats or visors and sunglasses can protect your eyes from the rays of the sun.

Avoiding eyestrain is still another way to keep your eyes healthy. When you read or study, be sure you have adequate light and look up occasionally from your work to relax your eyes and change their focus.

Regular eye examinations can help to detect, prevent, or control many eye problems, such as nearsightedness, far-sightedness, and astigmatism. Regular eye exams can also aid in the early detection of glaucoma and cataracts. In fact, regular eye examinations can reveal a good deal about your health. For example, by looking through your pupils with a special instrument an eye doctor can see the blood vessels of the retina. Changes in the blood vessels can offer early warn-ings of illnesses.

Section Review

1. What are the three layers of the eye?
2. Where are the two kinds of light-receptor cells found in the eye?
3. What causes astigmatism?
4. What is glaucoma?

What Do You Think?

5. What are some habits that you could change to help protect the health of your eyes?

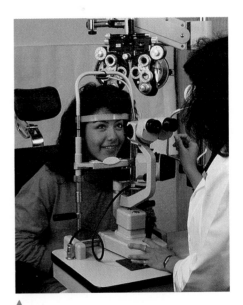

▲
Figure 7-12. Regular eye examinations can help to prevent or correct many vision problems.

3. YOUR EARS

You may think your ears are only for hearing, but did you know they also help to keep your balance? Your ears convert sound waves into nerve signals that your brain can understand. At the same time, your ears sense the position and movement of your head so you can adjust your body and keep your balance.

Structure of the Ear

Your ear is divided into three parts—the outer ear, the middle ear, and the inner ear. These parts are illustrated in Figure 7-13. The outer and middle parts of the ear transfer sound waves to the inner ear, which deals with hearing and your sense of balance.

THE OUTER EAR When you look in a mirror, you can see a part of the outer ear. This part is called the **auricle (or ih kul)**. The auricle, which is covered with a thin layer of skin, acts as a collecting funnel for sound waves. It channels the sound waves into the **ear canal**, a narrow cavity that leads to the middle ear. Glands in the skin lining the ear canal release a wax that helps fight infections in the ear. At the end of the ear canal is a thin membrane called the **eardrum**. The eardrum vibrates when sound waves strike it.

O━┓

Your ears allow you to hear and to keep your balance.

Figure 7-13. In which part of the ear is the cochlea?

▼

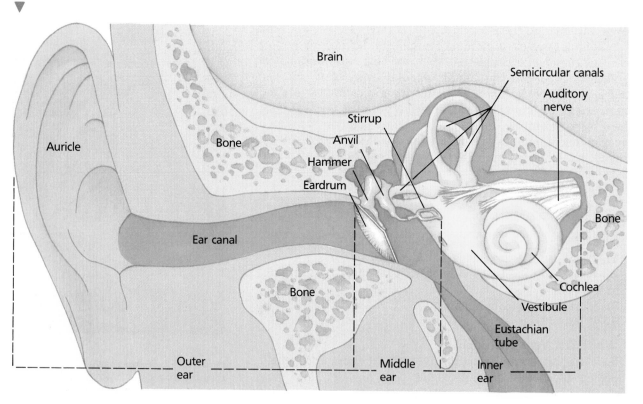

THE MIDDLE EAR The eardrum marks the beginning of the middle ear, which contains three small bones—the hammer, the anvil, and the stirrup—named for their shapes. The hammer receives the vibrations from the eardrum and pushes the anvil, which then moves the stirrup. The movements of the hammer, the anvil, and the stirrup magnify gentle sounds and soften loud ones. Often, too much sound passing to the inner ear will damage its delicate hearing mechanism permanently.

Have you ever felt your ears pop when you go up or come down in an elevator? This happens when the air pressure in the outer ear is different from the air pressure in the middle ear. As you can see in Figure 7-13, a narrow tube, known as the **eustachian** (yoo **stay** shun) **tube**, connects the middle ear to the back of the throat. Most of the time the eustachian tube is closed. When you cough, swallow, or yawn, however, it opens, allowing the air pressure in the middle ear to become the same as the air pressure in the outer ear. This is why swallowing usually relieves ear popping. If the eustachian tubes did not help to maintain equal air pressure, your eardrums could burst, or rupture.

THE INNER EAR The hammer, the anvil, and the stirrup in the middle ear transmit the sound vibrations to a small membrane, called the **oval window**, which separates the middle ear from the inner ear. As Figure 7-13 illustrates, the oval window is actually a part of the wall of the **cochlea** (kahk lee uh), a hollow, fluid-filled, coiled tube. Special vibration-sensing cells line the inside of the cochlea. Vibrations of the oval window cause vibrations in the fluid in the cochlea which, in turn, stimulate the cells lining the cochlea. These cells then send out nerve signals that travel through the **auditory** (aw duh tor ee) **nerve** to the brain, where they are interpreted as sound.

Other structures in the inner ear help you to maintain your balance. One of these structures, the **vestibule** (**ves** tuh byool), is a fluid-filled chamber that senses the position of your head. The inside of the vestibule is lined with pressure-sensitive, or weight-sensing, cells. As you change the position of your head, small particles in the fluid of the vestibule fall to the lowest point in the chamber and rest on some of the pressure-sensitive cells. These cells send nerve signals to the brain. At the same time, the **semicircular canals**, a set of three hollow tubes also in the inner ear, detect changes in body position. Each canal is lined with cells that respond to the motion of the fluid that partially fills each canal. When you change position, the position of fluid in the canals changes. As the fluid flows across the cells, the cells send signals to the brain. Your brain interprets these signals with the signals from the vestibule and sends signals to your muscles so that you can maintain your balance.

Figure 7-14. Balance is a complex skill that depends on the functioning of the inner ear.

Hearing Disorders

Ear infections, especially in young children, are a common problem. Because the eustachian tubes lead from the back of the throat to the middle ear, it is possible for bacteria from the nose or the throat to enter the middle ear, causing an infection. Severe middle-ear infections may cause the eardrum to rupture. An infected ear usually aches, feels warm, and may feel as if fluid is running in it. Doctors usually prescribe antibiotics, medicines that kill germs, for people who have ear infections.

Sometimes, a tear in the eardrum, caused by placing an object too far into the ear canal, leads to an ear infection. Although the eardrum will heal, it will also be scarred. Every time the eardrum is torn, a scar forms. Scar tissue makes the eardrum less flexible and less able to transmit sound. Therefore, scarred eardrums can lead to a loss of hearing. A buildup of wax in the ear can also cause hearing loss because sound waves cannot reach the inner ear. Sometimes, a hearing loss is caused by the abnormal growth of bone tissue in the ear, which prevents movement of the three small bones of the middle ear. These types of hearing loss can be corrected. A doctor can remove wax from a blocked ear or prescribe a wax softener. Sometimes, surgery can correct abnormal bone growth.

When the vibration-sensitive cells in the cochlea are damaged, the hearing loss is permanent. Loud noises, some diseases, and large doses of certain medications can damage or kill the vibration-sensitive cells, usually a few at a time. Whenever cells are damaged or killed, some sensitivity to sound is lost.

Usually hearing aids can help people with mild hearing losses due to damaged vibration-sensitive cells in the cochlea. A hearing aid makes sounds louder. People who are totally deaf cannot hear any sound. Total deafness results when many of the cells in the cochlea are damaged. A relatively new device, known as a cochlear implant, may help these people hear some sounds. The device, which is placed in the ear, electrically stimulates the cochlea. Total deafness also can occur when the auditory nerve is damaged. As of now, there is no way to restore hearing when the auditory nerve is damaged.

Ear Care

Proper ear care is not difficult. You can use a wet washcloth to clean your outer ear and the front part of your ear canal. Dry your ears thoroughly after washing. Never insert a cotton-tipped swab or any other object into your ear canal to clean it.

Wearing earplugs when you are swimming keeps water out of your ears, which will help to prevent ear infections.

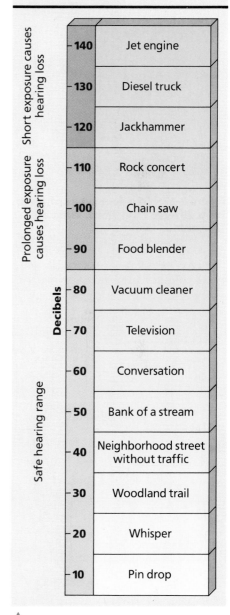

Figure 7–15. You can enjoy music but not damage your hearing if you keep the volume in headphones low.

This is especially important if you have had repeated ear infections or a recent puncture of the eardrum.

Because loud noises can damage the cochlea cells, you should wear foam-rubber earplugs or earmuff-type devices to protect your hearing when you are working around loud equipment. The intensity, or loudness, of sound is measured in units called **decibels**. As shown in Figure 7-16, sound above 80 decibels can cause hearing loss. Motorcycles, televisions, radios, and stereos also can generate sound levels damaging to your hearing. If you wear headphones when you listen to music, keep the volume to a level at which you can enjoy the music but not damage your ears. Any noise that is so loud that it makes conversation with a person three feet (about 1.0 meter) away difficult is too loud. If you have trouble hearing normal conversation, if the conversation sounds muffled, or if you experience a ringing in your ears after listening to some sounds, the sound was too loud.

If you think you have been exposed to too much noise or cannot hear as well as you once could, see an ear doctor. An ear doctor can test your hearing to determine whether or not you have suffered a hearing loss.

Section Review

1. Name the three bones of the middle ear.
2. What is the function of the eustachian tube?
3. What is the sound-sensing organ of the inner ear?
4. Why does loud noise cause hearing loss?

What Do You Think?

5. In what ways can you take better care of your ears?

Sound Levels

	Decibels	
Short exposure causes hearing loss	140	Jet engine
	130	Diesel truck
	120	Jackhammer
Prolonged exposure causes hearing loss	110	Rock concert
	100	Chain saw
	90	Food blender
Safe hearing range	80	Vacuum cleaner
	70	Television
	60	Conversation
	50	Bank of a stream
	40	Neighborhood street without traffic
	30	Woodland trail
	20	Whisper
	10	Pin drop

Figure 7-16. What are some typical sources of sound levels above 80 decibels?

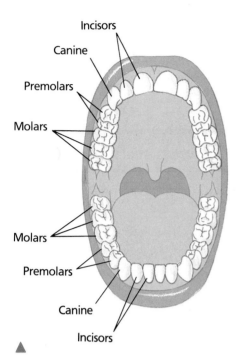

Incisors
Canine
Premolars
Molars
Molars
Premolars
Canine
Incisors

Figure 7-17. Your four types of teeth have different functions. What are the canines used for?

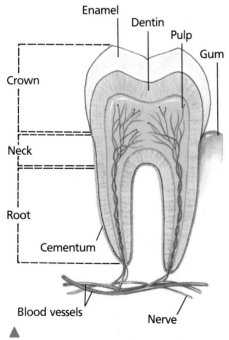

Enamel
Dentin
Pulp
Gum
Crown
Neck
Root
Cementum
Blood vessels
Nerve

Figure 7-18. Teeth have a structure that is well-suited to their function.

4. YOUR TEETH AND GUMS

Your teeth not only help you to chew your food, they also help you to produce certain sounds when you speak. Try pronouncing the word *think* without pressing your tongue against the back of your front teeth! Your teeth also give shape and fullness to your cheeks and lips. Whenever you talk, laugh, or smile, your teeth are on display.

Good oral hygiene is essential for maintaining the health of your teeth and gums. Healthy teeth and gums will last a lifetime and will help you look and feel your best.

Kinds of Teeth

As you can see in Figure 7-17, you have four types of teeth. Each type has its own special function. **Incisors** (in **sy** zurz), teeth with sharp edges, are at the front of your mouth. They are used to cut your food. **Canines** (**kay** nyns) are the teeth with a single point that are used for tearing food. These teeth are on either side of your incisors. Teeth that have flat surfaces with two rounded ridges for crushing food are called **premolars** (pree **moh** lurz). Located at the back of your mouth are the **molars** (**moh** lurz), the largest of your teeth. Molars have large flat surfaces that grind food.

Structure of Teeth

Although your teeth vary in size and shape, they all have the same basic structure, illustrated in Figure 7-18. The part of any tooth you see when you look at your teeth in a mirror is called the crown. The crown is the part of the tooth that comes into contact with the food you eat. Just below the gumline is the neck of a tooth. The neck forms the middle section of a tooth, between the crown and the roots. The roots are cone-shaped extensions of the tooth that attach it to the jawbone.

Each tooth is made of several kinds of tissue. The hard outer layer that covers the crown is a tissue called **enamel** (ee **nam** ul). Enamel is the hardest substance in your body. Below the enamel and forming the outer tissue of the neck and some of the root is **dentin** (**den** tin), a yellowish, dense, bonelike tissue. Most of a tooth consists of dentin. **Cementum** (si **men** tum) is the outer tissue of the roots that covers the root dentin.

A soft tissue, called **pulp**, fills the center of each tooth. The pulp contains nerves and blood vessels. These blood vessels and nerves pass through a channel known as the **root canal** and connect with the other blood vessels and nerves in the upper and lower jawbone.

The gum, or **gingiva** (jin **jy** vuh), is the tissue that surrounds the teeth and covers the bone around your teeth.

Each tooth is implanted in this tissue. Because your gums help to hold your teeth in place, they should fit tightly around the neck of each tooth.

Most people get two sets of teeth, primary teeth and permanent teeth. Primary teeth, the first teeth a person gets, begin to break through the gums when a baby is about 6 months old. By the age of 3, a child will have all 20 primary teeth, 10 in the upper jaw and 10 in the lower jaw.

Between the ages of 6 and 12, the primary teeth begin to fall out. They are replaced by 32 larger permanent teeth. The last permanent teeth, known as wisdom teeth, break through the gums between the ages of 17 and 21. Some people never develop wisdom teeth.

Tooth and Gum Problems

Teeth can grow in a way that affects your appearance, your ability to speak, or your ability to chew food. When the upper and lower teeth do not meet properly, the condition is known as a **malocclusion** (mal uh **kloo** zhun), or improper bite. When the top teeth stick out too far, the malocclusion is called an overbite. When the bottom teeth stick out beyond the top teeth, it is called an underbite.

People with malocclusions need the help of an **orthodontist** (or thuh **dahnt** ust), a dentist who specializes in correcting the position of teeth. Orthodontists use brackets and wires—known as braces—to help move teeth to their proper positions. Once the teeth have been moved, an orthodontist may use other mechanical aids to keep the teeth in position until they become fixed in place.

Tooth decay occurs when teeth are not properly cared for. **Plaque** (plak) is a sticky, colorless film of bacteria that covers the surface of teeth. When plaque is not removed regularly, the bacteria grow and multiply, producing an acid that eats away tooth enamel. As shown in Figure 7-19, at first, a tiny hole, or cavity, forms. If the cavity is not treated by a dentist, it becomes larger and deeper.

To prevent further decay, a dentist removes the decay and bacteria that are present and fills the cavity. Dentists frequently use gold or a material called an **amalgam** (uh **mal** gum), a silver-colored mixture of several metals, to fill cavities. Cavities in teeth near the front of the mouth may be filled with a material that matches the color of tooth enamel. This material, which is usually a type of plastic, is not as strong as gold or amalgam.

If tooth decay is not treated at an early stage, it will eventually spread to the pulp and its roots. When this happens, the dentist must remove the infected pulp from the tooth and replace it with a special material. This type of treatment is known as root canal therapy. Root canal therapy may also be necessary if a tooth is severely damaged or broken.

Rinsing Away Tooth Decay

Researchers have found a new weapon to fight cavities—"super saliva" mouth rinses.

Cavities are caused by plaque, an invisible, bacteria-laden film that sticks to teeth. As the bacteria break down sugars and starches in foods, acids form. These acids erode tooth enamel. Saliva washes these acids away. Saliva also contains minerals such as calcium and phosphorus that strengthen teeth and help repair newly forming cavities.

Super saliva mouth rinses contain high concentrations of calcium and phosphorus, which help reduce decay in all areas of a tooth. But, different regions of a tooth have different calcium and phosphorus requirements. By adjusting the proportion of calcium to phosphorus in a mouth rinse, it can combat decay in specific areas of the teeth. Studies have shown that super saliva rinses work best if used twice a day for two minutes each time. This two-minute rinse may soon become part of a regular brushing and flossing regimen.

Super saliva rinses fight decay.

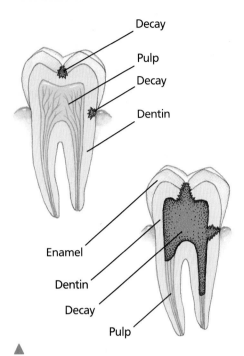

Figure 7-19. Tooth decay begins at the tooth's surface and spreads to the inner tissues.

When a tooth is lost either because of disease or an accident, it is often replaced with a false tooth, or a fixed bridge. If several neighboring teeth are lost, a removable partial denture, several false teeth, may be required. Unlike a fixed bridge, a removable partial denture can be taken out of the mouth for cleaning. Complete dentures are sets of upper and lower false teeth.

Plaque can also affect the gums when it builds up along the gumline and under it. If the plaque is not removed within 48 hours, it begins to harden. Hardened plaque is called tartar, or **calculus** (**kal** kyuh lus). It irritates the gums, causing them to become red and swollen and to bleed easily. This condition is called **gingivitis** (jin juh **vy** tis).

If gingivitis is not treated, it can develop into **periodontitis** (pehr ee oh dahn **ty** tis), a more advanced stage of gum disease. In periodontitis, the buildup of plaque and calculus causes the gums to pull away from the teeth, forming pockets between the teeth and gum, as illustrated in Figure 7-19. Plaque, calculus, and food collect in the pockets, and the gums may become infected. If the infection is not treated, it can spread to the jawbone. Periodontitis can be treated surgically by dentists who specialize in gum diseases.

Bad breath, or **halitosis** (hal uh **toh** sis), is another common problem. Tooth decay, gum disease, and oral cancer can

Health careers

A dental laboratory technician's work requires care and precision.

There are many people who work with a dentist to help care for your teeth. The **dental laboratory technician** makes dentures (artificial teeth), braces, and other dental fixtures, using models of a patient's teeth and mouth.

Dental laboratory technicians craft dental fixtures from plastics, ceramics, and metals, using drills, torches, electric lathes, and high-heat furnaces. Their jobs require patience and skill at using their hands.

A high-school diploma is recommended for this job. Many people learn the craft either on the job or by working as apprentices. Some colleges offer a two-year program that leads to an associate's degree.

Dental hygienists work directly with patients. They clean teeth, process x-ray films, and instruct patients in proper oral care. Dental hygienists must be licensed before they can work. To obtain a license, a person must be a high-school graduate, complete a two-year dental hygiene program, and pass an examination.

cause halitosis. You can learn more about oral cancer in Chapter 18. These, however, are not the only causes of bad breath. Infrequent brushing and spicy foods also can cause halitosis. Keeping the mouth clean is the best way to control halitosis. Although mouthwashes do not cure halitosis, they can improve breath odor temporarily.

Dental Care

There are a few simple steps you can follow for healthy teeth and gums. These steps include eating a well-balanced diet, low in sugar, brushing your teeth three times a day, using dental floss, and seeing your dentist regularly.

Brushing your teeth after eating and before bedtime helps to remove the food and some of the plaque that can cause cavities and gum disease. Use a soft-bristled toothbrush and fluoride toothpaste. Fluoride, a tasteless, odorless chemical, combines with tooth enamel to strengthen the enamel and make it more resistant to decay. When you brush your teeth, tip the toothbrush slightly so that some of the bristles reach below the gumline. Gently brush away food and plaque by moving the toothbrush in short back-and-forth and circular motions. Dental floss, a nylon string, either waxed or unwaxed, removes food and plaque from between the teeth and between the teeth and gums, areas that a toothbrush cannot reach. You should use dental floss at least once a day, preferably at bedtime. Figure 7-20 illustrates how to floss your teeth. Ease the floss between two teeth by moving it back and forth gently. Bend the floss toward one tooth and scrape the floss up and down against the tooth. Then, bend the floss toward the other tooth and do it again. Each of your teeth should receive this treatment.

If you think you may have a dental problem, see your dentist right away. Even if you do not have problems, you should see your dentist twice a year or on a schedule that your dentist recommends. Regular dental checkups can stop problems before they become painful or hard to treat.

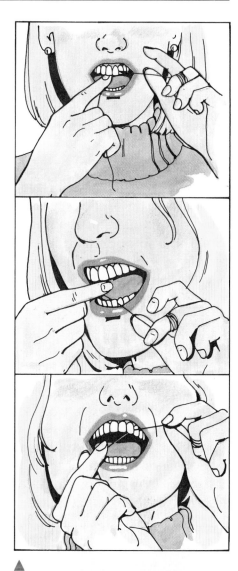

Figure 7-20. Flossing is the most effective method for removing plaque.

Section Review

1. Name the four kinds of teeth.
2. What tissue covers the crown of a tooth?
3. How does plaque affect tooth decay?
4. What does flossing accomplish?

What Do You Think?

5. How would you convince a friend to stop neglecting his or her teeth? What specific suggestions for dental care would you make to your friend?

Time Management

John has overslept again. He has to rush off to school without eating a good breakfast, brushing his teeth, or combing his hair. In his haste he also may forget to do something important or leave something behind. At the very least John starts his day feeling anxious and tense.

Many people are like John. They rush from one activity to another with no clear goal or schedule. These people usually never have enough time to do everything they want to do. John, for example, wants to get his driver's license. But he has no idea how he will fit driver's education classes into his life.

John and many other people could be more productive if they managed their time better. A good time manager is someone who completes daily tasks, works toward long-term goals, and still finds time to relax, all in a day's work. The time management process outlined below will help you to plan your day-to-day schedule so you can accomplish the tasks that are important to you.

1. List Your Goals

Make a list of all the things you would like to accomplish in the next six months. Then, rate each goal according to how important it is to you. Use this scale:

A = very important
B = somewhat important
C = not very important

My Six-Month Goals	
Get my driver's license	A
Buy a new bicycle	C
Make the baseball team	B
Pass math	A

2. Outline Your Tasks

For each of the goals you gave an A rating to, list all the activities you need to do in order to accomplish the goal. If possible, break down each activity into smaller, more manageable tasks. This makes it easier to tackle an activity.

You may also wish to outline the tasks for a few of your more important B goals, although these are of lower priority. Do not focus on your C goals unless you have extra time.

3. Outline an Overall Plan

For each task, assign a specific and realistic deadline. To do this, estimate how long the task will take and when you want it completed.

Top "A" Goal		
Activities	Time Needed	Deadline
1. Take driver's ed. course		
a. Find out schedule + fee	20 mins	today
b. Sign up for course	½ hr	tomorrow
2. Learn to drive		
a. Take permit test	2 hrs	next Fri.

Time management skills will help you to use your time well.

4. Make a Daily Schedule

Each day, list the tasks from step 3 that you want to accomplish. Also list the chores and other commitments you have that day.

Do not schedule too many tasks each day. It is wise to allow more time for a task than it may require. Allow some time for unplanned events.

Things to Do Today	
Find out driver's ed. schedule	A
Finish Math assignment	A
Take trash out	A
Help Matt rebuild bicycle	B

5. Prioritize Your Daily Tasks

Assign an A, B, or C rating to each task and chore. Do A tasks and chores first each day, followed by B and C tasks, even if a C task is easier.

6. Ask Yourself at Different Points of the Day, "Is this the best use of my time?"

If your answer is "no," you may be procrastinating, or putting off, an A task. If so, consider these questions:

■ Is the task too overwhelming? If so, break it into smaller steps. Make a list of tasks that you can do in less than five minutes.
■ Do you have enough information? If not, list the information you need and where you can find it.
■ Are you afraid you will fail or make mistakes? If so, list your fears. You may realize the task is not as difficult as you thought.
■ What are you doing instead? Are these activities as important to you? Will they help you achieve your long-term goals?

APPLY THE SKILL

1. Take ten minutes to list the goals you want to accomplish in six months.

2. Rate the goals according to how important they are to you. Use the A-B-C rating scale. Which goals will most benefit you in the long run? Assign an A rating to each of those goals.

3. Break down each A goal into simple activities and even simpler tasks. Assign specific and realistic deadlines for these tasks.

4. Each day for a week, make a daily schedule and prioritize your tasks using the A-B-C scale. Do your A tasks first each day, followed by B and C tasks. If you find that you are putting things off, ask yourself the questions in step 6. At the end of the week, report to your class on how helpful the time management process really has been for you.

7 | Chapter Review

Chapter Summary

- Skin functions to keep foreign matter from entering the body, to maintain a constant body temperature, and to prevent the loss of the body's fluids.
- Skin is made up of two main layers—the epidermis and the dermis. Oil glands and sweat glands are found in the dermis.
- Cleaning and protecting skin from the sun's rays, a well-balanced diet, and regular exercise and sleep help to keep skin healthy.
- Hair is a part of the skin. Hair insulates the body from heat and cold. Eyelashes and eyebrows help to keep foreign objects from entering the eyes. Ear and nostril hairs help keep foreign objects from entering the ears and nose.
- Fingernails and toenails are outgrowths of the skin that protect the sensitive upper surfaces of the tips of fingers and toes.
- Vision occurs when the light-receptor cells in the retina are stimulated by light and send signals through the optic nerve to the brain. The brain interprets the signals as images.
- Protective glasses or goggles, sunglasses, and proper light when reading help to protect the eyes.

- Sound waves entering the ear canal cause the eardrum to vibrate. The vibrations are transmitted by small bones in the middle ear to the inner ear. The vibrations set into motion the fluid in the inner ear, causing nerve impulses to travel to the brain where they are interpreted as sound.
- The sense of balance depends on structures in the inner ear that detect head position and changes in body position. Nerve messages from these structures are sent to the brain where they are interpreted.
- Keeping ears clean, protecting them from loud noises, and preventing water from entering them are ways to keep ears healthy.
- Teeth function to break apart food, to help make certain sounds of speech, and to give shape and fullness to the cheeks and lips.
- A tooth is made up of a crown, a neck, and one or more roots.
- Acid produced by bacteria in plaque begins the process of tooth decay.
- Eating a well-balanced diet, low in sugar, brushing the teeth after eating, flossing once a day, and having regular dental checkups help to protect the teeth.

Vocabulary Review

Listed below are some of the important terms in this chapter. Choose the term that best matches the phrase in the exercise that follows:

astigmatism
calculus
choroid
cochlea
cornea

dentin
dermatitis
dermis
epidermis
eustachian tube

gingivitis
iris
malocclusion
melanin
optic nerve

periodontitis
plaque
retina
semicircular canals
vestibule

1. the layer of skin that contains blood vessels and hair follicles
2. pigment produced by special skin cells
3. the light-sensing layer of the eye
4. an advanced stage of gum disease
5. equalizes pressure on the eardrum

6. curved, hollow tubes in the inner ear
7. hardened plaque
8. the tissue that makes up most of a tooth
9. disorder characterized by red, swollen gums that bleed easily
10. an overbite or an underbite

What Have You Learned?

1. What is the smallest unit of the body?
2. How does your skin help maintain a constant body temperature?
3. What are the two main layers of the skin?
4. Why is it important to use a sunscreen while you are in the sun?
5. What determines the color of the nails?
6. What is the relationship between the iris and the pupil?

7. What is the function of the lens?
8. How do cones differ from rods?
9. Explain what causes ears to pop.
10. What nerve carries messages from the ear to the brain?
11. Name the four tissues of a tooth.
12. Explain how tooth decay is caused. How does the removal of plaque help to prevent tooth decay?

What Do You Think?

1. Is a deep, dark suntan healthful? Explain your answer.
2. Why do you think it is important to test the hearing and vision of school-aged children on a regular basis?
3. What function do you think is served by the dark color of the choroid?

4. How would you explain the brief period of dizziness that you experience when you spin around and then suddenly stop?
5. Why do you think a dental cavity can result in pain?
6. How would covering one eye with a patch affect your vision?

What Would You Do?

1. You are going to a friend's pool, but you have athlete's foot. What can you do to make sure you do not pass it along?
2. You have been given front row tickets to a rock concert. Explain why you will or will not use the tickets.
3. Your friend just got eyeglasses but will not wear them. How could you encourage your friend to wear the glasses?

4. You have a job as a camp counselor. During the first week of camp, an all-day trip to the beach is planned. Many of the children in your group could become sunburned. What will you do?
5. A friend with acne has been washing the affected areas with a strong detergent. Is your friend improving his skin? What would you advise your friend?

For Further Study

1. You probably have seen advertisements for hard, soft, and extended wear contact lenses. Research the differences between these vision aids and describe the different types of vision problems that can be aided by each kind of contact lens.
2. Interview a dentist or dental hygienist to find out how dental practices and technology have changed in the last decade and what the future holds.
3. Research and report on the discovery that flouride can prevent tooth decay. Include the history of flouride use in the United States and in other countries. Why do some communities object to flouride?

8

As you read, think about

▶ how your digestive and excretory systems work to keep you healthy.

▶ how the foods you eat affect the way you look as well as the way you feel.

▶ the kinds of foods your body needs in order to function at its best.

Food and Nutrition

The big circle of pizza spins high up in the air. The chef catches it and plops it onto the baking sheet. Now he liberally spreads on spicy tomato sauce. Next comes a thick coating of cheese. Finally, he adds the extras you ordered: onions and green peppers. As the pizza sizzles in the oven, the smells blend deliciously.

At last you get to take the first tasty bite, and you focus on the combination of tastes and textures. In fact, this pizza not only tastes good, it is good for you. In this chapter, you will learn what makes this food—and others—nutritious. You will learn how to choose a healthy, balanced diet that provides the energy you need for all the activities that make up your busy life. Finally, you will investigate the remarkable ways your body turns the food you eat into the fuel that keeps your life running full speed ahead.

Many of the foods you now enjoy can be part of a nutritious diet.

Check Your Wellness

How healthy are your daily eating habits? See how many of these questions you can answer yes to.

1. Do you eat three well-balanced meals, including breakfast?
2. Do you avoid fried or fatty foods?
3. Do you choose fresh foods whenever possible?
4. Do you avoid sweets, including sugary cereals and soft drinks?
5. Do you limit your intake of salt?
6. Do you eat plenty of fiber-rich foods, such as fruits, vegetables, and whole grains?
7. Do you limit your intake of fast foods and junk food?
8. Are your mealtimes relaxed and unhurried?
9. When you are physically active, do you drink water frequently?

1. YOUR DIGESTIVE SYSTEM

Imagine that you have just finished eating your favorite meal. As you sit back and relax, your body goes to work changing your meal into a form that your cells can use. You know that the foods you ate contain the substances your body needs to work well. Breaking down your food into those substances is the work of your digestive system.

How the Digestive System Works

The process of changing foods into a form your body can use is called **digestion** (dy **jes** chun). The many parts of the digestive system work together to carry out this important function. As you read about digestion, use the illustration in Figure 8-1 to trace the path of food through the digestive system.

THE MOUTH   Digestion begins in the mouth. When you begin to eat an apple, you take a bite of the apple and chew. Teeth begin the process of digestion by making the pieces of food you eat smaller.

Does your mouth ever "water" when you see or smell your favorite food? The water you feel is **saliva** (suh **ly** vuh), a tasteless liquid made by the salivary glands inside your mouth. Saliva moistens the food and makes it easier to swallow. Your saliva contains a substance that speeds up chemical reactions. This kind of substance is known as an **enzyme** (**en** zym). Different enzymes work on different kinds of food. For instance, **amylase** (**am** uh lays) is the enzyme in saliva that begins the digestion of starchy foods in the mouth.

After food is mixed with saliva, the tongue helps form it into a small ball and moves it to the back of the mouth so it can be swallowed. As you swallow, a small flap of tissue called the **epiglottis** (ep ih **glaht** is) automatically covers the opening to your windpipe. This prevents your air passage from being blocked by food. If your food is not adequately chewed, it may lodge in any part of the air passage and cause you to choke. You can avoid this danger if you remember not to talk or laugh with food in your mouth.

THE ESOPHAGUS   When you swallow food, it moves into your **esophagus** (ih **sahf** uh gus), a muscular tube about 12 inches (30 centimeters) long. Everything you eat or drink passes through the esophagus to the stomach. As the food moves down the esophagus, more moisture from the lining of the esophagus is added to it.

The smooth, muscular wall of the esophagus contracts and relaxes in wavelike motions, pushing the food toward the stomach. This wavelike muscular movement is what keeps the food moving throughout the digestive system.

THE STOMACH The **stomach** is a muscular, but stretchable, saclike organ that stores food. It is lined with glands that produce, or secrete, gastric juices. Gastric juices are made up of hydrochloric acid, protein-digesting enzymes, and mucus. The mucus coats the lining of the stomach to protect it from the hydrochloric acid. A circular band of muscle at the opening of the stomach can contract to prevent food and gastric juices or other substances in the stomach from backing into the esophagus. Layers of muscles in the stomach wall churn the food. This helps to break up the food and to mix it with the gastric juices.

After the food has mixed with the gastric juices in the stomach for a period of time, the food becomes a thick liquid called **chyme** (kym). The amount of time food stays in the stomach varies. Liquids, for example, leave the stomach within about 10 minutes. Fatty foods may stay in the stomach for three to four hours.

As a part of the process of digestion, food is broken up and mixed with gastric juices inside the stomach.

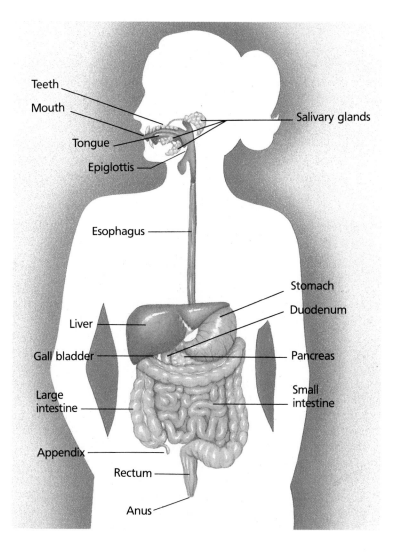

Teeth
Mouth
Tongue
Epiglottis
Salivary glands
Esophagus
Stomach
Duodenum
Liver
Gall bladder
Pancreas
Large intestine
Small intestine
Appendix
Rectum
Anus

◀ **Figure 8–1. The digestive system breaks down food into essential nutrients that your body can use.**

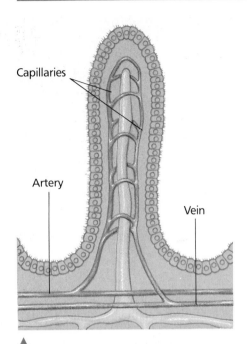

Capillaries

Artery

Vein

▲
Figure 8–2. Nutrients absorbed by villi enter the bloodstream through capillaries to nourish the cells in all parts of your body.

O━━┱

Most of the food that you digest is absorbed into your bloodstream from the small intestine.

THE SMALL INTESTINE   In time, the chemical breakdown of the food is complete enough for the chyme to leave the stomach. Wavelike muscle contractions move the chyme out of the stomach and through another circular band of muscles into the small intestine.

The **small intestine** is a long, coiled organ about 1 inch (2.5 centimeters) in diameter and about 20 feet (6 meters) long. Most of the remaining digestion takes place within the first 10 inches (25 centimeters) of the small intestine. This part is called the **duodenum** (doo uh **dee** num).

Glands in the lining of the small intestine secrete digestive juices and enzymes that help complete the digestive process. Other digestive juices are secreted by the **pancreas** (**pang** kree us), an elongated gland behind the stomach, and the **liver,** a large organ that also removes harmful substances from the blood. The pancreas produces pancreatic juice, which contains enzymes that help in the digestion of your food. The digestive juice produced by the liver is **bile.** Bile is stored in the **gallbladder,** a membranous sac attached to the liver. It is released into the intestine where it helps in the digestion of fats.

Eventually the chyme is broken into the substances your body uses to carry out all of its daily activities. These substances are absorbed into the bloodstream for use by all the cells of your body.

The inner wall of the small intestine, where this absorption occurs, is covered with millions of tiny, fingerlike projections called **villi** (**vil** eye). As Figure 8-2 illustrates, each villus contains tiny blood vessels called **capillaries** (**kap** uh lehr ees). As the substances pass by these villi, they are absorbed into the blood within these vessels. Once in the bloodstream, the substances are carried to all the cells of the body to be used in carrying out the body's activities.

THE LARGE INTESTINE   Not all the food you eat is broken down in the small intestine. Any undigested food, along with water, passes into the **large intestine,** a tube about five feet (1.5 meters) long. This undigested food is called waste. Getting rid of waste is the job of the large intestine.

Bacteria feed on the waste within the large intestine. They produce small amounts of vitamin K and some of the B vitamins. These vitamins are absorbed through the lining of the large intestine into the bloodstream. As the waste is moved through the large intestine, most of the water is absorbed by the lining of the large intestine. At this point, the waste becomes a solid material called **feces** (**fee** seez).

The **rectum,** which is the last few inches of the large intestine, holds the feces until they are released from the body. The process of releasing wastes from the body is called **elimination.** Elimination may take place anywhere from 24 to 48 hours after food is eaten.

Disorders of the Digestive System		
Disorder	**Prevention**	**Treatment**
Constipation (infrequent or difficult elimination of feces)	high-fiber diet; adequate water intake	increased fiber and water in diet; medication to soften feces
Diarrhea (too rapid passage of wastes through the digestive system)	well-balanced diet of clean, well-cooked foods; purified water	bland, low-fiber diet; medication to slow movement of feces
Indigestion (difficulty digesting meals)	small meals, eaten slowly; diet low in coffee and alcohol; control of stress	medication to neutralize acids; control of stress
Ulcers (break in lining of stomach or small intestine)	well-balanced diet low in coffee and alcohol; control of stress	medication to coat stomach and intestine and reduce acid; controlled diet

◀ **Figure 8–3. Digestive disorders often call for a change in diet. When is a diet low in fiber recommended?**

Disorders of the Digestive System

Some disorders of the digestive system are fairly common. More information on the prevention and treatment of these disorders is given in Figure 8-3. Most people suffer occasionally from **indigestion,** or difficulty digesting food. Soon after eating, they may experience sharp chest pain, abdominal cramps, gas, or nausea. Usually, you can prevent indigestion by eating calm, relaxed meals.

When food moves too quickly through your digestive system you may experience loose, watery, frequent bowel movements, or **diarrhea.** Minor cases of diarrhea usually come and go quickly and respond to home therapy, such as drinking plenty of fluids. Prolonged cases can result in **dehydration,** a condition in which water and mineral losses are severe. If diarrhea continues for more than 48 hours, or if you begin to experience the signs of dehydration, such as little or no urination, dry lips, or lack of tears, be sure to seek medical help.

A condition called **constipation** occurs when too much water is removed from partially digested food as it passes into the lowest part of the large intestine. When this happens, waste builds up in the large intestine and becomes difficult to pass. To avoid constipation, be sure to include enough fluids, fruits, vegetables, and grains in your diet and get plenty of exercise. Limit your intake of high-fat foods such as chocolate and fatty meats, which pass through the digestive system slowly.

Some common disorders of the digestive system can be improved through a carefully planned diet.

Most people experience indigestion, diarrhea, and constipation at some time. However, there are other, more serious disorders of the digestive system that, fortunately, are less common. For example, an **ulcer** (**uhl** sur), or open sore, may occur in the lining of the stomach or small intestine. Pain results when this sore comes in contact with the acid in digestive juices. Poor diet and stress are thought to cause ulcers in some people. Treatment includes dietary changes, medicines, and surgery. Surgery may also be needed to treat **ulcerative colitis** (ul suh **ray** tiv koh **lyt** us), a chronic inflammation of the lining of the lower part of the large intestine. Although the exact cause of ulcerative colitis is not known, it appears to be related to stress.

Enlarged veins in the anal area, called **hemorrhoids** (**hem** uh roids), are usually caused by straining during bowel movements and by chronic constipation. Regular, daily exercise and a diet that includes plenty of whole grains and fresh fruit and vegetables can help to relieve many of the symptoms of hemorrhoids.

Sometimes hard, rocklike masses called gallstones form from substances in the bile of the gallbladder. Severe pain may arise when gallstones get caught in the tube that leads from the gallbladder to the small intestine.

Keeping the Digestive System Healthy

How you eat is one key to maintaining a healthy digestive system. You should try to eat your meals when you can relax and enjoy them. Plan time to eat in a pleasant environment. Chew your food slowly and thoroughly to aid digestion. Drink small amounts of water during your meal to help the digestive enzymes work more effectively. Eat in moderation. Overeating places a strain on your digestive system and can lead to overweight.

Eating is a necessary part of your life. You can make the most of it by taking time to enjoy your food. Your health will benefit from it.

O—— Poor diet and stress are common causes of some serious disorders of the digestive system.

▲
Figure 8–4. Calm, relaxed meals in pleasant surroundings help your body to get the most out of your diet. Try not to rush or overeat.

Section Review

1. Trace the path of your meal during digestion.
2. What is an enzyme?
3. In what parts of the digestive system are the substances in food absorbed?

What Do You Think?

4. What changes in your eating habits or diet will help the functioning of your digestive system?

2. YOUR EXCRETORY SYSTEM

Have you ever watched a building under construction? Large quantities of materials are brought to the site and used. As the building nears completion, leftover materials are hauled away. Your body, which builds and rebuilds itself, also produces waste materials that must be removed.

How the Excretory System Works

As you know, your digestive system changes the substances that you eat into forms that your body can use. When the cells of your body use these substances to carry out the body's activities, waste products are produced.

The process by which the body collects and removes wastes produced by its cells is called **excretion** (ek **skree** shun). The organs that are involved in excretion are the liver, the skin, the kidneys, and the bladder.

THE LIVER   Your liver plays an important role in excretion. It chemically changes wastes, impurities, poisons, alcohol, and drugs to less harmful substances that can be excreted in urine or feces. Your liver is one of the most vital organs in your body. It can be damaged by alcohol, drug abuse, and toxic chemicals. While you can survive without some organs, you must have a functioning liver to live.

THE LUNGS   Your lungs not only supply your body with oxygen but also remove wastes. As blood circulates through your lungs, carbon dioxide and some water are removed and pass out of the body as you exhale. On cold days, you can see this moisture condense when you breathe.

THE SKIN   **Perspiration** (pur spuh **ray** shun), another term for sweating, is one way in which the body cools itself. Perspiration is also a form of excretion. Water, containing dissolved mineral salts, travels from the sweat glands deep in the skin tissue to the surface of your skin.

THE URINARY SYSTEM   **Urea** (yoo **ree** uh) and **uric** (**yoor** ik) **acid** are two of the wastes produced by your body. These and other substances, such as certain drugs, would poison you if they built up or remained too long in your bloodstream. The organs of the urinary system filter these chemicals from your blood and then excrete them. As you can see in Figure 8-5, the urinary system is made up of your two kidneys and the urinary tract. Your **kidneys,** fist-size organs that filter the waste products from your bloodstream, are located on either side of your spine at elbow height.

Your excretory system prevents the buildup of wastes produced by your cells.

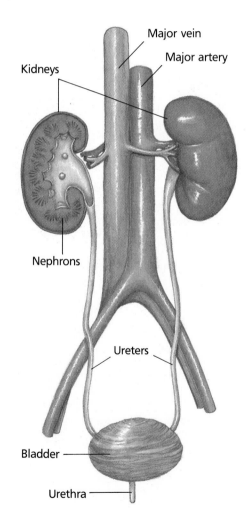

▲ **Figure 8–5. The urinary system rids your body of waste products produced by your cells and excess fluid.**

Lasers Shatter Kidney Stones

Approximately 350,000 people in the United States are admitted to hospitals each year for kidney stone treatment. To get rid of the stones, doctors may prescribe medication or use a device called a lithotripter (lih thoh **trip** tehr), which generates sound waves that crush the stones. Until recently, large stones and stones that are shielded from sound waves by the pelvic bones had to be removed by surgery. Now, a new technique that uses laser light provides an option to surgery.

To treat kidney stones with laser light, a doctor threads an optic fiber of the instrument up through the bladder and places it in contact with a stone. A pulse of light is sent through the fiber. When the light hits the stone, it produces a sparklike flash, which shatters the stone. Shattered stones can generally be passed in the urine.

In addition to reaching areas the lithotripter cannot reach, laser light is less expensive and less cumbersome to use. Furthermore, the use of laser light may be extended to treat some cases of gallstones.

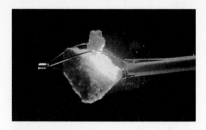

Kidney stones can be crushed using laser light.

Your blood reaches the kidneys through large blood vessels. Once in the kidneys, the blood passes through clusters of capillaries. These capillaries come in close contact with **nephrons** (**nehf** rahns), the working units of the kidneys.

The fluid passed through to the nephron and its collecting tube contains water, urea, uric acid, and many substances essential for maintaining your body's activities. Most of the water and essential substances are reabsorbed by cells in the tube wall and returned to the capillaries. The filtered blood returns to the heart to be recirculated.

The substances that remain in the collecting tube cannot be reused by the body. They are waste products. These waste products, which include urea, uric acid, and excess water, are then carried away as **urine** (**yoor** in). After urine is formed, it passes down a long tube called a **ureter** (**yoo** rih tur). One ureter from each kidney leads into the **bladder,** a muscular sac that stores the urine.

When the bladder is full, nerve endings in the bladder wall signal the brain that the bladder needs to be emptied. Muscles in the bladder squeeze the urine down a short tube called the **urethra** (yoo **ree** thruh). The ureters, bladder, and urethra make up your **urinary tract.**

The kinds and amounts of substances in urine can act as important clues to your overall health. Your doctor can use urine analysis to diagnose many illnesses.

Disorders of the Urinary System

Because of the importance of the kidneys and urinary tract, you should be aware of some of the common disorders that can afflict them. **Nephritis** (nuh **fry** tis) is an inflammation (swelling) of the nephrons of the kidneys. A bacterial infection somewhere in the body is usually the cause. Bacteria also can directly infect the bladder.

Two more serious disorders are **uremia** (yoo **ree** mee uh) and kidney stones. Uremia is the poisoning of the body caused by the failure of the kidneys to remove waste products. **Kidney stones** are painful, pebblelike masses in the kidneys or urinary tract. Until recently, surgical removal of the stones was necessary. Now, an ultrasound machine can be used to smash the stones by bombarding them with sound waves. The small bits of the stones can then pass through the urinary tract. Figure 8-6 shows the symptoms, causes, prevention, and treatment of these conditions.

Sometimes, the kidneys fail and a life-threatening situation develops. If kidney failure is severe enough, a patient must undergo **kidney dialysis** (dy **al** uh sis), a process in which a machine is used in place of the kidneys. This treatment takes a few hours each week. Blood is removed from the body by tubes that then carry it through the dialysis machine where it is filtered for wastes and returned to the body.

Disorders of the Urinary System

Disorder	Symptoms	Causes	Prevention	Treatment
Nephritis (inflammation of the nephrons)	decrease in urine production	bacterial infection	prompt treatment of any infection; 6 to 8 glasses of water each day	antibiotics
Bladder infections	pain when urinating; frequent urination	bacterial infection	good personal hygiene	antibiotics
Uremia (poisoning due to kidney failure)	nausea; vomiting; headache; body swelling in severe cases	kidney failure due to infection or prolonged high blood pressure	maintenance of normal blood pressure; 6 to 8 glasses of water each day	antibiotics kidney dialysis
Kidney stones (hard, stonelike masses in kidneys or urinary tract)	severe pain as stone passes through the ureter	undetermined	foods and beverages with high acid content	ultrasound treatment to break up stones; or surgical removal

Sometimes, the only means of survival in cases of kidney failure is a kidney transplant. In a kidney transplant, the patient's diseased kidney is replaced with a healthy one. The biggest obstacle to overcome in a kidney transplant is the body's tendency to reject the new kidney as a foreign object.

▲ **Figure 8–6. In what kidney disorders would antibiotics be used? What else do you need to do in these cases?**

Keeping the Kidneys and Urinary Tract Healthy

Your kidneys are resourceful organs. If one of them is damaged, the other kidney can do the work of two. To keep your kidneys healthy, you should try to drink six to eight glasses of water a day. If you have a fever or some other infection, your kidneys must work even harder to remove impurities. At these times, it is especially important to drink lots of water.

Section Review

1. What are two nitrogen-containing wastes that your body excretes?
2. What is the basic working unit of the kidneys?
3. What three structures make up the urinary tract?

What Do You Think?

4. To maintain or improve the health of your kidneys, what precautions would you take?

▲ **Figure 8–7. Drinking six to eight glasses of water a day helps to keep your kidneys healthy.**

3. YOUR NUTRITIONAL NEEDS

Now that you understand how your digestive and excretory systems work, you can see why food is more than something that satisfies your hunger. It affects the way you look and the way you feel. It even has an influence on the way you perform mentally and physically.

How can food have such a tremendous effect on your well-being? Food does all this because it supplies you with nutrients. **Nutrients** (**noo** tree unts) are the substances found in food that the body needs to regulate bodily functions, promote growth, repair body tissues, and obtain energy.

Your body requires over 40 different nutrients for these tasks. The process by which the body takes in and uses these nutrients is called **nutrition.**

Food and Energy

Whether you are sleeping or running in a race, you use energy. In fact, energy is used for everything you do. Energy is needed to maintain your body temperature, keep your heart beating and your lungs breathing, and enable you to read and understand the words on this page.

When your body uses the nutrients in foods, a series of chemical reactions occurs inside your cells. During these reactions, certain nutrients are burned or broken down. As a result, heat energy is released. The amount of heat energy released when nutrients are burned is measured in units called **calories** (**kal** ur eez). The more calories a food has, the more energy it contains. As you can see in Figure 8-8, the

Your body needs the energy that nutrients provide to function properly, to grow, and to repair damaged tissues.

Figure 8–8. Which of the foods shown below would you choose for a 300 to 350 calorie meal?

The Calorie Content of Some Common Foods

Tomato
1 medium
25

Whole Milk
1 cup
150

Cheese Pizza
1 slice
290

Egg
1 large
80

Apple
1 medium
80

Green Pepper
1 medium
20

Wheat Bread
1 slice
65

Potato
1 medium
145

Ice Cream
1 cup
270

Orange
1 medium
60

calorie, and thus the energy, content of different foods varies greatly. How would you compare the energy that you can get from a slice of cheese pizza with the energy that you can get from a three-ounce (85-gram) hamburger?

To find out how many calories you need in a day, you must consider a number of factors. For example, the more active you are, the more calories you need to power your activities, as you see in Figure 8-9. The colder the air temperature, the more calories you require to maintain a constant body temperature. Your **basal metabolic** (**bay** sul met uh **bahl** ik) **rate** (**BMR**) also helps to determine your energy needs. The basal metabolic rate is the rate at which you use energy when you are completely at rest. The term **metabolism** (muh **tab** uh liz um) refers to all the reactions going on inside the cells of your body. The BMR varies according to age, sex, weight, and body size and shape.

For good health, the number of calories you eat daily should match the daily calorie needs of your body. Too many calories may cause you to become overweight; too few calories may cause you to become underweight.

The Six Basic Nutrients

There are six basic classes of nutrients: carbohydrates, fats, proteins, vitamins, minerals, and water. Each of these is essential for good health. Too much or too little of any one nutrient can result in poor health.

CARBOHYDRATES Sugars and starches are nutrients known as **carbohydrates** (kar boh **hy** drayts). Carbohydrates are made of carbon, hydrogen, and oxygen. Sugars are simple carbohydrates found in fruits, vegetables, and milk. They can be linked together chemically to form complex carbohydrates. Starch is a complex carbohydrate found in many plant foods, such as potatoes. When you eat foods containing starch, your digestive system breaks the starch into simple sugars that can be absorbed into your bloodstream. The major carbohydrate in your blood and used by your cells for energy is the sugar, **glucose** (**gloo** kohs).

At a meal, you usually eat more carbohydrates than your body can immediately use. When this happens, some cells in your body change the glucose into a type of starch called **glycogen** (**gly** kuh jun). Glycogen is stored in these cells until more glucose is needed. The glycogen is then converted again to glucose, which reenters the bloodstream. If you eat so many carbohydrates that the excess cannot be stored as glycogen, your body stores this excess in the form of fat.

Many nutrition experts believe that about 55 percent of our calories should come from carbohydrates. The carbohydrates they recommend are those that come from starches, rather than sugars.

Comparative Calorie Needs

Teenager 120 lbs. (Calories per hour)	Teenager 180 lbs. (Calories per hour)
65	98
260	390
456	672

▲
Figure 8–9. When would you burn more calories—while reading, jogging, or playing basketball? On a hot day or on a cold day?

Figure 8–10. Your body needs energy from the complex carbohydrates found in cereal grains and potatoes. ▶

Starchy carbohydrates, like those found in bread and pasta, usually contain a variety of nutrients. Sugary carbohydrates, like those found in candy and soft drinks, usually have few, if any, nutrients. That is why they are called "empty calorie" foods. The best way to have sugar in your diet is to eat naturally sweet foods, such as fruits and fruit juices, which also provide vitamins and trace amounts of some of the minerals you need.

Another kind of carbohydrate is **fiber,** the undigestible material that makes up the walls of plant cells. Fiber is necessary for the proper functioning of your digestive system. It plays an important role in preventing constipation, hemorrhoids, appendicitis, and gallstones. Adequate fiber may even reduce the risk of lower bowel cancer and the risk of certain types of heart disease.

For normal, healthy people, a diet that includes whole-grain breads and cereals, vegetables, fruits, and seeds will provide enough fiber. Fiber supplements are not necessary if you are eating a diet rich in these foods. Excessive fiber

Friend to Friend

José:

Hey, David, get your gear and let's go grab a cheeseburger at the diner.

David:

Forget the diner, José. I need to drop five pounds to get into shape for the regional trials.

José:

But I've been dreaming about the Diner Special. I thought it was a favorite of yours too.

may prevent essential minerals, such as zinc, calcium, and iron, from being absorbed into your body. Laxatives or supplements should not be used unless they are prescribed by a doctor for a particular medical reason.

FATS The nutrients with the highest energy content are the **fats.** The number of calories supplied by one ounce (28 grams) of fat is more than twice the number of calories supplied by one ounce (28 grams) of carbohydrates. Like carbohydrates, fats are composed of carbon, hydrogen, and oxygen. However, the proportions of carbon, hydrogen, and oxygen in fats are different from those in carbohydrates.

Fats not only supply your body with energy, but they also form part of the structure of your cells. Although fats are clearly important nutrients, researchers believe that many American diets are too high in fats. Many nutritionists recommend that no more than 30 percent of your calories come from fats. Some typical sources of fat in the American diet are shown in Figure 8-11.

Fats are sometimes classified as saturated or unsaturated. **Saturated** (**sach** uh ray tid) **fats** are fats that contain as much hydrogen in their structure as chemically possible. These fats are "saturated" with hydrogen. Animal fat, such as that in beef, pork, chicken, lamb, and dairy products, has a high saturated fat content. Usually saturated fats are solid at room temperature. **Unsaturated fats** are fats that have less than the maximum possible amount of hydrogen. Unsaturated fats usually are liquid at room temperature. Vegetables, nuts, and seeds are sources of unsaturated fats.

Saturated and unsaturated fats are important because of their effects on the cholesterol level in the blood. **Cholesterol** (kuh **les** tuh rawl) is a waxy, fatlike substance found in the cells of all animals. It is not present in plants. In humans,

▲ **Figure 8–11. A variety of foods in your diet supply saturated and unsaturated fats.**

David:
It is, but the regionals are coming up in a few weeks and they're very important to me. How about trying that restaurant with the big salad bar instead? What do you say?

José:
You know I'd die for the Diner Special. But, for a wrestling buddy, I'll sacrifice. On to the salad bar.

183

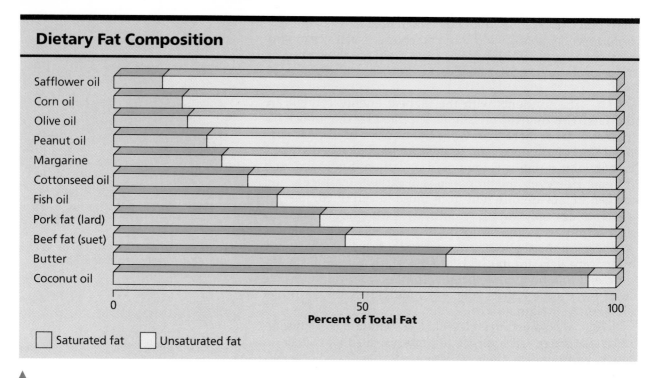

Dietary Fat Composition

Safflower oil
Corn oil
Olive oil
Peanut oil
Margarine
Cottonseed oil
Fish oil
Pork fat (lard)
Beef fat (suet)
Butter
Coconut oil

0 50 100

Percent of Total Fat

☐ Saturated fat ☐ Unsaturated fat

Figure 8–12. Which of the fat sources listed above is lowest in saturated fat?

Too much saturated fats in your diet can lead to high cholesterol levels and the risk of heart disease.

cholesterol is made in the liver and circulated throughout the body in the bloodstream. Although cholesterol is needed by your body, certain diets can cause cholesterol levels to become too high. When this occurs, the cholesterol may collect in the blood vessels leading to the heart and clog them. This is why elevated levels of cholesterol in the blood frequently are associated with heart disease.

Scientific studies have indicated that levels of blood cholesterol often rise when dietary fats are mostly saturated. These levels drop when dietary fats are mostly unsaturated. For these reasons, you should try to limit your intake of the saturated fats and cholesterol found in butter, eggs, and meats. When you do eat fats, try to use sources that are high in unsaturated fats, such as vegetable oils. As you can see in Figure 8-12, all fats are actually mixtures of saturated and unsaturated fats, and the amounts of saturated and unsaturated fats in different foods vary greatly. One way to lower the amount of cholesterol in your diet is to consume more fruits and vegetables, which are cholesterol-free.

PROTEINS Nutrients that contain nitrogen as well as carbon, hydrogen, and oxygen are called **proteins.** Like carbohydrates and fats, proteins make up a part of every cell in your body and serve as a source of energy. The really important function of proteins, however, is their role in the growth and repair of your body's tissues.

Proteins are made of about 21 different chemical substances known as **amino acids** (uh **mee** noh **as** ids). The protein you eat is broken down to amino acids in your digestive system. These amino acids are absorbed into your bloodstream and reassembled by the cells to form the kinds of proteins you need. Because your body cannot store excess amino acids, some of the amino acids are converted to sugar and used for energy or stored as glycogen or fat.

When you do not eat enough carbohydrates, your body starts to break down some of its own proteins. The amino acids from these proteins are converted to glucose to maintain the glucose level needed in the blood. Although fats can be used directly as an energy source by most tissues, they cannot be converted to glucose.

To make its own protein, your body needs all 21 amino acids. It can make 12 of these. The remaining 9 amino acids must be supplied by your diet. The 9 amino acids that the body cannot manufacture are called **essential amino acids.**

Animal protein is said to be complete protein because it contains all the essential amino acids in the proportions needed to make human proteins. Most plants have incomplete protein. This is protein that lacks the correct proportion of one or more essential amino acids. This problem can be overcome by combining in a single meal incomplete protein sources that complement each other. Suppose, for example, you prepare a casserole of rice, beans, and tomatoes. The protein found in the rice and beans individually is incomplete. When they are combined, however, the rice and the beans together supply all the essential amino acids needed by your body. This principle is the basis for combining a bean with a cereal grain in such foods as refried beans and tacos, peanut butter and bread, or beans and rice. If you do not eat meat, it is especially important for you to make sure that you eat complementary combinations of protein so that you get all the necessary amino acids.

VITAMINS Nutrients that are made by living things, that are required in only small amounts, and that assist many of the chemical reactions in the body are **vitamins.** Your body can make some vitamins, such as vitamin D, but most vitamins must be supplied in the food you eat.

There are two classes of vitamins: fat-soluble vitamins and water-soluble vitamins. Vitamins A, D, E and K are fat-soluble vitamins that are stored by the body. They can be harmful if consumed in excess. Usually this can only happen if you take vitamin supplements that contain large amounts of these vitamins.

Vitamin C and all of the B vitamins, are water-soluble vitamins that are not stored by your body. Because of this, it is important for you to eat foods that supply these vitamins on a daily basis. Figure 8-14 shows the function and food sources of all the vitamins and some of the essential minerals that you need.

Figure 8–13. Yogurt is a good source of protein and also provides plenty of carbohydrates, vitamins, and calcium.

By combining sources of incomplete complementary protein, you can receive the protein your body needs.

Essential Vitamins and Essential Minerals

		Functions	Food Sources
Water-Soluble Vitamins	**B₁ Thiamine**	aids in carbohydrate use; necessary for heart, nervous system, and appetite	pork; liver; legumes; whole grain products; fresh vegetables
	B₂ Riboflavin	aids in energy production in cells; promotes healthy skin	liver; milk; yogurt; eggs; lean meats
	B₃ Niacin	aids in digestion and carbohydrate use; necessary for nervous system functioning	liver; meat; fish; peanuts; fortified cereals
	B₆ Pyridoxine	aids in protein, fat, and carbohydrate metabolism	red meat; fish; liver; vegetables; whole grain cereals; bananas
	B₁₂ Cobalamin	aids in red blood cell formation and synthesis of RNA and DNA	meat; poultry; fish; cheese; eggs; fortified cereal
	Folic acid	aids in blood cell formation, protein production and enzyme functioning	liver; kidney beans; green, leafy vegetables
	Pantothenic acid	aids in functioning of digestive tract	organ meats; poultry; fish; eggs; whole grains; broccoli; yeast
	Biotin	aids in metabolizing carbohydrates and other B vitamins	organ meats; poultry; fish; egg yolk; peas; bananas; melons
	C Ascorbic acid	aids in connective tissue, bone, teeth, and skin formation, resistance to infection, and iron assimilation	citrus fruits; melons; green vegetables; potatoes
Fat-Soluble Vitamins	**A**	maintains healthy skin, bones, and eyes	liver; carrots; spinach; sweet potatoes; whole milk products
	D	aids in calcium and phosphorous use	fortified milk; cod liver oil; eggs
	E	aids in maintenance of vitamin A and the body's fats	vegetable oils; egg yolk; milk fat; liver; nuts; wheat germ
	K	aids in blood clotting	dark-green leafy vegetables; liver
Minerals	**Calcium**	aids in bone/tooth formation and blood clotting; needed for muscle and nerve activity	milk and dairy products; dark-green vegetables; sardines; canned salmon
	Chlorine	aids in digestion and cellular water balance	table salt; meat; milk; eggs
	Magnesium	maintains muscles and nerves; aids in metabolism	legumes; nuts; chocolate; whole grains; dark-green vegetables
	Phosphorus	aids bone/tooth formation and in maintenance of acid balance in blood	meat; eggs; nuts; fish; poultry; whole grains
	Potassium	helps to maintain heartbeat, water balance, and nerve transmission; aids in carbohydrate and protein metabolism	orange juice; citrus fruits; bananas; green, leafy vegetables
	Sodium	helps to maintain water balance; aids in nerve and muscle transmissions	table salt; shellfish; organ meats; carrots; beets

▲
Figure 8–14. What essential vitamins and minerals does liver contain? And eggs?

MINERALS Nutrients that occur naturally in rocks and soil, that are not made by living things, and that are required in small amounts, are **minerals.** Twenty-four different minerals have been shown to be essential for good health. You need six of these minerals in amounts of at least 100 milligrams daily. These minerals are calcium, magnesium, phosphorus, sodium, potassium, and chlorine. You need only trace amounts of the remaining minerals fluorine, iodine, iron, manganese, selenium, sulfur, and zinc.

WATER Although you may not think of water as a nutrient, about 65 percent of your body weight is water. Water is the primary component of blood and tissue fluids. It carries dissolved waste products out of the body, helps digest food, and provides the environment for nearly all of the body's chemical reactions. Water also plays a critical role as a temperature regulator. If the body heat generated when you are physically active is allowed to build up, your body temperature can rise dangerously. Perspiring helps your body to cool down.

Heavy perspiring also reduces your body's mineral and water content. Failure to cool off properly and drink enough water can lead to heat illness. Heat illness may range from muscular cramps, one of the first signs of mineral and water depletion, to severe dehydration, or heat stroke. Heat stroke is a life-threatening condition due to a breakdown of the sweating mechanism. It is important to prevent these problems by drinking adequate amounts of water before, during, and after strenuous physical activity. Drinking one cup (250 milliliters) of water every 20 minutes when you are exercising can help you to avoid these problems.

The water you lose daily through perspiring, urination, and breathing must be replaced. Although drinking water is the obvious way to make up for these losses, most foods and beverages contain water.

▲
Figure 8–15. Choose fresh, healthful foods to add to your intake of vitamins and minerals. Avoid "empty calorie" foods.

⚊🗝

Drinking plenty of water helps to replace the water your body loses through perspiration, urination, and breathing.

Section Review

1. Name three functions nutrients perform in your body.
2. What types of fat tend to decrease the levels of cholesterol in the blood?
3. Which vitamins must be supplied every day in the foods that you eat?
4. What nutrient makes up most of your body weight?

What Do You Think?

5. Is your present diet high in sugar or fat? What practical changes could you make in your diet or eating habits to improve this situation?

4. MEETING YOUR NUTRITIONAL NEEDS

Good nutrition requires serious planning. A dietary plan will help you to develop good eating habits and to keep your body functioning at its best.

The Basic Four Food Groups

The foods you eat are divided frequently into five major groups. Of these groups, four are good sources of nutrients. Nutritionists often call these groups the Basic Four Food Groups. They include the Meat-Poultry and Fish-Beans group, the Vegetable-Fruit group, the Bread-Cereal group, and the Milk group. You can fill your daily diet with a variety of nutritious foods from each of these groups.

THE MEAT-POULTRY AND FISH-BEANS GROUP

This group includes all foods that come from animal sources and **legumes** (**leg** yoomz). Legumes are plants that bear seeds in pods, such as beans, peas, and peanuts. These foods, some of which are shown in Figure 8-16, are a rich source of protein and minerals, such as iron and calcium.

Teenagers and adults should have two servings from this group every day. A typical serving would consist of three ounces (85 grams) of meat, poultry, or fish; two eggs; or one cup (250 milliliters) of cooked legumes.

THE VEGETABLE-FRUIT GROUP

As you can see in Figure 8-17, all fruits and vegetables, except legumes, are included in this group. Fruits and vegetables supply carbohydrates, a variety of minerals, and some protein. All of your vitamin C and much of your vitamin A come from foods in

▲
Figure 8–16. Meat, fish, eggs, legumes, and nuts are rich sources of the protein and minerals that your body needs.

Figure 8–17. You can choose from a variety of fruits and vegetables that contain carbohydrates, vitamins, and minerals.

this group. For example, dark-green, leafy vegetables provide calcium, iron and vitamin K. The skins of fruits and vegetables are also rich in fiber.

Teenagers and adults should have at least four servings from this group each day. It is important to vary your choices of fruits and vegetables in order to receive a variety of vitamins and minerals. A serving from this group could be a medium-size fruit, one-half cup (125 milliliters) cooked vegetable, or one-half cup (125 milliliters) of juice.

THE BREAD-CEREAL GROUP Grains and grain products, such as cereals, breads, and pasta, make up the Bread-Cereal group, which is illustrated in Figure 8-18. These foods supply carbohydrates, fiber, iron, and B vitamins.

You should have four servings from this group daily. One serving is equal to one slice of whole-grain bread; one-half cup (125 milliliters) of cooked cereal, pasta, or rice; or one cup (250 milliliters) of ready-to-eat cereal.

THE MILK GROUP This group, shown in Figure 8-19, includes all the foods you will find in the dairy case of a grocery store—milk, butter, cheeses, yogurt, and ice cream. These foods supply much of the calcium in your diet. They are also good sources of protein and vitamins but may be high in fats. The low-fat and nonfat milk products found in this group have had the fat-soluble vitamins A and D taken out of them at the same time fat was removed. This is why labels on some low-fat products indicate that these vitamins have been added.

Teenagers need four daily servings from the Milk group, while adults need two daily servings. One cup (250 milliliters) of milk or yogurt, two ounces (56 grams) of cheese, or two cups (500 milliliters) of ice cream equals one serving from this important group.

Figure 8–18. Grain products provide energy in the form of carbohydrates and some vitamins and minerals.

Figure 8–19. Milk products are a good source of the calcium needed to make your bones strong.

▲
Figure 8–20. Foods like fruits, carrots, pizza, fish, or chicken supplement your diet better than those high in calories and low in nutrients.

OTHER FOODS IN YOUR DIET There are some foods that do not fit into any of the Basic Four Food Groups. Nutritionists sometimes call this fifth group of foods the Fats-Sweets group. Foods in this group include candies, soft drinks, mayonnaise, jams, syrups, and salad dressings.

These foods are low in nutrient value but high in fats or sugars. Foods like these are said to be low in nutrient density. **Nutrient density** is the proportion of nutrients in a food compared to the number of calories the food provides. For example, one cup (250 milliliters) of yogurt supplies protein, carbohydrates, and vitamins, along with 120 calories. Nutritionists call this type of high nutrient density food "friendly calorie food." The same amount of cola, on the other hand, provides almost no nutrients and 145 calories. Cola and other low nutrient density foods are known as "empty calorie foods." In planning your own diet, you may find it useful to determine nutrient density by reading the labels on food packages. First, find the number of calories the food provides. Then look for a listing of the nutrients, especially vitamins and minerals, that the food supplies. Finally, compare the number of nutrients in the food to the number of calories the food provides. If this ratio is high, you may want to consider incorporating the food into your diet. If the ratio is low, you may want to limit your intake of the food so that it does not take the place of more nutritious food. Figure 8-20 shows some foods that have high nutrient densities. In planning your diet, which food would you choose for higher nutrient density—a baked potato or a serving of french fries?

Recommended Daily Allowances

There is at least one other guide in addition to the Basic Four Foods classification system that helps you to meet your daily nutritional needs. This nutrition guide, called the **United States Recommended Daily Allowances (U.S. RDA),** is based on the allowances established by the Food and Nutrition Board of the National Academy of Sciences. The U.S. RDA guide specifies the amount of calories, protein, vitamins, and minerals you should have every day. Food labels indicate the percentage of the U.S. RDA for each nutrient provided by a single serving of the food. One serving of cereal with milk, for example, may supply 15 percent of the U.S. RDA for protein.

The U.S. RDA is a general guide. It gives allowances slightly higher than necessary since dietary needs vary. Nutrient needs are affected by age, sex, heredity, life style, and your emotional and physical state. As a general rule, nutrient needs are greatest during the growth years through adolescence. Pregnant women and nursing mothers also need extra nutrients. If you are physically active, ill, or injured, you may need more of some nutrients.

O═▬
The U.S. RDA provides useful information to help you meet your nutritional needs.

Improving Your Diet

Scientists who have studied the eating habits of Americans have identified some ways in which we can improve our diets. Their recommendations can help you to plan a healthy diet.

- **Eat a variety of foods.** In choosing your servings from the Basic Four Foods Groups, vary your choices. By not limiting your selection within these groups, you can be sure to get all the nutrients your body needs.
- **Limit your intake of saturated fats and cholesterol.** There are a number of ways in which you can meet this goal. Choose lean meats, fish, poultry, and legumes instead of fatty meats. Limit fried foods, including potato chips, french fries, and doughnuts.
- **Eat foods with adequate starch and fiber.** To do this, eat more whole-grain breads and cereals, fruits, vegetables, and legumes. Remember that the skins of fruits and vegetables often are rich in vitamins and fiber.
- **Avoid too much sugar.** Foods that are high in sugar are high in calories but often low in nutrients. Limit your intake of sweet snacks, candy, and soft drinks. Avoid foods that contain large amounts of sugar, honey, corn syrup, or other high-calorie sweeteners. Eat fresh fruits instead of sweets for snacks.
- **Limit your intake of sodium.** To decrease your salt intake, avoid eating too many salty snacks, pickled foods, cured meats, and canned soups. Season your foods with herbs and spices instead of salt, and do not add salt to foods at the table.

The graphs in Figure 8-21 compare the average American diet with a diet recommended by many scientists. Most Americans can improve their diets by recognizing their nutritional needs, developing a plan for meeting these needs, and by making wise food choices.

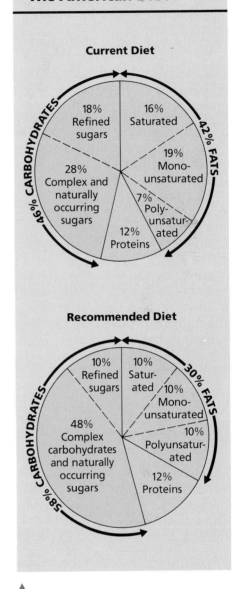

The American Diet

Current Diet

Recommended Diet

▲

Figure 8–21. What percentage of the American diet is made up of saturated fats? What is recommended?

Section Review

1. Foods from which food group supply all of your vitamin C needs?

2. Give two examples of foods with high nutrient densities and then give two examples of foods that have low nutrient densities.

3. What is the best way to get all the different nutrients you need?

What Do You Think?

4. How can you determine whether or not your diet meets your nutritional needs?

8 | Chapter Review

Chapter Summary

- The foods people eat must be broken into simpler forms before they can be used by the body. Once the foods are broken down, the nutrients can be absorbed into the bloodstream and transported throughout the body.
- The organs of the digestive system work together to break down foods physically and chemically.
- The body's cells produce waste products during bodily processes. The kidneys filter and remove these wastes from the blood.
- The skin, lungs, and liver also function in removing metabolic wastes from the body. Perspiration, an excretory function of the skin, also serves to cool the body when it is overheated.

- Nutrients provide the raw materials necessary for the growth, repair, and maintenance of your body's cells and tissues.
- The human body requires six types of nutrients: carbohydrates, fats, proteins, vitamins, minerals, and water.
- Foods are classified into four food groups, according to the nutrients they provide. These groups are the Meat-Poultry-Fish-Bean group, the Vegetable-Fruit group, the Bread-Cereal group, and the Milk group. Nutritional needs can be met by selecting a variety of foods from each group every day.
- The U.S. Recommended Daily Allowances (U.S. RDA) and the dietary goals set by scientists are additional guides for a healthy, well-balanced diet.

Vocabulary Review

Listed below are some of the important terms in this chapter. Choose the term that best matches the phrase in the exercise that follows.

amino acids	digestion	glucose	perspiration
bladder	enzyme	legumes	proteins
calories	excretion	metabolism	unsaturated fats
carbohydrates	fats	nephron	urinary tract
cholesterol	gallbladder	nutrient density	vitamins

1. a muscular storage sac for metabolic wastes produced by the body
2. the working unit of the kidney
3. a nutrient that provides concentrated energy to the body
4. all the reactions that occur in your body

5. a nutrient that contains nitrogen
6. sugars and starches
7. removal of bodily wastes
8. chemical that helps break down foods
9. plants that bear seeds in pods
10. a sugar that supplies energy for cells

What Have You Learned?

1. How do essential amino acids differ from other amino acids?
2. Trace the path of food through the digestive system.
3. How does fiber aid in digestion?

4. Why is it a good idea to eat foods with high nutrient densities?
5. Describe how nephrons first remove and then return fluids to the blood.
6. List three functions of fat in the body.

7. Which three minerals work together to build strong bones and teeth?

8. How does your body cool itself?

9. List the major nutrients supplied by foods in each of the Basic Four Food Groups.

10. What role does the liver play in digestion?

11. How do simple carbohydrates differ from complex carbohydrates?

12. How do nutrients pass from your digestive system into your bloodstream?

What Do You Think?

1. Researchers have found that a significant number of American teenagers do not have good diets. Why do you think this is so?

2. In many cultures, people include very little protein from animal sources in their diets. How might these people be able to obtain all the protein they need?

3. What kind of information do you think a urinalysis could provide?

4. Many children's television programs carry advertisements for presweetened cereals, sugary snacks, and vitamins shaped like cartoon characters. How might these advertisements affect the eating habits of the children watching them?

5. Why do you think food manufacturers are required to print nutritional information and ingredients on their products?

What Would You Do?

1. Your friend is overweight and is thinking about trying a weight-loss program. He has heard that he will lose weight quickly if he eliminates all carbohydrates from his diet. What advice would you give your friend about trying this plan?

2. You are planning a week-long backpacking trip in the mountains with a group of friends. You must carry all of your food in backpacks. What kind of food will you take to meet your nutritional needs?

3. It is a hot summer day. You have finished two hours of yard work and are perspiring heavily. What should you do and why?

4. Recently, your sister has been skipping lunch to work on a school project. She is not worried about her diet because she takes a vitamin supplement each day. What would you tell her?

5. What foods would you choose to eat the day before you plan to participate in a five-mile race? Explain.

For Further Study

1. Research and report on the eating habits of people in another country. What are the most popular foods? Are diets well-balanced or do nutritional problems exist? Describe some food-related customs practiced in the country.

2. Currently, there is a shortage of kidneys and other organs available for transplants in this country. Find out about the nationwide system of organ distribution and the methods to educate the public about organ donation. Write a report on your findings.

3. For one week, analyze lunch menus offered by your school cafeteria. Are foods from all four food groups included in each meal? Are the foods high in nutrient density? What changes would you recommend? Report your findings and suggestions to your class.

9

As you read, think about

▶ how you can use nutrition labeling and comparison shopping to select the foods you eat.

▶ what strategies can be used to reduce or gain body weight wisely.

▶ how you can plan your diet to meet your needs.

A Healthy Diet

What a perfect day for a barbecue! The sizzling shish kabob sends fragrant wisps of smoke into the deep blue of the sky. Steam from the roasting corn on the cob adds to the aroma. The bright green of the big mixed salad and the basket of shiny, red apples, golden pears, and purple grapes make a striking contrast with the rich brown of the meat. All your senses help you look forward to the meal, and your mouth is watering as you sit down at the table.

Tasty, healthful food makes any meal a celebration. This chapter will help you to plan balanced meals that are fun to eat and good for you. You will learn shopping tips to help you plan those meals and stay within your budget, too. Finally, you will learn how to maintain your ideal weight while consuming the well-rounded diet that you need for your active life style.

When you eat right, you have the energy to do all the things you want to do.

1. YOU THE CONSUMER

How do you go about selecting the foods you eat? Like most people, you probably choose foods because you like them, not because you know they are nutritious. Yet there is an important connection between the foods you choose at the grocery store or in the school cafeteria and your well-being. It is the kinds and amounts of nutrients in these foods that determine what your level of energy will be, how well your body will function, and whether or not you will grow as you should.

Nutrition Labeling

The United States Food and Drug Administration (FDA) requires every prepackaged food to be labeled with four kinds of information: the name of the product, the name and address of the manufacturer, the weight of the food without its container (its net weight), and a list of ingredients in descending weight order. Many manufacturers also list nutritional information, based on the U.S. Recommended Daily Allowances (U.S. RDA). Look at the food labels displayed in Figure 9-1. What percentage of the U.S. RDA for vitamin C is in one serving of canned tomatoes? of green beans? Would either of these foods be a good choice for someone who is trying to increase protein intake?

Check Your Wellness

Every day you make decisions about the foods you eat, often without even thinking about them. To determine whether your dietary habits are healthy ones, see how many of these questions you can answer yes to.

1. When you eat out, do you select nutritious foods?
2. Do you choose nutritious between-meal snacks, such as fresh fruits, raw vegetables, popcorn, and nuts?
3. Do you eat only when you are hungry and stop when you are full?
4. Do you avoid either overeating or undereating when you are bored or depressed?
5. Do you read food labels in order to decide which foods to buy?
6. Do you think your weight is appropriate for your height and body frame?
7. Do you avoid weight-loss or weight-gain diets that are not well-balanced?
8. Do you feel that your eating habits are healthful?

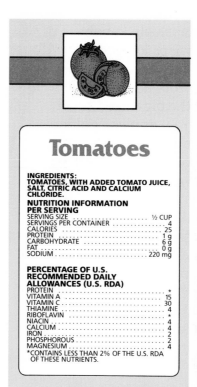

Tomatoes

INGREDIENTS:
TOMATOES, WITH ADDED TOMATO JUICE, SALT, CITRIC ACID AND CALCIUM CHLORIDE.

NUTRITION INFORMATION
PER SERVING

SERVING SIZE	½ CUP
SERVINGS PER CONTAINER	4
CALORIES	25
PROTEIN	1 g
CARBOHYDRATE	6 g
FAT	0 g
SODIUM	220 mg

PERCENTAGE OF U.S. RECOMMENDED DAILY ALLOWANCES (U.S. RDA)

PROTEIN	*
VITAMIN A	15
VITAMIN C	30
THIAMINE	4
RIBOFLAVIN	4
NIACIN	4
CALCIUM	4
IRON	2
PHOSPHOROUS	2
MAGNESIUM	4

*CONTAINS LESS THAN 2% OF THE U.S. RDA OF THESE NUTRIENTS.

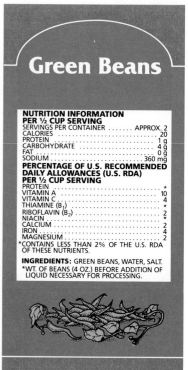

Green Beans

NUTRITION INFORMATION
PER ½ CUP SERVING

SERVINGS PER CONTAINER	APPROX. 2
CALORIES	20
PROTEIN	1 g
CARBOHYDRATE	4 g
FAT	0 g
SODIUM	360 mg

PERCENTAGE OF U.S. RECOMMENDED DAILY ALLOWANCES (U.S. RDA)
PER ½ CUP SERVING

PROTEIN	*
VITAMIN A	10
VITAMIN C	4
THIAMINE (B₁)	*
RIBOFLAVIN (B₂)	2
NIACIN	*
CALCIUM	2
IRON	4
MAGNESIUM	2

*CONTAINS LESS THAN 2% OF THE U.S. RDA OF THESE NUTRIENTS.

INGREDIENTS: GREEN BEANS, WATER, SALT.
*WT. OF BEANS (4 OZ.) BEFORE ADDITION OF LIQUID NECESSARY FOR PROCESSING.

Figure 9–1. Food labels provide a list of ingredients, the calorie content per serving, and the percentage of the U.S. RDA for the vitamins and minerals in the food. ▶

ADDITIVES If you have ever examined a food label, you may have noticed a series of long chemical names in the ingredients list. These are the names of food additives. **Additives** are chemicals that are added to a food to prevent spoilage, to control or improve color and texture, to replace or add vitamins and minerals, and to improve or give more flavor. They can be as simple as extra sugar or salt or as complex as their names. Additives that are used to prevent spoilage or to keep foods from losing their natural color or texture are called **preservatives**. Some preservatives prevent fats from becoming stale. These types of preservatives are added to prepared foods such as potato chips, salad dressings, and cake mixes. Other preservatives are used to keep peeled and cut fruits from becoming brown. Bakers often add the preservative calcium propionate to their baked goods to prevent mold from growing on them.

Look again at the food labels in Figure 9-1. Which food would be the better choice for people who need to limit salt in their diet? Which food contains more additives?

Often when food is canned, treated with chemicals, or processed in some other way, some of its vitamins and minerals are lost. To replace the nutrients lost during processing, foods are **enriched**, that is, nutrients are added by the manufacturer. Some breads and cereals are enriched with thiamine, niacin, riboflavin, and iron. If vitamins, minerals, and even proteins are added to a food that does not contain these nutrients, the food is said to be **fortified**. Milk is fortified with vitamin D. The foods you see in Figure 9-2 frequently are enriched or fortified.

Sometimes, manufacturers use additives to improve the texture, taste, or preparation of foods. An **emulsifier** (ih **muhl** suh fy ur) is an additive that is used to keep the ingredients in a food from separating. Emulsifiers are often added to salad dressing to prevent the mixture from separating. A **stabilizer** keeps solid ingredients from separating out of liquids. Stabilizers make ice cream smoother by holding the fluids and fats together to make finer ice crystals. They also prevent the loss of flavors from cake and pudding mixes. A **thickener** is an additive that is used to give a food a thicker, consistency. You may have seen the name of a thickener, such as starch, pectin, or vegetable gum, listed on the labels for some commercial gravies, puddings, or canned soups.

Probably you have heard people express concern over the use and safety of food additives, especially artificial colors and sweeteners. If you are allergic to certain food additives or concerned about their use, read the labels on the foods you purchase. Keep in mind that convenience foods are likely to contain the most additives. Foods least likely to contain additives are fresh foods that you prepare yourself every day. These include fresh fruits and vegetables, fresh meats, eggs, and fish.

Figure 9–2. Manufacturers often add vitamins and minerals to foods that have lost these nutrients during processing.

Food additives are substances added to processed foods to prevent spoilage, improve color and texture, and maintain or improve nutritional value.

HEALTH FOODS, NATURAL FOODS, AND ORGANIC FOODS

Sometimes people are confused by the terms health foods, natural foods, or organic foods. Should you make a special effort to buy foods with these labels? Should you purchase only organically grown apples and all-natural peanut butter?

Health foods are foods that the manufacturers claim have special, "health-giving" qualities. These qualities may have no scientific basis. **Natural foods** are foods that contain no additives. **Organic foods** are foods grown in soil fertilized only with manure or humus rather than chemical fertilizers. The food itself has not been treated with synthetic chemicals. Since the terms *health food*, *natural food*, and *organic food* have no legal definitions in most states, they can be applied to almost any food. The terms themselves, however, usually indicate higher prices.

Buying Food

When you shop for food, compare foods on the basis of their nutrient density, or the proportion of nutrients to calories, as you learned in Chapter 8. Try to avoid foods that are high in calories and low in nutrients. These foods have low nutrient density. Instead, choose friendly calorie foods: fruits, vegetables, whole-grain breads, milk, and fruit juices. These foods are high in nutrient density.

You can use the information on food labels to help you evaluate foods. Food labels will show you the number of calories as well as any low food value nutrients such as sugar and fat. It will also help you to compare the levels of vitamins

Advertisers use the terms "health food," "natural food," and "organic food" without strict regulation.

Figure 9–3. Reading food labels helps you to learn about a food's nutrient density, calorie level, and freshness.

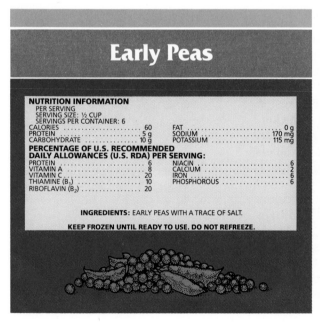

Early Peas

NUTRITION INFORMATION
PER SERVING
SERVING SIZE: ½ CUP
SERVINGS PER CONTAINER: 6

CALORIES 60	FAT .... 0 g
PROTEIN .... 5 g	SODIUM .... 170 mg
CARBOHYDRATE .... 10 g	POTASSIUM .... 115 mg

PERCENTAGE OF U.S. RECOMMENDED DAILY ALLOWANCES (U.S. RDA) PER SERVING:

PROTEIN 6	NIACIN 6
VITAMIN A 8	CALCIUM 2
VITAMIN C 20	IRON 6
THIAMINE (B₁) 10	PHOSPHOROUS 6
RIBOFLAVIN (B₂) 20	

INGREDIENTS: EARLY PEAS WITH A TRACE OF SALT.

KEEP FROZEN UNTIL READY TO USE. DO NOT REFREEZE.

Peas & Onions with Cheese Sauce

NUTRITION INFORMATION PER SERVING AS PACKAGED

SERVING SIZE: 5 OZ.	SERVINGS PER PACKAGE: 2
CALORIES 140	FAT .... 5 g
PROTEIN .... 6 g	SODIUM .... 435 mg
CARBOHYDRATE ...... 18 g	

PERCENTAGES OF U.S. RECOMMENDED DAILY ALLOWANCES (U.S. RDA)

PROTEIN 10%	NIACIN 8%	PHOSPHOROUS 15%
VITAMIN A 35%	CALCIUM 10%	MAGNESIUM 6%
VITAMIN C 25%	IRON 6%	ZINC 6%
THIAMINE 15%	VITAMIN E 4%	COPPER 4%
RIBOFLAVIN 10%	VITAMIN B₆ 6%	PANTOTHENIC
	FOLIC ACID 15%	ACID 4%
	VITAMIN B₁₂ 2%	

CONTAINS 1.0% NON-NUTRITIVE CRUDE FIBER (1.4 GRAMS PER SERVING).

STORE IN FREEZER AT 0°F.

INGREDIENTS: PEAS, PEARL ONIONS, SAUCE MADE FROM: WATER, AMERICAN CHEESE, PARTIALLY HYDROGENATED SOYBEAN AND COTTONSEED OILS, CORNSTARCH, WHEY (FROM MILK), NONFAT MILK, WHEAT FLOUR, SALT, SUGAR, SODIUM PHOSPHATE (FOR BETTER DISPERSION), CHEDDAR CHEESE, ONION POWDER, MILK FAT, NATURAL AND ARTIFICIAL FLAVORS, SORBIC ACID AND SODIUM BENZOATE (PRESERVATIVES), ARTIFICIAL COLOR, VITAMIN A PALMITATE.

and minerals. Look at the food labels for two types of frozen peas in Figure 9-3. A serving of the plain frozen peas contains no fat and provides 70 calories. How would you compare the two products for additives?

Freshness is an important factor when you buy food. If the food you are buying is a prepackaged product, look at the date stamped on it. It is an estimate of how long the product is usable. Foods advertised for quick sale may not be bargains if the use-by date has already passed.

Of course, nutrient density is your first concern when you shop. Yet, cost is also important. Suppose you are trying to decide which of two loaves of bread to purchase. To find out which is the better buy for your money, compare the **unit price**, or the cost per ounce of each product. Look at the two bread products in Figure 9-4. The 20-ounce (571-gram) loaf of bread made with six whole grains costs $1.50. The 16-ounce (457-gram) loaf of white bread costs $1.30. What is the unit price of each loaf of bread? Which is the better buy in terms of cost and nutrient density? Why?

Section Review

1. What information must be on the label of prepackaged food? What other information may be there?
2. List several reasons why preservatives may be added to certain foods.
3. Distinguish between the following labels: health food, natural food, organic food.
4. When you shop for prepackaged foods, what are three factors you should consider?

What Do You Think?
5. How do you choose your breakfast cereal?

Issues in Health

Should Food Additives Be Banned?

Some people feel that the use of food additives should not be allowed. They claim that many food additives are hazardous to our health. Some artificial colors and sweeteners, and chemical preservatives, such as nitrites, have been linked to cancer in laboratory animals. Other additives, such as monosodium glutamate (MSG), cause allergic reactions in some people. And even the most common additives, sugar, and salt, contribute to tooth decay, obesity, hypertension, and diabetes.

Other people feel that additives play a vital role in the food industry. Some additives are put into foods to improve their taste, appearance, or nutritional value. This makes foods more appealing to consumers. Chemical preservatives are necessary to prevent food spoilage. Without preservatives, food poisoning might be a common occurence. Food additives also make it possible for us to have year-round supplies of seasonal foods and to have all the convenience foods we now depend on.

Do you think additives should be banned? Why or why not?

2. MANAGING YOUR WEIGHT

Like most people, you probably carry around a mental image of yourself that you compare with photographs of athletes, models, or friends you admire. From time to time you may want to change this image so that it is slimmer, has its curves or muscles rearranged, or is taller. Some of the changes you long for will occur naturally as you acquire your full growth. Other changes will depend on your heredity, nutrition, and level of physical activity.

Malnutrition and Ideal Weight

When you hear the word *malnutrition*, you may think of starving people. **Malnutrition,** however, refers to any condition of poor nutrition. Its cause can be too little food, too much food, an unbalanced diet, or the failure to digest or absorb nutrients properly. In the United States many people suffer from malnutrition due to overeating rather than from eating too little. Figure 9-5 lists some of the health risks associated with overeating.

Eating more calories than your body can use results in their storage as fat. It is this storage of fat that leads to being **overweight**, more than 10 percent over the weight that best suits your height and body frame. **Obesity** (oh **bee** sut ee) refers to a weight that is 20 percent or more above your most comfortable weight.

Malnutrition can result from being overfed as well as from being underfed.

Figure 9–5. Being overweight increases the risk of developing certain diseases. ▶

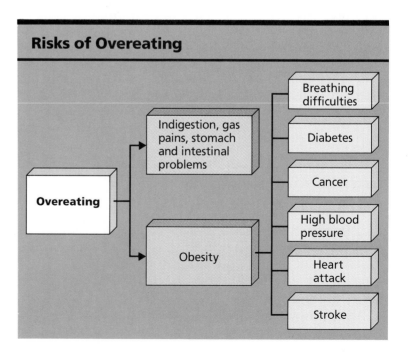

Risks of Overeating

Overeating → Indigestion, gas pains, stomach and intestinal problems

Overeating → Obesity → Breathing difficulties, Diabetes, Cancer, High blood pressure, Heart attack, Stroke

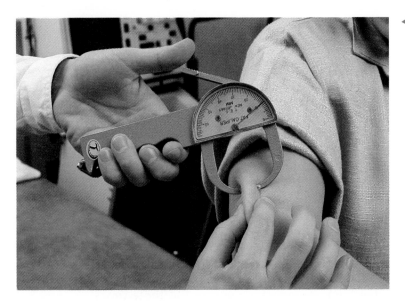

▲ Figure 9–6. A fat caliper helps you to gauge whether your body fat is within the limits of good health.

The weight at which you look and feel most comfortable is your **"ideal" weight**, or the healthiest weight for your body. As you compare yourself to your classmates, keep in mind that there is no single ideal weight for persons with the same body size and shape. An athlete may weigh more than others of his or her age and height, but the extra weight is in the form of muscle mass, not body fat. A person who gets little or almost no exercise may weigh as much as the athlete does but have too much body fat in comparison with his or her muscle mass.

You can test yourself for excess body fat by pinching a fold of skin on one side of your wrist or upper arm. If the fold of skin you pinch is more than one inch (2.5 centimeters), you may have excess fat. In Figure 9.6, this test is performed with a special instrument, called a caliper. After the measurement is taken, an index is used to determine what percentage of a person's body weight is fat.

There is no single ideal weight for persons who have the same body size and shape.

Reducing Body Weight and Body Fat Safely

Suppose that after you have targeted your ideal weight you decide to lose a few pounds. This is the time for you and your doctor to plan a sensible program for weight loss. Your program should involve choosing nutritionally balanced foods, based on the Four Basic Food Groups. It should also involve regular exercise. Researchers know that dieting alone is not as effective as dieting combined with a program of exercise because as you decrease your caloric intake, your metabolic rate also decreases. Thus, unless you exercise, your body does not burn calories as rapidly as it did, and your weight loss slows or stops.

▲ Figure 9–7. You can control body weight by eating plenty of fresh vegetables and other healthful foods that are low in fat.

After you have planned your diet, think what you can do to help yourself stick to it. Learn to take your time while eating so that you can really taste and enjoy your food. Watch the size of your portions. If smaller portions look lost on your dinner plate, switch to a salad plate. Your meal will look larger, and you may feel more satisfied. When you eat in a restaurant or in your school cafeteria, choose foods carefully. Baked or broiled meats and fish will fit into your diet better than those that are fried.

Some people get so hungry that they abandon their diets. To avoid this problem, you may want to try eating small meals more frequently. Perhaps, instead, you will want to save your fruit or vegetable from your regular meals for a snack when you are hungry. If you feel like snacking right after a meal, take a walk, ride your bike, or visit a friend instead of visiting the refrigerator.

You may find it helpful to keep a diary of what you eat, when you eat, and how you feel at these times. As you review your diary, you may discover eating patterns or behaviors you were not aware of. You may even find out what triggers your overeating. Some people overeat when they are disappointed, depressed, frustrated, or excited.

There are many ways to approach a program of weight loss. Your approach to weight loss is a personal decision that only you make. Remember that good eating habits, based on common sense, are essential for good looks and good health. When these habits are combined with a sensible exercise program, the rewards are lifelong.

Fad Diets, Diet Aids, and Fasting

Many young people want a weight-loss diet that brings instant results. This is unrealistic, and it is not always safe. A **fad diet** is a currently popular diet that may help a person lose weight temporarily. Fad diets range from high-protein-low-carbohydrate diets to diets with a special ingredient that is supposed to help you burn fat. These diets may exclude certain nutrients necessary for healthy development. Frequently, fad diets so restrict food choices that people tend to eat more of everything when the diet ends.

Diet aids, such as pills and candies, are usually ineffective and can be habit forming. They do not provide long-term weight control; nor do they involve changes in eating patterns. Some diet aids may cause nervousness, insomnia, and high blood pressure.

Refraining from eating all or certain foods is known as **fasting**. Although fasting may result in quick weight loss, it is not usually a healthy way to lose weight because you lose muscle tissue as well as some fat. Fasting may stunt your growth; put a strain on your kidneys and liver; and possibly cause hair loss and irregular menstrual cycles.

○━┳
Fad diets, diet aids, and fasting are usually unhealthful and ineffective for long-term weight control.

You can lose weight on almost any weight-loss plan if the number of calories you consume is less than the number of calories you use. However, you will be more likely to follow a diet that offers a variety of foods. The best weight-loss plan is one that has your doctor's approval and contains enough nutrients to sustain healthy growth.

Gaining Body Weight Wisely

Although underweight teenagers may be the envy of their friends, being too thin can be as emotionally painful as being too heavy. If you are underweight, remember that some teenagers who are just beginning to develop use a large number of calories in growth. This will not last. As your growth rate slows, you will fill out.

You may want to change any habits that keep you too thin. Eliminate snacks before mealtimes that spoil your appetite, and try to eat regular meals. Never skip a meal! When you do snack, enjoy nutritious foods such as those listed in Figure 9-8.

You may want to keep a daily diary of the kinds and amounts of foods you eat. The diary should help you to discover what your eating patterns are. Do you eat well-balanced meals or do you snack here and there, frequently

Nutrient Dense Foods

	Calories	
	135	Banana-nut bread 1 slice
	280	Bean salad ¾ cup
	150	Whole milk 8 oz. (202 gm)
	332	Cheddar cheese 3 oz. (86 gm)
	492	Salmon 8 oz. (202 gm)
	582	Peanut butter 3.5 oz. (100 gm)
	654	Brazil nuts 3.5 oz. (100 gm)

Figure 9–8. Eating high-nutrient-density foods is an important part of any diet. Which of these foods do you include in your diet?

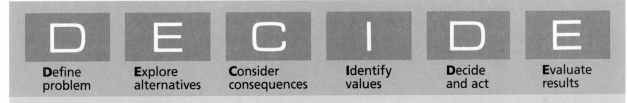

Define problem	**E**xplore alternatives	**C**onsider consequences	**I**dentify values	**D**ecide and act	**E**valuate results

A BULIMIC FRIEND?

Your girlfriend is a dancer. Most of her life revolves around dancing. She has always been on the thin side, but lately she has been worrying that she's becoming too fat to be a dancer.

Recently, you've noticed that she either eats very little or overeats and then forces herself to throw up. Although she doesn't seem to have lost that much weight, you are worried about her. You've heard about the eating disorders anorexia nervosa and bulimia, and you are beginning to wonder if she could be developing one of them.

1. Use the DECIDE process on page 16 to decide what you would do in this situation. Explain your reasons for making this decision.

2. Suppose the action you decided to take did not bring satisfactory results. What would you do next? Explain.

Could your weight-conscious friend be harming herself?

Fish Oils and Heart Disease

Drugstores have begun to carry a new product—fish oil capsules. These capsules contain oils taken from the tissues of deep water ocean fish, such as sardines and salmon. Some scientists believe fish oils help reduce a person's risk of heart disease.

Researchers studying the health of the Eskimos in Greenland noticed that these people have a low incidence of heart disease, despite their high-fat diets. The Eskimos eat over a pound of whale and seal meat daily, including intestines and blubber. Scientists began to wonder if the fish contained some substance that provided protection from heart disease.

Studies have shown that fish oils may guard against heart attacks and strokes by preventing the buildup of fats within arteries. Scientists are still not sure if fish oil capsules provide any protection from disease. Meanwhile, the American Heart Association simply advises people to eat fish regularly.

Can fish oil capsules help to curb heart disease?

skipping meals? Do you tend to lose your appetite when you are nervous or depressed? Are you constantly on the go, with little time to eat?

Exercise is important in gaining or losing weight. If you are trying to gain weight, increase your caloric intake and exercise on a regular basis. Exercise will turn the weight you gain into muscle tissue rather than fat.

Eating Disorders

Some young people use dieting as a way to solve emotional problems. They become obsessed with the idea of not eating. Some genuinely fear being overweight. Most, however, fear rejection by others or seek approval. People who deliberately starve themselves in this way suffer from **anorexia nervosa** (an uh **rek** see uh nur **voh** suh). Anorexia nervosa is a life-threatening disorder that frequently results in depression, hyperactivity, and a distorted body image. Anorexics are usually adolescent girls or women in their early twenties who lose 20 to 40 percent of their body weight. They are frequently extremely sensitive to cold temperatures and have a low pulse rate as well as low blood pressure. They may also experience dry skin, brittle hair, a growth of fine body hair, and the loss of their menstrual periods.

Another eating disorder, known as **bulimia** (boo **lim** ee uh), begins for many of the same reasons as anorexia nervosa. A teenager with bulimia frequently eats too much food (binges) and then gets rid of it (purges) by vomiting and taking laxatives. Although many bulimics do not become dangerously underweight, there are other serious health effects. Bulimics may suffer from dehydration. The enamel on their teeth may become eroded from the stomach acid introduced into the mouth when vomiting occurs. Some bulimics experience vitamin and mineral deficiencies as well as tearing and bleeding of the gums, tongue, and esophagus. Typically, bulimics become depressed and fantasize about suicide or abuse alcohol or other drugs.

Section Review

1. What is a simple method for determining whether or not you are overweight?
2. Explain how a person can be overweight but still suffer from malnutrition.
3. List four strategies for reducing body weight safely.
4. Describe two problems associated with fad diets.

What Do You Think?
5. Which eating habit of your own would you most like to change?

3. EATING FOR HEALTH

Do you ever feel that your parents continually nag you to eat a well-balanced diet? Frustrating as this may be, there is a reason for it. At this point in your life you have a great deal of control over what you eat. Since nutrition is so important, you need to make wise food choices for yourself.

Planning a Balanced Diet

Although a well-balanced diet is important, it is not limited to only a few foods. Within the Basic Four Food Groups you have many choices as the breakfast suggestions in Figure 9-10 illustrate. There are many ways you can combine the Basic Four Food Groups to make enjoyable meals for yourself. If you dislike vegetables, try new varieties; or try the same variety in a different form. With a little imagination, you can have a variety of well-balanced meals.

MEALS   You may have heard it said that breakfast is the most important meal of the day. Unfortunately, in many homes, breakfast is neglected in the morning rush.

In fact, most nutritionists believe that breakfast really is the most important meal. Your stomach is empty after a night without food, and breakfast should provide one-fourth to one-third of your food needs for the day ahead. When your

▲
Figure 9–9. The Basic Four Food Groups offer a surprising variety of choices for a nutritious meal anytime.

Figure 9–10. Breakfasts can be as varied as you want them to be. Which of these breakfasts would you choose? Why?
▼

Nontraditional Breakfast Foods				
Breakfast menu	Vegetable-Fruit Group	Milk Group	Meat-Poultry and Fish-Beans Group	Bread-Cereal Group
Cream of tomato soup Crackers and cheese	X	X X		X
Cottage cheese and fruit Toast or English muffin	X	X		X
Peanut butter on toast Orange juice Milk	X	X	X	X
Tomato juice Toasted cheese sandwich	X	X		X
Leftover meat/pasta casserole Milk		X	X	X
Tortilla with beans Orange juice Milk	X	X	X	X

breakfast is inadequate, you are likely to eat high-calorie, low-nutrient-density snacks to give you energy.

A balanced breakfast includes foods from each of the Basic Four Food Groups. These do not have to come from typical breakfast foods at all. You may want to try cottage cheese, fruit, or tuna on toast one day and a toasted cheese sandwich and tomato juice another day.

Perhaps more than at any other meal, at lunch, you are in control of the foods you eat. School cafeterias almost always provide choices from each of the Basic Four Food Groups. Many school cafeterias even offer nutritious snacks, salad bars, and special diet foods and vegetables. Since lunch makes up another third of your food needs for the day, you may want to choose a high-protein sandwich, such as chicken on whole wheat bread, a piece of fruit or a salad, and a carton of milk.

Dinner is frequently the heaviest meal of the day. Since you may be less physically active after this meal, it should not account for more than the final third of your calorie needs for the day. Use the dinner meal to make up for the nutrients you did not choose at breakfast and lunch. If you chose fruit from the Vegetable-Fruit Group for both breakfast and lunch, a green salad or some other green or yellow vegetables will be a good choice at dinner.

SNACKS Snacks are not necessarily bad for you if you choose them wisely, but it is possible to become poorly nourished from snacking. Frequent snacking may result in unnecessary weight gain because snack foods are often high in calories. Many snack foods are the empty-calorie, or low-

Foods you select for a day's meals should include a balance of foods from each of the Four Basic Food Groups.

Figure 9–11. Snacks can be nutritious. What would you choose when you are hungry and want something tasty?

Nutritious Snacks from the Basic Four Food Groups

Snack or Mini-Meal	Vegetable-Fruit Group	Milk Group	Meat-Poultry and Fish-Beans Group	Bread-Cereal Group
Peanut butter Bread Milk or yogurt		X	X	X
Slice of cheese pizza Tomato juice	X	X		X
English muffin with tomato and melted cheese Apple juice	X X	X		X
Deviled egg Toasted rye bread Milk		X	X	X

nutrient-density, variety that replace the high-nutrient density foods that you need.

If you tend to be a frequent snacker, you may want to modify the types of foods you snack on. Instead of an evening snack of chocolate chip cookies, try substituting a tablespoon of peanut butter on crackers. Rather than a sweet roll and coffee at mid-morning, try a bagel with cream cheese and a glass of juice. You may even begin to think of the nutritious snacks listed in Figure 9-11 as small meals. Many doctors recommend these kinds of small meals to maintain energy throughout the day.

VEGETARIANISM A person who eats no meat is called a **vegetarian**. The diet of a strict vegetarian includes fruits, vegetables, legumes, cereal grains, and plant oils. As shown in Figure 9-12, the protein that strict vegetarians eat comes primarily from cereals, legumes, and nuts. Other types of vegetarians may add eggs and dairy products to their diets. For these vegetarians, half of their protein comes from milk, cheese, and eggs and the other half from plants.

Vegetarians are less likely than others to suffer from overweight and heart disease, problems associated with eating too much animal protein and fat. Variety, however, is especially important in a vegetarian diet. Eating only green salads, vegetable sticks, and sprouts is monotonous and not nutritionally sound. To introduce variety, you may want to experiment with new sources of protein, such as tofu and tempeh. If your family is not vegetarian, you may also need to learn how to prepare a cheese souffle or a vegetable-bean soup. Using fish and seafood in a vegetarian diet is another way to introduce variety.

If a vegetarian diet appeals to you, you may want to make up a week's worth of menus, using some of the foods in Figure 9-13. Check your menu plans with your doctor or school nurse to be sure your meals are well balanced.

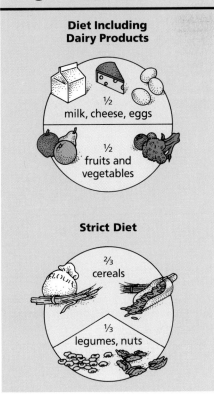

Vegetarian Diets

Diet Including Dairy Products

½ milk, cheese, eggs

½ fruits and vegetables

Strict Diet

⅔ cereals

⅓ legumes, nuts

▲
Figure 9–12. In which of these two vegetarian diets would you satisfy your protein needs more easily?

Figure 9–13. Protein sources such as seaweed and tofu, a soy bean product, help to add variety to vegetarian meals.
▼

Figure 9–14. A salad can be a pleasant, healthful change from a typical fast-food meal.

Fast-food meals that are high in fat and low in nutrient density should be eaten in moderation or modified to include high-nutrient density foods.

FAST FOODS   Tom and his friend Dave drop by their favorite fast-food restaurant several times a week for a meal of hamburgers, fries, and shakes. Their parents complain that this fast food will not provide the vitamins and minerals needed by growing teenagers. Their coach insists that their diet of high-fat, high-calorie food will interfere with their athletic performance. The boys, who are active and not overweight, see no reason to change their eating habits.

Fast-food meals like Tom's and Dave's are the cause of much discussion. Diets that continue to be high in fat may be linked with heart disease and certain cancers in later years. High-calorie diets may result in a gradual weight gain, which is difficult to lose once growth has stopped and a taste for such foods has formed. A typical meal of a cheeseburger, fries, and a shake provides a whopping 1,000 calories. This kind of caloric intake when you grow older could cause serious weight problems.

If you enjoy fast-food meals once in a while, consider substituting milk or orange juice for shakes and sodas. Use the salad bar in place of fries and onion rings. If you form wise food habits now, they will help you throughout your adult years.

Special Diets

Dietary needs can vary greatly. If you swim for two hours a day and walk a mile to school, you may need more calories than your friend, who is rehearsing for a choral concert and riding the bus. If you are allergic to milk and eggs, you need to avoid these foods. Sometimes, special physical conditions require special diets. A pregnant or nursing woman, for example, requires extra nutrients to provide for her own needs as well as those of her developing baby.

FOOD ALLERGIES Have you ever eaten a shrimp salad and developed an unpleasant rash? If so, you probably have an allergy. A **food allergy** is a condition in which the body's cells respond to a particular food by releasing substances that cause fluid to leak into the surrounding tissues. Symptoms such as rashes (hives), a runny nose, diarrhea, coughing, and sneezing are generally caused by the release of **histamine (his tuh meen)**. Histamine, a substance normally released in small amounts, is released in toxic amounts when you eat foods to which you are allergic.

If your doctor does not know for sure which foods are causing your allergy, he or she may refer you to an allergist, a person who specializes in the diagnosis and treatment of allergies. The allergist may conduct a series of scratch tests or skin tests. In a **skin test**, tiny portions of the suspected foods are injected just below the surface of your skin, usually on your back. If your skin swells or becomes red, you are probably allergic to that food.

Once the allergist has identified the foods to which you are allergic, you can eliminate these foods from your diet. Of course, this can be frustrating when you crave the foods you should avoid. Furthermore, you must become even more skilled at making sure you get the nutrients you need from each of the Four Basic Food Groups. If you are allergic to cow's milk, for example, you may need to discover other sources of calcium. If you are allergic to wheat, you will need to check the ingredients label on cereal boxes and breads, among other things, to find foods containing oats, rice, or some other grain.

If you have food allergies, you may receive a series of desensitization shots to help you build up protection against the irritating substance. These shots are not effective for severe allergies.

DIETS FOR DIABETICS As you learned in Chapter 8, the principal carbohydrate circulating in your blood and used by your cells for energy is glucose. Normally, the body makes a substance called **insulin (in** suh **lun)**, which allows glucose to enter the cells. If insulin is lacking, glucose levels in the blood will build up, and a disorder called diabetes mellitus (dy uh **bee** tis muh **ly** tus) may result. Diabetes mellitus is a chronic disorder in which the body does not produce or properly use insulin. Symptoms may include sudden excessive thirst, an increase in appetite but a loss in weight, and frequent urination. Some people also feel fatigued, irritable, and confused. If you have a combination of any of these symptoms, you should see a doctor.

If your doctor suspects you have diabetes, you will need to have your blood and urine tested. These tests indicate whether or not there is excess sugar in your urine and bloodstream and show how your body absorbs and uses sugar.

Diabetes mellitus occurs when there is insufficient insulin in the body, which prevents glucose in the blood from entering the body's cells.

Diabetes usually can be controlled. You may need to take daily insulin injections, which must be adjusted according to the amount of exercise you get and the kinds of foods you eat. You will also need to eat well-balanced meals on a regular schedule. Your meals should help to control blood glucose levels by leaving out foods high in sugar and focusing on complex carbohydrates. The American Diabetes Association also emphasizes the importance of foods high in fiber and low in sodium and fat. Frequently, people with diabetes carry a snack, such as fresh fruit, raw vegetables, or cheese with them at all times. This type of snack helps diabetics to regulate their blood glucose levels if they are unable to eat a regular meal on a schedule they have established.

MANAGING HYPOGLYCEMIA THROUGH DIET If too much insulin is produced by the body, there may be a dramatic fall in the level of blood glucose. The result is a condition known as **hypoglycemia** (hy poh gly **see** mee uh), or low blood sugar. Although hypoglycemia may be caused by a malfunctioning of the liver or pancreas, it may also be triggered by skipping meals, fasting, or eating a diet high in sugar. People with hypoglycemia may experience hunger, weakness, severe headaches, and shakiness as their blood glucose levels fall. To counteract these symptoms, you need three well-balanced meals a day that are high in protein and complex carbohydrates. Your digestive system breaks down these substances more slowly than the sugars found in soft drinks, for example. A mid-morning and a mid-afternoon snack, such as cheese, whole-grain bread, or peanut butter, also help to maintain a regular level of insulin release. If your symptoms continue after you have altered your diet to include more frequent small meals with protein-rich snacks in between, you should see your doctor.

DIET AND HIGH BLOOD PRESSURE High blood pressure is a higher than normal pressure on the walls of the blood vessels. It is sometimes called the "silent disease" because many people with high blood pressure experience no symptoms at all. Others may experience dizziness, headaches, and nervousness.

High blood pressure may occur at any age, even during adolescence. Sodium, found in table salt and many other foods, is thought to be a factor in the disease. When the body is unable to rid itself of extra sodium, the excess stays in body tissue and holds in water, increasing the total blood volume. This increased blood volume then pushes more forcefully on the walls of the blood vessels, elevating blood pressure. For this reason, people with high blood pressure are told to limit their sodium intake. Figure 9-15 offers some suggestions for controlling your intake of salt. Some people enjoy experimenting with herbs and spices to add flavor to their foods.

Figure 9–15. Salt is high in sodium. Which of these tips are you likely to follow to limit your intake of salt?

▼

Avoiding Sodium

- Learn to enjoy flavors of foods by using herbs instead of salt.
- Cook with only small amounts of added salt.
- Substitute another salt, such as potassium chloride, for table salt, also known as sodium chloride.
- Limit your intake of foods such as potato chips, pretzels, crackers, salted nuts and popcorn, cured meats, and cheese.
- Read food labels carefully to determine the amounts of sodium they contain.

NUTRITION DURING PREGNANCY You may have heard it said that a pregnant woman is eating for two. In a very real sense, this is true. A woman's nutrition during pregnancy must provide for her needs as well as the needs of the developing baby. This double nutritional task requires a diet high in protein and rich in vitamins and minerals. For example, two ounces (56 grams) of protein per day are recommended for women who are not pregnant. Pregnant women need twice that amount. They also need more of most vitamins and minerals, especially iron and calcium. Iron is necessary for the formation of red blood cells. Red blood cells contain a substance called **hemoglobin** (**hee** muh gloh bun), which carries oxygen to all parts of the body. If the mother is not getting enough iron, her blood will contain too little hemoglobin to supply the developing baby with adequate oxygen. For this reason, extra iron often is prescribed during pregnancy. Calcium is another mineral important to pregnant women. Calcium is necessary for the formation of strong bones and teeth. Since the baby's teeth start to bud early in pregnancy, the mother's calcium intake in the first four months is extremely important. Milk and other dairy products are useful sources of calcium, as are leafy vegetables, whole grains, legumes, and nuts.

Pregnant women also need carbohydrates for energy. Sugary foods, such as cakes, candy, and cookies, should be replaced with some of the complex carbohydrates, which contain other valuable nutrients.

During pregnancy, the body's need for fat also increases, but a nutritious diet usually contains enough fat to meet this need. While it is normal to gain between 25 and 35 pounds (11 to 16 kilograms), if foods rich in fats and carbohydrates make up most of the diet, a woman may put on unnecessary weight. Recent research on nutrition in pregnancy suggests that when a diet is inadequate, the mother may give birth to a premature baby or a baby of lower birth weight!

▲
Figure 9–16. During pregnancy, a woman needs to provide for herself and the developing baby.

○━━▄
Nutrition during pregnancy must meet the needs of the mother as well as the needs of the developing baby.

Section Review

1. Why is breakfast the most important meal of the day for you?
2. Why are vegetarians not likely to suffer from overweight and heart disease?
3. What steps can you take to enjoy occasional fast-food meals and get the nutrients you need?
4. Why is nutrition important during pregnancy?

What Do You Think?
5. If you suddenly developed an allergy to eggs, what would you do to adjust your diet?

Breaking a Bad Habit

The teenager below has developed a poor nutritional habit. Although he may wish to cut down on the amount of cola he drinks each day, he may not think he has the willpower to do so. We all can develop habits that are not good for us. Yet, because they are habits, we continue to do them. Did you ever try to break a bad habit? Did you decide you didn't have the willpower?

It may surprise you to learn that breaking a habit does not depend on willpower. Instead, what you need more than anything else is "skillpower." You need to learn and practice the skill of behavior change.

It is difficult to break an old, ingrained pattern of behavior. But, the key to breaking a bad habit is to replace it with a new, positive habit. The process works best if it is done in small steps and if everything is put in writing on a behavior contract.

The steps given here will help you to break almost any bad habit. By using this process, you can develop the "skillpower" to direct your life toward wellness.

1. Define Your Bad Habit

Be sure to describe your bad habit in a specific manner. For example, instead of saying "I don't eat very well," describe a specific behavior that demonstrates the problem: "I drink too much cola" or "I eat too many candy bars" or "I never eat fruit."

2. Set Your Goal

A goal describes the behavior you would like to be doing instead of your bad habit. Your goal should be specific and clear and should have a realistic deadline. The goal should emphasize *doing* something, rather than *not* doing something. If a goal is large, break it down into small subgoals.

3. Design an Action Plan

(a) Monitor Your Bad Habit: Spend a week carefully observing and recording your bad habit. This will help you understand the things that trigger and reinforce the habit.

Bad Habit Record			
BEFOREHAND		**BEHAVIOR**	**AFTERWARDS**
Scene	Feelings	Details	Results
Monday 12 noon lunch at school	tired and bored	12 oz. can of cola	more energetic

(b) Write Your Plan: Describe in detail the specific day-to-day changes you will make to reach your goal. Your plan should be a gradual, step-wise process.

(c) Keep a Log: Log your new behavior daily, including any setbacks you may have.

Behavior Log							
	M	T	W	Th	F	Sa	Su
Action Plan	← 1 juice substition daily →						
Behavior	✓	forgot juice	✓	craved cola	✓	✓	✓

4. Build a Supportive Environment

Since breaking a habit is not easy, you will need help from many sources. Plan to reward yourself for accomplishments along the way to your goal. Ask family and friends to keep an eye on your progress and keep a list handy of the benefits of your new behavior. Structure your surroundings to support your efforts. For example, if you are trying to break a cola habit, try not to keep any cola in your house and avoid carrying loose change for cola machines.

A few skills and a will to change can help you break any bad habit.

APPLY THE SKILL

1. Choose three habits that you would like to break. Look back over the "Check Your Wellness" inventories you have taken to help you identify poor habits you have.

2. Out of the three habits, choose the one habit you would *most* like to change and clearly define it. Then, set a specific goal of eliminating the habit. Fill this information in on a behavior contract.

3. For a one-week period, monitor your bad habit. Every time you exhibit the habit, record where and when it occurred, along with your thoughts and feeling both before and after. Can you detect any patterns in your behavior?

4. Devise a specific action plan for breaking your habit, using your new knowledge of your behavior patterns. Record your plan in detail on your contract. Also, fill in the ways that you will build a supportive environment.

5. Log your behavior for a three-week period.

6. After three weeks, evaluate your performance. Did you stick to your plan? If not, what were the things that made it hard for you? What aspects of your plan worked for you?

Behavior Contract

Bad Habit: drinking too much cola

I Sam Brown

plan to substitute water or juice for cola by May 4th.

I will reach this goal by doing the following target behavior substituting water juice once a day at first and gradually increasing to four times a day

To create a supportive change environment, I will get help from the following role models: Mom and Loretta, reward myself by going to the movies with friends after successful weeks along the way and by buying myself a new baseball glove when I reach my goal.

Signed Sam Brown Date March 6th

Chapter Summary

- Labels on prepackaged foods provide the product's name, an ingredients list, the manufacturer's name and address, and the net weight. Labels may provide nutritional information based on the U.S. RDA.
- Food additives are used to prevent spoilage, to control color and texture, to replace or add vitamins, and to improve flavor.
- When purchasing prepackaged food, the shopper should consider nutrient density, unit price, and the use-by date.
- Overweight and obesity are the common forms of malnutrition in the United States.
- A person's ideal weight should be based on the ratio of body fat to muscle mass.
- To be effective, a weight-loss or weight-gain program should combine sensible eating with regular exercise.

- Fad diets are generally ineffective because some important nutrients are left out of them, and it is difficult to maintain the weight loss.
- Each of the main meals of the day should supply about one-third of a person's caloric needs and come from the Four Basic Food Groups. Snacks should provide a variety of nutrients rather than calories.
- Vegetarian diets must contain enough variety from nonmeat sources to meet the requirements for good nutrition.
- By choosing wisely, people can lessen calories, fat, and salt in fast-food meals.
- Diets can be modified to meet the nutritional requirements of people who have food allergies, are diabetic or hypoglycemic, have high blood pressure, or are pregnant.

Vocabulary Review

Listed below are some of the important terms in this chapter. Choose the term that best matches the phrase in the exercise that follows.

additives
anorexia nervosa
bulimia
diabetes mellitus
emulsifier

fad diet
food allergy
hemoglobin
high blood pressure
histamine

hypoglycemia
ideal weight
malnutrition
organic foods
overweight

preservatives
stabilizer
thickener
unit price
vegetarian

1. a person who eats no meat
2. chemicals added to a food
3. a condition of poor nourishment
4. a disorder in which the body does not produce or properly use insulin
5. an additive used to prevent the separation of ingredients

6. increased stress on the walls of the blood vessels in your body
7. low blood sugar
8. cost per unit measure of a product
9. a substance released in toxic amounts when you eat a food to which you are allergic.
10. disorder resulting from self-starvation

What Have You Learned?

1. Describe the role of emulsifiers, stabilizers, and thickeners in various foods.
2. What kinds of nutritional information can you get from labeling that has the U.S. RDA.

3. How can you evaluate foods for nutrient density? What is the advantage of choosing friendly calorie foods?
4. Why is fasting a poor way to lose weight?

5. Describe some steps you can take to eat in a restaurant and still diet successfully.
6. Why use a diet diary when dieting?
7. Why is it frequently said that plain foods are better buys?
8. How do anorexia nervosa and bulimia differ? How are they alike?
9. List three reasons why it is a good idea to avoid snacks such as candy bars or sweet rolls.
10. Explain what happens when you eat a food to which you are allergic. How can you go about getting help for allergies?
11. List the causes, symptoms, and treatments of diabetes mellitus and hypoglycemia.
12. Why do iron requirements increase during pregnancy?

What Do You Think?

1. Research has shown that some additives cause cancer in test animals. Why do you think that food manufacturers continue to use these additives in their products?
2. How can you explain the fact that Jean gained weight after she began a sensible diet and exercised with weights four days a week?
3. Explain why skipping meals to eliminate calories is not an effective way to lose weight.
4. Why can diabetes and hypoglycemia, be managed, in part, by eating nutritious snacks between regular meals?
5. How can you explain why someone who is not overweight becomes bulimic?

What Would You Do?

1. Your older sister is pregnant. Before her pregnancy, she was overweight. Now, you notice, despite her doctor's advice, she is trying to control her weight and restrict her weight gain to 10 pounds. What might you say to your sister?
2. Your friend tells you he is taking diet pills to qualify for the wrestling team. What advice would you give him?
3. You and a diabetic friend are far from home without insulin when she begins to feel ill. What should you do?
4. You have been asked to a dance. You decide to lose those extra pounds in the two weeks before the dance and are considering a fad diet. What should you do and why?
5. You will be traveling next summer. Design a plan for (a) eating nutritious foods, (b) maintaining your weight, and (c) occasionally avoiding restaurants.

For Further Study

1. Save the ingredients labels of two brands of cereal, bread, or another prepackaged product. Compare each brand for the kinds of additives, level of sodium, calories per serving, and nutrient density. If possible, calculate the unit price and note the use-by date. Which of the brands is the better buy? Why?
2. Prepare a questionnaire to help other students analyze their eating habits. Include such questions as: Do you eat when you are angry, anxious, or bored? Do you eat faster than most people you know? Do you skip breakfast?
3. Report on the breakthroughs that make it possible for diabetics to (a) monitor blood sugar levels at home, (b) have a constant flow of insulin based on their needs, and (c) use surgery, perhaps, to cure diabetes.

10

As you read, think about

▶ how your nervous system coordinates your actions and thoughts.

▶ how your skeletal and muscular systems support your body, give it shape, and produce movement.

▶ how your circulatory and respiratory systems work together to supply your body with oxygen and nutrients and to remove waste products.

▶ how you can find your level of physical fitness.

Fitness and Your Body Systems

The frisbee arcs high above your head. With a tremendous leap, you fly into the air. Your lungs fill with oxygen, your heart pumps faster, and your muscles pull hard as your body sails upward. Who-eee! You've caught it.

Your body is an amazing instrument. No manufactured machine can match it. Your respiratory system sends oxygen to your heart; your circulatory system carries the blood from your heart to fuel the muscles and bones that balance and move all parts of your body. Your brain and nervous system send out the messages that control your body's actions. This chapter tells you about these wonderful, complicated systems. It also shows you how to keep them all in top form.

Your body is designed for action. Keeping it fit helps it function at its best.

Check Your Wellness

Do you know if you are in good physical condition? See if you can answer yes to the questions below.

1. Do you breathe easily after climbing a flight of stairs?
2. Can you do light exercise or household chores without feeling sore afterwards?
3. Are bending, twisting, and reaching movements easy for you?
4. Do you usually have enough energy to do the things you want to do?
5. Can you participate in a vigorous activity, such as running, biking, or swimming, for at least 15 minutes?
6. Do you avoid foods that are high in cholesterol and saturated fats?
7. Are you a nonsmoker?

Sensory neurons, interneurons, and motor neurons make up your nervous system.

1. THE NERVOUS SYSTEM

Have you ever stopped to think about the hundreds of actions you perform each day and the thousands of thoughts you have in one hour? All of your actions and thoughts are coordinated by a complex group of organs and nerves called the nervous system. The nervous system consists of two parts. Your brain and spinal cord make up one part. Forty-three pairs of nerves connecting the brain and spinal cord to other parts of your body make up the other part.

Your nervous system coordinates your thoughts and actions in three basic steps. First, it receives information about your environment and the other parts of your body. Then, it interprets this information. Finally, it causes the body to respond to the information. If you are coasting down the sidewalk on your bike when a woman pushing a baby stroller approaches from the opposite direction, you receive this information through your eyes. The information moves from your eyes to your brain. Your brain decides that you may run into the woman and stroller. The brain also decides that you should stop your bike and sends a message through your spinal cord to the nerves of your feet. These nerves cause the muscles in your feet to apply the brakes on your bicycle. All these events happen in less than a second. But, what makes it possible for your nervous system to receive, send, and act upon these messages?

Nerves and Nerve Cells

The basic cell of the nervous system is the **neuron** (**noor** ahn). It carries nerve impulses, or messages, from one part of your body to another. A typical neuron, as illustrated in Figure 10-1, has three parts: a **cell body**, which controls the growth of the nerve cell; **dendrites** (**den** drytz), short, branched fibers that carry nerve messages toward the cell body; and an **axon** (**ak** sahn), a long, thin fiber that carries messages away from the cell body. Axons are sometimes called nerve fibers. Bundles of these fibers bound together by connective tissue are known as **nerves**.

Look again at Figure 10-1. As you can see, there are three kinds of neurons: sensory neurons, interneurons, and motor neurons. **Sensory neurons** are nerve cells that pick up information about your body—your skin, your muscles, your sense organs, and your internal organs. They carry this information to the **interneurons**, nerve cells found only in your brain or spinal cord. These interneurons receive the sensory messages and send responses to your **motor neurons**, nerve cells that tell your muscles or glands to act.

Interneurons, then, act as a type of central receiving area for your nervous system. The two areas where interneurons are found make up the central nervous system.

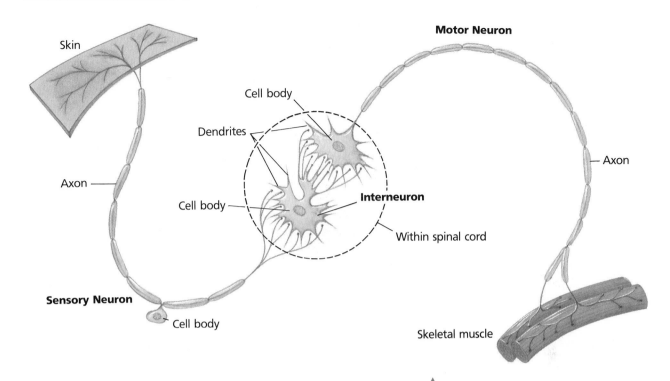

Skin

Motor Neuron

Cell body

Dendrites

Axon

Cell body

Interneuron

Cell body

Within spinal cord

Axon

Sensory Neuron

Cell body

Skeletal muscle

▲

Figure 10-1. Sensory neurons, interneurons, and motor neurons are the three basic types of nerve cells in your body.

The Central Nervous System

The **central nervous system (CNS)**, where the interneurons receive and pass on messages, consists of the brain and the spinal cord. The brain is the control center of the CNS. The spinal cord relays sensory and motor information to and from the brain and other parts of the body.

THE BRAIN   The **brain**, a moist, spongy organ weighing about three pounds (1,400 grams), is made up of 10 billion neurons that control everything you do—your thoughts, your movements, your memory—and everything you sense. The brain produces waves of electrical impulses that vary in length and frequency, depending upon your activity. Every individual has a different brain wave pattern, just as every individual has a different fingerprint.

A thin layer of tough bone, known as the skull, protects the brain. Beneath the skull are three layers of skinlike membranes that completely cover the brain and give it further protection. These membranes are called **meninges** (muh **nin** jeez). **Cerebrospinal** (suh ree broh **spy** nul) **fluid**, a substance found between the middle and inner meninges and in certain spaces within the brain, helps to cushion and protect the brain and spinal cord.

The brain is divided into three areas: the cerebrum, the cerebellum, and the brain stem. The large upper region of the brain is called the **cerebrum** (suh **ree** brum). Its surface is folded into many ridges and depressions like the shell of

Ten billion neurons make up your brain, the organ that controls your thoughts, your movements, and your memory.

O—⊤

The cerebrum controls muscular movement, reasoning, and memory and interprets messages from the senses.

a walnut. As you can see in Figure 10-2, the cerebrum consists of a number of different, specialized regions. Some regions control muscular movement; others control memory and reasoning. Some regions receive messages from the sense organs. These regions interpret the messages as smells, tastes, touch sensations, sights, and sounds.

The cerebrum itself is divided into left and right sides, known as the left hemisphere and the right hemisphere. The outside layer of each of the hemispheres is a thin layer of tissue, called gray matter. This tissue completely covers the cerebrum. The rest of the cerebrum is made of white matter, the same soft tissue that makes up most of the brain.

Nerve fibers from each hemisphere pass down through the brain and spinal cord and cross to the opposite side of the brain or spinal cord at some point along their pathway. Because of this crossing over, the right hemisphere of your brain controls the muscles on the left side of your body, and the left hemisphere controls muscles on the right side of your body. If a person received an injury to the left side of the cerebrum, which side of the body would be affected?

O—⊤

The cerebellum coordinates the movements of your muscles.

The **cerebellum** (sehr uh **bel** um), just beneath the back part of the cerebrum, coordinates your muscles for movement. Like the cerebrum, the cerebellum has an outer layer of gray matter and an interior of white matter. Unlike the rest of the brain, which produces signals that trigger reactions in other parts of the nervous system, the cerebellum processes and then reduces or stops some of these signals. By adjusting the signals, the cerebellum can coordinate the

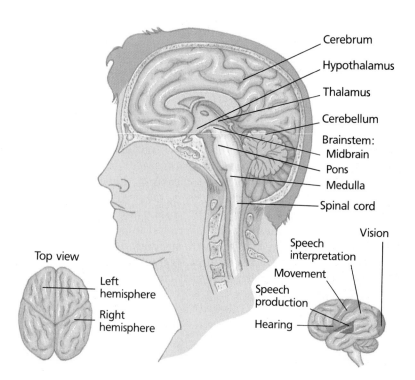

Figure 10-2. Your brain controls everything you do. What activities does the cerebellum control?

movement of your muscles. Without the cerebellum's work, simple movements, such as picking up a glass of water without spilling it or walking without staggering, would be impossible for you.

The **brain stem**, located below the cerebellum at the base of the skull, acts as the body's life support system. It controls heartbeat, breathing, and blood pressure. As you can see in Figure 10-2, the brain stem has several parts. Each part shares some of its functions with the others. The **medulla** (muh **duhl** uh) controls breathing, heart rate, and swallowing. The **pons** regulates breathing and helps to control eye movement. The **midbrain** is also linked to vision. It controls the movement of the eye and pupil size.

Two smaller parts of the brain, the thalamus and the hypothalamus, grow out from the brain stem. The **thalamus** (**thal** uh mus) is a relay station for the senses. It processes information from the sense organs and provides some control over muscle activity. The **hypothalamus** (hy poh **thal** uh mus), another bundle of nerve fibers, regulates the body's temperature, use of water, blood pressure, and the release of regulatory chemicals.

SPINAL CORD   The **spinal cord**, the other part of the central nervous system, is simply a rod of brain tissue. It extends about two-thirds of the way down the back to just below the ribs. As you look at Figure 10-4, you will notice that, like the brain, the spinal cord is covered with three meninges and bathed in cerebrospinal fluid. More than 24

▲ **Figure 10-3. A healthy nervous system enables body movements to be well-coordinated.**

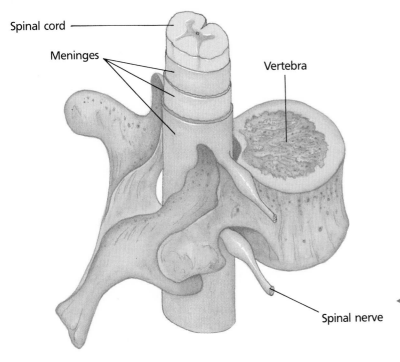

Spinal cord

Meninges

Vertebra

Spinal nerve

◀ **Figure 10-4. The spinal cord connects the brain with the rest of your body. What protects the spinal cord from injury?**

ring-shaped bones, called **vertebrae** (**vur** tuh bree), make up the spinal column, which protects the spinal cord and allows you to bend and turn.

Thirty-one pairs of threadlike nerves branch off the spinal cord. These nerves connect the CNS with almost every part of the body. Messages traveling along these nerves move at more than 300 feet (91.4 meters) per second. The speed with which the nerves send messages enables you to react quickly in an emergency.

The pairs of nerves that branch off from your spinal cord connect with almost every part of your body.

The Peripheral Nervous System

The **peripheral** (puh **rif** ur ul) **nervous system (PNS)**, the other half of the entire nervous system, includes all the parts of the nervous system except the brain and spinal cord. The PNS is made up of the **cranial** (**kray** nee ul) **nerves** and the **spinal nerves**. The cranial nerves are 12 pairs of nerves that emerge from the brain. Those that connect with your eyes, ears, and nose contain mostly sensory nerve fibers. The other cranial nerves are made up of sensory and motor nerve fibers. Spinal nerves are 31 pairs of nerves that branch off from the spinal cord. Each pair serves a particular part of your body. One pair of spinal nerves, for example, accelerates the heartbeat; another pair relaxes the bladder.

Like the central nervous system, the PNS is divided into two parts: the somatic nervous system and the autonomic nervous system. The **somatic nervous system** is responsible for actions that you control. The **autonomic nervous system** controls your heartbeat, breathing, and digestion. These are actions that you do not usually control.

Disorders of the Nervous System

A severe bump to the head can cause the soft brain tissue to come into contact with the skull. This is known as a concussion. Frequently, a concussion is accompanied by a small, hairline crack in the skull. Although paleness, and dizziness are two signs of concussion, more serious signs are vomiting, sleepiness, and unconsciousness. A concussion may result in a coma, a prolonged period of unconsciousness.

Headaches, as common as they are, are also a disorder of the nervous system. Tension headaches are felt at the base of the skull or at the front or on the sides of the head. When the blood vessels around the brain dilate, or swell, a **migraine** (**my** grayn) headache occurs. A migraine headache first throbs with each heartbeat, then becomes a steady pain that may continue for several hours or even a day or more. A person with a migraine is usually sensitive to light and noise and may experience nausea and blurring of vision.

The name given to disorders of the nervous system that occur early in life is **cerebral palsy** (suh **ree** brul **pawl** zee).

▲
Figure 10-5. People once thought of a headache as it is shown in this early drawing.

These disorders result in a lack of full control of physical movement. The causes of cerebral palsy vary from a lack of oxygen at birth to head injury and meningitis.

Occasionally, the electrical impulses produced by the brain become disturbed. This causes a condition known as **epilepsy** (ep uh lep see). The sudden storm of electrical activity in the brain results in an epileptic attack, or **seizure.** During a severe seizure, the individual may lose consciousness, the arms and legs may jerk, and the teeth may lock together. A milder form of epilepsy causes only one or two seconds of unconsciousness, much like daydreaming, when the person stares or stiffens momentarily.

Spinal cord injuries can result in paralysis, or the loss of the ability to move or have sensation in some part of the body. Paralysis occurs when some nerves are so damaged that they no longer can signal the muscles they control.

Meningitis (men in **jy** tis), an inflammation of the meninges of the brain or spinal cord, may be caused by a bacterial infection or a virus. Before antibiotics were discovered, the bacterial form of the disease was fatal. Symptoms include high fever, severe headache, vomiting without nausea, stiff neck and back, and sometimes spotting of the skin.

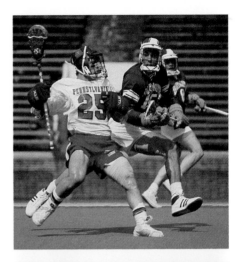

Keeping the Nervous System Healthy

Since your nervous system controls your actions and thoughts, it is important for you to keep it functioning well. Rest, sleep, good nutrition, and daily exercise help to keep your nervous system in good condition. Mind-altering substances, such as drugs or alcohol, can cause permanent damage to your nervous system.

Following a few basic safety rules will also help you to protect your nervous system. Wear your seat belt every time you are in a car. Do not risk a head or spinal injury by diving in unfamiliar swimming areas. Be sure to wear protective head gear when you work on mechanical equipment, play contact sports, or ride a bicycle or motorcycle.

Section Review

1. What is another name for a nerve cell?
2. Name three types of nerve cells and their functions.
3. Name the two parts of the central nervous system. Identify the parts of the peripheral nervous system.

What Do You Think?

4. Do you engage in activities in which you should take precautions to protect your nervous system?

▲
Figure 10-6. Protective head gear is required in situations where there is risk of head injury.

Figure 10-7. All physical activities involve bones and muscles working together in a coordinated fashion.

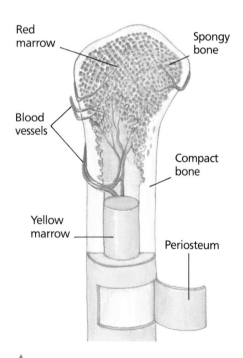

Red marrow

Spongy bone

Blood vessels

Compact bone

Yellow marrow

Periosteum

Figure 10-8. Bones are made of a number of different tissues. What are two bone tissues?

2. THE SKELETAL AND MUSCULAR SYSTEMS

You probably take your ability to move for granted, but what holds you erect or allows you to collapse into the nearest chair? The bones that make up your skeleton are one thing. They support your body and give it shape, but they cannot move your body. Your muscles can. Because your bones and muscles work together, you can sit in a chair, play the piano, or lift weights.

The Skeletal System

The skeletal system, the bones of the body, shields the important parts of your body and gives your body shape. Your skull protects your brain; your ribs protect your heart and lungs; your backbone protects your spinal cord. There are approximately 206 bones in this protective skeletal system. Each one is made of nonliving mineral matter, mostly calcium, and living tissue with blood vessels and nerves.

THE STRUCTURE OF BONES Before you are born, your skeleton first appears as **cartilage** (**kar** tuh lij), a tough, supportive tissue, similar to bone but softer and more flexible. Feel, for example, the cartilage in your ears. It is softer and more flexible than the bone in your arm, but it still offers support. Gradually, minerals, such as calcium and phosphorus, are deposited within most of the cartilage in your body, and it changes to bone. This process, which starts before birth and continues until you are 20 to 25 years old, is called **ossification** (ahs uh fih **kay** shun). As you grow older, your bones can become thinner. This condition is called **osteoporosis** (ahs tee oh puh **roh** sis), the thinning of the bones.

As you can see in Figure 10-8, all of your bones are covered with a tough membrane called the **periosteum** (pehr ee **ahs** tee um). The periosteum contains bone-forming cells that produce new bone for growth and repair. Blood vessels run through the periosteum, branch into the bone, and nourish the cells of the bone. Beneath the periosteum are two types of bony tissue. The outer layer is a strong, dense material called compact bone. The inner layer, known as spongy bone, is made of the same material, but it contains many hollow spaces. Because of these hollow spaces, spongy bone acts as a shock absorber for the rest of the bone. Some of your bones produce blood cells. A soft tissue called **marrow** (**ma** roh) fills the spaces inside the hollow bones and hollow spaces within spongy bone. There are two types of marrow—red marrow and yellow marrow. Red marrow makes red blood cells and some types of white blood cells. Fat cells make up most of the yellow marrow, which can also make red blood cells in an emergency. Yellow marrow also produces some white blood cells.

To make your study of the human skeleton easier, look at it in two parts, the **axial** (ak see ul) **skeleton** and **appendicular** (ap un **dik** yuh lur) **skeleton**. The axial skeleton includes the skull, vertebral column, ribs, and sternum, or breastbone. The bones of the arms, legs, shoulders, and hips make up the appendicular skeleton. Figure 10-9 identifies the major bones in the axial skeleton, shown in blue, and the major bones in the appendicular skeleton, shown in red. Is your clavicle a part of the axial or appendicular skeleton?

Your skeletal system gives shape, support, and protection to your body.

Figure 10-9. The human skeleton provides the framework to support the rest of your body.

▼

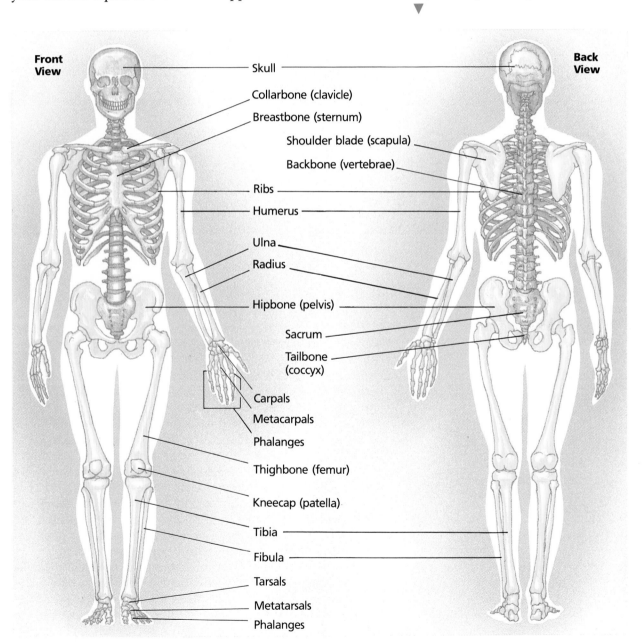

Front View

Back View

Skull
Collarbone (clavicle)
Breastbone (sternum)
Shoulder blade (scapula)
Backbone (vertebrae)
Ribs
Humerus
Ulna
Radius
Hipbone (pelvis)
Sacrum
Tailbone (coccyx)
Carpals
Metacarpals
Phalanges
Thighbone (femur)
Kneecap (patella)
Tibia
Fibula
Tarsals
Metatarsals
Phalanges

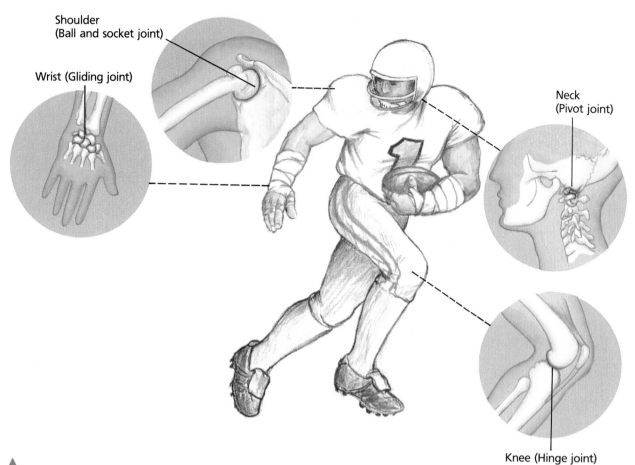

Shoulder
(Ball and socket joint)

Wrist (Gliding joint)

Neck
(Pivot joint)

Knee (Hinge joint)

Figure 10-10. Movable joints allow you to bend, twist, and turn. What type of joint is your knee?

The different types of movable joints in your body make a variety of movements possible for you.

JOINTS A **joint** is the point at which two bones come together. The joints in your body may be classified according to the type of movement they permit. Joints in which the bones are so tightly fitted together that they cannot move are called immovable joints. Joints that allow the bones to bend, twist, or turn are known as movable joints. Figure 10-10 illustrates the four kinds of movable joints: the hinge, the ball-and-socket, the pivot, and the gliding joint. Your fingers, knees, and elbows have hinge joints, which permit these bones to move back and forth. Your hips and shoulders have ball-and-socket joints. This type of joint allows movement in all directions. A pivot joint, like the one found in your neck, allows some bones to move from side to side and up and down. Your wrists and ankles are flexible because the bones there have gliding joints. A gliding joint allows bones to slide over one another. Strong, fibrous bands, called **ligaments**, prevent the bones from popping apart at these joints.

To keep your bones from rubbing against each other at the joint, they are covered with a smooth layer of tough cartilage. Membranes around the joint produce a secretion called **synovial** (suh **noh** vee ul) **fluid**, which flows over the bones at the joint, reducing wear on the bones.

The Muscular System

Without your muscles, you could not walk, breathe, digest your food, or swallow. Your muscular system even helps to produce heat. When you are cold, you shiver. Shivering is the contraction of your muscles to generate heat.

TYPES OF MUSCLES There are three types of muscles in your body—skeletal, smooth, and cardiac. **Skeletal muscle** is voluntary muscle. You control its movement. It is attached to your bones by thick strands of connective tissue called **tendons**. **Smooth muscle** is involuntary muscle. It works automatically to control movements inside your body, such as breathing, digestion, and blood circulation. Smooth muscle makes up the walls of your stomach, intestines, and blood vessels. **Cardiac muscle**, another involuntary muscle, is found only in the walls of your heart. It is the strongest muscle in your body.

All muscle—skeletal, smooth, and cardiac—causes movement by contracting, or becoming shorter and thicker. To contract, however, your muscles must receive messages from your nervous system. These messages travel along the nerve cells that are attached to your muscles.

When a muscle receives a message from a nerve, the muscle contracts. When the message stops, the muscle relaxes, or lengthens. To react to a message from a nerve, your muscles need a constant supply of energy. They get the energy they need by using some of their glucose or fat.

Your skeletal muscles work in pairs. One contracts as the other relaxes. As you can see in Figure 10-11, tendons at the shoulder and the top of the forearm hold the biceps muscle in place. When the biceps muscle contracts, the tendon attached to the forearm pulls the forearm up, and the triceps muscle relaxes. When the triceps contracts, the forearm straightens, and the biceps relaxes. The tendon that holds

The three types of muscles in your body contract and produce movement when they receive messages from your nervous system.

Figure 10-11. Skeletal muscles work in pairs. What muscles is this athlete using?

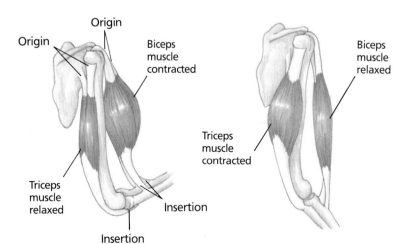

Origin

Origin

Biceps muscle contracted

Biceps muscle relaxed

Triceps muscle contracted

Triceps muscle relaxed

Insertion

Insertion

the biceps muscle to the shoulder is attached to the periosteum at a point known as the **origin**. The origin, then, is the stationary attachment of one end of a muscle to a bone. The tendon at the other end of the biceps is attached to the periosteum of a movable bone, in this case, the humerus, at a point known as the **insertion**. Every skeletal muscle has an origin and an insertion.

Disorders of the Skeletal and Muscular Systems

Because your bones, joints, and muscles get constant use, they sometimes develop problems. Most of these problems occur when you push your skeletal and muscular systems beyond their endurance or you are not properly prepared for an activity. A few problems, however, occur as a result of disease or poor development.

A **fracture** is a break in a bone. The bone may be cracked or broken into two pieces. When the bone does not break through the skin, it is called a closed fracture. In a more serious fracture, a bone end breaks through the surface of the skin. This is known as an open fracture.

When the ligaments around a joint are severely stretched or torn, a bone can pop out of a joint. This kind of injury is a dislocation. Dislocations are common sports injuries. Torn cartilage occurs when the cartilage is pulled away from the bone or muscle by the stress put on a joint.

Curvature of the spine, or **scoliosis** (skoh lee **oh** sis), occurs when the spine develops an abnormal curvature to one side during childhood or adolescence. Although this condition may be inherited, it can also result from certain diseases, such as polio, rheumatoid arthritis, and cerebral palsy. Early symptoms of scoliosis include shoulders that are not level, uneven hips, and an uneven waistline. Sometimes, exercises will improve mild scoliosis. Severe scoliosis may require braces or even surgery.

Muscle strains are tears through part or all of a muscle. Muscle sprains are overstretched or torn ligaments. These injuries occur when your muscles are overworked or stretched too far or too quickly. Sometimes, an injury or a strain on a muscle, low levels of some minerals, such as salt and potassium, poor circulation, or eating just before you exercise can cause all the fibers of a muscle to contract suddenly. This is known as a muscle cramp.

Runners frequently experience shin splints, or tears in the tissue covering the shinbone. Shin splints are caused by a muscle imbalance. The calf muscles that pull the front of the foot down overpower the shin muscles that pull the front of the foot up. The best treatment for shin splints is to strengthen the weaker shin muscles and stretch the stronger calf muscles.

▲
Figure 10-12. Braces or even surgery may be required to treat severe scoliosis.

Keeping the Skeletal and Muscular Systems Healthy

While your bones and muscles are still forming, you need calcium in your diet every day. To absorb calcium efficiently, you need adequate amounts of vitamin D. If you have milk, bread, cereals, and other foods to which vitamin D has been added as a regular part of your diet, you will be better able to absorb the calcium you need.

Exercise keeps your muscles toned and flexible. Although exercise will not increase the number of muscle fibers you have, it does make the individual fibers grow, which, in turn, causes the entire muscle to become thicker.

A 10-minute warm-up period before you exercise increases the blood supply to your muscles, raises their temperature, and makes them more flexible and resistant to injury. After exercising, a cool-down period of mild exercise can prevent muscle problems by gradually stretching the muscles that you have used.

A healthful diet and regular exercise can help to strengthen your bones and muscles.

Section Review

1. What is the major function of the skeletal system?
2. Name two parts of the bone and their functions.
3. Name three kinds of joints.
4. Name three types of muscle and their functions.

What Do You Think?

5. Have you ever experienced a muscle strain or a sprain? How could you avoid such an injury?

3. THE CIRCULATORY AND RESPIRATORY SYSTEMS

The circulatory system, also known as the cardiovascular system, and the respiratory system supply your body with oxygen and nutrients and remove carbon dioxide and other waste products produced by your cells.

The Circulatory System

The circulatory system, shown in Figure 10-14, consists of your heart and a branching network of large and small blood vessels. Your **heart**, which is located in the middle of your rib cage, is the strongest and most efficient muscle in your body. It pumps about six quarts (5.7 liters) of blood per minute throughout your body.

Your blood vessels are the paths for delivering oxygen and blood to your body. If laid out from end to end, there would be over 100,000 miles (160,930 kilometers) of them.

THE HEART Your heart, which is about the size of your fist, has a left and right side that are separated from each other by a thick wall of muscle. Each side has two chambers: an **atrium** (**ay** tree um) and a **ventricle** (**ven** trih kul). The atrium is a small chamber that has valves to separate it from the large ventricle below. The valves allow blood to flow through the heart in one direction only.

In Figure 10-15, you can see that the atrium on the right side of the heart receives oxygen-poor blood from the body. The right ventricle pumps this blood to the lungs. The pathway that blood follows from the heart to the lungs is called

Heart
Artery
Vein
Lung
Spleen
Kidney

Figure 10-14. Blood flows to all regions of your body through the circulatory system.

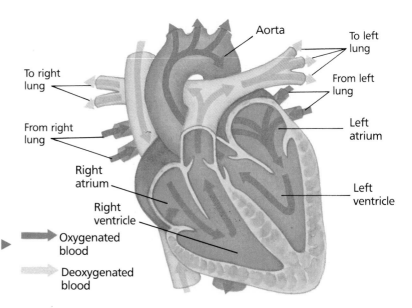

Aorta
To left lung
To right lung
From left lung
From right lung
Left atrium
Right atrium
Left ventricle
Right ventricle

Oxygenated blood

Deoxygenated blood

Figure 10-15. The left and right ventricle both pump blood. Which ventricle pumps oxygen-poor blood to the lungs?

pulmonary circulation. As the blood travels through the lungs, it gains oxygen and gets rid of carbon dioxide.

On the left side of the heart, the left atrium receives oxygen-rich blood from the lungs. This blood passes to the left ventricle where it is pumped out into a large blood vessel, the **aorta** (ay **or** tuh), and from there to all parts of the body except the lungs. The pathway oxygenated blood follows from the heart to all parts of the body is called **systemic** (si **stem** ik) **circulation**. Because the left side of the heart works harder to pump blood throughout the body, the muscles on this side are larger.

In the wall of the right atrium is a node, or group of cells, that acts as a control center for the heart. This **sinoatrial node**, or **SA node**, regulates the heartbeat when it is 60 or more beats per minute. A backup node, the **atrioventricular** (ay tree oh ven **trik** you lur) **node**, or **AV node**, is also in the right atrium. It regulates the heartbeat when it is less than 60 beats per minute. These nodes and a special group of fibers make up the pacemaker, which keeps the heart beating. If the pacemaker begins to malfunction, an artificial pacemaker can be surgically placed inside the person's body. The **artificial pacemaker** delivers an electric shock to the heart at regular intervals to keep it beating.

BLOOD VESSELS **Arteries** are thick-walled, elastic vessels that carry blood away from the heart to the tissues and organs of the body. As an artery enters a tissue or an organ, it divides many times to form smaller arteries, called **arterioles** (ar **teer** ee ohlz). Branching off the arterioles are capillaries, the smallest blood vessels in your body. Oxygen, dissolved nutrients, and various waste products are exchanged between the blood and the body cells when blood flows through the capillaries.

From the capillaries, blood flows into **venules** (**ven** yulz), tiny vessels that join together to form veins. **Veins** (vaynz) are thin-walled, slightly elastic vessels that return blood from the body tissues to the heart. Valves inside the veins allow the blood to flow toward the heart.

As the blood is pushed through your arteries by the beating of your heart, the arteries expand and contract. Your blood pressure is a measurement of the push of blood against the walls of the arteries. When your blood pressure is measured, two different readings are taken. The first, and higher, number is the **systolic** (sis **tahl** ik) **pressure**. The systolic pressure is the amount of force recorded when the ventricles of the heart contract and your heart beats. The second number is the **diastolic** (dy uh **stahl** ik) **pressure**, or the amount of force recorded when the ventricles relax between beats. Although your blood pressure will vary depending on your level of physical activity, an average reading for normal young adults at rest is about 120/80.

Pulmonary circulation involves the flow of blood from the right ventricle to the lungs. Systemic circulation involves the flow of blood from the left ventricle to the rest of the body.

▲
Figure 10-16. Checking blood pressure is advisable at any age. Do you know what your blood pressure is?

The Respiratory System

The respiratory system consists of the lungs and the body's air passages. Together, these organs take in oxygen from the air and remove carbon dioxide.

THE PATHWAY OF AIR   As Figure 10-17 illustrates below, air follows a regular path to reach your **lungs**, two large, elastic organs that consist of tubes, blood vessels, and spongy tissue. As you inhale, air enters your nose where it moves past special moist cells and hairs that warm and clean it. The air then travels to your **larynx** (**la** ringks), or voice box, at the base of your tongue. From there, the air moves into your trachea (**tray** kee uh), or windpipe, and on into your lungs.

The **bronchi**, two cartilage-ringed tubes that branch off the trachea, go to each lung. The bronchi divide and subdivide, like the branches of a tree, into smaller and smaller passages, known as **bronchioles** (**brahng** kee ohlz). At the end of these passages are balloonlike air sacs, called **alveoli** (al **vee** uh ly). These sacs are surrounded by capillaries in which the exchange of oxygen and carbon dioxide occurs. As oxygen moves out of the air sacs into the bloodstream, carbon dioxide moves from the blood into the air sacs.

Your respiratory system supplies oxygen to, and removes carbon dioxide from, your blood.

Figure 10-17. Air moves into and out of your lungs as you breathe. What air passage connects the lungs with the larynx? ▶

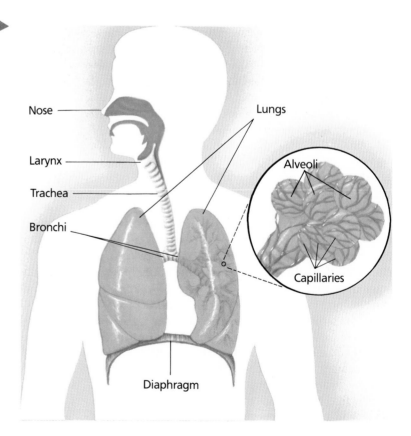

Nose

Larynx

Trachea

Bronchi

Lungs

Alveoli

Capillaries

Diaphragm

BREATHING   Each breath begins with a contraction of the **diaphragm** (**dy** uh fram), a dome-shaped sheet of muscle that lies just below the lungs. When you inhale, your diaphragm contracts, or flattens downward. This contraction creates a vacuum, causing oxygen-rich air to move through the nose and mouth, down the trachea, and into the lungs. When you exhale, your diaphragm relaxes, increasing the pressure on the lungs and forcing air, now filled with carbon dioxide, out of the body.

What causes your diaphragm to contract and relax? As you know, your brain controls everything you do. The small area within the brain stem known as the medulla regulates your breathing. It senses the amount of carbon dioxide in the blood and sends signals to your diaphragm. The more carbon dioxide there is, the faster you breathe.

Disorders of the Circulatory and Respiratory Systems

Most of the time, the circulatory and respiratory systems behave as efficient machines. Occasionally, however, something goes wrong. The heart may become damaged or fail to pump blood efficiently, or blood may not be able to flow smoothly through the vessels. Figure 10-18 illustrates some common circulatory and respiratory problems.

High blood pressure, usually considered to be a diastolic reading above 90 with a systolic pressure of 140 or more, is a common cardiovascular problem among Americans. Some people may experience dizziness, headaches, and nervousness, but many people have no symptoms. Diet, weight, stress, heredity, and exercise are thought to influence your blood pressure.

If the pressure on a vessel wall in the brain becomes so great that the wall breaks, and blood leaks into the surrounding tissues, it is called a **stroke**. Bleeding into delicate brain tissue can cause paralysis and even death.

Heart disease is a term that covers many different cardiac problems, including a malformed heart, which occurs before birth. Heart malformations may take various forms, such as faulty valves and openings between chambers. **Coronary heart disease** results when the arteries of the heart become clogged with cholesterol. When the muscles of your heart do not get enough blood because the arteries are blocked, a heart attack may occur, and some of the muscles of the heart may die. This happens to over 1 million Americans a year.

There are a number of common respiratory disorders that affect people. Pneumonia, for example, is an inflammation of the air-filled alveoli, caused by either a bacterium or a virus. The disease results in a buildup of fluid in the air sacs, which lessens the lungs' ability to take in oxygen and

Atherosclerosis and Apo-B

Approximately one-half of all deaths in the United States are caused by atherosclerosis, or hardening of the arteries. Atherosclerosis results when blood vessels become clogged with deposits of cholesterol. If untreated, this disease can lead to heart attack or stroke.

Cholesterol travels through the body in tiny protein-containing packets called lipoproteins. There are two types of lipoproteins, low density lipoproteins (LDL) and high density lipoproteins (HDL). Scientists know that LDL, rather than HDL, plays an important role in causing heart disease.

A new study now suggests that the real villain in cardiovascular disease may be the protein found in LDL, called apolipoprotein B-100 (apo-B). Researchers think that the structure and concentration of apo-B in the blood may determine if a person will fall victim to heart disease. Studies have shown that people with high apo-B levels are likely to have heart trouble, even if they have normal cholesterol and LDL levels. Scientists are now developing a method for measuring apo-B levels in the blood to help evaluate a person's risk of heart disease.

Compare the normal artery (left) with the clogged artery (right).

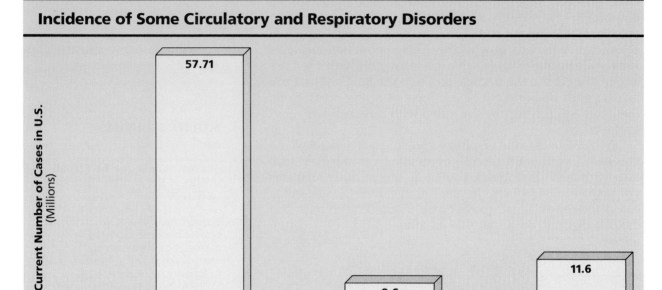

Incidence of Some Circulatory and Respiratory Disorders

Current Number of Cases in U.S. (Millions)

Heart attack	High blood pressure	Stroke	Asthma	Emphysema	Bronchitis
4.81	57.71	1.96	8.6	2.08	11.6

▲

Figure 10-18. Heart and lung diseases affect many Americans. Which disease listed in the chart affects the most individuals?

get rid of carbon dioxide. Although symptoms of pneumonia vary, they may include cough, fever, chills, sweating, and shortness of breath.

Bronchitis occurs when a cold invades the mucous membranes lining the bronchi. The membranes respond by becoming inflamed and secreting a thick sticky mucus. Hoarseness and coughing are some of the symptoms of bronchitis. People who smoke are more susceptible to this disease than nonsmokers.

Asthma (**az** muh) and **emphysema** (em fuh **see** muh) are two breathing disorders that are not brought about by illness. Emphysema is a breathing disorder in which the small air sacs in the lungs lose their elasticity. Asthma may be an allergic reaction to a substance. It causes wheezing, coughing, and difficulty in breathing. During an attack, the muscles in the bronchioles go into spasms, squeezing the air passages.

Developing Healthy Circulatory and Respiratory Systems

You can start now to build strong circulatory and respiratory systems. Diet, exercise, stress, weight, and life style all affect your circulatory and respiratory systems. A diet low in cholesterol and other animal fats helps to prevent clogged arteries, which force the heart to work harder. Maintaining

a body weight that is appropriate for you and avoiding alcohol and tobacco will also help ensure the health of your circulatory and respiratory systems.

A program of regular exercise can help to strengthen these two systems and relieve stress, which can cause the blood vessels to constrict and result in high blood pressure. Regular exercise causes your heart to pump more efficiently. Working muscles take oxygen from the blood more easily. Exercise helps you to maintain healthy respiratory and circulatory systems. Fast walking, swimming, biking, and cross-country skiing are forms of exercise that you may enjoy.

Some people benefit from relaxation exercises that combine deep breathing and muscle stretches to relieve stress. These exercises help to loosen tight muscles. Other people find that sharing their feelings of anger, fear, anxiety and frustration with a trusted friend or family member helps them to relax and eases stress.

A balanced diet and regular exercise can improve the health of your circulatory and respiratory systems.

Section Review

1. Identify the chambers of the heart. What is the function of each chamber?
2. What is the difference between arteries and veins?
3. What is the function of the respiratory system?
4. Trace the flow of air to the lungs.

What Do You Think?
5. Do you have any habits that may improve or harm your circulatory or respiratory systems?

4. THE IMPORTANCE OF FITNESS

Do you think you are physically fit? You may think that a program of vigorous exercise leads to fitness. Certainly it helps you to become fit, but it is not the only factor. Rest, sleep, and good nutrition help your body to build and repair itself and prepare you for exercise.

When you are physically fit, your body's systems work as a team, allowing you to breathe easily and contract your muscles in coordinated movement. **Physical fitness** is the ability of the heart, blood vessels, lungs, and muscles to work together to meet the body's needs. Everyone—from the handicapped to the athlete—can be physically fit.

Although there are tests that will measure the fitness of your heart, blood vessels, and lungs, there may be some that you cannot perform. This does not mean that you are not physically fit. It does mean that these tests do not meet your particular needs. Perhaps your doctor or gym instructor can suggest alternatives for you.

Health careers

Coaches help athletes perform at peak levels.

If you participate in any sport, you know the importance of the **coach**, the person who trains you to become a better athlete.

During practice sessions, coaches teach athletes the techniques of their sport. In competition, coaches decide who will play, when they will play, and what strategies to use. Coaches also motivate their players to master their sport and to excel.

Many coaches work in schools, where they teach classes as well as coach sports. Some coaches move on to work with professional athletes. To become a coach, you must complete a four-year college program in health and physical education and then become certified by your state as a teacher.

Another person who trains people in athletics is the **fitness instructor**. Fitness instructors work in health spas, gyms, hotels, and camps, where they plan programs in sports like aerobics or weight training. To become a fitness instructor a person needs either a college degree in adult fitness or a high-school diploma and thorough on-the-job training.

Components of Fitness

There are four components, or parts, to fitness. They are cardiorespiratory endurance, muscular strength, muscular endurance, and flexibility. **Cardiorespiratory endurance** is the ability of your heart, blood vessels, and lungs to deliver nutrients and oxygen to your muscles and to remove wastes. When you exercise, your heart and lungs must supply more oxygen to your muscles than they need when you are resting. Your heart, for example, pumps 5 to 6 quarts (4.7 to 5.7 liters) of blood per minute when you are at rest and 20 to 25 quarts (18.9 to 23.6 liters) when you are exercising.

Muscular strength is the ability of a muscle to exert or resist a force. Muscular strength is basic to all sports and many everyday activities. When you push, pull, or lift an object, for example, your muscles are exerting a force. **Muscular endurance** is the ability of a muscle or a group of muscles to apply force over a period of time. When you rake leaves, shovel snow, or do sit-ups, you are performing acts of muscular endurance.

Flexibility is the ability to use a muscle throughout its entire range of motion. This means that you can bend, stretch, and twist your joints easily. If your muscles are flexible, you are less apt to become stiff when you exercise. You can also improve your flexibility through a program of slow, steady stretching, followed by a brisk walk.

Measuring Fitness

Now that you know the components of fitness, you may want to try to measure your own fitness. Each of the following tests is designed to find out about one or more components of fitness. Keep in mind that individual differences, such as age, weight, height, bone structure, and muscle and fat distribution affect your performance.

You can rate your cardiorespiratory endurance, or the ability of your heart and lungs to supply your body with oxygen, by using the step test. For this test, you need a partner with a stopwatch and a sturdy box or stair that measures about 8 inches (20.3 centimeters) high. Before you take the test, count your pulse. To count your pulse, find your pulse with your forefinger and middle finger either on the inside of your wrists or under your jawbone on your neck, as illustrated in Figure 10-20. Count the beats for one minute and record the count.

Now, step up on the box or stair with one foot; then bring your other foot up. Take your first foot down and then the other foot. Continue stepping on and off the step every two seconds for three minutes. Have your partner count the seconds for you. If you experience pain, shortness of breath, or dizziness while taking the test, stop at once. Otherwise,

Cardiorespiratory endurance, muscular strength, muscular endurance, and flexibility are the four components of physical fitness.

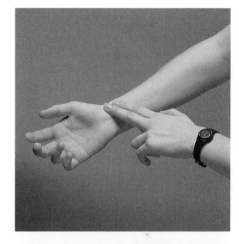

▲ **Figure 10-20. Checking your pulse is a skill you can easily learn. What is your resting pulse rate?**

Step Test

Rating	Pulse rate (30 seconds)
Outstanding	50 or less
Excellent	51–55
Good	56–60
Average	61–65
Fair	66–70
Low	71–75
Poor	76 plus

Figure 10-21. You can rate your fitness by comparing your test results with this chart.

complete the test, then count your pulse for 60 seconds. This count will allow you to compare your heart rate before and after exercising. As you can see in Figure 10-21, the lower your score, the better your heart recovers from strain.

To measure your muscular strength and endurance, lie on your back with your knees bent. Lock your hands behind your head and have your partner hold your feet flat on the floor. Carefully curl your back and raise your trunk until your lower back is perpendicular to the floor. Then, lower yourself to the starting position. Do as many of these sit-ups as you can in 60 seconds. Look at Figure 10-22 to find your score.

You can determine your general flexibility by taking the sit-and-reach test. Sit with your legs straight and your feet flat against a box. Bend forward from the waist while stretching your arms forward as far as you can. Hold this position for a count of three. Have a partner use a ruler to measure the distance you reach. If you cannot reach, or can only reach, the edge of the box, your score will be negative. If you reach beyond the edge, your score will be positive. Check the chart in Figure 10-23 to find your degree of flexibility.

Figure 10-22. How good is your muscular strength and endurance?

Sit-ups

Rating	Girls	Boys
Outstanding	40+	45+
Excellent	35–39	40–44
Good	30–34	35–39
Average	25–29	30–34
Fair	20–24	25–29
Low	15–19	20–24
Poor	Less than 15	Less than 20

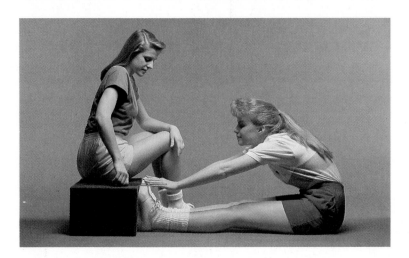

Sit-and-Reach Test		
Rating	Girls	Boys
Good	+2 to +4 in.	+1 to +3 in.
Fair	−1 to +2 in.	−3 to +1 in.
Low	−4 to −2 in.	−6 to −3 in.

▲
Figure 10-23. Flexibility is an important part of fitness. What is your level of flexibility?

The FIT Principle

Having some idea of how you rate in the areas of cardiorespiratory endurance, muscular strength and endurance, and flexibility is the first step in setting up a fitness program geared to your needs. As you learn more about setting up such a program in Chapter 11, you may find it helpful to retest yourself. As you improve in each component of fitness, you may notice some changes in yourself. You may find that you look better, sleep better, and feel more alive.

Even though your fitness program should be geared to meet your needs, all fitness programs should contain three basic ingredients. These ingredients make up the FIT principle, which stands for **f**requency, **i**ntensity, and **t**ime. To stay physically fit, you should exercise frequently, at least four times a week. To stimulate your heart, lungs, and muscles, you must work your cardiorespiratory and muscular systems with greater-than-normal effort, or intensity. This means raising your heart rate during exercise. Finally, you must exercise a certain amount of time during each exercise period. Most research suggests that 20 to 30 minutes of vigorous exercise four times a week will lead to greater fitness.

Applying the FIT principle to your life is a helpful way of achieving physical fitness.

Section Review

1. What are the four components to fitness?
2. List the factors that might affect your performance on fitness tests.
3. Describe two tests that can be used to rate different types of endurance.

What Do You Think?
4. Explain how you could use the FIT principle in your own exercise program.

10 ▮ Chapter Review

Chapter Summary

- The nervous system consists of the central nervous system, which contains the brain and spinal cord, and the peripheral nervous system, which contains the cranial nerves and the spinal nerves.
- The human skeletal system consists of the axial skeleton—the skull, vertebral column, ribs, and sternum—and the appendicular skeleton—the bones of the arms, legs, shoulders, and hips.
- The bones provide support and shape for the body, attachment for muscles, and protection for organs.
- Most of the body's cartilage gradually changes to bone during the process of ossification.
- There are four types of movable joints in the body. These are known as hinge, ball-and-socket, pivot, and gliding.
- The body has over 600 muscles that are either skeletal, smooth, or cardiac. When muscles receive messages from nerve cells, they contract, producing movement.

- Skeletal muscles work in pairs, contracting and relaxing, to produce movement.
- The circulatory system consists of the heart and the blood vessels.
- The respiratory system consists of the lungs and the body's air passages.
- Breathing results from contractions and relaxations of the diaphragm.
- Together, the circulatory and respiratory systems supply the body with oxygen and nutrients and remove carbon dioxide and other waste products.
- Fitness is the ability of the heart, muscles, blood vessels, and lungs to work well together to meet the body's needs.
- The components of fitness are cardiorespiratory endurance, muscular strength, muscular endurance, and flexibility.
- Exercise should meet the FIT principle, which includes frequency (at least four times a week), intensity (greater than normal effort), and time (20 to 30 minutes).

Vocabulary Review

Listed below are some of the important terms in this chapter. Choose the term that best matches the phrase in the exercise that follows.

artery	cerebrum	larynx	periosteum
asthma	CNS	lungs	physical fitness
axon	diaphragm	marrow	pons
capillary	flexibility	muscular strength	scoliosis
cerebellum	joint	neuron	vein

1. ability to use a muscle throughout its entire range of motion

2. brain and spinal cord

3. curvature of the spine

4. blood vessel that returns blood from the body tissues to the heart

5. breathing disorder in which the muscles in the bronchioles go into spasms and the air passages become squeezed

6. part of neuron that carries messages away from the cell body

7. muscle used in breathing

8. part of the brain that coordinates muscles for movement

9. point at which one or more bones meet

10. ability of the heart, muscles, blood vessels, and lungs to work well together to meet the body's needs

What Have You Learned?

1. Identify and describe the parts of a neuron.
2. Distinguish between the somatic nervous system and the autonomic nervous system. To what system do they belong?
3. Distinguish a migraine headache from a tension headache.
4. List three ways you can protect your nervous system.
5. Describe the structure of a typical bone. Where are blood cells produced in a bone?

6. Describe the two major parts of the human skeleton.
7. What is cartilage and where can it be found in the body?
8. Distinguish a tendon from a ligament.
9. Distinguish between pulmonary circulation and systemic circulation.
10. What is the aorta?
11. How is the diaphragm used in breathing?
12. What factors help you to become fit?

What Do You Think?

1. Why is being physically fit important today? Which do you believe our society puts greater emphasis on, sickness or fitness? Why?
2. Why are not more Americans physically fit? What might be done to bring about a greater emphasis on fitness in our society?

3. Why do you think so many people have high blood pressure?
4. How can alcohol and other drugs permanently damage your nervous system?
5. How might smoking and air pollution lead to respiratory problems?

What Would You Do?

1. You notice that one of your sister's shoulders is lower than the other. Her waistline appears to be thicker on one side than the other. What might have caused these changes? What would you urge your sister to do?
2. Your friend mentioned that his father, who is overweight and gets little exercise, seems nervous and has complained of dizziness lately. Your friend seems puzzled by his father's sudden change in behavior. Can you suggest some reasons for the change?
3. Your soccer coach insists that you follow

every practice session with a period of stretching exercises. Why?
4. What advice would you offer a classmate who wants to remain physically fit even though she has broken her ankle and will be in a cast for several weeks?
5. Your friend insists that there is no reason to exercise when he keeps in shape by eating the right foods, watching his weight, avoiding alcohol and tobacco, and doing yard work. Would you agree with your friend? Why or why not?

For Further Study

1. Research and report on the use of arthroscopic surgery in removing damaged cartilage. Alternatively, find out more about artificial joints, such as the artificial hip, and report your findings to the class.
2. Go to a physical therapy unit in a hospital or sports medicine clinic to see the types of therapies and artificial limbs used for injuries. Report on topics such as the electrostimulation of paralyzed muscles, exercises for nervous system disorders, and the progress that has been made in the design of artificial limbs.

11

As you read, think about

▶ what benefits you derive from a program of regular exercise.

▶ how you can determine your fitness progress.

▶ what happens during the sleep cycle and how you can improve the quality of your sleep.

Fitness and Your Life Style

Y ou're beginning to get it right at last. Your practice is paying off, and now you realize what the ancient art of Tai Chi is all about. You're relaxed but alert; your mind and muscles are working in harmony. Your motion is slow and controlled, but you feel the strength of your movements. As you concentrate on centering your weight on one foot, you swing around easily, and your other foot moves up smoothly in a perfect arc.

Tai Chi, other martial arts, aerobics, and various exercise programs can contribute to your physical fitness. A part of staying fit, however, is getting enough sleep. You need both activity and rest to stay healthy. In this chapter, you will learn about finding a fitness program that is right for you. You will also explore why you need sleep and the disorders that sometimes interfere with it.

By choosing activities you enjoy, fitness can become a natural part of your life.

1. EXERCISE AND YOU

Because your body was made for activity, stimulating your muscles, bones, heart, lungs, and blood vessels with regular exercise is as important to your health as getting enough rest and eating nutritious foods. Regular exercise helps you to stay at or move toward the wellness end of the Illness-Wellness continuum.

The Benefits of Exercise

What happens inside you when you run, swim, hike, or enjoy some other form of exercise? As the muscles in your arms, shoulders, or legs alternately contract and relax, they burn food to generate the energy they need. Because your muscles are using up energy more quickly than when you are sitting still, they need to be supplied more rapidly with food and oxygen. To meet the increased needs of your muscles, your heart beats two to three times its normal resting rate. You breathe more rapidly and deeply. The flow of blood to your heart, lungs, and skeletal muscles increases as your blood vessels dilate, or widen. Your blood pressure and body temperature rise, and you begin to sweat.

PHYSICAL BENEFITS Because blood circulates more rapidly through vessels dilated from exercise, it brings oxygen and nutrients to, and removes wastes from, your body more quickly. This increased circulation is one reason why you feel refreshed and energetic after a hard workout. Over time, exercise that increases your heart and breathing rates may increase the number of capillaries in your body.

When you run, swim, or do other endurance types of exercise on a regular basis, you strengthen your entire body. Your heart, for example, becomes stronger and pumps blood more efficiently. Your back and abdominal muscles become stronger, and stronger back and abdominal muscles help to protect you against back pain. Strong abdominal muscles also help to hold the stomach and intestines in place and are important for good digestion and elimination.

Not only does regular exercise strengthen your muscles, it also strengthens your bones. As you exercise, you place some pressure and stress on your bones. This causes them to deposit extra calcium and phosphorus along the lines of stress. As your bones become thicker and denser, they become stronger. This means, for example, that if you run or walk regularly, the bones in your legs gradually become stronger. In fact, any bone you place some pressure and stress on through regular exercise becomes thicker and stronger. If you play squash, racquetball, or tennis frequently, the bones in the arm you use for play will be thicker and stronger than those in the other arm.

Figure 11-1. Regardless of age, people can enjoy regular exercise to stay fit.

As you know from Chapter 9, weight loss or weight maintenance is more successful when you follow a program of regular exercise. A regular workout that you repeat every day for at least 30 minutes will help to replace fat tissue with muscle tissue.

PSYCHOLOGICAL BENEFITS Have you ever experienced a sense of physical and emotional exhilaration after a hard workout? This feeling results from more than just knowing that you have done something good for your health. It is at least partly the result of certain substances called **endorphins** (en **dor** funs) that are produced in your brain. Endorphins, which are sometimes described as your body's natural painkillers, help to produce a sense of satisfaction and pleasure within you. When you engage in vigorous endurance exercise, cells within your brain produce greater amounts of these endorphins.

Peer pressure, hormonal changes, and the expectations of teachers or parents can make life seem overwhelming at times when you are a teenager. A program of regular exercise, tailored to your particular needs, can help you handle this stress. Simple stretching exercises, for example, can help you to relax tense muscles and allow you to sleep better, which is also important in reducing stress and achieving a healthy appearance. Recent studies have noted that people who exercise on a regular basis are likely to sleep better, feel more self-confident, be better able to cope with stress, and focus more productively on their work.

Regular exercise can help you to feel good, reduce stress, and work more productively.

Some Benefits of Regular Exercise	
Physical Benefits	**Psychological Benefits**
1. increases muscle strength and endurance 2. increases efficiency of heart and lungs 3. increases physical stamina 4. increases bone strength 5. improves appearance 6. improves posture 7. reduces blood pressure 8. reduces risk of cardiovascular disease 9. helps in losing excess body fat 10. helps to maintain desired body weight 11. helps to control appetite 12. increases resistance to muscle and bone injury	1. improves mental alertness 2. increases ability to concentrate 3. increases resistance to mental fatigue 4. improves self-image 5. improves self-confidence 6. helps to relieve stress and to improve relaxation 7. helps to control anxiety and depression 8. improves quality of sleep

Figure 11-2. Regular exercise offers physical and psychological benefits. Which of these benefits are you most interested in?

In fact, many health professionals suggest exercise as a treatment for depression. One doctor who prescribed running on a regular basis for depressed patients found that their depression was eased, their need for medicine was lessened, and their dependence on cigarettes or alcohol was reduced or eliminated. Figure 11-2 summarizes all the physical and psychological benefits you may obtain from a regular, vigorous exercise program.

Types of Exercise

There are two major types of exercise—aerobic and anaerobic. **Aerobic exercise** is exercise that involves continuous physical activity lasting for at least 10 minutes. During aerobic exercise, the heart rate and breathing rate become elevated, and the oxygen supplied to the muscles meets the muscles' demand for oxygen.

When you run, swim, skip rope, dance, or do other continuous, rhythmic activities, you breathe rapidly and deeply and bring in more oxygen to your lungs. This increased amount of oxygen is carried through your bloodstream to your muscles, where it is used to burn glucose or fat. When glucose or fat is burned, energy is released to the muscles to carry on their work.

Aerobic activities, such as those pictured in Figure 11-3, involve the large muscles of the body in repeated patterns of motion, as well as increased breathing and heart rates. These types of exercise condition the cardiovascular and respiratory systems but do not improve muscle speed. They can, however, improve your endurance, and lower your blood pressure and heart rate.

Figure 11-3. Aerobic exercises, like running, increase your cardiovascular and respiratory endurance.

Fitness Ratings of Physical Activities

Activity	Cardiorespiratory Endurance	Muscular Strength	Muscular Endurance	Flexibility
Aerobic dancing	3–4	2	2	3
Ballet	3	2	2	4
Baseball/Softball	1	1	1	2
Basketball	3–4	1	2	2
Bicycling (at least 10 mph)	3–4	2	3–4	1
Bowling	1	1	1	2
Calisthenics	3	3–4	3–4	3–4
Canoeing	2–3	3	3	2
Football	2–3	2	2	2
Golf	1	1	1	2
Gymnastics	1	4	3	4
Handball/Squash	3	2	3	2
Hiking (uphill)	3	1	2	2
Hockey	2–3	2	2	2
Horseback riding	1	1	1	2
Jogging/Running (at least 6 mph)	3–4	1	3	2
Judo/Karate	1	2	1	3
Jumping rope	3–4	1	3	2
Racquetball	3–4	1	3	2
Rowing	3–4	3	3	2
Skating (ice, roller)	2–3	1	2–3	2
Skiing (cross-country)	4	2	3–4	2
Skiing (downhill)	3	2	2–3	2
Soccer	3	2	2	2
Swimming	4	2	3	2
Tennis (singles)	3	1	2–3	2
Volleyball	2	1	2	2
Walking (brisk)	3	1	3	2
Weight training	1–2	4	3	2
Wrestling	3–4	2	3	3

Rating scale: 1 = Low, 2 = Moderate, 3 = High, 4 = Very high

To receive the cardiovascular and respiratory benefits of aerobic exercise, you should exercise continuously for 20 to 30 minutes at least three times a week.

Anaerobic (an uh **roh** bik) **exercise** is intense physical activity that lasts only a few seconds to a few minutes. For example, although you may lift weights for an overall time of 15 minutes, the periods of intense physical activity come only when you actually lift the weight. During anaerobic exercise, muscles use up oxygen faster than the blood can supply it even though your heart and breathing rates may be elevated. Anaerobic exercise usually improves movement, strength, and sometimes speed. It does not specifically condition the cardiovascular and respiratory systems. Figure 11-4 compares the fitness benefits you can receive from some activities you may already enjoy.

Figure 11–4. Which of these physical activities rate highest for cardiovascular and muscular endurance?

Aerobic exercises improve breathing and blood circulation. Anaerobic exercises improve muscle strength.

Figure 11–5. Pole-vaulting involves the burst of speed and intense muscular activity typical of an anaerobic exercise.

Most anaerobic exercises are designed to develop specific skills, agility, flexibility, or strength. Lifting weights, sprinting, and some forms of gymnastics, for example, usually are considered anaerobic activities. Some anaerobic exercises may provide cardiovascular and respiratory benefits if they are performed quickly and continuously for prolonged periods of time.

Isotonic (eye suh **tahn** ik), **isometric** (eye suh **met** rik), and **isokinetic** (eye suh kih **net** ik) **exercises** are three kinds of exercise that can increase strength and endurance in specific groups of muscles. Fitness experts usually consider these exercises to be anaerobic, although with constant repetition, some can be aerobic.

Isotonic exercises involve the contraction and relaxation of muscles through the full range of their motion. These exercises are performed with or without weights and are repeated to develop muscle strength. An example of isotonic exercise is bending and straightening your arm.

Isometric exercises are exercises in which a muscle contracts but does not shorten. If you push against a wall or place your palms together and push them against each other, you are performing an isometric exercise. There is no movement, but your muscles are contracting and thus working. If you continue this exercise over a long period of time, the result will be greater strength in your chest and arms. Isometric exercises increase strength, but only at the joint angle at which the exercise is performed.

Isokinetic exercises are other forms of exercise that make use of special types of weight-training machines. These exercises involve muscle movements performed at a constant rate of speed through the full range of muscle movement. Isokinetic exercises are used for physical therapy and rehabilitation. Athletes who have injured themselves sometimes use weight-training machines during rehabilitation.

Section Review

1. What kinds of changes occur in your body during vigorous exercise?
2. List three physical benefits of regular exercise. Then list three psychological benefits.
3. How does aerobic exercise differ from anaerobic exercise? Classify running, swimming, gymnastics, lifting weights, cycling, and sprinting as either aerobic or anaerobic types of exercise.

What Do You Think?
4. How would you convince a friend that he or she should start an exercise program?

2. FINDING THE RIGHT EXERCISE PROGRAM

Now that you know the physical and mental benefits of exercise, you may want to set up your own exercise program. It should be based on the fitness ratings you received in Chapter 10 and your own interests, abilities, and needs. This means that you must decide what you want to gain from an exercise program before you set up the program.

Defining Your Goals

Do you want to increase your stamina, have a trimmer body, achieve better coordination, or just feel more alert? Your goals help to determine the best exercise program for you. If your goal is to strengthen muscles, for example, your program will probably include lifting weights or using a strength-training machine. In other words, you may want more anaerobic exercise than aerobic exercise. If your goal is to improve your cardiorespiratory endurance, you may want to develop a program of aerobic exercise in which you have to sustain the proper intensity of exercise and monitor it closely. Jogging, bicycling, swimming, or brisk walking will fit into this type of program. Most likely, you have a combination of goals in mind. For example, you may want to increase your flexibility and endurance in order to set a personal-best record in the five-mile (8 kilometer) race.

As you create your own exercise program, remember that your fitness program should be fun! Choose an activity or sport that you enjoy. Taking up jogging, for example,

▲ **Figure 11-6. Proper instruction and strong arms and shoulders can make gymnastics seem easy.**

◀ **Figure 11-7. Many people aim to gain muscular strength and size with anaerobic exercises.**

A Weekly Exercise Program

Sunday

- Slow 20-minute run around the pond
- Two flights of stairs taken three times

Monday

- 20-minute brisk walk to school
- Gym class at school
- 20-minute walk home

Tuesday

- Walk to school
- 30-minute swim after school
- Walk home

Wednesday

- Bike to school
- Gym class
- 40-minute basketball practice session

Thursday

- 20-minute walk to school
- Basketball game after school

Friday

- Gym class
- 30-minute aerobic dance class
- 20-minute walk home

Saturday

- Leaf raking for 40 minutes
- Slow 20-minute run

▲

Figure 11–8. What changes would you make in this balanced weekly exercise program to suit your special needs?

when you really want to be with other people may improve your cardiorespiratory endurance, but you may become too bored to continue it. You should look forward to your exercise program, or you probably will not stick with it.

You can begin to develop your program by reviewing all the physical activity that is already a part of your life. Suppose, for example, that you walk a half mile (0.8 kilometer) to school each day, swim once a week, and enjoy weekend backpacking or occasional quiet walks on the beach. You already have the basis for an exercise program tailored to your own interests. If you apply the FIT principle from Chapter 10 to these activities, you may discover that while you exercise with a frequency of at least four times a week, there is not enough intensity and time in your program to achieve the most important component of fitness, cardiorespiratory endurance. Since it appears that you enjoy more solitary activities, you may want to continue these activities but pick up your pace and increase your time to 20 or 30 minutes each. You could, for example, try walking home from school by a new, longer route at a brisk pace or take a 30-minute walk in the late afternoon before supper. The chart in Figure 11-8 illustrates how one person built an exercise program around daily activities.

Suppose, on the other hand, that you are on the school basketball team, skateboard with friends for an hour or two, and help out at home by shoveling snow and raking leaves. In this case, you are involved in a number of vigorous, endurance-type exercises, but the intensity and frequency with which you do them varies. Since you enjoy being with friends, why not arrange regular biking or jogging outings with someone whose pace is comparable to yours?

How to Exercise

The FIT guidelines from Chapter 10 will help you to set limits on how often you should exercise, how fast your heart should beat when you exercise, and how long you should spend in an exercise session. Exercises for stretching, warming up, and cooling down help to prevent injuries as you follow the FIT guidelines.

Before you begin any new exercise program, it is a good idea to go over your program with your doctor. Your doctor will tell you whether the program is suited to you and, if not, suggest modifications.

FREQUENCY OF EXERCISE How often you exercise depends on your goals. If you want the cardiorespiratory benefits of aerobic exercise, you should exercise at least four times a week. As you become more fit, some studies suggest that five times a week is more effective. Exercising vigorously more than five times a week can cause injuries. If you want to lose weight, most experts recommend six days a week of moderate exercise.

No matter what your goal is, you will want to spread your exercise out over the week. It is not a good idea to do all your exercising on weekends only. Being inactive during the week does not prepare your body for a workout. Weekend athletes are more likely to injure themselves than those who exercise regularly throughout the week.

INTENSITY OF EXERCISE The intensity of a workout is indicated by the number of times per minute your heart beats during your activity. As you recall from Chapter 10, the faster your heart rate, the more intense the exercise is. There are a number of ways to determine how fast your heart should beat. These methods take into account your age, your resting heart rate, your maximum heart rate, and your current level of fitness.

Your **target heart rate** is the heart rate you need to maintain during a workout to improve your cardiorespiratory fitness. It will be somewhat lower than your maximum heart rate. You might think of your **maximum heart rate** as your heart's top speed, or the rate of heartbeat when exhausted. Your maximum heart rate depends on your age, and it de-

How often, how long, and how hard you exercise affect your level of fitness.

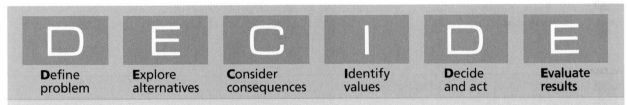

Define problem	**E**xplore alternatives	**C**onsider consequences	**I**dentify values	**D**ecide and act	**E**valuate results

KEEPING FIT?

After weeks of looking for a part-time job, you've been hired by the local ice cream parlor to work after school and on weekends. Now you will be able to save money to help pay for your upcoming college expenses.

Since your new job will take up much of your time, you are concerned about keeping physically fit. Until now, you have always played on sports teams at school and worked out in your spare time. It is important to you to stay in good shape. But, how you will be able to keep fit while working?

1. Use the DECIDE process on page 16 to decide what you would do in this situation. Explain your reasons for making this decision.

2. What does your decision say about you—your values, your goals, your strengths, and your weaknesses?

3. What steps would you need to take in order to implement your decision? Explain.

How would you combine exercise with a part-time job after school?

creases as you get older. You can estimate your maximum heart rate by subtracting your age from 220. For example, if you are 15 years old, your maximum heart rate is 220 minus 15, or 205 beats per minute. Working out at your maximum heart rate can lead to heart strain and muscle soreness.

Your target heart rate is a percentage of your maximum heart rate. The percentage depends on your level of fitness. The higher your fitness level, the greater your percentage will be. If you scored poorly on the fitness tests in Chapter 10, you should use 50 to 60 percent. If your score indicated an average level of fitness, you should use 70 to 75 percent. If your score indicated your fitness level was good or excellent, you should use 80 to 85 percent.

To calculate your target heart rate in beats per minute, multiply your maximum heart rate by the percentage that is appropriate for your level of fitness. Suppose, for example, your maximum heart rate is 205 beats per minute and your fitness is average. If you multiply 205 by .70 (70 percent), you will get a target heart rate of 144. Figure 11-9 shows the maximum heart rates for different ages and the target heart rates that are appropriate for different levels of fitness.

You need to check your heart rate regularly while exercising to discover whether or not you are exercising at the right intensity. The proper exercise intensity will maintain your heart rate within 5 beats per minute above or below your calculated target heart rate. For example, if your target

Figure 11-9. What should be your target heart rate during workouts?

Maximum and Target Heart Rates

Age	Maximum Heart Rate (MHR) (beats per minute)	Target Heart Rate (beats per minute)		
		Person in Poor Condition (60% of MHR)	Person in Average Condition (70% of MHR)	Person in Good Condition (80% of MHR)
5	215	129	151	172
10	210	126	147	168
15	205	123	144	164
20	200	120	140	160
25	195	117	137	156
30	190	114	133	152
35	185	111	130	148
40	180	108	126	144
45	175	105	123	140
50	170	102	119	136
55	165	99	116	132
60	160	96	112	128
65	155	93	109	124
70	150	90	105	120
75	145	87	102	116
80	140	84	98	112

Some Exercise Guidelines		
Fitness Component	**Health Goal**	
	Improve Cardiovascular Fitness	**Reduce Body Fat**
Frequency	Minimum: 3 times per week Maximum: 5 times per week	Minimum: 4 times per week Maximum: 6 times per week
Intensity	*Poor Starting Condition:* 60% of Maximum Heart Rate *Average Starting Condition:* 70% of Maximum Heart Rate *Good Starting Condition:* 80% of Maximum Heart Rate	60% of Maximum Heart Rate
Time	Minimum: 20 minutes per session Maximum: 30-40 minutes per session	Minimum: 30 minutes per session Maximum: 40-60 minutes per session

heart rate is 144, your actual heart rate during exercise should be between 139 and 149 beats per minute. To check your heart rate, you need to stop exercising for a moment and count your pulse. Because your heart rate slows down quickly, you will not get an accurate count if you take your pulse for a full minute. To get an accurate count of the number of beats per minute, take your pulse for only 10 seconds and multiply by 6.

The "talk test" is the easiest way to check your level of intensity. If you are so out of breath while exercising that you cannot talk at all, your exercise level is too intense. You will not be able to continue exercising for long at that intensity. If you can sing while you are exercising, you probably are not working hard enough. You are working at the proper intensity when you can talk comfortably during your exercise period.

EXERCISE TIME If your goal is cardiorespiratory improvement, your minimum time for aerobic exercise is 20 minutes per session. This means that you reach your target heart rate and maintain it for 20 to 30 minutes.

If your goal is to lose body fat, you need to lower your target heart rate to 60 percent of your maximum heart rate. This is because, at a moderate intensity level, your muscles tend to burn mostly body fat rather than the other energy source, glucose, that your body burns during high intensity exercise. At the lower intensity, you will need to exercise longer, for a minimum of 30 minutes, in order to burn up a significant amount of fat. Figure 11-10 offers some exercise guidelines for improving cardiovascular fitness and losing body fat.

Figure 11-10. How do you balance the three components of fitness when trying to reduce body fat?

You can check your heart rate or use the talk test to see if you are exercising at the right intensity.

What Should Be Done About Violence in Sports?

Today's newspapers frequently carry reports of fights both on the playing field between players and by spectators watching the events. Is this violence a permanent part of our sports scene, or can it be controlled?

Some people think that sports violence results from the emphasis placed on winning. Because professional and college sports bring in large amounts of money, players and coaches are under tremendous pressure to win. Some fans expect to see their team play hard even if there is a fight. Violence also occurs in youth sports when some youths imitate what they see in professional sports. People against violence in sports want strict penalties imposed on violent players. They would also like to see violent sports, like boxing, eliminated. They want to see fair play, rather than winning, emphasized at the youth level.

Other people think that nothing should be done to make sports safer. They claim that sports serve as a healthy outlet for hostility and that it is better to have violence on the field than off.

What do you think we should do about violence in sports?

STRETCHING About five minutes of stretching before you begin your warm-up increases your flexibility and helps you to avoid injury and strained muscles. Stretching should be a constant, even pull on your muscles on both sides of your body. Because muscles work in pairs, you need to stretch both muscles in a pair. As you stretch each muscle group, you should feel tension but not pain. Hold each stretch for 5 to 30 seconds. Do not bounce. Bouncing can strain your muscles and ligaments.

WARMING UP The **warm-up** is a 5-to-10 minute period during which you prepare your body for vigorous exercise. As you stretch the parts of your body you are going to use, you generate heat in the muscle and joint tissues, which makes them more elastic and less likely to become injured. Mild exercise during the warm-up gradually increases your heart rate and prepares your cardiorespiratory system for the workout. Some people go through the motions of the sport, with or without equipment, when they warm up. If you are going to play tennis, for example, you will want to warm up your shoulder and arm muscles, and you may go through the motions of a serve without a racket.

THE WORKOUT If the workout you have prepared for is aerobic, it will be made up of consistent, repetitive movements involving the large muscles of the body. Once your heartbeat reaches its target rate, maintain the rate for at least 20 minutes. As you become more fit, you may want to increase your workout to 30 or 40 minutes.

Figure 11-11. As your fitness improves with exercise, you can extend your exercise time for a longer period. ▶

If your workout is anaerobic, you should plan on at least a 45-minute workout. This time, however, will consist of short periods of physical activity, such as weight lifting, followed by rest periods during which the muscles can recover. You will not reach your target heart rate since anaerobic exercise does not usually involve a sustained elevated heart rate. You should, however, try to space the exercise periods evenly throughout the workout and avoid straining your muscles.

COOLING DOWN The **cool-down** is a 10-to-15 minute period of milder exercise that allows your body and heart rate to return to their resting states slowly. As you can see in Figure 11-12, your cool-down should be as long as, or even slightly longer than, your warm-up. If you stop exercising abruptly, blood can pool in the muscles you were using. When this happens, less blood reaches your heart, and you may feel lightheaded.

Walking is an effective way to cool down. When you walk, your leg muscles squeeze the blood vessels in your legs, which helps the blood return to your heart. Your cool-down period should continue until your heart is less than 100 beats per minute. Because some forms of exercise tighten your muscles, you may need to stretch thoroughly to prevent muscle soreness after you have cooled down.

Avoiding Injury

Anyone who exercises faces the risk of injury. The equipment you use and the foods and fluids you consume are almost as important as a thorough warm-up in preventing injury. Recognizing signs of overexertion is another important factor that can reduce your risk of injury.

THE RIGHT EQUIPMENT Your only exercise equipment may be sneakers and sweat clothes, but choosing the right kind of each is important. Because your feet take a pounding in most sports, buy the best footwear you can afford. Look for shoes with cushioned soles that fit properly and provide good support. Many sports call for canvas shoes, or sneakers. Court shoes are designed for sports such as tennis, basketball, and racquetball that are played on a court. They have thick soles and padded sides to cushion your feet during quick, hard turns. Jogging shoes are much lighter since they do not need extra padding for sideward movements. The jogging shoe's lifted heel helps to cushion the shock of your heel hitting the ground before the ball of your foot when you run.

When you exercise in warm weather, wear light-colored clothing to reflect the sun's rays, and dress lightly to expose as much of your skin as possible. Dressing lightly increases

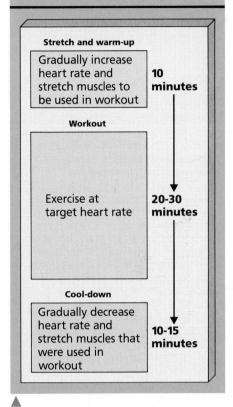

Components of an Exercise Session (minimum times)

Stretch and warm-up
Gradually increase heart rate and stretch muscles to be used in workout — **10 minutes**

Workout
Exercise at target heart rate — **20-30 minutes**

Cool-down
Gradually decrease heart rate and stretch muscles that were used in workout — **10-15 minutes**

▲
Figure 11–12. An exercise session is best divided into three parts. Why do you need to warm up and cool down?

Proper clothing, footwear, and protective gear help you to avoid discomfort and injury during exercise.

Talking Exercise Machines

When top athletes train, they depend on a personal coach for advice and encouragement. Now, computer technology has made it possible for anyone to have a "personal coach."

This modern-day coach is really an exercise machine with a computer-synthesized voice box and computer screen. When a person uses the machine, the "coach" offers verbal advice and encouragement. A face appears on the computer screen with an expression that matches the coach's words.

Many health clubs have several of these exercise machines, each one specializing in a different part of the body. Each may have a distinct voice, personality, and a sense of humor.

These coaches track each user's progress from day to day and electronically communicate with the other coaches about a user's specific problems or accomplishments. As a result, workouts can be geared to the user's individual needs.

Can computers replace coaches?

▲
Figure 11–13. Proper sports equipment will prevent injuries.

the skin's contact with the air, which allows sweat to evaporate and cool your body. When it is cold, you may need warm-up suits, sweat shirts, and sweat pants for warmth, but avoid wearing them to force your body to sweat. Since sweat cannot evaporate under layers of clothing, you run the risk of becoming overheated.

Shoulder pads, helmets, and other protective gear should be designed to prevent injuries in contact sports, such as football and hockey. Hard-shell helmets, worn by football players and hockey players as well as baseball players at bat, are designed to protect the head from a direct blow. Of course, you would not play a contact sport without a helmet, but did you know that you should regard a helmet as standard operating equipment if you are a biker? It should be worn each time you bike, not just when you are riding on heavily trafficked streets.

THE NEED FOR FLUIDS AND FOOD When you are active, never wait until you are thirsty to take a drink of water. You will not become thirsty until you have lost two to four pounds (0.9 to 1.8 kilograms) of water. By then, you are risking dehydration.

You can improve your performance in any exercise that takes more than 45 minutes by taking fluids while you exercise. This is especially important in hot weather. To help prevent dehydration on warm days, you should have a cup of cold water a few minutes before you exercise and every 15 minutes during your exercise. Cold water, which is less likely to cause stomach cramps than warm water, causes your stomach to contract, pushing the water into your intestines, where it can be absorbed into your bloodstream.

You may have heard that some athletes eat large amounts of pasta or other complex carbohydrates before a marathon. This practice is known as carbohydrate loading. **Carbohydrate loading** is an attempt to store more than the usual amount of carbohydrates, in the form of glycogen, in the muscles and liver in order to continue longer in an endurance event. Carbohydrate loading may have some food-storing benefit for highly conditioned athletes who participate in long-term activities, but for most athletes, the best policy is to eat normally three to five hours before a competitive event. You will want to avoid fat and sugar-rich foods, which will give you only a brief burst of energy. During vigorous exercise that takes more than 3 hours, you will need to eat enough food to avoid exhaustion. Wise bikers, for example, include bananas, peanut butter and jelly sandwiches, and other high-energy foods in their backpacks.

THE SYMPTOMS OF OVEREXERTION If your exercise level is too intense or your exercise session too long, you may feel unusually tired during the session or even a few hours after it. This is a signal that you have overworked your body. Other signs of overexertion include nausea or vomiting during or after a workout and muscle or joint aches and pains that do not go away quickly. If you experience any of these symptoms, you need to reduce your exercise intensity and time. A consistent exercise schedule, rather than occasional bursts of activity followed by periods of inactivity, is one way to avoid these symptoms.

Drinking plenty of water and eating the right foods help to prevent dehydration and exhaustion during exercise.

You can avoid the ill effects of overexhaustion by following a consistent program of exercise.

Figure 11-14. Marathon runners may resort to carbohydrate loading to meet their energy needs.

Sample Form For Exercise Journal

Date	Weight	Measurements	Resting Heart Rate	Appetite	Sleep Pattern

▲

Figure 11-15. A fitness journal keeps track of your progress. What target heart rate should you aim for?

○━┳

Logging basic information about yourself in a journal will help you to measure your progress.

Checking Your Progress

In most exercise programs, you will begin to notice changes in your body within at least 12 weeks. Because these changes happen gradually, some people like to track their progress in a fitness journal like the one shown in Figure 11-15. If you keep a journal, write down some basic information about yourself, such as your weight, measurements, resting heart rate, appetite, and the amount of sleep you are getting, at the start of the program. At the end of 12 weeks, update your observations. You ought to be able to see the progress you have made toward your goals. Perhaps you will notice that your resting heart rate is lower or that you have lost weight or gained muscle tone.

YOUR RESTING HEART RATE As you know from Chapter 10, someone with average cardiorespiratory fitness has a resting heart rate between 72 and 84 beats per minute. A rate of 85 or above usually shows a poor fitness level. If you have recorded your resting heart rate before beginning your fitness program, you may notice a change in the rate after three to four weeks. Take time from your program to check it again. You may find that it has decreased by as much as 5 to 10 beats per minute.

A resting heart rate below 72 beats per minute usually indicates a good fitness level. On the average, males have lower resting heart rates than females. A young athlete in top condition usually has a slow resting heart rate, perhaps only 40 beats per minute. The athlete's heart is so strong and efficient that it does not need to beat more rapidly to meet the body's needs.

YOUR CHANGING SHAPE As you track your progress in your exercise program, keep in mind that all muscle and no fat is not a goal of a fitness program. To be healthy, your

body must store some fat. It is important, however, to have a body fat level that is right for your age and sex. Healthy adolescent males can have between 11 and 16 percent of their weight as body fat. For example, a 15-year-old boy who weighs 130 pounds (59 kilograms) should have between 14 and 21 pounds (6 and 10 kilograms) of stored fat. Healthy adolescent girls can have 16 to 22 percent of their weight as body fat. A 120-pound (54 kilogram) adolescent girl, for example, should have between 19 and 25 pounds (9 and 12 kilograms) of fat.

It is possible to lose fat tissue without losing weight. If you lose fat and gain muscle, you may find that you weigh more because muscle tissue is heavier than fat. This results, however, in a trimmer body. If you measure your body at various points every 12 weeks, you will be able to track the changes. Use a standard measuring tape and measure your chest, waist, hips (females only), upper arm, and upper leg. Record your measurements in your journal.

Your exercise program should be geared to maintain appropriate levels of body fat and muscle.

Section Review

1. What are two things you should consider when choosing a personal exercise program?
2. List two ways to reduce your risk of injury during your exercise program.
3. Why can you lose fat tissue without losing weight?
4. How is your resting heart rate an indicator of your fitness level?

What Do You Think?
5. What goal would you set for yourself if you were planning to begin an exercise program?

3. SLEEP AND FEELING FIT

Sleep, like nutrition and exercise, affects your level of fitness. Although scientists do not know all the ways sleep helps people, they do know that the body releases pent-up tension and repairs damaged tissues during sleep. In fact, much of your body's growth takes place while you are asleep.

What Is Sleep?

Sleep is the deep relaxation of the body and mind during which the eyes are usually closed and there is little conscious thought or movement. During sleep, your muscles relax, your breathing and heart rates decrease, and your body temperature drops slightly.

Any 24-hour cycle is known as a **circadian** (sur **kay** dee un) **rhythm.** Your body follows a circadian rhythm. Your temperature, mood, alertness, and chemical levels rise and fall at roughly the same time every day. During the most active period of the circadian rhythm, your mind is most alert, your body temperature is high, and your physical dexterity is at its peak. Usually this state occurs during daylight when you are awake. The least active period of the circadian rhythm usually occurs at night when you are asleep.

While most people tend to follow a 24-hour cycle of sleep and wakefulness that matches the circadian rhythm, sleeping habits, such as when you sleep, are learned. Although you probably sleep for one long stretch during the night, in some countries, particularly those with hot climates, people may wake before dawn to begin work, rest or nap in the afternoon when it is warmest, then return to work in the early evening.

THE SLEEP CYCLE   There are two different kinds of sleep—rapid eye movement sleep and nonrapid eye movement sleep. Sleep during which your eyes flicker back and forth behind your closed eyelids is called **rapid eye movement (REM) sleep.** REM sleep makes up about 25 percent of your sleep. Sleep in which your eyes are relaxed is called **nonrapid eye movement (NREM) sleep.** NREM sleep can range from drowsy to deep sleep.

The typical sleep cycle consists of four stages of NREM sleep followed by REM sleep, which is stage five. Each stage of sleep is marked by certain kinds of brain waves. As you can see in Figure 11-17, different kinds of brain waves indicate different activities taking place in the brain.

The first stage of NREM sleep is the gradual period of falling asleep. Sometimes during this state, you experience a sudden jerk of your muscles. This is known as a **myoclonic** (my oh **klawn** ik) **jerk.**

After you have fallen asleep, you pass through NREM stages two, three, and four. During these stages, your brain

O⌐ㅡ▬
Your body is able to relax and to repair damaged tissues during sleep.

Brain Wave Patterns During the Sleep Cycle

Figure 11-17. There are five stages to a typical sleep cycle. In what stage do dreams occur?

waves slow down, your sleep becomes deeper, and your muscles become more relaxed. It appears that these stages of deepest sleep help to restore and revitalize the body. People who exercise regularly spend more time in third and fourth-stage NREM sleep than people who do not exercise.

Once you have reached stage four of NREM sleep, you begin to reverse the cycle. You go back to stage three, then stage two, and then into REM sleep, as Figure 11-18 illustrates. Each cycle lasts approximately 90 minutes and is repeated four to six times until you wake up.

Look again at Figure 11-18. During REM sleep, the most active stage of sleep, the rapid brain waves recorded are associated with dreaming. While people rarely report dreaming during NREM sleep, eighty percent of the people wakened during REM sleep report dreaming. The first REM period usually lasts about 5 to 15 minutes. As you continue sleeping, later REM periods increase to about 28 minutes.

SLEEP DISORDERS   There are a number of disorders that can turn sleep into a frustrating or frightening experience. People who have severe nightmares, for example, may wake up suddenly with a sense of anxiety, heaviness in the chest, and little or no recollection of their dreams.

Some people suffer from **sleep apnea,** which means that they stop breathing for short periods during sleep. For unknown reasons, sleep in some people signals the brain to stop the diaphragm and rib muscles or to collapse the windpipe. As a result, air cannot enter the lungs. After not breathing for as long as two minutes, an individual's oxygen supply becomes so low that the person wakes up suddenly, exhales forcefully, and snores loudly. This may happen 300 to 500 times a night without the person becoming aware of it, although he or she may be extremely tired the next day.

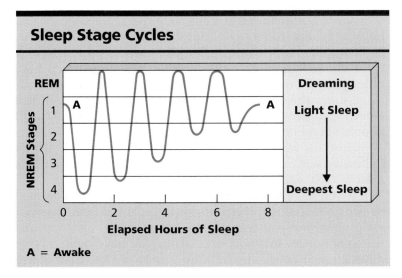

Sleep Stage Cycles

A = Awake

◀ **Figure 11-18. Each sleep stage has its own brain-wave pattern. How does the pattern change in deep sleep?**

People who fall asleep suddenly without warning and inappropriately for short periods of time may suffer from **narcolepsy** (**nahr** kuh lep see). Narcolepsy is a disorder of REM sleep that can develop during adolescence or in the early twenties. Sleep specialists think that narcoleptic people frequently enter REM sleep without passing through NREM stages of sleep. People with narcolepsy often experience sleep paralysis, hallucinations, and **cataplexy** (**kat** a plex ee), or a sudden loss of muscle tone that may result in falling and weak muscles around the eyes and mouth.

Almost everyone experiences **insomnia,** difficulty in falling asleep or staying asleep at some point. Occasionally, insomnia can be caused by stress, anxiety, or physical problems. If you are bothered by insomnia, getting more exercise during your waking hours may ease the problem.

Being pleasantly tired when you go to bed is the best way to get a good night's sleep. Heavy-duty exertion, like calisthenics or aerobics, just before bedtime elevates your metabolism and increases your alertness, making it harder to fall asleep. As a rule, if you are still awake after 15 minutes, or if you find yourself lying awake during the night, do not stay in bed. Get up and have some warm milk or do something relaxing, such as reading.

Changing your sleep schedule or sleeping on an irregular schedule can interrupt your circadian rhythm. People who travel from one time zone to another and face a day-night cycle that does not match their circadian rhythm must face this problem. The term **jet lag** refers to the fatigue and disorientation often suffered by air travelers whose circadian rhythms are interrupted. If the traveler stays in the new time zone long enough, the body usually adjusts to the cycle and jet lag disappears.

How Much Sleep Is Enough?

No two individuals have exactly the same sleep needs. Healthy adults usually get 7 or 8 hours of sleep out of every 24 hours. People who are sick or depressed sometimes sleep even more. Infants and adolescents need more sleep than other people because of the changes occurring in their bodies. Usually the older you are, the less sleep you need. Some elderly people sleep only five hours a day. All in all, most people spend one-third of their lives asleep!

How do you know how much sleep you need? If you fall asleep without trouble and wake up feeling refreshed you are probably getting enough sleep.

If you have trouble falling asleep, keep a notebook next to your bed. Note in it the time you go to bed, the time you wake up, how you feel when you wake up, and any disturbances or dreams you have. After you have done this for a week, see if your notes indicate a pattern. Does getting less

▲
Figure 11–19. Regular, sound sleep is fundamental to good health.

than eight hours of sleep make you irritable? Does an afternoon nap delay your sleep at night?

The quality of your sleep is as important as the amount of time you sleep. Establishing a nighttime routine before you go to bed often helps to relax you for a good night's sleep. Try to go to bed at the same time every night so that your body can establish a pattern for sleeping. Avoid going to bed late and getting up late on weekends. You cannot store or catch up on sleep.

While you will want to sleep in a position that is comfortable for you, sleeping on your stomach places more strain on your back and neck than any other position. Sleeping with music or lights on also is not a good idea, since these conditions may prevent you from reaching or staying in the deep stages (NREM stages three and four) of sleep. It is best to sleep in a dark, quiet room with some ventilation.

When you fall asleep easily and wake up refreshed, you know your body has got the rest it needs.

Section Review

1. Describe the sleep cycle in terms of its stages and the kinds of sleep involved.
2. Identify and describe three kinds of sleep disorders.
3. During which stages of life do people need the greatest amounts of sleep?
4. How can you determine whether or not you are getting enough sleep?

What Do You Think?
5. How much sleep do you get? How might you adjust your daily schedule if you feel you are not getting the right amount of sleep?

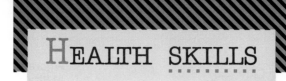

Warm-Up and Cool-Down Exercises

Imagine you are about to go on a 20-mile bicycle ride or participate in your favorite sport. What would be the best way for you to prepare your body for these activities? Try warming up.

Warming up is important for stretching out muscles and gradually increasing heart rate. It prepares your body for more strenuous work.

Cooling down is equally important, because it helps return blood to your heart and brain after exercising. Stretching your body after a workout also helps prevent muscle stiffness.

Although no single warm-up or cool-down routine is appropriate for every activity, the exercises below provide a good base for you to build on. The key point to remember is *don't rush*! A pulled muscle can hold you up much longer than the few extra minutes it takes to do your warm-up and cool-down exercises properly.

1. Hand Grasp

Grasp your hands behind your back and hold. Stand with your feet apart, knees slightly bent, and lean over at the waist. Pull up your arms behind you 5 times.

2. Side Stretch

Stand with feet apart, knees bent and one hand on your hip. Extend the opposite arm overhead and stretch to the side. Hold 5 seconds. Repeat in the other direction. Do 5 times in each direction.

3. Lower Back Curl

Lie on your back with legs extended. Bring one knee up to your chest. Grasp the leg and pull the knee closer to your chest. Hold 5 seconds. Next, curl your head and shoulders toward your knee. Hold 5 seconds. Switch to opposite leg. Do 4 times on each side.

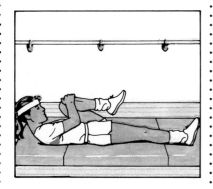

4. Raising/Lowering Heart Rate

Either walk, jog slowly, or do the activity you are about to participate in at a reduced pace to increase/decrease circulation to muscle groups. Do this after stretching out in the warm-up phase and before stretching out in the cool-down phase. Do for 3 to 5 minutes.

5. Hamstring and Calf Stretch

Stand in a stride position with right leg forward and hands on hips. Lean your upper body forward. Simultaneously bend your right leg and extend your left leg back in a continuous line with your upper body. Push your left heel to the ground. Hold 5 seconds. Repeat with other leg. Do 5 times on each side.

A warm-up makes any physical activity you participate in safer and more enjoyable.

6. Hamstring Stretch

Sit on the floor and extend one leg, toes facing up as you can see in the picture. Tuck your other foot against your extended thigh. Reach forward over the extended leg and slide hands down the leg until you feel a stretch. Hold 5 seconds. Switch to opposite leg. Repeat with each leg twice.

APPLY THE SKILL

1. Read over the warm-up/cool-down exercises in this section and take 5 minutes to practice them.

2. Each morning for one week do the 5-minute stretching routine and record how you felt before and after the routine, including any soreness or stiffness. At the end of the week evaluate the stretching routine and your reactions to it. What would be the benefits of making this part of your daily exercise routine?

3. Select a favorite sport or other physical activity and then ask your physical education teacher or coach to suggest good stretching exercises for that activity. Write down the instructions, including the number of repetitions, and include them in your daily exercise routine.

11 | Chapter Review

Chapter Summary

- During vigorous exercise many changes occur in the body. These include increases in heart rate, blood pressure, and breathing rate.
- An exercise program can strengthen the cardiovascular system, build muscle strength and endurance, and aid in weight control. Regular exercise also can improve sleep and contribute to a sense of well-being.
- Exercise can be aerobic or anaerobic. Aerobic exercise improves cardiovascular and respiratory health; anaerobic exercise improves flexibility, muscular strength, and sometimes speed.
- Three types of anaerobic exercises are isotonic, isometric, and isokinetic.
- The frequency with which you exercise, the intensity of your workouts, and the length of your exercise time should be based on the goals you have established for yourself.
- Every fitness program should include a stretching period and a warm-up period to avoid muscle strain and injury, the workout itself, and a cool-down period.
- Injuries can be prevented during exercise by using the proper equipment, drinking enough fluids, and avoiding overexertion.
- When planning an exercise program, choose an activity or sport you enjoy and decide what you want to gain from your program.
- Changes in body fat, body measurement, and resting heart rate are some of the indicators of progress in a fitness program.
- Getting proper sleep is necessary for physical fitness.
- The sleep cycle consists of four stages of NREM sleep and a period of REM sleep.
- Some sleep disorders are apnea, narcolepsy, insomnia, and the effects of interrupting the circadian rhythm.
- No two people have exactly the same sleep needs. A regular sleeping schedule and a nighttime routine before going to bed can help you sleep well.

Vocabulary Review

Listed below are some of the important terms in this chapter. Choose the term that best matches the phrase in the exercise that follows.

aerobic exercise	cool-down	isotonic	REM
anaerobic exercise	endorphins	myoclonic jerk	sleep apnea
carbohydrate loading	insomnia	narcolepsy	stress test
cataplexy	isokinetic	NREM	target heart rate
circadian rhythm	isometric	oxygen debt	warm-up

1. natural painkillers

2. anaerobic exercise that involves the use of special machines

3. high-carbohydrate diet consumed before a marathon or some other endurance event

4. period of stretching and mild exercise that gradually increases heart rate

5. exercise that improves the cardiovascular and respiratory systems

6. period of sleep in which dreaming occurs

7. twenty-four-hour cycle

8. exercise in which the demand for oxygen exceeds the supply of oxygen

9. a period after vigorous exercise during which the heartbeat is allowed to return to its resting state slowly

10. difficulty in falling asleep or staying asleep

What Have You Learned?

1. How does your body meet its increased need for oxygen during aerobic exercise?
2. What effect do the endorphins produced in your brain have on your body?
3. List two cardiovascular improvements that result from regular vigorous exercise.
4. List three elements of fitness that can be improved by anaerobic exercise.
5. Compare isotonic and isometric exercise.
6. What is the simplest way to calculate your target heart rate?

7. How often and for how long should you exercise for cardiovascular improvement?
8. What is the purpose of the warm-up period? What is the cool-down period?
9. Describe two symptoms of overexertion.
10. How can you tell if your heart is more fit as a result of an exercise program?
11. List three changes that occur in your body during sleep.
12. Describe three ways that you can improve the quality of your sleep.

What Do You Think?

1. Studies have shown that many school-aged children and teenagers have low fitness levels. Why do you think this is so?
2. What evidence have you seen that fitness has become more popular recently?
3. If you were to try building up your arm strength, which type of exercise—isotonic, isometric, or isokinetic—would you use? Why?

4. Why do you think that true anaerobic exercises can be performed only for short periods of time?
5. An 18-year-old gymnast who works out anaerobically each day to improve her performance has a resting heart rate of 85. Does this heart rate show that the athlete is fit? Why or why not?

What Would You Do?

1. Your friend believes exercise takes too much energy, causes pain, and requires several hours each day. How would you convince him or her that these ideas are false?
2. Your friend is having trouble sleeping and has begun to stay in bed all morning on weekends to catch up on sleep. What advice would you give your friend?

3. What forms of aerobic exercise could you take up if you did not want to spend money on a fitness club, lessons, or special exercise equipment other than proper footwear?
4. If you could buy any piece of fitness equipment, what would you buy? Why?
5. How would you go about learning how to play a new sport?

For Further Study

1. Jim Fixx was the author of a best-selling book titled, *The Complete Book of Running*. Research and report on his life style before and after he began his running program and the cause of his early death.
2. Find out what free exercise or sports facilities are available in your community and the hours and days they are available. For example, does your community have free tennis courts, swimming pools, jogging tracks, or bicycle paths? Are there any free or inexpensive exercise programs, such as aerobics or yoga classes, offered through the recreation department in your community?

Believe it or not, I'm looking forward to being retired. I see myself relaxing, having fun with my grandkids, no work, and no worries. That sounds great to me.

UNIT

4

The Human Life Cycle

12

As you read, think about
▶ how the endocrine system controls many of your body's activities.
▶ how the male and female reproductive systems function.
▶ how to keep your reproductive system healthy.
▶ how traits are passed from parent to child.

Reproduction and Heredity

You and your dad are returning from your morning run. He cracks a joke, and you both chuckle. It's a joke probably no one else would laugh at. You glance at him as he begins to stretch out, and you think, "No wonder everyone says I'm just like my dad: same laugh, same hair, same nose. And come to think of it, we're both kind of shy."

Of course, you're not *exactly* like your dad; you are separate individuals. Nevertheless, you are similar to him and to your mother in many ways. You even have the freckles that "missed" your mom but "come from" her side of the family.

Many of your physical characteristics and personality traits are inherited from your parents and through them, from your grandparents and so on. In this chapter, you'll find out how the human reproductive system works and how traits are passed from one generation to the next.

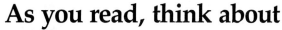

Parents pass on traits to their children. This depends on a healthy reproductive system.

1. THE ENDOCRINE SYSTEM

Every day, your body must perform many functions in order to survive. Growth, metabolism, and sexual development are just three of the many things occurring inside you right now. **Metabolism,** as you read in Chapter 8, is a complicated process by which food is converted into energy by the body. To control your metabolism and other important processes, some structures of the body work together as a giant communications system that carries chemical messages throughout the body. This system, known as the **endocrine** (**en** duh crin) **system,** not only controls many of your body's daily activities but also controls its overall development.

How Your Endocrine System Works

Your endocrine system is made up of a group of organs, or body structures, called **endocrine glands.** A **gland** is a cell (the smallest living unit in the body) or a group of cells that produces and releases a chemical substance. Some glands, such as sweat glands, have ducts, or passages, that carry the chemicals to the place where they will be used. An endocrine gland is a gland that does not have a duct. Because endocrine glands are ductless, their chemicals are released directly into the bloodstream. Figure 12-1 shows the location of the major endocrine glands in the body.

The chemical substances produced by endocrine glands are known as **hormones.** Hormones act as chemical messengers in the body. Once released into the bloodstream, hormones travel to other parts of the body where they stimulate a response. Some hormones affect only certain cells of the body, while others stimulate a response in many body cells. Some hormones are only produced at certain times in a person's life while others are produced continually.

The endocrine system is a complicated system of checks and balances that works to keep the body healthy. When the endocrine system is working properly, hormones from one gland send chemical signals to another gland, which responds by regulating the chemicals of the first gland. Just as a thermostat may turn on when the temperature is below 68° and may turn off when the temperature is above 68°, so the endocrine system turns on and off in response to hormone levels. Each of the hormones of the endocrine system is kept in check by the production of another hormone or a series of hormones. This control of hormones keeps the body's activities functioning smoothly. When the endocrine system is not functioning properly, your health, your physical appearance, your energy level, the balance of water in your body, and your ability to produce children may be affected.

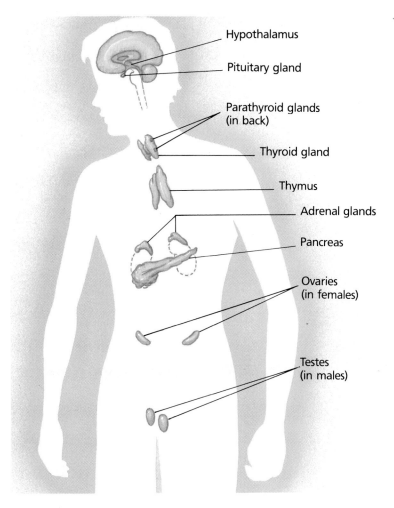

Hypothalamus

Pituitary gland

Parathyroid glands (in back)

Thyroid gland

Thymus

Adrenal glands

Pancreas

Ovaries (in females)

Testes (in males)

Endocrine Glands in the Body

Each of the endocrine glands in your body plays a specific and important role in your body. Figure 12-2 lists some of the hormones produced by the endocrine glands and their functions. To keep your body functioning properly, the endocrine glands interact in a complex but well-organized manner. In rare cases when the endocrine system fails to work properly, physical and mental disorders may result. In some of these cases of endocrine problems, doctors are able to identify and eventually correct the problem with specific hormone treatments.

THE PITUITARY GLAND AND HYPOTHALAMUS

Two of the body's endocrine glands are located in the brain. The **pituitary** (pi **too** uh tehr ee) **gland** is a small gland at the base of the brain. It controls many of the activities in your body, including growth rate, cellular metabolism, and **reproduction,** the producing of offspring. The pituitary gland also regulates many of the other endocrine glands in the body.

The pituitary gland regulates the activity of other endocrine glands in the body.

For this reason, the pituitary gland was once referred to as the "master gland."

In fact, the pituitary gland is controlled by the **hypothalamus** (hy poh **thal** uh mus), that part of the brain that regulates your body temperature, use of water, and blood pressure, among other things. The hypothalamus is connected to the pituitary gland by blood vessels. In addition to

Figure 12-2. The endocrine system consists of nine major glands. Which glands are in the brain?

▼

Endocrine Hormones and Their Functions

Gland	Hormone	Function
Adrenal glands	Adrenaline (epinephrine)	Controls "fight or flight" response: increases heart rate and blood pressure; directs blood to muscles and brain; converts glycogen to glucose
	Aldosterone	Increases uptake of sodium and water by kidney
	Cortisol	Increases glucose, fat, protein metabolism; controls inflammation of connective body tissue
	Testosterone, estrogen	Controls development of secondary sex characteristics in both sexes
Thyroid gland	Thyroxine	Regulates body's overall metabolic rate
	Calcitonin	Controls calcium level in bloodstream
Parathyroid glands	Parathyroid hormone	Regulates level of calcium and phosphorus in bloodstream
Pancreas	Insulin	Regulates glucose level in bloodstream
	Glucogen	Stimulates liver to convert glycogen to glucose
Testes (males)	Testosterone	Regulates development of male sex organs in embryo and secondary sex characteristics at puberty; controls sex drive
Ovaries (females)	Estrogen	Regulates development of female secondary sex characteristics at puberty; controls sex drive
	Progesterone	Controls development of endometrium during menstrual cycle and maintenance of uterus during pregnancy
Hypothalamus	Releasing factors	Stimulates pituitary gland to secrete specific hormones
	Oxytocin	Controls muscle contractions of uterus and milk production in mammary glands
	Antidiuretic hormone (ADH)	Increases water uptake in kidney
Pituitary	Adrenocorticotropic hormone (ACTH)	Stimulates adrenal gland to secrete specific hormones
	Thyroid stimulating hormone (TSH)	Stimulates thyroid gland to secrete specific hormones
	Growth hormone	Regulates growth of skeletal system
	Prolactin	Stimulates milk production in mammary glands
	Luteinizing hormone (LH)	In females: Stimulates ovulation, maturation of egg cell, and progesterone production In males: Stimulates sperm and testosterone production
	Follicle-stimulating hormone (FSH)	In females: Stimulates maturation of egg cell in ovary and estrogen production In males: Stimulates sperm production

its other functions, the hypothalamus oversees all the hormone levels in the body. When the level of a hormone is low, the hypothalamus produces a **releasing hormone,** a chemical that causes the pituitary gland to release a specific hormone.

ADRENAL GLANDS   Under the control of the pituitary gland and the hypothalamus are a pair of glands known as the **adrenal** (uh **dree** nul) **glands.** The adrenal glands are found on each side of your body, one above each of the kidneys. Adrenal glands produce a number of hormones that affect the functioning of your kidneys, cellular metabolism, and your response to stressful situations. As you read in Chapter 3, the hormone **adrenaline** (uh **dren** uh lin), also known as **epinephrine** (ep uh **nef** rin), causes the **fight or flight response** during which your heartbeat, breathing rate, and blood pressure increase, preparing you to either face or run away from a danger. The adrenal glands secrete both male and female sex hormones in both sexes. The importance of these hormones will be discussed in more detail in the next section.

THYROID GLAND   The **thyroid** (**thy** royd) **gland** is a large gland, shaped like a bow tie and located at the front of the neck. The thyroid gland, which is under the control of the pituitary gland, regulates the rate of metabolism in the body. One of the hormones produced by the thyroid gland, known as **thyroxine** (thy **rahk** sin), contains iodine, a mineral found in some foods. If a person does not have enough iodine, he or she may develop **goiter,** a swelling of the thyroid gland. This condition is uncommon in the United States because most table salt has had iodine added to it.

OTHER ENDOCRINE GLANDS   The **parathyroid glands** are four tiny glands attached to the back of the thyroid gland. These glands regulate the levels of two important minerals in the body, calcium and phosphorus. As you read in Chapter 8, these minerals are necessary for proper bone and tooth formation and for muscle and nerve activity.

The **pancreas** (**pang** kree us) is a large gland located behind the stomach. This gland is a part of the digestive system and the endocrine system. As an endocrine gland, the pancreas controls the level of sugar in the blood. As you read in Chapter 9, when the pancreas does not work properly, **diabetes,** a condition in which there is a high level of sugar in the blood, or **hypoglycemia** (hy poh gly **see** mee uh), low blood sugar, can occur.

The **thymus** is a gland located in the upper chest near the heart. The function of this gland is not thoroughly understood. The thymus gland appears to be most active early in life and plays a role in developing some of the body's defenses against infection.

Figure 12-3. Proper endocrine function is necessary to meet the high-energy needs of active teenagers.

The adrenal glands, thyroid gland, parathyroid glands, and pancreas play a role in regulating metabolism.

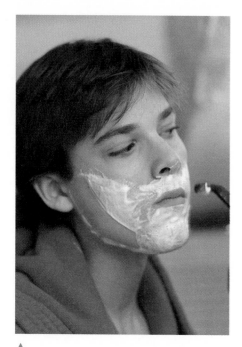

Figure 12-4. In males, the growth of facial hair is controlled by the sex hormone testosterone.

LH and FSH are produced in males and females. These hormones affect the production of sex hormones.

The reproductive glands, two other endocrine glands, include the **ovaries** (**oh** vuh reez) in females and the **testes** (**tes** teez) (singular: testis) in males. These two glands play an important role in reproduction.

Reproduction and the Endocrine System

Like other glands in the endocrine system, the reproductive glands are controlled by the pituitary gland, which is controlled by the hypothalamus. Until about the age of ten, the reproductive glands work at low levels in both girls and boys. After this age, hormone levels begin to increase, and physical changes occur. The hypothalamus releases certain substances that signal the pituitary gland to begin producing two hormones important for reproduction: **folli-cle-stimulating hormone (FSH)** and **luteinizing** (**loo** tee in y zing) **hormone (LH).** These two hormones are produced in both males and females. These hormones affect the testes in men and the ovaries in women.

In males, LH signals the testes to begin producing **tes-tosterone** (tes **tahs** tuh rohn), the male sex hormones. Testosterone with FSH controls the production of **sperm,** the male sex cells. Testosterone is also responsible for developing and maintaining other traits that develop during the teenage years in men. These traits, which are not involved in reproduction, include the growth of facial hair.

In females, the pituitary hormones LH and FSH stimulate the ovaries to produce **estrogen** (**ehs** truh jun) and **progesterone** (proh **jes** tuh rohn), the female sex hormones. Estrogen and progesterone are responsible for the development and maintenance of other traits not directly connected with reproduction in females, such as breast development. In addition, these hormones work with FSH and LH to produce **ova** (singular: ovum), or mature egg cells, the female sex cells. This will be discussed later in the chapter.

Section Review

1. What is an endocrine gland? What does it produce?
2. Name two hormones and their functions.
3. Why has the pituitary gland been called the "master gland"? Which other gland controls the pituitary gland?

What Do You Think?

4. Suppose a friend began to lose weight and noticed that his appetite had increased greatly. Could this problem be caused by a malfunctioning endocrine gland? Explain your answer.

2. THE MALE REPRODUCTIVE SYSTEM

During the early to mid-teen years, most boys notice many physical changes taking place in their bodies. Their voices may deepen, and hair growth may appear on their faces, underarms, legs, chests, and above the reproductive organs. These changes mark the onset of **puberty,** a period of sexual development during which males and females become able to produce children. At puberty, a boy's body begins to produce sperm. As you have read, sperm development is controlled by the production of the male hormone testosterone by the testes.

At puberty, physical changes occur in a boy's body, and sperm production begins.

Structure and Function

The male reproductive system is made up of both internal and external organs, shown in Figure 12-5. The internal organs are a series of glands and ducts that transport, store, and nourish the sperm cells once they are produced. The external organs produce, store, and release the sperm. Once released, a sperm cell must unite with an egg from a female for reproduction to occur. The joining of a sperm cell with an egg cell, called **fertilization,** begins the process of producing a new life.

Figure 12-5. Which structure of the male reproductive system is responsible for the production of sperm cells?

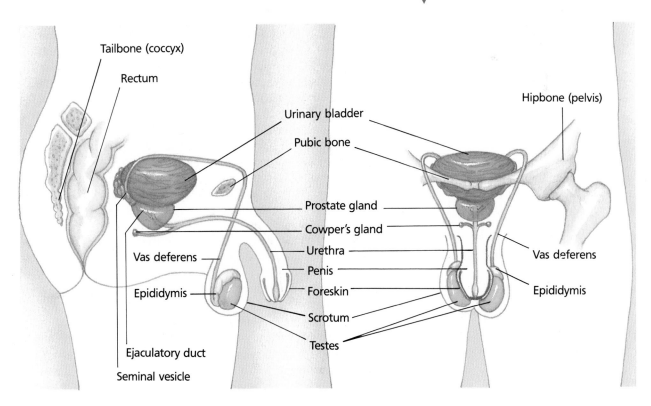

Tailbone (coccyx)

Rectum

Urinary bladder

Pubic bone

Hipbone (pelvis)

Prostate gland

Cowper's gland

Urethra

Vas deferens

Penis

Vas deferens

Epididymis

Foreskin

Epididymis

Scrotum

Ejaculatory duct

Testes

Seminal vesicle

Testes produce sperm and the hormone testosterone.

TESTES The testes, or **testicles** (**tes** ti kuhls), have two major functions: the production of testosterone, the male hormone, and the production of sperm. The testes are made up of coiled tubules in which the sperm are produced. The testes hang outside the body within a sac of skin called the **scrotum** (**skroh** tum). The scrotum protects the sperm by keeping the temperature of the testes slightly lower than the normal body temperature. Sperm must be kept at this lower temperature in order to survive.

EPIDIDYMIS The **epididymis** (ep ih **did** uh mis) is a J-shaped tube located on the back of each testicle. This tube is coiled and folded upon itself. It stores the sperm for two to four days after they have been produced. While in the epididymis, the sperm mature and gain the ability to move.

PENIS The **penis** (**pee** nis) is the external sexual organ through which sperm are delivered into the female's body. In its normal state, the penis is a soft, tubular organ that hangs from the front of the body. An **erection** is a condition in which the penis becomes larger and stiffer due to an increased flow of blood through it. When the penis is in an erect state, **ejaculation** (ih jak yuh **lay** shun), the ejection of sperm from the penis, can occur. An erection does not need to result in ejaculation; in fact, most do not. Erections can be caused by different factors, including sexual excitement or tight clothing. Sometimes an erection may occur for no reason at all. This is especially common during puberty. It is also common for a teenage male to experience a **nocturnal emission** or "wet dream," which is erection and ejaculation during sleep. This occurs because sperm production during puberty causes an increased pressure in the reproductive system. Sometimes a nocturnal emission occurs because of a sexually arousing dream. This is a normal occurrence and may happen frequently.

The tip of the penis, called the head, or **glans,** is covered with loose skin, called the foreskin. In some males the foreskin is removed surgically shortly after birth. This surgical procedure is known as **circumcision** (sur kum **sizh** un). In other males the foreskin is not removed. Over the years, circumcision has been performed for both religious and health reasons. Some doctors believe that removing the foreskin helps to keep the penis clean and free from possible infection. Other doctors believe regular daily cleanliness will prevent any possible problems.

OTHER GLANDS AND DUCTS There are several other glands and ducts that play an important role in storing and releasing sperm. The **vas deferens** (vas **def** ur unz) is an 18-inch (45 centimeter) tube that receives sperm from the epididymis of each testicle. The two vas deferens loop over the

didymis of each testicle. The two vas deferens loop over the bladder and join at the **urethra** (you **ree** thruh) a tube that passes through the penis to the outside of the body. The urethra carries urine and sperm, but a valve within the urethra prevents the two fluids from mixing. As the sperm travel through the vas deferens, they combine with fluids from other sex glands: the **seminal vesicles** (**ves** i kulz), paired glands located near the bladder; **Cowper's** (**kow** purz) **glands,** paired glands located at the base of the penis; and the **prostate gland,** which is near the bladder at the midline of the body. The mixture of sperm and the fluids from these glands is known as **semen** (**see** mun). As you will see in the next section, the fluids from these glands nourish the sperm and lubricate the passageways through which the sperm must travel.

Sperm Production

Once a male reaches puberty, millions of sperm are produced in his body on a daily basis. The process by which sperm are produced is known as **spermatogenesis** (spur mat uh **jen** i sis). Spermatogenesis occurs when the hypothalamus signals the pituitary gland to release FSH and LH, which stimulate the cells of the testes to produce testosterone. These three sex hormones—FSH, LH, and testosterone— work together to produce sperm within the testes and move them to the epididymis where they are stored for two to four days. As you know, in the epididymis, the sperm gain the ability to "swim." Figure 12-6 shows the structure of a mature sperm cell. By wiggling its long tail like a fish, the sperm propels itself through the vas deferens toward the urethra. Along the way, the fluids from the other glands are added to the sperm to form semen. The fluid added by the seminal vesicles, which makes up 60 percent of the semen, provides a source of energy for the active sperm. The Cowper's glands produce a clear fluid that lubricates the urethra; this fluid accounts for 5 percent of the semen. The prostate gland produces a milky white fluid that makes up 35 percent of the semen. The fluid from the prostate gland protects the sperm as it travels through the female reproductive tract.

Before entering the urethra, the semen passes through the **ejaculatory** (ih **jak** yuh luh tor ee) **ducts,** tubes that are lined with muscles. These muscles contract to force semen out of the body during ejaculation. About 400 million sperm cells in about one-tenth of an ounce (3.5 milliliters) of semen are released during one ejaculation. When the semen enters the female, the sperm swim upward through the female reproductive system for a possible joining with an egg. The fluid in which the sperm are bathed contains nutrients that enable the sperm to survive for several days inside of the female's body.

Sperm are produced in a process known as spermatogenesis.

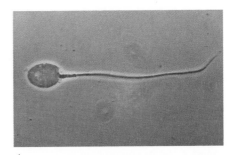

▲ **Figure 12-6. The long tail of a mature sperm cell allows it to swim through the reproductive system.**

Disorders of the Male Reproductive System

There are a number of medical conditions that involve the organs of the male reproductive system. Chapter 17 will discuss some infections, known as sexually transmitted diseases, that also affect the reproductive system.

STERILITY   When a person is unable to reproduce, the condition is known as **sterility** (stuh **ril** ih tee). It may be present in either males or females. In males, sterility may be caused by a number of conditions. Sometimes a male is unable to produce healthy sperm. Sometimes environmental factors, such as exposure to certain chemicals, may cause sterility. Adult men who develop mumps, usually a childhood illness, may become sterile. Medical research is discovering more about the causes of sterility and how it can be prevented.

UNDESCENDED TESTES   Most men have two testes. In some males, a condition known as **undescended** (uhn dih **send** ed) **testes** results when one of the testes does not descend into the scrotum at birth. This condition does not necessarily cause any medical problems, and it is not considered a disease. In some cases, undescended testes can be corrected by surgery or hormonal treatments.

HERNIA   A **hernia** (**hur** nee ah) is the condition in which an organ in the body pushes outward through the wall of the body normally containing the organ. Hernias can occur in various parts of the body. One of the most common hernias is called an **inguinal** (**in** gwuh nul) **hernia.** An inguinal hernia occurs when a part of the intestine pushes into the scrotum through a weak spot in the wall near the scrotum. Surgery is almost always necessary to correct this condition.

ENLARGED PROSTATE   Enlargement of the prostate gland is a common problem in men after middle age. Doctors often say every male will develop an enlarged prostate if they live long enough. Enlargement does not have to indicate either disease or illness, but it can cause some pain and discomfort. Surgery is required for an enlarged prostate.

PROSTATE CANCER AND TESTICULAR CANCER
There are many kinds of cancer and many causes for it. **Cancer** is an area of uncontrolled cell growth that invades the surrounding tissue and destroys it. After lung cancer, cancer of the prostate is the most common form of cancer among men. At this time, surgical removal of the prostate is the usual treatment for prostate cancer. **Testicular cancer,** or cancer of the testicles, can occur in men between the ages of 15 and 34. Hard lumps, enlargement of the organ, or an unusual

Sterility in men has many causes, including environmental factors and disease.

Prostate cancer is the second most common cancer among men.

◄ **Figure 12-7. When playing a sport, males should wear a protector or supporter to prevent injury to the groin area.**

thickening of tissue should be checked by a doctor. Cancer of the testes can be treated in a variety of ways. Like all cancers, treatment is most effective when the cancer is in its early stages.

Keeping the Reproductive System Healthy

Healthy habits start with cleanliness. It is important to thoroughly clean the external organs—the penis and scrotum—daily, preferably during a shower or bath.

Good health also requires protection and prevention. The **groin area,** the area of the external sexual organs, should be protected during athletic activities by wearing a protector or supporter. Tight clothing should be avoided since tight trousers, jeans, or underwear can irritate or cause pain in the groin area. To prevent hernias, men should be careful when lifting heavy objects. Males should also examine their testes on a monthly basis for signs of cancer. By discovering lumps or thickenings early, testicular cancer often can be treated successfully. Figure 12-8 describes how to perform this simple self-examination.

Figure 12-8. By performing this self-examination each month, cancer of the testes may be detected early.

Testicular Self-Examination

- Perform the self-examination each month after a bath or shower.
- Roll each testicle gently between the thumb and fingers of both hands.
- Feel for hard lumps, thickening, enlargement, tenderness, or change in texture.
- Report any abnormalities to your doctor.

Section Review

1. Name the male external sexual organs.
2. What are the two major functions of the testes?
3. What is semen and how is it formed?

What Do You Think?
4. What sexual changes would you tell your younger brother to expect as he reaches puberty?

3. THE FEMALE REPRODUCTIVE SYSTEM

Just as there are physical changes in a boy's body during puberty, so are there changes in a girl's. When a girl enters puberty, the most obvious physical changes are the development of the breasts and the widening of the hips. At this time too, a girl's body begins to produce ova, mature egg cells. Many hormones in the endocrine system work together to produce a mature egg, which, if fertilized by a sperm cell, may develop into a new life.

Structure and Function

Figure 12-9. The female reproductive system provides the environment for a fertilized egg to develop into a baby.

The female reproductive system, like the male reproductive system, is made up of both external and internal structures. In the female, it is the internal organs that provide the environment in which a fertilized egg can develop into a baby. Figure 12-9 shows the internal organs of the female reproductive system.

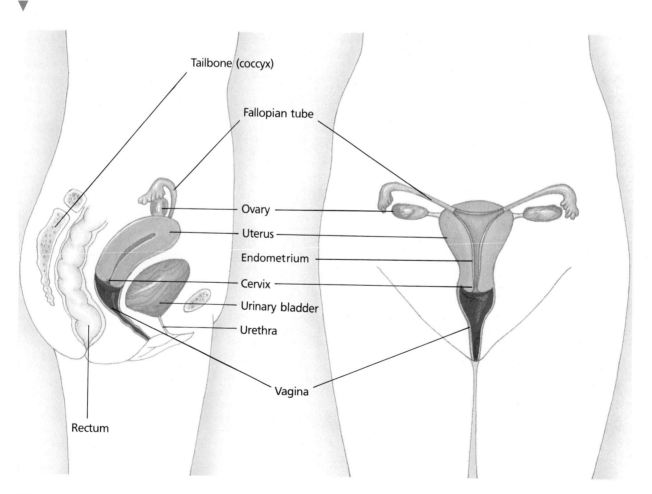

Tailbone (coccyx)

Fallopian tube

Ovary

Uterus

Endometrium

Cervix

Urinary bladder

Urethra

Vagina

Rectum

OVARIES The two ovaries are small organs, each about the size of an almond. They are located inside the female, one on each side of the body a few inches below the waist. As you know, the ovaries have two important functions: they release estrogen and progesterone and produce mature egg cells. When a girl is born, each ovary contains about 200,000 eggs. These eggs are not mature. They begin to mature, or ripen, when the female reaches puberty. Once puberty begins, the ovaries usually produce and release one ripened egg every 28 days in a process called **ovulation** (oh vyuh **lay** shun). The tiny egg that is released is no larger than a typewriter dot.

FALLOPIAN TUBES The two **fallopian** (fah **loh** pee un) **tubes,** or oviducts (ducts that carry eggs), are small tubes that carry the released eggs from the ovaries. The fallopian tubes lie on each side of the body. They are slightly curved so that one end of each tube lies close to an ovary. Each month, one of the ovaries releases a mature egg into a fallopian tube. Because eggs, unlike sperm, cannot swim, small hairs in the fallopian tubes sweep the egg into and through the tube. If sperm are present in the fallopian tubes, the egg may be fertilized.

UTERUS Each of the fallopian tubes leads into the **uterus** (**yoo** tur uhs), a hollow, muscular, pear-shaped organ located between the two ovaries. Another name for the uterus is the **womb (woom)**. It is here that a fertilized egg will develop and grow into a baby. The uterus has several layers of tissue and a rich supply of blood to protect and nourish a developing baby. The base of the uterus is called the **cervix.** When a baby is ready to be born, the cervix expands to allow the baby to exit.

VAGINA The **vagina** (vuh **jy** nuh), or birth canal, is a hollow tube leading from the uterus to the outside of the body. It is through the vagina that the baby passes out of the body. The walls of the vagina are very elastic, which allows it to expand dramatically during childbirth.

The Menstrual Cycle

You may recall from the discussion of sperm production that males produce millions of sperm cells daily. Females, on the other hand, produce one mature egg cell each month. The process by which women produce and release egg cells is known as the **menstrual** (**men** stroo ul) **cycle.**

The menstrual cycle, which is shown in Figure 12-10, begins when an egg starts to mature in one of the ovaries. At the same time, the **endometrium** (en doh **mee** tree um), the lining of the uterus, thickens. If the egg is not fertilized,

The ovaries produce mature egg cells and release the female sex hormones.

If an egg is fertilized, it will grow and develop into a baby inside the uterus.

Changes in Ovary and Uterus in the Menstrual Cycle

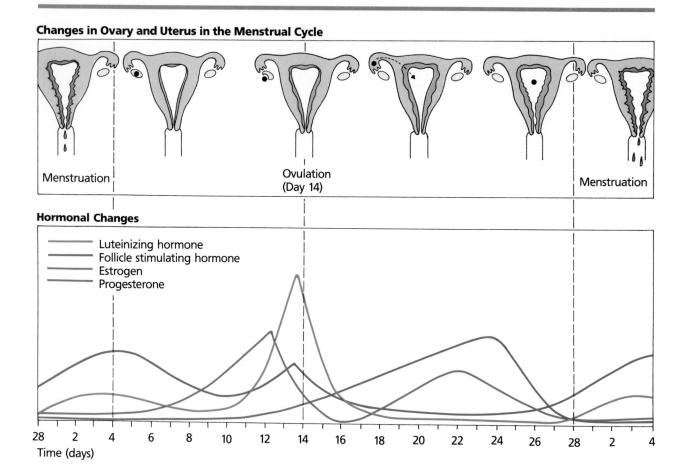

Hormonal Changes

Luteinizing hormone
Follicle stimulating hormone
Estrogen
Progesterone

Time (days)

Figure 12-10. The female endocrine system regulates the menstrual cycle. Which hormone level is highest when ovulation occurs?

A woman is most fertile around the time of ovulation.

the endometrium breaks down and is discharged from the body. This discharge of blood and tissue, known as **menstruation** (**men** stroo ay shun) or the menstrual period, marks the end of the menstrual cycle. On the average, the menstrual cycle lasts 28 days, although cycles as short as 21 days or as long as 35 days are normal.

The menstrual cycle is controlled by the endocrine system. During the first half of the cycle (days 1–14), the pituitary hormone FSH stimulates an egg to mature inside one of the ovaries. As the egg develops it releases estrogen, which causes the endometrium, the lining of the uterus, to thicken. At about the middle of the cycle (day 14), the level of LH begins to rise, and ovulation occurs. The mature egg is released by the ovary and travels into the fallopian tube. A woman is most fertile (able to produce children) around the time of ovulation.

It takes about 7 days for the egg to travel through the fallopian tube into the uterus. During this time, the production of progesterone increases, which maintains the growth of the endometrium. If the egg has not been fertilized when it reaches the uterus, progesterone and estrogen levels drop. The endometrium breaks down and, along with the unfertilized egg, passes out of the body through the vagina. In general, a menstrual period lasts about 3 to 5 days. About two ounces (50–60 milliliters) of fluid is lost during menstruation. Most women wear either a sanitary pad or a tampon (sanitary protection worn inside the vagina) to absorb the menstrual flow.

Although the endocrine system controls ovulation and menstruation, many other factors can influence menstrual cycle. Diet, stress, illness, and weight gain or loss can all affect the menstrual cycle. Every woman's menstrual cycle is different. The age when menstruation begins, the length of the menstrual cycle, and even the number of days it takes to discharge the menstrual flow varies from woman to woman. It is common for a woman's menstrual cycle to be irregular at times, especially for the first few years. Some women may experience cramps or other discomfort during the menstrual period. Often a warm bath, the use of a heating pad, exercise, or a change in diet can relieve cramps. For severe cramps or for any other menstrual concerns, see your doctor.

The menstrual cycle is a normal, natural sign of a healthy reproductive system. Except during pregnancy, menstruation occurs each month from puberty until about the age of 45 to 55. At that time of life, called **menopause** (**men** uh pawz), the ovaries slow down their hormone production and no longer produce mature eggs. At this point, menstruation stops, and the woman is no longer fertile.

Disorders of the Female Reproductive System

Some diseases of the reproductive system are transmitted sexually and will be discussed in Chapter 17. This section will focus on common medical conditions that affect the female reproductive system.

VAGINITIS   At some point in her life, every female probably will experience **vaginitis** (vaj uh **ny** tis), a vaginal infection or irritation. There are several types of vaginitis, but the symptoms are similar—a thick discharge, vaginal itching, and a burning sensation during urination. Only a doctor can diagnose the specific type of vaginitis and provide the correct medication for it.

STERILITY   There are a number of reasons for sterility. Some of the most common causes of female sterility include blocking of the fallopian tube, the failure of the ovaries to produce eggs, and **endometriosis** (en doh mee tree **oh** sis). Endometriosis is a condition in which the endometrium grows somewhere other than the uterus. This condition can sometimes be corrected with hormones or through surgery.

New Treatment for Endometriosis

About 5 million women in the United States suffer from endometriosis. The disease causes pain in the pelvic area, especially during menstrual periods. Often this disease can lead to sterility.

Although no cure for endometriosis exists yet, a new treatment is available to relieve pain and, in some cases, reverse sterility. The treatment, called laser laparoscopy, uses two older surgical instruments, a laparoscope and a laser.

A laparoscope is a rigid tube-like device that a surgeon inserts into the abdomen through a small cut made near the belly button. Lights and an eyepiece on the laparoscope allow the surgeon to see the internal reproductive organs.

The surgeon uses the laparoscope to guide a laser, which is inserted through a separate incision. By concentrating light into a narrow, high-energy beam, the laser then destroys any unwanted tissue with pinpoint precision.

Compared to conventional surgery, laser laparoscopy is quicker and safer and leads to a faster recovery.

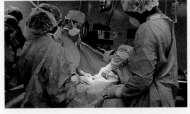

Endometriosis can now be treated by laser surgery.

TOXIC SHOCK SYNDROME (TSS) Sometimes a bacterial infection can cause a rare disease known as **toxic shock syndrome (TSS).** TSS usually is found in menstruating women who are using tampons. Although no one is certain about the connection between tampons and TSS, it is important to change tampons regularly to avoid infection. Some doctors also recommend that women do not use super-absorbent tampons.

The symptoms of TSS include a sudden high fever, a rash, vomiting, diarrhea, and dizziness. Contact a doctor or get the person to an emergency room immediately since TSS can lead to death.

PREMENSTRUAL SYNDROME (PMS) As you have just read, some women experience discomfort during their menstrual period. For most of these women, the pain is minimal, and they continue their usual activities. Some women, however, experience severe discomfort some time before menstruation. This condition, known as **premenstrual syndrome (PMS)** is marked by nervous tension, mood swings, headaches, bloating, and irritability. Although PMS is not well understood, it is believed to be caused by a dramatic change in hormone levels. To treat PMS, some doctors recommend that women alter their diets to reduce their intake of salt, sugar, caffeine, and alcohol. Regular exercise and other stress-reduction techniques can also help relieve PMS.

CYSTS AND CANCER An **ovarian cyst** (sist) is a growth on the outside of an ovary. Small cysts are common in women of all ages and often dissolve on their own. Large cysts may be painful and must be surgically removed.

Friend to Friend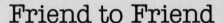

Donna:
Carol, what do you think I should do about Steve? He keeps pressuring me to have sex.

Carol:
How do you feel about it?

Donna:
I'm afraid of losing him, but I don't feel ready for sex.

Carol:
Have you talked to him about your feelings?

4. HEREDITY

When a baby is born, people often say, "she looks just like her father" or "he has his grandmother's eyes." Think about the ways in which you resemble your parents, grandparents, and any other relatives. The color of your eyes, the texture of your hair, your height—these are traits you inherit from your parents. **Heredity** is the passing on, or transmission, of biological characteristics from parent to child.

Chromosomes and Genes

How are characteristics passed on from a mother and a father to their child? What determines the combination of characteristics that are passed on? To answer these questions, you must first understand the process that takes place in almost every cell in your body. This process involves **chromosomes** (**kroh** muh sohmz), tiny structures found within almost every cell. Your chromosomes carry the information about the characteristics you will inherit. Chromosomes are made up of a chemical substance known as **deoxyribonucleic** (dee ahk see ry boh noo **klee** ik) **acid,** or **DNA.**

Most of the cells in your body contain 23 pairs of chromosomes—46 chromosomes in all. Your sex cells (the sperm or egg), however, contain half this number, or 23 chromosomes. When a sperm and egg unite, the fertilized egg ends up with 46 chromosomes—23 from each parent.

Each of the chromosomes in your body is made up of many genes. A **gene** is a section of a chromosome that determines a single trait, such as eye color. Genes are considered the basic units of heredity. Like the chromosomes that contain them, genes come in pairs. Since a sex cell con-

Chromosomes carry information about the characteristics you will inherit.

◀ **Figure 12-12. Your looks are determined by the traits you inherit from your parents.**

Inheritance Patterns

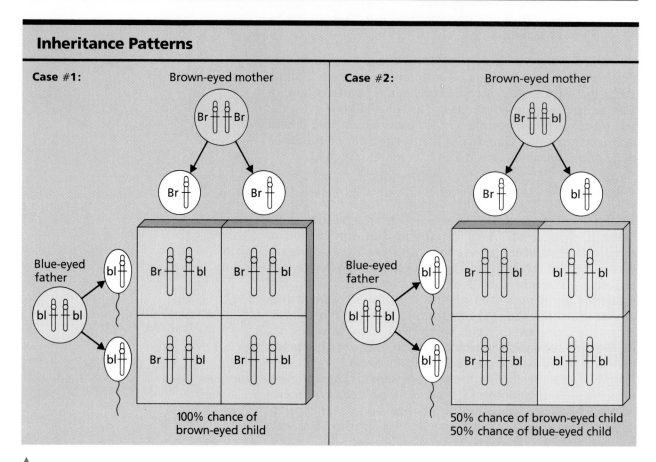

Case #1: Brown-eyed mother

Blue-eyed father

100% chance of brown-eyed child

Case #2: Brown-eyed mother

Blue-eyed father

50% chance of brown-eyed child
50% chance of blue-eyed child

▲
Figure 12-13. If a baby receives one gene for brown eyes and one gene for blue eyes, it will have brown eyes. Only if a baby receives two genes for blue eyes will it have blue eyes.

tains only one of each chromosome pair, it also has only one of each gene pair. Once the egg is fertilized, however, it contains two genes for each trait—one from the father and one from the mother. This is how hereditary information is passed from one generation to the next.

DOMINANT AND RECESSIVE GENES Imagine that a father had blue eyes and a mother had brown eyes. What color eyes would the child have? Although the child would receive both a blue-eye and a brown-eye gene, only one of these traits will show up, or be expressed, in the child. This is because many genes are either dominant or recessive. **Dominant genes** are genes that are expressed whenever they are present. **Recessive genes** are genes that are expressed only when the dominant gene is not present. With eye color, the brown-eye gene is dominant, and the blue-eye gene is recessive. The child, then, probably would have brown eyes.

There is a way that a brown-eyed mother and blue-eyed father can have a child with blue eyes. This is shown in Figure 12-13. Suppose the child's mother had one brown-eye gene and one blue-eye gene. She would have brown eyes because brown is the dominant trait. Each of her egg cells, however, would have an equal chance of receiving either the brown-eye gene or the blue-eye gene. Any egg cell that receives the blue-eye gene will result in a blue-eyed child.

Some other examples of dominant genetic traits are curly hair, freckles, and dimples. Other recessive traits include straight hair, blonde hair, and even a "turned-up" nose. Could a child end up with curly, blonde hair if the mother has straight, blonde hair and the father has curly, blonde hair? How could the child inherit a turned-up nose?

SEX DETERMINATION Among the 23 pairs of chromosomes in each body cell is a single pair called the sex chromosomes. The genes on the sex chromosomes determine whether you are male or female and control most of your sexual characteristics. If you are a female, the two sex chromosomes in your cells are called X chromosomes. If you are a male, one of your sex chromosomes is an X chromosome and the other is called a Y chromosome.

What happens to the sex chromosomes when egg and sperm cells form? As you read, only one chromosome of each pair is contained in the egg and sperm cells. Since females have only one type of sex chromosome, all eggs receive one X chromosome. In males, however, there are two different sex chromosomes. This means that half of a male's sperm cells have an X chromosome and half have a Y chromosome. When a sperm cell with an X chromosome fertilizes an egg, the egg will develop into a girl. When a sperm with a Y chromosome fertilizes an egg, it will develop into a boy. It is the sperm cell that determines the sex of a child.

Genetic Disorders

Along with hair and eye color and other traits, some genetic disorders can also be passed from parent to child. A **genetic disorder** is any abnormal condition that a person inherits through genes. A gene that can cause a genetic disorder is sometimes called a defective gene. Just like all other inherited traits, the genes that cause genetic disorders are either dominant or recessive. Some examples of disorders caused by dominant genes include extra fingers on the hands and Huntington's disease (a disease of the nervous system). Because the genes for these disorders are dominant, the disorder will show up in people who receive one defective gene from either parent.

RECESSIVE DISORDERS Most genetic disorders are recessive disorders. With recessive disorders, a child must receive two defective genes—one from each parent—for the disorder to show. People who receive one defective recessive gene are called carriers. Carriers do not express the disorder because it is masked by the dominant normal gene. They can, however, pass the defective gene to their children.

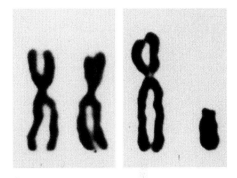

Figure 12-14. Females have two X chromosomes while males have one X and one Y chromosome.

Figure 12-15. How are normal red blood cells (top) different from sickle cells (bottom)?

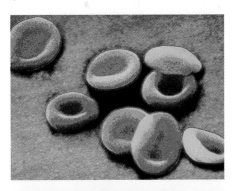

Sickle cell anemia is a recessive genetic blood disorder that occurs most frequently among people of African descent. People who inherit two defective genes for this disease will have abnormally shaped red blood cells and may die at an early age. People who have one sickle-cell gene may show few, if any, signs of the disease.

Another recessive genetic disorder, known as **Tay-Sachs disease,** is characterized by the lack of an important chemical in the brain. Tay-Sachs disease is found primarily among eastern Europeans. Infants with two defective Tay-Sachs genes appear healthy at first but soon show signs of brain damage. There is no treatment for this disease, and those who are born with Tay-Sachs usually die within their first five years of life.

Phenylketonuria (fen ul kee tah **nyoor** ee uh), or **PKU,** is a rare disorder that can cause severe mental retardation in infants. Babies who inherit two defective genes for this disease cannot break down phenylalanine, a chemical commonly found in food. As phenylalanine builds up in the body, the brain is affected. Although PKU is a serious disease, it can be treated successfully if the infant follows a special diet. Because PKU can be treated when it is recognized early in life, babies are routinely tested for this disorder, even though it occurs only rarely.

Cystic fibrosis (**sis** tik fy **broh** sis) is another recessive disorder. In children with two defective genes, some glands produce too much mucus, which clogs and damages the lungs. As the disease progresses, it becomes increasingly difficult for the child to breathe. Although the disease is fatal, many children born with cystic fibrosis today will live to early adulthood.

SEX-LINKED DISORDERS There are a small number of recessive genetic disorders that are **sex-linked disorders,** that is, the gene for the disorder is found on the X chromosome. Sex-linked disorders are more common in men than in women. This is because men have only one X chromosome, so all defective genes on that chromosome will be expressed. Since women have two X chromosomes, a recessive defective gene on one X chromosome can be covered by a normal gene on the other X chromosome. The woman carrying the defective gene, however, may pass it on to her children.

The most common sex-linked disorder is **color blindness,** the inability to distinguish certain colors. Other, more serious sex-linked disorders are **Duchenne muscular dystrophy** (**dis** truh fee) and **hemophilia** (hee muh **fil** ee uh). Duchenne muscular dystrophy is a condition in which muscle tissue begins to break down during childhood. A person with this disease cannot walk and usually does not live beyond his or her teens. In hemophilia, a person's blood cannot clot. Hemophilia is dangerous because the smallest cut or

Sex-linked disorders are more common in men than women.

Figure 12-16. People who have inherited a common form of color blindness cannot see the number within the circle.

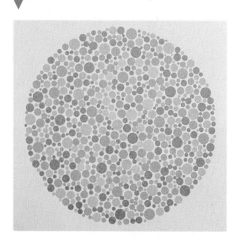

bruise can cause a person to bleed to death. Blood plasma transfusions and injections of a blood-clotting substance are used to treat hemophilia. Many hemophiliacs are now living into adulthood.

DOWN'S SYNDROME There are some genetic disorders that are the result of too few or too many chromosomes. One disorder, called **Down's syndrome,** results when a child receives an extra chromosome (chromosome 21). People with Down's syndrome are mentally retarded and have a distinctive physical appearance. Mental retardation can range from mild to severe. Although the reason is not fully understood, women over the age of 35 have a greater chance of having a Down's syndrome child. Children with Down's syndrome often lead full lives within their limitations.

Section Review

1. What is a chromosome? What is a gene?
2. Explain the difference between dominant and recessive genes. Give examples of dominant and recessive genetic traits.
3. Why do most sex-linked genetic disorders affect males and not females?

What Do You Think?
4. List some physical traits exhibited by members of your family that you would say are controlled by dominant genes. Then, list some you think are controlled by recessive genes. Explain your reasoning.

12 | Chapter Review

Chapter Summary

- The endocrine system allows one part of the body to communicate with another through chemical messengers called hormones. Endocrine glands control growth, metabolism, and reproduction.
- The endocrine glands that play a role in reproduction are the testes, the ovaries, the pituitary gland, and hypothalamus.
- In the male, the testes produce sperm cells and the male hormone testosterone.
- Fluids produced by the seminal vesicles, prostate gland, and Cowper's glands mix with sperm to form semen.
- Internal female reproductive organs are ovaries, fallopian tubes, uterus, and vagina.
- The ovaries produce the female sex hormones estrogen and progesterone. Under the control of the pituitary gland, the ovaries produce and release a mature egg in a process called ovulation.
- Ovulation is part of a monthly process known as the menstrual cycle. During this cycle, the lining of the uterus thickens in preparation for a fertilized egg. If the egg is not fertilized, the uterine lining is discharged from the body in a process called menstruation.
- Disorders of the female reproductive system include premenstrual syndrome, cancer, vaginitis, and sterility.
- Males and females should perform self-examinations to assure early detection of testicular and breast cancer.
- Heredity is the physical transmission of traits from parents to children.
- Chromosomes are the structures in cells that carry hereditary characteristics.
- A gene is a section of a chromosome that determines a single trait. A child's genes come equally from mother and father.
- Some genetic disorders are sickle cell anemia, Tay-Sachs disease, phenylketonuria, cystic fibrosis, and Down's syndrome.
- Females possess two X chromosomes in their cells, while males possess one X chromosome and one Y chromosome.

Vocabulary Review

Listed below are some of the important terms in this chapter. Choose the term that best matches the phrase in the exercise that follows.

chromosomes
color blindness
gene
endometrium
epididymis
fertilization

follicle-stimulating
   hormone
menstruation
ovary
ovulation

pituitary gland
progesterone
prostate gland
seminal vesicles
sickle cell anemia

spermatogenesis
testes
thyroid gland
uterus
vagina

1. the lining of the uterus
2. a genetic disorder of red blood cells
3. male reproductive structure in which sperm acquire the ability to swim
4. male reproductive glands that produce testosterone and sperm
5. the process by which a mature egg is released from the ovary

6. pituitary hormone that plays a role in reproduction
7. the birth canal
8. structure on which genes are located
9. the process by which sperm are produced in the testes
10. endocrine gland that controls metabolism, growth, and reproduction

What Have You Learned?

1. What is the endocrine system?
2. How are hormone levels regulated?
3. Name two hormones produced by the pituitary gland that are important for reproduction.
4. Describe the process of spermatogenesis.
5. What is the function of the fallopian tubes?
6. What is the menstrual cycle? Which hormones play a role in this cycle?
7. List some causes of sterility in both males and females.

8. What is the difference between sperm and semen?
9. How often should breast or testicular self-examination be done? Why are self-examinations important?
10. Explain why recessive genes are often not expressed in the body.
11. How many chromosomes are contained in your body cells? Your sex cells?
12. Explain why the father, rather than the mother, determines the sex of their offspring.
13. What is Down's syndrome?

What Do You Think?

1. Your 16-year-old sister does not menstruate regularly. Should she be concerned about this? Why or why not?
2. Some athletes misuse steroids, chemicals similar to testosterone, because of their effect on building muscles. Why do you think that steroid misuse might have a harmful effect on the reproductive system?

3. If only one sperm is needed to fertilize an egg, why do you think that 100 million sperm are released during ejaculation?
4. Because color-blindness is a sex-linked trait, it is more common in males than females. For a girl to be color-blind, what genes would she have to inherit from her parents? Would either of her parents be color-blind?

What Would You Do?

1. Suppose that a friend of yours has confided in you that during a testicular self-examination, he detected a lump. Your friend is reluctant to see a doctor. What would you do?
2. Your friend tells you that her younger sister has recently begun to menstruate but seems confused about the process. Your friend would like to help her sister feel more

comfortable about her changing body. What should she say or do?
3. If you were worried that your body was not developing properly, what would you do?
4. A man with hemophilia is considering marriage. He is concerned his children might be born with hemophilia. What questions should he ask his future wife? Explain.

For Further Study

1. Contact the March of Dimes to find out what is being done to combat genetic disorders such as sickle cell anemia, cystic fibrosis, hemophilia, muscular dystrophy, and Tay-Sachs disease. For one disorder, write a report explaining ongoing research, any possible cures, and hope for the future.
2. Choose three endocrine glands discussed in this chapter and find out about some disorders that affect them. Construct a chart describing the disorders, their causes, and their treatments. Include photos of the disorders, if possible.

13

As you read, think about

▶ the lifelong responsibilities and requirements of being a parent.

▶ the process of human development from conception to birth.

▶ the physical and emotional changes that parents undergo during pregnancy and afterward.

▶ the stages of childhood development from birth to 12 years of age.

Birth and Parenthood

You call out, "Say cheese!" Everyone smiles, and you quickly snap the picture. You started taking pictures of your sister's family soon after your nephew was born. You have a whole album of pictures. It's fun to look through these photographs and see how quickly he's developed. He's not a baby any longer.

Soon there will be a new baby to add to the album. Your sister and brother-in-law are planning a large family. You can hardly wait. Will it be a girl this time?

In this chapter, you'll learn about pregnancy and fetal development, including ways to protect the health of both mother and baby. You'll also look at how babies and children grow and develop. Finally, you'll examine the responsibilities of having a child and learn what you should consider in deciding to become a parent.

Being a parent is one of life's most rewarding—and most difficult—experiences.

297

1. DECIDING TO HAVE CHILDREN

Becoming a parent is the biggest commitment a person can make in his or her life. It is for keeps. There is no such thing as undoing parenthood "if it doesn't work out" or if you become bored with it.

Reasons for Having Children

Why do people have children? Usually there are a combination of reasons. If you were the baby-to-be, what would you think of the following reasons?

- "The world needs more people like us!"
- "We have good jobs, nice cars, and a house. It's time to have children."
- "We have lots of love to give to a child."
- "My mother wants to be a grandma before she's 50."
- "If I get pregnant, maybe he will marry me."
- "All of our married friends are having babies. Maybe we should, too."
- "Once I have a baby, the world will know I'm an adult."
- "I need someone to love."
- "I need someone to love me."
- "It's now or never. We're almost 40!"
- "If we have one more, maybe it will be a girl."
- "I know our marriage will improve if we have a baby."

Check Your Wellness

How much do you know about conception, pregnancy, birth? Decide whether these statements are true or false.

1. The decision to have a child involves considering the financial means, emotional maturity, and the time you have for a family.

2. Fertilization occurs when an egg cell joins with several hundred sperm cells.

3. The most critical period in a baby's development is the first three months of pregnancy.

4. By the fourth month of pregnancy, most of the fetus's body systems have been formed.

5. The symptoms of early pregnancy often include fatigue and nausea.

6. A pregnant woman must eat nutritiously and avoid alcohol and drugs not prescribed by her doctor.

7. Teenagers are more likely than older women to give birth to premature babies.

8. Birth occurs 40 weeks after fertilization.

9. Because the first year has the greatest risk of death, babies need great care.

Figure 13-1. The joys of parenthood are many but so are the responsibilities. ▶

The baby-to-be might not care for some of these reasons. It needs parents who can focus on what they will give, not what they will get. If the baby could choose, it would want parents who

- are adults who like children and who really want to have a baby.
- love each other, are emotionally mature, and have a happy, stable marriage.
- have completed their educations and are financially able to support a child.
- know the responsibilities of parenthood and are committed to carrying them out.
- accept the fact that their lives will change a great deal once the baby is born.
- are eager and able to give a child all the love, guidance, and attention it needs to be happy and healthy.
- are prepared to enter into a lifelong relationship with a new and unknown person.

Parenthood has many joys and satisfactions, but it is also stressful and involves a lot of hard work. The responsibilities of parenthood go far beyond most other occupations. Babies are demanding and totally helpless. Along with the loving feelings, smiles, and cuddles, new parents must face sleepless nights, times of worry about illness, and the giving up of many freedoms and pleasures they used to enjoy. Couples with the qualifications listed above have the best chance of coping successfully with all of the demands and responsibilities of parenthood.

O——⚐
Parents who understand the realities and demands of having a child have the best chance of coping.

◀ **Figure 13-2. Caring for a young child is a full-time responsibility.**

Planning a Family

At least one part of planning a family is purely practical. A couple has to review their budget to find out whether or not they can afford to provide food, clothing, shelter, and medical care for a child. They need to discuss who will care for the child if both of them must continue to work. They need to find out if their employers grant maternity or paternity leave, so that at least one of them can stay home with the baby for a few months and still return to the same job. They also need to investigate the costs of day care.

The next step in planning a family is to find out if either parent could possibly pass on an inherited disease to a child. The couple should examine their health histories and ask their own parents whether any of the inherited diseases mentioned in Chapter 12 run in the family. If this possibility exists, the couple should receive **genetic counseling.** In genetic counseling, a genetic counselor explains to a couple what the chances are that they will pass on a disease to a child. The couple then has to weigh the risks and decide whether or not to have a baby.

Health careers

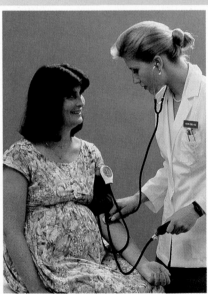

Obstetricians closely monitor mothers and their unborn babies.

What kind of doctor cares for two patients at the same time? Answer: an **obstetrician,** a doctor who has specialized in caring for pregnant women and the unborn babies they carry.

Obstetricians know about the special medications, dietary needs, risks, and possible complications associated with pregnancy. They use special instruments, such as ultrasound and heartbeat monitors, to track the baby's progress, while also watching the mother's health. Obstetricians may also counsel expectant couples to prepare them for their new child. When the time comes, obstetricians help the newborns come into the world.

To become an obstetrician, a person must graduate from college and attend four years of medical school. This is followed by several more years of study and training in obstetrics.

If a woman's pregnancy proceeds without complications, she can choose to be cared for by a **nurse-midwife.** A nurse-midwife must have a bachelor's degree in nursing and an additional year of study in obstetrics.

Even before a woman becomes pregnant, she has to start taking care of herself. She should be in good physical condition and eat a balanced diet. She should not use tobacco, drink alcohol, take any drugs that are not prescribed by her doctor, or handle or be exposed to any harmful substances or fumes in the environment. Any of these substances can harm the unborn child.

It is also important to plan for **prenatal** (pree **nay** tul) **care,** or medical care during pregnancy. Before becoming pregnant, the woman should visit her doctor, who will recommend an obstetrician. An **obstetrician** (ahb stih **trish** un) is a doctor who specializes in caring for pregnant women and assisting at the birth of babies. Good prenatal care is crucial to maintaining the health of the mother and to having a healthy baby.

Finally, the couple has to stop using any method of preventing pregnancy. Preventing pregnancy is known as birth control or **contraception** (kahn trah **sep** shun). If pregnancy does not occur within one year after a couple has stopped using contraception, the couple may be **infertile** (in **fur** til), or unable to have biological children. At this time many infertile couples may undergo tests to determine the cause of the infertility. Treatments are available to correct some forms of infertility in men and in women. If, after treatment, pregnancy does not occur, or if the fertility problem cannot be corrected, the couples may consider a number of alternatives. One of the alternatives is **adoption**, a legal procedure in which a child is taken into a family to be raised in the same way as any child born to the parents. Adopted children are their parents' children in every respect except genetic inheritance. Another alternative involves becoming foster parents. **Foster parents** take care of children whose parents are unable to do so. The child may live with foster parents for a few weeks or several years, depending on the situation.

Section Review

1. Name four responsibilities of parenthood.
2. What is the purpose of genetic counseling?
3. Name two ways a woman can start taking care of her baby before she becomes pregnant.
4. What is contraception for?

What Do You Think?
5. Of the reasons for having children that are listed on page 298, which ones do you think a baby-to-be would like the best?

Issues in Health

Should Surrogate Motherhood Be Legal?

Sadness and frustration are the feelings often experienced by couples who want but cannot have children. Now, scientific advances have provided some new options, including surrogate motherhood.

A surrogate mother bears a baby for others, usually in exchange for a fee. She is artificially inseminated with sperm from the male. The mother signs a contract that requires her to turn the baby over to the couple when it is born.

Some people approve of surrogate motherhood as a way to aid infertile couples. They favor laws that ensure that surrogate contracts are enforced. Many argue that surrogate mothers should be carefully screened and that psychological counseling be provided to them during and after pregnancy.

Other people are against surrogate motherhood. Some feel that contracts should at least allow the mother time to change her mind after the baby is born. Others believe that a woman's body and baby should not be for sale. They fear that wealthy people may take advantage of poor women and that surrogate children may suffer psychological damage.

Do you think that surrogate motherhood should be legal? Explain your thoughts.

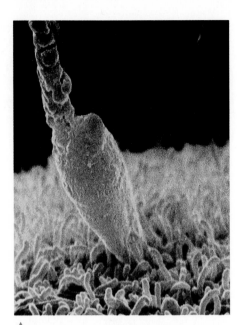

Figure 13-3. Fertilization occurs when a sperm unites with an egg.

2. CONCEPTION AND PREGNANCY

Every individual begins when two cells, one from the mother and one from the father, join. These cells are too small to be seen without a microscope, yet their union is the beginning of every human being.

Fertilization

Fertilization, also called conception, is the union of an egg (ovum) from the mother and a sperm from the father. As you learned in Chapter 12, an egg is released from one of the ovaries about once every 28 days. After its release, the egg enters the fallopian tube to begin its journey to the uterus. If sperm are deposited in the woman's vagina while the egg is on its way to the uterus, fertilization can occur. Fertilization is shown in Figure 13-3.

Although as many as half a billion sperm may be deposited in the vagina, only a few hundred will survive the six-inch swim to the fallopian tubes. Most will die along the way. Of the sperm that do reach the egg, only one will fertilize it. Within seconds of fertilization, the surface of the egg changes so that no more sperm can enter the egg. At the moment of fertilization, the sex and genetic traits of the future individual are set.

THE ZYGOTE The united egg and sperm are called a **zygote** (**zy** goht). Within 36 hours, while the zygote is still traveling through the fallopian tube, it begins to divide, first into two cells, then into four, and so on, until it is made up of dozens of cells, shown in Figure 13-4.

IMPLANTATION About three days after fertilization, the growing structure reaches the uterus, where it floats free for a few days and forms itself into a hollow sphere called a **blastocyst** (**blas** toh sist). Once the blastocyst is formed, it begins to attach itself to the wall of the uterus. The process of attachment is called **implantation** (im plan **tay** shun). After the blastocyst has been implanted, it is known as an **embryo** (**em** bree oh). Over the next few weeks, the attachment holding the embryo in place will become more complex.

Pregnancy can be detected once an embryo is implanted in the uterus.

PREGNANCY TESTING Pregnancy can be determined as soon as implantation has occurred. This is possible because the mother's body begins to produce the hormone **human chorionic gonadotropin (HCG)** (kor ee **ahn** ik) (goh nad uh **troh** pin) at the time of implantation. A laboratory test can find HCG in the blood of a pregnant woman six to eight days after fertilization. One week after menstruation

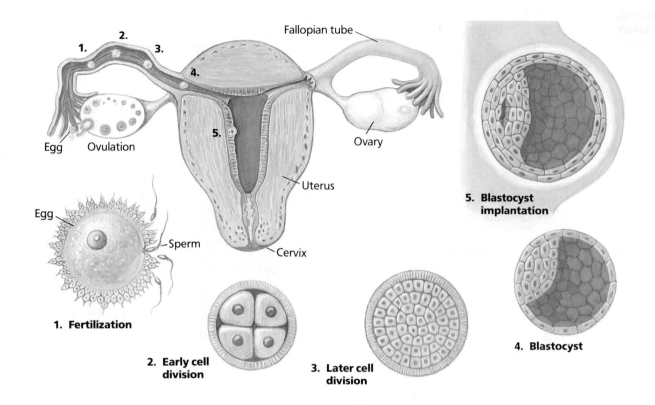

Egg
Ovulation

Fallopian tube

Ovary

Uterus

Cervix

Egg

Sperm

1. Fertilization

**2. Early cell
division**

**3. Later cell
division**

4. Blastocyst

**5. Blastocyst
implantation**

▲
**Figure 13-4. The embryo becomes
implanted in the wall of the uterus.**

should have begun, HCG can be found in a pregnant woman's urine. A pregnancy test is more reliable, however, if HCG is measured a full two weeks or more after menstruation should have begun.

Although the classic sign of pregnancy is a missed menstrual period, not all missed menstrual periods are caused by pregnancy. A menstrual period can be missed because of diet, stress, illness, weight gain or loss, or simple irregularity.

The Embryo

The attachment that holds the embryo to the wall of the uterus is called the **placenta** (pluh **sen** tuh). About 25 days after fertilization, a cord develops between the embryo and the placenta. This cord, shown in Figure 13-5 on the following page, is called the **umbilical** (uhm **bil** ih kul) **cord.** The umbilical cord is the embryo's lifeline. It contains blood vessels that carry nutrients and oxygen from the placenta to the embryo and wastes from the embryo to the placenta. The placenta acts as a filter between the mother's bloodstream and the embryo's bloodstream. Many different substances can pass through this filter, including alcohol, drugs, the chemicals in tobacco smoke, and some **viruses** (microscopic germs that cause disease). Any of those substances can seriously harm the developing embryo.

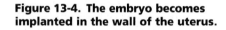

The placenta allows for an exchange of materials between the bloodstreams of the mother and the embryo.

Figure 13-5. The embryo is surrounded by many protective structures.

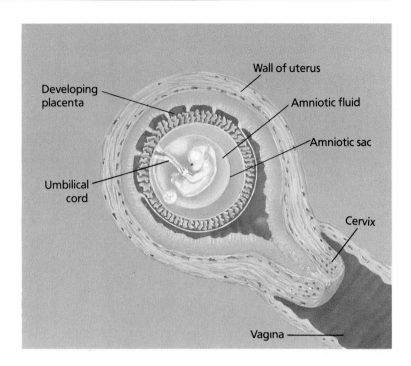

The developing embryo is enclosed in a bag of thin tissue called the **amniotic** (am nee **aht** ik) **sac.** The embryo floats within the sac in fluid called **amniotic fluid.** Amniotic fluid acts as a shock absorber and helps to keep the embryo's temperature constant.

By the end of the second month of pregnancy, the embryo is about 1.2 inches (3 centimeters) long and has a recognizable human form. At this point and until birth it is called a **fetus** (**fee** tuhs).

The Fetus

Between the third and sixth months, the fetus will grow until it is 11 inches (28 centimeters) long and weighs about 1.5 pounds (680 grams). Hair grows on the head and body, and facial features and ears develop. Because the fetus has little fat under its skin, the skin is wrinkled. During this period, the fetus begins to move and kick, a sign that its skeleton and muscles are developing. As its nervous system continues to grow, the sense organs begin to function. The fetus becomes sensitive to light and sound and alternates periods of activity with periods of sleep. A fetus born at this stage probably will not survive. At 23 weeks, the fetus has less than a 1 percent chance of survival. At 26 weeks, it has about a 7 percent chance of survival.

From the sixth to the ninth month, the fetus continues to grow and develop until it is ready to be born. The size of the body increases so that it becomes more in proportion to

As the fetus develops, it becomes more and more active.

the size of the head. The eyelids open and close, and the skin becomes less wrinkled as body fat accumulates. By the end of the ninth month, the average fetus is 20 inches (51 centimeters) long and weighs seven pounds (3.2 kilograms). A full-term fetus has approximately a 99 percent chance of survival at birth.

Expectant Parents

During the nine months that the baby is developing in the uterus, the expectant parents are preparing for its birth. The mother experiences the many physical changes of pregnancy. Both parents spend a lot of time thinking and talking about the baby to come. It is a time of excitement, expectation, and anxiety.

PHYSICAL CHANGES   The nine months of pregnancy are divided into three periods that are known as **trimesters** (try **mes** turz). Each trimester is three months long. The mother experiences many different physical changes during each trimester.

Early in the first trimester, while the embryo is developing into a fetus, the mother may experience **morning sickness.** Morning sickness consists of attacks of nausea and sometimes vomiting, which can occur in the morning or at any time of day. The cause is related to changes in the levels of certain hormones that occur as a result of the pregnancy. Morning sickness is the response of the mother's body as it adapts to these changes. Morning sickness usually disappears after a few weeks. Other changes that occur during the first trimester are an increase in breast size and breast tenderness, the need to urinate frequently, and times of overwhelming sleepiness. Some of these changes last throughout pregnancy. Some may not occur at all. Every pregnancy is different. By the end of the first trimester, the mother's abdomen looks more rounded than usual, but the pregnancy is not obvious.

During the second trimester, the mother's abdomen begins to swell, and she begins to feel the fetus moving. As the fetus and placenta grow, the enlarged uterus pushes against the mother's digestive tract. This can cause the mother to have constipation or indigestion—mostly "heartburn" and the need to burp. Toward the end of the second trimester, a thin fluid may begin to leak from the nipples. This fluid is the forerunner of breast milk.

By the third trimester, the mother is close to the upper limit of the recommended weight gain during pregnancy, which is 25 pounds. As the fetus grows to its birth size and exercises its muscles, its movements can be seen and felt on the mother's abdomen. Indigestion and frequent urination continue and may even increase as the fetus takes up more

▲
Figure 13-6. The fetus has a recognizable human form and begins to make its presence felt.

Most expectant parents feel excited and anxious.

▲

Figure 13-7. Parents experience many joys and concerns as they prepare to welcome their baby.

Figure 13-8. By following an exercise program approved by her doctor, a mother increases the chances for a healthy baby.

▼

and more room in the abdomen. During the last few weeks of pregnancy, some irregular contractions may be felt by the mother. The uterus is preparing its muscles for the work of pushing the fetus out. Finally, at a time anywhere from two weeks to a few days before birth, the fetus's head begins to move lower in the uterus.

EMOTIONAL CHANGES   What will our baby be like? Will it be a girl or a boy? Will it be healthy? Will we be good parents? These are only a few of the questions that parents ask themselves while they are waiting to welcome their child into the family.

During the first trimester of pregnancy, excitement and happiness are mixed with worries about responsibility and concerns about the physical discomfort of the mother. The bond between expectant parents can be especially strong during this time. In fact, some fathers experience **sympathetic pregnancy,** a condition in which they share some of the mother's discomfort, such as morning sickness or frequent urination. Both parents worry about the health of the embryo or fetus and the possibility that something could go wrong in the course of its development.

These worries do not go away entirely until the baby is born, but by the second trimester, the parents are more confident. This is usually a pleasant time. The fetus begins to kick, and the parents begin to think of it as a person. As the time of birth approaches, they choose a name for the baby and shop for things the baby will need. These activities help them to adjust to their role as parents. By the ninth month of pregnancy, both mother and father are anxious to experience the birth of their child.

PRENATAL CARE   The chances of having a healthy baby greatly increase if the mother practices good health habits and visits her obstetrician for regular checkups throughout pregnancy. In addition to a well-balanced diet, most women require extra protein, iron, calcium, and B vitamins during pregnancy. Pregnant women require extra calories, but usually they should gain no more than 25 pounds. Exercise is another part of a healthy pregnancy. It helps to keep the heart fit so that it can meet the extra demands of providing for the developing fetus. Having muscles that are in good condition helps during childbirth.

As soon as pregnancy is suspected, a woman should avoid alcohol, smoking, and any drugs not prescribed or approved by her obstetrician. These substances and others can cross into the baby's circulation and cause birth defects. Women who drink three ounces (88 milliliters) or more of alcohol per day have a one in three chance of giving birth to a baby with fetal alcohol syndrome. **Fetal alcohol syndrome** is mental retardation caused by alcohol, which damages the fetus's brain cells. Other birth defects can be caused by viral infections during pregnancy or conditions that prevent the fetus from receiving enough oxygen. A woman who smokes during pregnancy exposes her fetus to many of the harmful chemicals present in the smoke. Smoking also increases the chance that the fetus will not get enough oxygen, causing slow growth or other problems.

Regular checkups during pregnancy allow the obstetrician to detect and deal with any problems as early as possible. If a fetal problem is suspected, the obstetrician can recommend a number of special tests. For example, more than 70 inherited disorders can be detected with either one of two methods. The older method, called **amniocentesis** (am nee oh sen **tee** sus), involves the removal of a small amount of amniotic fluid from around the fetus at about the sixteenth week of pregnancy. Figure 13-9 illustrates how this procedure is carried out. After four weeks, this fluid is examined for the presence of substances that may indicate an inherited disorder. Because of the four-week wait, the results of amniocentesis cannot be obtained until the twentieth week of the woman's pregnancy.

The newer method, called **chorionic villus** (vil us) **sampling,** allows results to be available by the eighth week of pregnancy. In this test, a small piece of the **chorion,** a part of the developing placenta, is removed for examination. Chorionic villus sampling detects many of the same disorders as amniocentesis.

Regular checkups and a healthful life style during pregnancy are important for the health of the fetus.

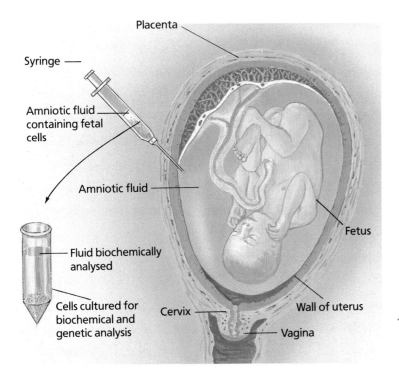

Syringe

Amniotic fluid containing fetal cells

Amniotic fluid

Fluid biochemically analysed

Cells cultured for biochemical and genetic analysis

Placenta

Fetus

Cervix

Wall of uterus

Vagina

◀ **Figure 13-9. In amniocentesis, a sample of amniotic fluid is used to detect certain disorders in the developing fetus.**

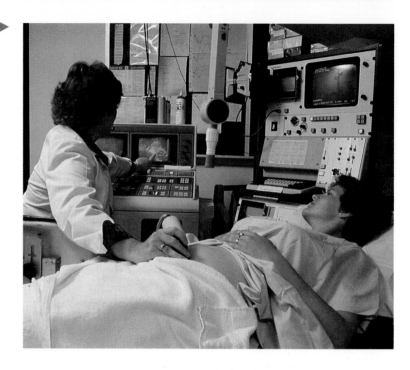

Figure 13-10. Ultrasound "pictures" can reveal defects or problems that may be treated during or after birth.

Ultrasound can detect abnormal bone, muscle, and heart formation in a developing fetus.

Sometimes high-frequency sound waves, known as **ultrasound,** are used to make a "picture" of the developing fetus. Ultrasound can detect abnormal bone, muscle, and heart formation. It is also used to confirm the position of the fetus in the uterus or the presence of more than one fetus.

Amniocentesis, chorionic villus sampling, and ultrasound are not done for every pregnancy. They are done only if the woman is over 35 years of age or if the obstetrician or couple have reason to believe that something might be wrong with the fetus. Some of the disorders revealed by these tests can be treated before birth or during the newborn period. Should a test show that the fetus has an extremely serious genetic defect or other disorder, the couple might choose to end the pregnancy.

Section Review

1. Name the two cells whose union causes fertilization.
2. Where does implantation occur?
3. How long is a trimester? How many trimesters are there in a pregnancy?
4. What is the purpose of amniocentesis?

What Do You Think?

5. If you were a woman used to swimming for your daily exercise, would you give it up during pregnancy? Why or why not?

3. BIRTH

As a pregnancy progresses, expectant parents begin to arrange for the birth of their baby. Most couples choose to have the baby in a hospital and sometimes in a **birthing room,** a room that looks just like a bedroom. Hospital births are assisted by the obstetrician and specially trained nurses. Having a baby in a hospital is a good idea because doctors, nurses, and special equipment are available to help immediately should something go wrong. If the pregnancy has gone well and the mother is in good health, the parents may choose to have the baby at home with the help of a nurse-midwife. A **nurse-midwife** is a person trained to assist in the birth process.

Many expectant parents take childbirth classes during pregnancy. Childbirth classes teach the parents what to expect during the birth process and how they can help the process along.

Most couples choose to have their baby in a hospital, assisted by a trained medical team.

The Stages of Birth

At the end of the ninth month of pregnancy, the fetus's head moves lower in the uterus. Birth begins when the muscular wall of the uterus begins contractions that will push the fetus out of the mother. The work of pushing the fetus out is called **labor.**

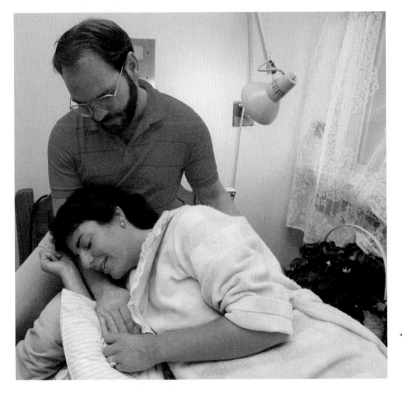

◀ **Figure 13-11. A hospital birthing room combines a homelike environment with modern medical facilities.**

Labor has three stages. Refer to Figure 13-12 as each stage is described. The first stage usually lasts from 4 to 24 hours. During this time, strong contractions cause the cervix, the "neck" of the uterus, to dilate, or increase its width, from one inch to four inches (2.5 to 10 centimeters). Each contraction lasts 30 to 90 seconds. At first, the contractions may be minutes apart, but by the end of the first stage, they are usually only a few seconds apart. The sac containing the amniotic fluid breaks, and the cervix becomes softer to allow the fetus to pass through.

Stage two lasts from half an hour to 2 hours and involves actual birth, or **delivery,** of the baby. Contractions continue, and the baby is pushed out through the cervix and vagina. The baby usually enters the world head first.

Once the baby is out, the umbilical cord is clamped and cut. There are no nerve endings in the cord, so this does not hurt the baby or the mother. The baby's nose and mouth are suctioned to remove mucus and make breathing easier. Spe-

Figure 13-12. The three stages of labor include delivery of the baby and the placenta.

▼

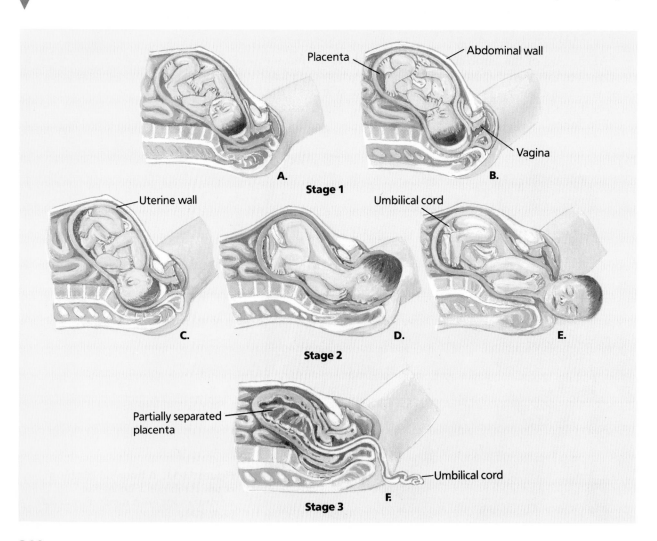

Placenta — Abdominal wall

Vagina

A.

B.

Stage 1

Uterine wall — Umbilical cord

C.

D.

E.

Stage 2

Partially separated placenta —

— Umbilical cord

F.

Stage 3

cial eyedrops are put on the baby's eyes to prevent infection, and an injection of vitamin K is given to prevent excessive bleeding from the cut umbilical cord.

Within one minute of birth and then again five minutes later, the baby is examined and given an Apgar score. The **Apgar score** is a way to determine the baby's need for emergency care. The baby is rated from zero to two in five areas: heart rate, breathing, muscle tone, the ability to react to a stimulus by moving and crying, and skin color. A score of two in each area, for a total of ten, means the baby has come through the birth process in the best condition possible.

The third stage of birth consists of delivery of the placenta, which is sometimes called the **afterbirth.** This stage lasts from 15 to 30 minutes.

Complications of Pregnancy and Birth

Sometimes problems can develop during pregnancy and birth. Staying in good health, avoiding drugs, alcohol, and tobacco, and having regular checkups are the best ways of reducing the possibility of these problems.

PROBLEMS IN PREGNANCY Although most pregnancies go well, occasionally problems do occur. Sometimes the zygote does not travel down the fallopian tube to the uterus. The blastocyst forms and becomes implanted in the fallopian tube or elsewhere in the abdomen. This condition, called **ectopic** (ek **tahp** ik) **pregnancy,** results in the death of the embryo. Sometimes the embryo blocks the fallopian tube and must be removed by a surgeon.

Another event that ends a pregnancy is **miscarriage.** Miscarriage is the expulsion of a dead zygote, blastocyst, embryo, or fetus from the uterus. The usual cause of death is a serious genetic defect, but sometimes death is due to the mother's illness or a drug the mother has taken. In other cases, there is no apparent reason for a miscarriage. Miscarriage almost always occurs during the first trimester, and sometimes it occurs before a woman is even aware of pregnancy. It is a natural event that ends 15 to 20 percent of all pregnancies. **Stillbirth** is the birth of a dead, full-term fetus. There may be a number of causes for a stillbirth, including physical injury to the fetus.

Some problems of pregnancy affect both the mother and the fetus. One of these is **toxemia** (tahk **see** mee uh). Toxemia is a serious condition characterized by high blood pressure, protein in the urine, and swelling, which is caused by fluid staying in the tissues. Toxemia requires hospital care. If toxemia is not treated, the mother can suffer convulsions, go into a coma, and die. Toxemia is most common in mothers for whom pregnancy is already a health risk: teenagers,

PUBS—Testing and Treating the Unborn

If a fetus needed a blood transfusion, how would doctors know? How would they solve the problem? The answer is PUBS, *p*ercutaneous *u*mbilical *b*lood *s*ampling, a new way of testing fetal health.

Doctors use the PUBS technique to draw a blood sample from a fetus. Then, they screen the sample for disorders such as sickle-cell anemia. They also can use PUBS to deliver medication to the fetus and to give it a blood transfusion.

To get a blood sample, the doctor must insert a needle into the mother's abdomen and carefully guide it through the uterine wall to the umbilical cord, where the blood sample is drawn. This sample is analyzed, and the results are used to diagnose any problems.

Eventually, PUBS may be able to find problems that can lead to mental retardation. PUBS also may be able to detect the absence of certain key substances and then supply them to help the fetus develop normally.

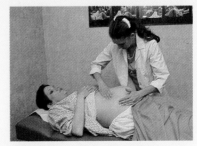

If problems occur during a pregnancy, PUBS may be used to treat the developing fetus.

women over the age of 40, women who had health problems before they became pregnant, and women who do not receive prenatal care.

Another problem that can occur in some pregnancies is caused by something called the Rh factor. The **Rh factor** is a substance that is present in the blood of some people. These people are said to be **Rh positive.** People who lack this factor are called **Rh negative.** As you learned in Chapter 12, a baby inherits many traits from its parents. If the father is Rh positive and the mother is Rh negative, it is possible for the fetus to inherit the Rh positive trait from the father and, therefore, be Rh positive. Should some of the baby's Rh positive factor get into the mother's bloodstream, the mother's blood will make a substance that attacks the Rh factor. This is known as **Rh incompatibility.** This does not present a problem for the mother or the baby if the woman is given an injection that prevents her blood from making any anti-Rh substance. If the treatment is not given, then the anti-Rh substances in the mother's blood may cross the placenta and harm the developing fetus's blood.

COMPLICATIONS AT BIRTH Although the birth process usually proceeds smoothly, problems can occur. Sometimes delivery through the cervix and vagina is not possible because of the position of the fetus in the uterus or the narrowness of the mother's pelvis. Sometimes illness or other conditions may make labor and vaginal delivery dangerous for the mother or the fetus. In these circumstances, the obstetrician will perform a **cesarean** (sih **zair** ee un) **section.** A cesarean section is a surgical method of birth. The operation takes about one hour to complete and the mother may be awake or asleep during the procedure, depending on the kind of **anesthesia** (an is **thee** zhuh), or painkilling method,

The Rh factor may cause a problem if an Rh negative mother has an Rh positive child.

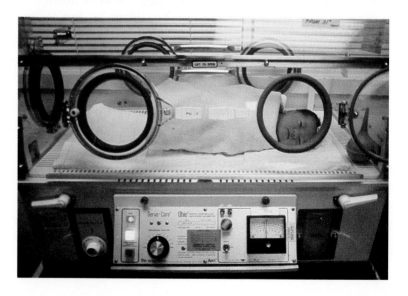

Figure 13-13. A premature baby usually needs to be kept in an incubator until it develops further.

used. About 25 percent of all babies born in the United States today are delivered by cesarean section.

Delivery of a live fetus before it is ready to be born is **premature birth.** Premature birth usually occurs during the third trimester. At this time the fetus's lungs may not be fully developed, so it cannot breathe by itself. Premature babies receive special care in **incubators,** special chambers designed to protect the baby until it is more developed.

The delivery of more than one fetus—twins, triplets, or quadruplets—is called a **multiple birth.** In the United States, twins account for 1 out of every 100 births, triplets for 1 out of every 8,000 births, and quadruplets for 1 out of every 500,000 births.

What causes more than one fetus to develop? Take the example of twins. There are two types of twins: identical twins and fraternal twins. **Identical twins** develop from the same fertilized egg, or zygote, when the zygote divides into two individual zygotes. They are, therefore, exactly alike. They have identical inherited traits and are the same sex. **Fraternal twins** develop if two eggs are released from the ovary and are fertilized by two sperm. Fraternal twins are no more alike than any other two siblings, and they may or may not be the same sex.

The Postpartum Period

The **postpartum period** begins with delivery and lasts about six weeks. It is a period of adjustment for the parents and their newborn.

CHANGES IN PARENTS The mother's body goes through many changes during the postpartum period. The uterus shrinks back to its normal size, and the breasts produce milk for the baby. These changes are caused by hormones. **Prolactin** (proh **lak** tin) causes milk to form in the breasts. **Oxytocin** (ox ih **toh** sin) causes the uterus to contract and get smaller. Oxytocin also helps the breast tissue to eject milk when the baby suckles. Other hormonal changes help the mother's body to switch from the pregnant to the non-pregnant state. Hormonal adjustments and fatigue are likely to cause the mother to become depressed during the postpartum period.

Both parents are likely to feel happy but tired. Emotionally and mentally, they are getting used to being parents. Physically, they are taking care of a newborn baby, which is demanding work that goes on around the clock. Despite their joy and delight with their baby, the parents of a newborn sometimes feel exhausted and irritable. These feelings usually go away once the baby is sleeping for a few hours at a time and the mother and father are able to resume some sort of daily routine.

▲
Figure 13-14. Identical twins (top) inherit identical traits, whereas fraternal twins (bottom) do not.

Figure 13-15. The parent-child bond
grows strong as the newborn baby
adjusts to its new life.

The newborn's lungs and digestive
system begin to function for the first
time during the postpartum period.

CHANGES IN THE NEWBORN   The newborn baby has
just made the biggest physical adjustment of its life. It has
been pushed from its cozy watery environment, where
everything it needed was received automatically, into a chilly
place where it has to breathe, cry, and suckle to survive.

During the postpartum period, the newborn's lungs and
digestive tract begin to function for the first time. Its circulatory system and heart undergo changes to send more blood
to the lungs, where the baby now gets its oxygen. Its nervous
system reacts to new sensations: light, air against the skin,
the touch of its parents, hunger, and pain. Even a healthy,
full-term newborn with an Apgar score of ten has a lot of
work to do during the postpartum period. While its body is
adjusting to life outside the uterus, the newborn is learning
to get what it needs by forming a strong bond with its mother
and father.

Section Review

1. What organ pushes the fetus out of the mother?
2. What ends the second stage of labor?
3. Why is a newborn baby given an Apgar score?
4. Name one problem of pregnancy and one complication of birth.

What Do You Think?
5. Babies who form a close, loving bond with their parents grow faster and are healthier than babies who do
not form this bond. Why do you think this is so?

4. INFANCY THROUGH CHILDHOOD

Babies and young children are not miniature adults. They do not behave, feel, or think the way older children and adults do. Growing up occurs slowly and in stages. At each stage, the child's physical and mental development determines how it will interact with the other people in its life and with its environment.

Birth to Eighteen Months

At birth, many of the baby's organs and systems are not fully developed. Its bones are still soft and flexible. A newborn baby can suckle, cry, and direct its gaze, but it will not learn to smile until it is about one month old.

By the time it is 3 or 4 months old, the baby's brain, nerves, and muscles are ready for more coordinated movement. It recognizes its parents and siblings and can get what it needs by crying or responding to attention with obvious delight. By the time it is 18 months old, the baby has grown a great deal. It has learned to sit, crawl, stand, and walk and may be able to say a few words. It has "baby" teeth and can chew solid food. Eighteen-month-olds have completed a stage of growth and development that will not be equaled until they are ready to change from child to adult.

Parents of babies between birth and 18 months have one main responsibility: the physical care of their child. Without hands-on, physical nurturing, the child will not survive. Part of physical nurturing involves regular checkups by a **pediatrician** (pee dee uh **trish** un), a doctor who specializes in caring for babies and children.

From birth to 18 months of age, a baby grows rapidly.

◄ **Figure 13-16. A baby delights its parents with the new things it learns each day.**

Eighteen Months to Three Years

Between 18 months and 3 years of age, the child loses its babylike appearance. Appetite decreases as the child's growth slows down. Baby fat is lost, and the arms and legs get longer. Physical coordination improves, and the child begins to talk.

During this time, children are learning to assert themselves and to manipulate objects, such as toys. They may show off around family and friends but be shy around strangers. When they are with others their age, toddlers tend to play alongside, but not with, each other. They are not ready to share or to play interactively because they are busy learning how to do things for themselves. Most children between these ages learn to use the toilet.

Physical nurturing continues to be an important parental responsibility, but it is slightly less intense. The child is no longer helpless. The main parental responsibility at this stage is to "keep an eye on" the child at all times. People who take care of toddlers have to be alert, because toddlers are too young to know when something can hurt them.

Three to Six Years

Between the ages of 3 and 6, all traces of babyhood disappear. The child becomes more independent and active. Muscles grow, energy is high, and the curious child is "into everything." Communication skills advance rapidly. Most 4-year-olds express themselves readily and are easy to understand. By the age of 5, the child begins to lose baby teeth.

During this stage, children learn to play interactively and to make friends. They begin school and learn how to behave in a group. Between 3 and 6, most children start spending less time with their parents and more time with their peers and teachers. This transition is sometimes difficult.

Figure 13-18. Children between the ages of 3 and 6 are curious about everything that surrounds them.

Parents of children between 3 and 6 find themselves in the role of teacher. The child still needs physical nurturing but times of physical contact are less frequent. These tend to occur at bath time or while reading the child a story.

Seven to Twelve Years

Between the ages of 6 and 8, the child's facial structure changes with the appearance of permanent teeth. Muscles and bones continue to grow, and coordination develops further. Children between the ages of 7 and 12 master all sorts of physical activities from climbing trees to dancing ballet. Toward the end of this stage, the bones begin to grow faster, mostly in the legs. Appetite increases, and the process of sexual maturation begins.

Mental development continues as the child learns higher-level thinking skills. The self-centeredness of early childhood lessens, and children learn values, such as honesty and fairness. Responsibilities at home increase with the ability to perform chores well.

The approval of peers and the desire to fit in with a social group become all-important at about the age of 10. While this can be a problem for some children, it helps many children to work well in group situations. Noise and enthusiasm are part of most group activities at this age. Having a best friend of the same sex is also important and will remain so into the teen years.

Parents of children between 7 and 12 have new responsibilities. Children at this stage need loving guidance, encouragement, and respect. The responsibility of providing food, clothing, medical care, and shelter continues until the child is legally of age. Love and concern for the child's well-being continue for life.

▲
Figure 13-19. Between the ages of 7 and 12, coordination improves.

Section Review

1. Of the four stages of childhood, which involves the fastest growth and development?
2. Why do 2-year-olds not play together readily?
3. At about what age does peer pressure become more important to a child?

What Do You Think?

4. You have just arrived to babysit a 20-month-old child for the afternoon. When the parents start to leave, the child begins to cry. The parents try to comfort the child by explaining where they are going and when they will be back. Who gets the most comfort from the explanation, the child or its parents? Why?

13 | Chapter Review

Chapter Summary

- In deciding to have children, couples must consider their emotional, mental, and financial readiness to become parents.
- Responsibilities of parenthood begin before pregnancy and include genetic counseling, if needed; the practice of good health habits by the woman; and prenatal care.
- Fertilization takes place in the fallopian tube. Implantation takes place in the uterus.
- Pregnancy tests measure the hormone HCG in the mother's blood or urine. The earliest reliable results are obtained about one month after fertilization.
- For the first two months of pregnancy, the developing baby is called an embryo. For the remainder of pregnancy, it is called a fetus.
- The embryo and fetus are protected within a fluid-filled sac and receive oxygen and nutrients from the mother's blood. These substances filter through the placenta, the structure by which the embryo attaches to the uterus.
- The nine months of pregnancy are divided into three trimesters, or three-month periods.

- Complications of pregnancy include ectopic pregnancy, miscarriage, toxemia, and Rh incompatibility. Complications of birth include cesarean section, premature birth, and multiple birth.
- During the postpartum period, hormones cause the mother's body to produce milk.
- During the postpartum period, newborns' bodies change so they can breathe, digest food, and react to the environment.
- Childhood is divided into four stages of development: birth to 18 months, 18 months to 3 years, 3 to 6 years, and 7 to 12 years.
- Pregnant women must avoid alcohol, smoking, and drugs not prescribed by an obstetrician. Alcohol, drugs, and viruses can injure the embryo or fetus.
- Regular checkups are necessary during pregnancy so that problems can be detected and treated immediately.
- Labor has three stages: (1) the amniotic sac breaks and the cervix begins to dilate and soften; (2) the baby is born; and (3) the placenta is delivered.

Vocabulary Review

Listed below are some of the important terms in this chapter. Choose the term that best matches the phrase in the exercise that follows.

amniotic fluid	fetal alcohol syndrome	nurse-midwife	postpartum period
Apgar score	fraternal twins	miscarriage	Rh incompatibility
afterbirth	HCG	morning sickness	stillbirth
cesarean section	infertile	oxytocin	umbilical cord
embryo	labor	placenta	zygote

1. hormone that helps the uterus to shrink after birth

2. the work of pushing the fetus out

3. the six weeks following birth

4. surgical method of birth

5. the attachment that holds the embryo to the wall of the uterus

6. nausea and vomiting during pregnancy

7. brain damage caused by mother's use of alcohol during pregnancy

8. hormone that indicates pregnancy

9. fertilized egg

10. the structure that carries nutrients and oxygen to the embryo

What Have You Learned?

1. What expenses do new parents have?
2. Infertile couples can explore three ways of becoming parents. What are they?
3. Name four things a pregnant woman can do to keep herself and her baby-to-be healthy.
4. What kinds of disorders are detected by amniocentesis and chorionic villus sampling?
5. How does smoking harm the fetus?

6. Besides prenatal care, how can expectant parents prepare for the experience of birth?
7. What stage of labor is the longest?
8. Why is premature birth dangerous?
9. Name two adjustments that both mothers and fathers face during the postpartum period.
10. At what stage of development do children begin to share and make friends?

What Do You Think?

1. Many expectant parents keep pregnancy a secret until after the first trimester. Why?
2. Rate (from 1 to 5) the following needs of children in order of importance:
- knowing what to expect
- being loved
- food, clothing, shelter, and medical care
- having two parents who love each other
- having parents who earn a lot of money

3. If you were the baby-to-be, what might bother you about the statement, "Once I have a baby, the world will treat me like an adult"?
4. Should a pregnant woman go on a starvation diet if she has already gained 25 pounds by the seventh month of her pregnancy? Explain your answer.
5. Why do you think newborn babies cry a great deal?

What Would You Do?

1. Your 6-year-old sister asks you where babies come from. How would you explain pregnancy and birth to a 6-year-old?
2. Your 10-year-old brother asks you where babies come from. To help him understand, would you give him this textbook to read? Explain your reasons.

3. Your 1-year-old cousin is crawling around on the living room floor. The phone rings in the kitchen. What do you do? Why?
4. Your older sister complains that her 2-year-old daughter has become a "picky eater." What can you tell your sister to stop her from worrying about her daughter's appetite.

For Further Study

1. How much does it cost to support a child for one month? Assume that the child is 10 months old and stays in a day care center from 8 a.m. to 5 p.m. Monday through Friday. The child has one checkup with its pediatrician during the month. It needs a new pair of shoes, diapers (you choose the type), and food for the month. Make an itemized list of expenses. What is the total cost?
2. Interview a parent who has a child at least 12 years of age. It can be your own parent. Ask which skills of parenthood were most important when the child was 1, 7, and 12 years old. You also might ask the parent to think of one phrase that sums up the responsibilities of parenthood at each age.

14

As you read, think about

▶ how you change physically, mentally, and emotionally during your adolescent years.

▶ how your body changes during puberty.

▶ what types of mental and emotional changes you experience during adolescence.

▶ why the adolescent years are a time of increased responsibility.

Adolescent Years

Y ou're coming to that low note. You take a deep breath and hit it—right on pitch. Last year you did not try out for the school musical because your voice was changing. You were never sure when it would leap an octave too high. Now, your vocal chords are stable, and you're singing again.

Of course, it's great to be in the show, but you're still not happy with your life. Sometimes you feel terrific, and other times you feel depressed without knowing why. You often lose your temper—particularly with your parents. You spend a lot of time thinking about relationships—especially relationships with girls. You wish the rest of your life would "settle down" just as quickly as your voice did.

During adolescence, both boys and girls go through physical, mental, and emotional changes as they move from childhood to adulthood. In this chapter, you will learn about these changes and ways to deal with them.

Adolescence is all about change. Adjusting to change is hard, but it allows you to grow as a person.

1. FROM CHILD TO ADULT

What's good about being a teenager?
Everything! There are lots of changes.
What's bad about being a teenager?
Everything! There are lots of changes.

Would you agree with this description of the teenage years? Is the author of these lines excited? Unhappy? Undecided? What would you add to the description?

The teenage years are a time of change, as you may have already realized. During these years, from about the ages of 12 to 19, you gradually change from a child into an adult. This period of change is called **adolescence** (ad'l es unz). During adolescence, your entire body grows and changes until you look like an adult, and you become able to produce children. In addition to these physical changes, you may also notice changes in the way you think, feel, and relate to others. With all these changes occurring at once, it is easy to understand why adolescence is often a time of confusion.

The Good News About Adolescence

Like most teenagers, you may be excited about some of the changes going on inside you. The statements below capture some of these positive feelings. As you read the statements, see if any sound familiar to you. You or a friend may have had a similar experience in the recent past.

"She thought I was in college!" The physical changes that occur during adolescence are exciting. You have a new look, and you are starting to get different kinds of looks from other people. As your body starts to look more like an adult's, you are treated more like an adult.

Figure 14-1. Borrowing the family's car is one sign of an adolescent's growing independence.

"I've got tickets to the concert!" Perhaps the most exciting thing about adolescence is your new independence. You are able to go places on your own, and you can decide for yourself how to spend your free time. You choose your friends, your interests, and the way you act and dress. You rely less and less on your parents to make your everyday decisions.

"I made the team!" Adolescence is also a time of discovery. You discover new talents and abilities that you did not know you had. You may try a new sport or activity and discover that you are good at it. You may find that you have a talent for music, acting, algebra, or helping your friends to understand their problems. You may get an after-school job and discover that you are a good worker. All of these discoveries help you understand yourself and your abilities.

"I finally made up my mind." Learning to make choices is one of the most challenging tasks of adolescence. You realize that your decisions can have important consequences both now and in the future. If you decide to study for an exam instead of going to the movies with friends, you will feel good when you do well on the exam. You may also feel good because you have mastered a difficult subject and because your grades may improve. It is even more satisfying knowing that it was a decision that you made on your own.

Feeling independent, discovering new abilities, and making your own decisions are positive aspects of adolescence.

The Bad News About Adolescence

Unfortunately, not all of the changes occurring during adolescence are as appealing as the ones you have just read. Some of the following complaints may also sound familiar to you. They show the not-so-positive side of adolescence.

"Oh no! Not another pimple!" Some of the physical changes of adolescence are not exciting. Your face may break out. Your hair may become oily, and you may perspire more heavily. You may even have to have braces on your teeth.

◀ **Figure 14-2. It is not easy to handle intense feelings of rejection.**

Some girls may experience discomfort with menstruation, while boys may experience nocturnal emissions. All of these changes may make you feel awkward and self-conscious. Talking about these changes with family members and friends may help you feel better about them.

"I'm in a really awful mood!" The physical and social changes you are experiencing can make you feel "up" one minute and "down" the next. Your moods seem to change for no reason at all. You try to remain calm and cool but cannot when someone snubs you in the hall or when your parents insist you be home by midnight. Sometimes you may get angry at a friend even though neither of you can figure out why. You may fight with your parents and say things that you do not really mean. Sometimes it may seem as if an alien being has taken over your feelings.

"I don't have a date for the prom." You may sometimes face rejection and disappointment. You may not be chosen for the team or make the honor roll or be accepted by the "in" crowd. Rejection happens to people of all ages, but it is especially difficult for adolescents. Because you are changing so rapidly, sometimes you are less secure about yourself and more sensitive to the opinions of others. As you grow older, you will become more self-confident, and you won't feel like "a reject" every time you suffer a disappointment.

"I don't know what to do." There are so many choices, and you have no idea which one is best for you. What should you do during your summer vacation? Should you take a job washing dishes at a restaurant, or should you volunteer as a camp counselor? Sometimes you face far more serious decisions. Should you do something you think is wrong just to go along with your friends? Will you lose your friends if you refuse? **Peer pressure,** a need to conform to the expectations of friends and classmates, can affect decision-making. Perhaps for the first time, you realize that decisions often involve giving up something. Making a choice is hard, especially if the thing you must give up is important to you.

Physical changes, moodiness, sensitivity to rejection, and learning to manage decision-making are the difficult aspects of adolescence.

Section Review

1. Can you think of one word that describes the experiences of adolescence? What is it?

2. At about what age does adolescence begin? When does it end?

3. Name two items of good news and two items of bad news about adolescence.

What Do You Think?

4. Which change of adolescence do you think is most important to ninth graders? To twelfth graders?

2. CHANGES IN YOUR BODY

If you were to compare a current photograph of yourself to one taken three years ago, you would notice many changes. You might notice specific changes in your appearance, such as your height or body proportions. You might simply say that you look more mature now without pointing to specific changes. Now try to imagine a photograph of yourself three years in the future. How different do you think you will look then?

As photographs can reveal, adolescence is a period of rapid physical growth. Photographs, however, can detect only some of the changes taking place. Important physical changes are also occurring inside your body during this time. All of these physical changes are controlled by the hormones of your endocrine system.

Puberty

Even before you read Chapter 12, you were probably familiar with the term *puberty*, although you may have heard it used in many different ways. Some people think that puberty is another word for adolescence; this is not correct. As you know, puberty is the period of sexual development in which the body becomes physically able to produce children. Usually puberty begins before you reach adolescence and ends during mid-adolescence or later.

As you also know, the changes that occur during puberty are controlled by the pituitary gland and the ovaries (in girls) or the testes (in boys). Between the ages of nine and fourteen, the pituitary gland signals the ovaries or testes to begin producing sex hormones. Figure 14-3 lists the hormones that play a role in puberty. Early in puberty, the body does not produce sex hormones consistently. As the glands mature, hormone production becomes more regular. Girls start to ovulate and menstruate while boys begin to produce sperm. Ovulation in girls and sperm production in boys signal **reproductive maturity,** the ability to produce children. It is important to realize that many girls begin to ovulate before their menstrual cycles become regular. In fact, in some girls, menstrual cycles do not become regular for many years.

The sex hormones have many other effects on the body during puberty. Feelings of sexual arousal increase in both boys and girls. You may notice that you feel excited around certain people. You also may experience sexual arousal and **orgasm (or** gaz um), the climax of sexual excitement, during sleep. This happens to both boys and girls, as well as to men and women. As you read in Chapter 12, the terms *nocturnal emission* and *wet dream* describe this occurrence in males.

Hormones Involved in Puberty

Pituitary Gland
  Follicle-stimulating
    hormone (FSH)
  Luteinizing hormone (LH)

Ovaries
  Progesterone
  Estrogen

Testes
  Testosterone

▲
Figure 14-3. How do these hormones affect the body during puberty?

Puberty in both boys and girls results in the ability to produce children.

The sex hormones also cause the development of **secondary sex characteristics,** physical changes that occur during puberty that are not directly related to reproduction. In girls, the breasts begin to enlarge, and the hips start to widen. In boys, the voice begins to deepen, and hair appears on the face, the arms, the legs, and sometimes on the chest. In both sexes, pubic hair begins to grow around the external sex organs, and underarm hair appears. In addition, the skin begins to secrete more oils, and body odor increases.

Some adolescents feel overwhelmed by all of the changes that accompany puberty. You may suddenly find that you have acne, oily scalp hair, and body odor. Regular bathing, shampooing, and deodorant use are important. Shaving may also become a regular part of adolescent boys' grooming habits. Girls may suffer menstrual discomfort. Some adolescents have difficulty adjusting to their changing body shape. Some adolescents may be embarrassed or confused about the new sexual feelings they are experiencing. Having someone to talk to, especially a trusted, older person, can help adolescents understand and accept their feelings.

Bone and Muscle Growth

Around the same time that puberty starts, the pituitary gland also increases its production of growth hormone, a chemical messenger that stimulates growth. You begin to get bigger. First your hands and feet grow, then your arms and legs. Growth does not occur in a regular fashion but rather in spurts. Some months little growth hormone is produced, and you do not seem to grow at all. Other months there is a surge of growth hormone, and you seem to jump several shoe sizes.

If you were to look at a group of young adolescents, you would notice that, for the most part, the girls were taller than the boys. The timeline in Figure 14-4 shows why. As you can see, boys usually begin their growth spurt around the middle of their tenth year and may reach adult height by the age of 16. Girls, on the other hand, start to grow earlier than boys. On the average, girls begin their growth spurt around the age of 9 and may reach adult height by the age of 14. By the time adolescents reach the end of high school, the situation has reversed; for the most part, the boys have grown taller than the girls.

Changes in height are followed by changes in overall body structure. As puberty continues, boys generally develop wider shoulders and larger muscles than girls. Girls become more rounded as hips widen and breasts develop.

Many adolescents find it difficult to adjust to the changes in body proportion. Rapid lengthening of the bones in your arms and legs can be painful; some adolescents feel aches and cramps in their growing limbs. Most adolescents feel

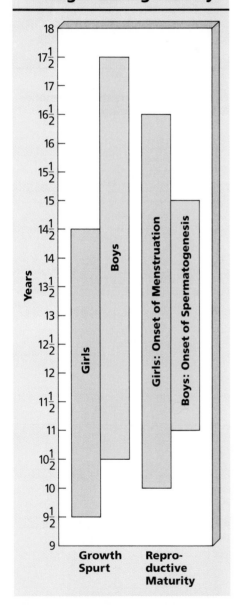

Average Age of Physical Changes During Puberty

Figure 14-4. The age range of normal physical development is wide.

awkward at times. You may feel as if you are tripping over your own feet, or you may find you are no longer comfortable in your favorite chair. You may also find that you need to alter your posture and walking style to accommodate your new, adult proportions. If you challenge your growing body with a variety of physical activities, you will adjust more rapidly to your new size and shape. Physical activity also will help to develop your muscles and your coordination. As unlikely as it may seem, your feelings of discomfort and awkwardness will disappear soon.

You may notice one other effect that growth has on your body: it makes you hungry. Your family may remark that your stomach seems to be a "bottomless pit." You may feel as if you are always hungry, and you may binge on foods sometimes. This is normal during adolescence because you need extra energy to fuel your growing body. It is important, however, to eat nutritious meals and snacks to supply your body with energy it can use. As you learned in Chapters 8 and 9, the quality of your new body will be only as good as the materials you use to build it. Adolescence is a good time to learn to make some healthy snacks and meals for yourself. Foods like lasagna, tacos, and muffins are easy to make. They are also satisfying and nutritious.

▲ **Figure 14-5. Learning how to cook a nutritious meal can be fun.**

Early Bloomers and Late Bloomers

If you are like most adolescents, you have probably compared your own physical development to that of your peers. As you look around your classroom, you may wonder why your classmates are all at such different stages of physical development. Some of your classmates may already look like adults while others may just be beginning to show signs of puberty. Since they are all about the same age, why do these differences exist?

The ages at which people mature sexually and grow to their adult height are determined by heredity. Chances are you are maturing at about the same age and speed as your parents did. Other factors that influence your unique timetable of development are nutrition and your overall state of health, including fitness.

Adolescents who develop at an early age are sometimes called **early bloomers.** Those who develop at a late age are called **late bloomers.** Most adolescents fall somewhere between these two extremes. Regardless of whether you see yourself as an early bloomer, a late bloomer, or someone in between, sometimes you may feel envious of adolescents in the other groups.

Late bloomers may feel that early bloomers have an easier time than they do. This is not necessarily true. If a person is expecting the physical changes and is eager for them, then being an early bloomer can be good. If the changes come as

Heredity, nutrition, and overall state of health determine whether you will be an early or late bloomer.

▲
Figure 14-6. Each of these girls is developing normally.

○━┳
Every individual's physical development is unique.

a surprise, however, then being an early bloomer can be difficult. Early bloomers often feel the same self-consciousness and awkwardness that many adolescents experience. Since their friends have not yet experienced the same changes, it may be difficult for them to understand the early bloomer's feelings. Some early bloomers may even have to put up with some unsympathetic jokes and stares.

Since physically mature boys and girls look like adults, people expect them to act like adults, too. Some early bloomers are mature enough to take on more responsibilities and handle these demands. Other early bloomers do not have the emotional maturity to take on adult responsibilities. These demands, along with the physical changes, are too much for them to handle.

Late bloomers have a different set of problems to contend with. Because they look young, late bloomers may not be treated as adults by others, even if they are mentally and emotionally mature. Some late bloomers feel weak or inadequate when they compare themselves to their peers. Their peers may even make inconsiderate comments that worsen these feelings. Late bloomers may compensate in a number of ways. Some late bloomers develop academic skills or become class clowns in an attempt to create a place for themselves among their peers.

Although they may not think so, most early bloomers and late bloomers are developing at a normal rate. If you turn back to Figure 14-4, you will see that "normal" includes early, average, and late physical development. Most adolescents worry that their development is not normal in some way. If you have these worries, you should tell them to your parents or your doctor. You are probably developing just as you should, but occasionally abnormal hormone production may cause accelerated or delayed puberty. In these cases, treatment usually can remedy the problem. Remember that these cases are rare. Everyone develops on his or her own schedule, which is as unique as he or she is.

Section Review

1. What is puberty?
2. Name three ways that increased hormone production affects the body.
3. Explain why growth spurts can cause some adolescents to feel awkward.
4. Who is likely to begin puberty first, a boy or a girl?

What Do You Think?
5. In your opinion, is it more difficult to be an early bloomer or a late bloomer? Why?

3. CHANGING THOUGHTS AND FEELINGS

When you were younger, it was probably difficult to imagine doing all the things adults do. For example, it may have been hard to imagine having a job or driving a car. You may have wondered how drivers knew how to get where they were going. After all, you just sat there and watched the scenery go by. Now you can read maps and street signs, and you know which bus to take when you want to go somewhere. You certainly can imagine driving a car!

Why are you now able to master adult skills that once seemed impossible? It is because of the mental and emotional growth that also takes place during adolescence. As your mind and feelings develop, you become capable of doing adult things such as solving problems, thinking about love, questioning your values, and planning the future. These mental and emotional changes are as important a part of adolescence as are the physical changes you just read about.

Mental Changes

Did you know that between the ages of 13 and 15 the human brain reaches its full capacity to think and reason? If you are at this point right now, you may notice that you are capable of thinking in ways that were not possible before. When you were a child, your thoughts and feelings were tied directly to your physical experiences at each moment. You

The mental and emotional growth that occurs during adolescence enables you to master adult skills.

◀ **Figure 14-7. The ability to think and reason is challenged during adolescence.**

The ability to think, reason, and remember matures during adolescence.

thought about hunger when your stomach was empty and pain when you were hurt. Now, however, your thoughts and feelings are no longer tied only to your immediate experiences. For example, you can think about things like hunger and pain in other people, rather than just in yourself.

Your ways of thinking have begun to change. You are now able to think about abstract ideas, such as honesty and justice. For example, you may find that you have good answers to questions like, "In what ways are all people equal?" These ideas may have nothing to do with your recent experiences. Now it is easier for you to predict consequences. You know, for example, that if you drop out of school, the action will change your life. Five years ago, you might not have been able to predict these changes. You will also find that you can classify things more carefully than before. Not all dogs are just large or small. Some are types of spaniels; some are types of retrievers. You group them according to specific characteristics that you have observed. Your memory is improving also. You find it easier to use symbols to stand for something more complex. In math, you use x to represent an unknown quantity. Figure 14-8 lists other ways your abilities to think are growing stronger. Can you think of times when you have used these thinking skills in school? Would you have been able to do this a few years ago?

Figure 14-8. Mature thought uses many different thinking skills. Which ones are your strength?

▼

Characteristics of Mature Thought

Thinking Skill	Definition	Example
Introspection	Looking inward; thinking about yourself and your own thoughts.	I'm a good person, although I could be better in science if I studied.
Abstract thought	Thinking about ideas or objects that are not visible.	Justice for all is difficult to achieve.
Ethical judgment	Making judgments based on your values and on others' intentions, rather than on how a situation affects you.	He drove up on the curb and frightened me, but he did it to avoid hitting the dog.
Memory skill	Remembering details about objects and events.	"Four score and seven years ago . . ."
Hypothesis testing	Approaching problem-solving by first predicting an outcome and then testing your prediction.	If I ask about the dance when we're alone, I'll have a better chance.
Classification skill	Creating systems based on similar characteristics.	Sharks and trout are fish, but whales are mammals.
Decentered thought	Understanding situations from someone else's point of view, considering the other person's intentions when you judge behavior.	I would have been angry, too, if I thought he took my radio.
Use of symbols	Using one thing to stand for something else, such as an idea or object.	X represents the unknown: $5 = 2 + X$.
Deductive logic	Developing general ideas and then looking to the real, concrete world for specific examples.	It is wrong to use people to satisfy one's own personal needs. That's why slavery was wrong.

You may have noticed that you use your new thinking abilities outside, as well as inside, of school. In fact, these skills affect your entire personal life. Perhaps you can already see that your new mental skills have changed some of the ways you have fun. You may become interested in more elaborate games, such as chess, that test your reasoning skills. You may start to enjoy participating in adult conversation on topics such as politics or world hunger. You may find that you enjoy fanciful discussions on topics such as "What if everyone in the world spoke the same language?" or "How are a fly and a tree alike?" If these kinds of questions interest you, it is because you now have the mental skills to think about them. You may find it fun to come up with your own questions and discuss them with friends.

Your new reasoning abilities will also affect the way you solve problems and make decisions. This is because you are now able to see all sides of a question and to weigh the pros and cons of specific events. For example, if you were trying to decide whether to write your history paper or watch television, you might analyze the choices by making two lists like the ones shown in Figure 14-9. You probably could not have made lists like these when you were a child. It is difficult for children to think about the consequences of something that has not yet happened. This is why children make decisions by trial and error; if one action does not bring satisfactory results, they try another. You may remember when you solved problems this way. Can you imagine learning to drive a car by trial and error? You can see how much your thinking has matured since then.

Like physical skills, your mental skills improve with practice. The saying "Use it or lose it!" applies as much to your mind as it does to your abilities as a gymnast or a singer. Throughout adolescence, you will be trying out your new capacity for reasoning and decision-making. For example, in deciding whether to write your history paper or to watch television, you are deciding whether to enjoy an immediate pleasure or to do something that will be better for you in the long run. If you gain experience making wise choices in matters like this one, you will find it easier to choose correctly in more difficult situations later. For example, what if the person who drives you to a party gets drunk? Should you find another ride home for both of you—which may be difficult or embarrassing—or get into the car with a drunk driver, which may cost you your life?

Emotional Changes

As you grow physically and mentally, your emotional needs and desires also become more like those of an adult. Adolescence is a time for questioning; you begin to question many things that you have simply accepted until now. You

---

TV or History Paper?

Pros of watching TV:
I need to relax for a while.
My favorite show is on.
I want to watch TV.
Cons of watching TV:
I won't get my paper done on time.
I will feel guilty about not writing my paper.
My grade in history will go down if the paper is late.

Pros of writing my history paper:
I will turn it in on time.
I will feel good about my decision.
My history grade might go up.
I will learn something.
Cons of writing my history paper:
I will not be able to relax for a while.
I will miss my favorite show.
I don't feel like writing it.

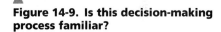
Figure 14-9. Is this decision-making process familiar?

Physical, mental, and experiential changes contribute to the emotional turbulence of adolescence.

may also start to question the values and actions of people around you, such as friends and family members. Most importantly, however, you may start to question yourself. Perhaps for the first time in your life you may wonder who you are, how you come across to others, what you stand for, and what you will do with your life.

Why is adolescence such an emotionally turbulent time? One reason, as you have studied, may be biological. The hormonal changes going on in your body affect your daily moods. Along with this, the physical changes you are experiencing may make you feel self-conscious and not in control of your own body. Another reason may be mental. As you have just read, your mental capabilities are changing dramatically. Your new mental skills help you see things in a different light. Your thoughts are more global, abstract, and future-oriented. You have new standards that people and things must measure up to—your friends, your school, and even your neighborhood. A third reason may be experiential; you are seeing and doing more things than ever before. As you are exposed to new and different things, it is natural to compare the old to the new. You may experience some confusion as you are torn between the old and the new. The result is emotional change.

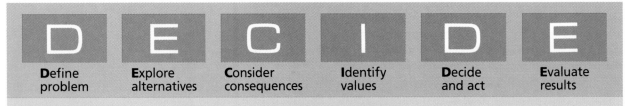

| **D**efine problem | **E**xplore alternatives | **C**onsider consequences | **I**dentify values | **D**ecide and act | **E**valuate results |

A DATING DILEMMA

Joe has been going out with Sheila for about a month. Although he has other friends, he really enjoys spending time with her and feels that he can talk to her about anything.

Joe's parents have objected to his relationship with Sheila. They say she has a bad reputation. They have made it clear that they do not want Joe to continue to see her.

1. Use the DECIDE process on page 16 to decide what you would do if you were Joe. Explain your reasons.

2. Name four other common areas of conflict between teenagers and parents that require teenagers to make important decisions.

3. From the areas in 2, choose one conflict that you are currently experiencing or have experienced recently. Use DECIDE to choose your best course of action for that particular situation.

Teenagers face hard decisions when parents disapprove of their actions.

SEARCH FOR MEANING It is not unusual during adolescence to suddenly question whether your friends are really true friends and whether happiness and love are possible to attain. These questions signal that you have begun to search for meaning in life. This search is important because in adolescence you are beginning to choose a way of life that is right for you. Some adolescents find answers to these questions by talking about them with parents or religious leaders. Other adolescents resolve these questions through their own experiences. Some adolescents volunteer their time to work in places such as hospitals, crisis centers, or runaway shelters. The experiences the adolescents have there often change the way they look at the world and help them decide what is important to them.

SEARCH FOR VALUES It is common for adolescents to begin to question the opinions and beliefs of others, especially those held by their parents. This questioning helps adolescents discover their own **values**, those beliefs and ideals that are important to them and that help them to clarify what they believe is right and wrong. Parents and other adults can help in your search for values. Although you may disagree with your parents at times and even reject some of their values, they can offer you guidance and serve as role models. For the most part, many of the values that adolescents eventually will come to accept are similar to those of their parents.

SEARCH FOR SELF Some of the most difficult questions that adolescents ask have to do with themselves and their place in the world. These questions are signs of a search for your **identity,** who you are. This search for your identity may take many forms. At times you may sit and think about who you really are, comparing yourself to people you admire, or you may discuss the question with others. Sometimes you may try on different personalities and behaviors in your daydreams. Other times you may actually try on new personalities by experimenting with new hairstyles, different clothing, and even new behaviors.

Your search for your identity is greatly influenced by your **self-concept.** As you read in Chapter 2, your self-concept is the physical and mental picture you have of yourself and your place in the world. How would you describe yourself? Do you feel good about yourself? Another influence is your **body image,** the way you think you look. Are you satisfied with your looks? How have your self-concept and body image changed over the last few years?

If you are like most adolescents, your self-concept and body image may not be as positive today as they were a few years ago. Right now, your image of yourself is strongly influenced by the opinions of others, particularly others of your

▲
Figure 14-10. Your identity can be expressed in unique ways.

Figure 14-11. During adolescence, ▶ it is important to feel good about yourself and the way you look.

Recognizing your strengths and achievements can help you deal with the question "Who am I?"

age. You may worry whether or not your peers approve of your clothing, your looks, your personality, and your interests. You may wonder whether or not members of the opposite sex find you attractive. You may worry that your looks do not measure up to those of movie stars and models.

It is difficult for teenagers to maintain a secure and positive identity during the adolescent years. Most adolescents, however, are able to recognize their strengths and achievements. Some teens find it useful to keep a list of their accomplishments and talents someplace where they can easily see it. Then, when the question "Who am I?" comes up, this list supplies them with some good answers.

Section Review

1. Describe three characteristics of mature thought.
2. How does decision-making in adolescence differ from that in childhood?
3. Give three reasons why adolescence is a time of many emotional changes.
4. What is self-concept? Name two things that influence an adolescent's self-concept.

What Do You Think?

5. "Developing an identity is the most important task of adolescence." Do you agree with this statement? Why or why not?

4. ADOLESCENCE AND RESPONSIBILITY

Adolescence brings increased privileges. You are treated more like an adult. Your opinion counts, and you make decisions that direct your life. You are allowed adult recreations, but the flip side of privilege is always responsibility. As an adult, you are expected to behave consistently and to assume responsibility for yourself and others. Often the move to this new status is not a smooth one. You may be anxious for the privileges but not so anxious for the responsibilities. Some days you may want to make all your own decisions; other days you may wish you could hide your head under your pillow and let someone older take charge. Although the progress may sometimes seem uneven, your pathway to adulthood will be marked by your growing and expanding sense of responsibility.

Learning to behave consistently and responsibly is an important task of adolescence.

Responsibility to Yourself

During adolescence you become responsible for taking care of yourself. Eventually no one will tell you not to have those five candy bars. No one will force you to eat nutritious meals, exercise, or go to the dentist. You will have to decide when to wear your heavy jacket or whether to take your umbrella with you.

You will also become responsible for your own wardrobe, deciding not only what to take out of your closet every morning but also what to put in your closet when you go shopping. If you pay for some or all of your clothes, you will learn to manage your resources, including balancing your budget. You will also have to consider the "messages" particular styles send to others. Do you want your clothes to reflect your personal uniqueness or the identity of a group you belong to—or wish you belonged to?

◀ **Figure 14-12. Learning to accept responsibility for yourself is a task of adolescence.**

Teenagers and Risk-Taking

Why are some teenagers so reckless? The growing number of serious accidents involving teens makes a question like this more and more important.

Researchers are finding a variety of answers. Some risk-taking is part of the normal adolescent search for independence. However, many teens do not yet have the ability—or interest—to understand long-term risks. Instead, they believe, "It can't happen to me." Teens also overestimate how many other teens engage in risky behaviors. Studies show that when teens say, "Everybody's doing it," only about 15 percent of their peers are "doing it."

Biology also plays a role. Research reveals that risk-takers have higher levels of sex hormones, particularly testosterone, than nonrisk-takers. They also have lower levels of the enzyme monamine oxidase, MAO, which regulates brain chemicals that affect mood. This combination of high hormone levels and low MAO levels makes adolescence a "risky" age.

Why do teenagers take risks?

While following the clothing styles of a particular "in-group" may be harmless fun, following all of their behaviors may have more serious consequences. Based on what you know is best for your own health and safety, you will have to make decisions about smoking, drinking, and drugs. Decisions about fad diets or after-school binges on junk food should also be based on your own health needs. You will also have to think about pressures to engage in sexual activity and the risks those behaviors involve. You will need to consult your own values as well as those of your family and community. Parents and other adults may make rules for you early in your teens, but eventually you will have to make these decisions on your own and take the responsibility for the results.

You will also be looking toward the future. Adolescence is a time to begin thinking seriously about career choices. During these years, you make many decisions that can affect your future career opportunities. You now know that you have to plan and work for what you want; these things do not just happen on their own. This means taking responsibility for your future self in several ways. Your grades and course selection in high school are important for getting into college or other career-preparation programs. High-school graduation is essential to most good jobs. Volunteer work or part-time jobs can help you sample different kinds of careers or gain valuable experience.

Responsibility to Your Family

Your status in the family is changing. You want and need more **autonomy** (aw **tahn** uh mee), or independence, and your family is learning to treat you more like an adult. How does your new status affect your relationships within your family?

Despite the image of teenagers as angry, rude, and rebellious, most teenagers are happy, healthy people who value their families. Research shows that most families work out the conflicts that normally arise as teenagers strive for more independence, and parents try to keep them from growing up too fast. These conflicts are often visible in clothing styles. One of the first ways many adolescents show their growing independence is in what they wear. Some of these styles and fads are seen by parents as a rebellion against adult standards; others are regarded as "too old" for younger adolescents. Most families work out these conflicts with some give and take. Parents acknowledge that adolescent taste may be different from their own, and teens tone down some styles, especially when going places with their parents. Showing respect for the feelings, taste, and values of other family members in minor issues, such as hair and clothing styles, sets the stage for increased autonomy on other issues.

▶ Figure 14-13. Babysitting is one way that teenagers can contribute to their family's needs. How do you help your family?

With increased autonomy comes increased responsibility. What are your responsibilities to your family? First, you may now be responsible for more of the physical work needed to maintain your household. You may need to learn new skills, such as house painting, grocery shopping, or laundering. You may be responsible for taking care of a younger brother or sister after school.

Second, you are responsible for becoming more of a "giver" in your family relationships. You are mature enough to offer understanding and support to other family members. You participate more fully in the emotional life of your family. Is your sister's birthday next week? You can create or buy a present without being reminded.

Your third responsibility is to follow family guidelines about clothing, dating, and other activities. This does not mean that your parents make all of the rules all of the time. You can help your parents to establish guidelines that are right for you. Look again at Figure 14-8. How many characteristics of mature thought will you need to use in negotiating guidelines with your parents? Just about every one of them!

Responsibility to Your Friends

In adolescence, you realize that friends are more than just people to have fun with. Friends are people who really listen when you talk and who are there for you when you have a problem. You have similar responsibilities to them. You should be willing to take time away from your other activities to help out a friend, to be a good listener, and to give comfort and encouragement when needed. You may also see some friends engaging in destructive or dangerous behaviors. When you have a real concern about a friend's health, safety, or well-being, you have a responsibility to

As you gain independence, your responsibility to your family and friends increases.

Figure 14-14. A friendship may grow stronger when friends help each other. ▶

intervene to try to help. Peer pressure—in spite of the way the term is usually used—is not always bad. You can use peer pressure to influence your friends in positive directions and to provide a network of concern and support in times of stress or crisis.

Responsibility to Your Community

As you continue through your teen years, your interests will expand and so will your responsibilities. You will begin to see yourself as an important part of a larger community and recognize that your actions directly affect community life. For example, you appreciate clean streets and parks and buses that arrive on time. You like knowing that cars will stop at the red light when you are crossing the street. Now you are mature enough to see that these benefits depend on you and people like you. Littering, vandalism, disruptive horsing around on buses, or reckless driving endanger the quality of life that you want. Some of these irresponsible behaviors are also dangerous, and many of them are against the law. During your teens, you become responsible for knowing the laws of your community and for obeying them. You are expected to think about the effect that your actions will have not only on yourself and your friends but on the community as a whole.

You may even want to go further in helping to improve your community. Participating in clean-up or fund-raising activities or giving more direct aid to less fortunate community members can be satisfying. During adolescence, many teens become more interested in public issues, and they find

○━━┳
Responsible behaviors reflect a mature understanding of community life.

Figure 14-15. Volunteering your time in a hospital is just one of many ways to help members of your community.

their actions can have a positive effect on their community. You may start with school or neighborhood projects and organize petitions or write letters to local politicians or newspaper editors. Later, you may want to join programs such as SADD, Students Against Driving Drunk, to work for important causes. Older adolescents often become involved in political issues. They do volunteer work for candidates and causes they believe in.

Eventually, you will have a say not only in local issues but in national elections, too. Your vote will mean as much as the vote of any other citizen, regardless of age. Becoming well-informed about candidates and issues and then exercising your right to vote will be a way of showing your sense of adult responsibility to your community.

Your involvement in a school, neighborhood, or community project can be a positive experience.

Section Review

1. Why do adolescents have more responsibilities than children have?
2. To whom are you responsible in adolescence?
3. When you eat healthfully, exercise, and get enough sleep, to whom are you being responsible?

What Do You Think?

4. Sometimes you have to decide whether to be responsible to yourself or to your family. Describe a situation in which a teenager might have to choose between responsibility to self and responsibility to family.

Coping with Change

How could they force her to come to a boring family picnic when her whole life was changing! Ann sat distracted by fears of entering a new school. Tomorrow everything would be different, and she was stuck here listening to the same old stories!

Conversations drifted by. Aunt Beth was concerned about her youngest daughter moving out, while Uncle Al, newly retired, wondered about his changed life style. Two cousins compared notes: Jen, expecting a baby, fretted over her new role as mom, while Mary was excited about moving cross-country for a better job. Suddenly Ann was struck by the idea that you could not escape from change. How could she ever cope with it all?

Ann's response to change is a common one. Many people feel overwhelmed or frightened—even if they are also looking forward to a new experience. The period between the old and new ways of life, called the transition time, can be difficult. The following guidelines will help you deal with transition periods in your life.

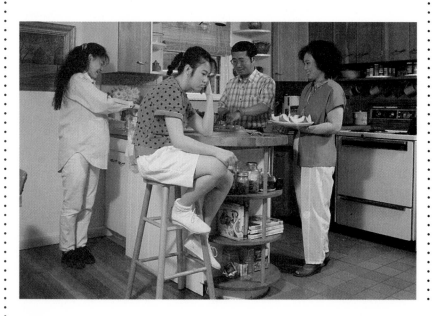

1. Accept Change as Normal

Change is a natural part of life. Some changes are a result of your decisions; others, such as the death of a loved one, are beyond your control. In either case, the transition is often stressful.

Think of some examples of changes from your past. List the positive and negative feelings you had about each one. Add to your list the strategies that you used to make the changes part of your life.

2. Expect Mixed Feelings

Because some fear and loss accompany even the most desirable new experience, change usually brings mixed feelings. Review the mixture of feelings in the list you just made.

When you are faced with a significant change, make a chart of the advantages and disadvantages the change will bring into your life. This "change chart" will help you to understand the source of your mixed feelings.

3. Understand Your Resistance

Moving on to "unexplored territory" is stressful, and resistance is common. Check your "change chart" to see which disadvantages are merely the short-term stresses of *making* the change. These will disappear if you integrate the new situation into your life. Now, circle the disadvantages over which you have no control. Remind yourself often that you must "let go" of things you cannot control.

4. Build an Inside Support System

(a) You are already experienced at dealing with change. Review your list of past changes to see how you can build on former successes and learn from the times when coping was more difficult.

(b) Focus on the positive aspects of the change you are now facing. Jot down the most important benefits, and add a reassuring message, such as "I can handle . . . and feel good!" Place your list where you will see it often.

5. Build an Outside Support System

List friends and family whose support was helpful to you in the past. Let them know you would appreciate their support again. Don't be discouraged if not all of them are able to help this time.

Seek out new sources of support. You may want to try organized groups that are working on similar issues, new friends, or counselors.

6. Start with Small Steps

Decide on a goal and put it in words, such as "feeling more a

Learning to cope with change can help you throughout life.

part of my new school." Take a small, positive step toward that goal, such as attending one meeting of one after-school club. Even a small step allows you to *demonstrate* that you can handle change in your life. Tell yourself "Great job!" Reward yourself for your new accomplishment.

7. Work Through Setbacks

It is not unusual to feel odd or scared, even as you are making progress. You may want to go back to what was safe and comfortable. Instead, remind yourself of your past successes and the steps you have already taken toward your goal. Tell yourself that you can do it . . . and you can!

APPLY THE SKILL

1. For two of Ann's relatives, list the positive and negative feelings they may be experiencing. Identify the factors they cannot control. How would "letting go" help them accept the changes?

2. List the positive and negative reactions you felt for at least two major changes in your life. Did you use any of the strategies above in coping with these changes? Explain.

3. Think about a change you are expecting. List its benefits and drawbacks, your mixed feelings, and your support system. Then decide on a first small step toward making the change a part of your life. Explain your choice.

14 | Chapter Review

Chapter Summary

- Adolescence is a gradual physical, mental, social, and emotional transition between childhood and adulthood. It begins at about age 12 and ends at about age 19.
- The changes of adolescence bring good and bad experiences. The good include physical maturation, the discovery of new abilities, independence, and the satisfaction of taking care of yourself. The bad include unpleasant physical effects, moodiness, the discovery of limitations, self-consciousness, and the difficulties involved in taking on new responsibilities.
- Puberty is the sexual development of the body that results in the ability to produce children. In girls, puberty is complete when ovulation occurs. In boys, puberty is complete when sperm is produced.
- During adolescence, hormones cause sexual maturation, the development of secondary sex characteristics, bone and muscle growth, and moodiness.
- At the start of puberty, growth hormone stimulates bone growth in the hands, feet, arms, and legs. Growth continues in spurts until adult height is reached, usually in the mid-teens or late teens.
- Puberty and growth usually occur earlier in girls than in boys. Both early and late blooming are almost always normal.
- Heredity, nutrition, and overall health and fitness affect the timetable of puberty, but the most important factor is heredity.
- Mental abilities also mature during adolescence. The ability to think and reason in new ways affects schoolwork, problem-solving and decision-making, and ways of having fun. Mental skills improve with use.
- During adolescence, teenagers often question values and opinions, search for meaning in life, and wonder about their identity. A teenager's identity is greatly influenced by the opinion of peers.
- Along with increased privileges, adolescence brings increased responsibilities. The responsibilities of adolescence include responsibility to yourself, your family, your friends, and your community.

Vocabulary Review

Listed below are some of the important terms in this chapter. Choose the term that best matches the phrase in the exercise that follows.

adolescence
autonomy
body image
early bloomers

identity
late bloomers
orgasm
peer pressure

reproductive
 maturity
secondary sex
 characteristics

self-concept
values

1. adolescents whose bodies develop at a later age than their peers
2. who you are
3. the physical and mental picture a person has of him or herself
4. a need to conform to friends
5. the climax of sexual excitement
6. the way you think you look
7. being independent of the influence or control of others
8. opinions and beliefs that become important to you
9. the teenage years, which are marked by physical, mental, and emotional change
10. physical changes during puberty that are not directly related to reproduction

What Have You Learned?

1. What changes occur in adolescence?
2. Name three adolescent physical changes.
3. Why do growth spurts occur?
4. What physical change establishes reproductive maturity in girls? In boys?
5. By what ages do boys and girls usually reach adult height?
6. What is difficult about being an early bloomer? A late bloomer?

7. Define introspection, hypothesis testing, decentered thought, and use of symbols.
8. How do mature thinking skills improve?
9. Why do adolescents go through many emotional changes?
10. Define self-concept. Why is self-concept important during adolescence?
11. Name two responsibilities you have to yourself, family, friends, and community.

What Do You Think?

1. In many cultures a special ceremony signals the end of childhood. What would be an appropriate ceremony in our society?
2. Name five physical activities you would encourage an adolescent to do as a way to challenge his or her new skills and strengths.
3. Schoolwork changes in high school as adolescents become more capable of mature thinking. Describe assignments you have had

that required the use of symbols, complex classification skills, and abstract thought.
4. You are the parent of a teenager who "tries on" an identity you dislike. How could you show disapproval without destroying your child's self-confidence?
5. In your opinion, what is the most difficult thing about the adolescent years? Why? How could it be made less difficult?

What Would You Do?

1. Your nine-year-old sister is worried about puberty. What can you tell her to expect?
2. Your friend is short, and overall he still looks as he did in seventh grade. What advice would you give him?
3. Suppose your parents want you home from a party at midnight, but you want to stay out later. How would you handle it?

4. You really want to play on the softball team, but you worry that your grades will suffer if you do. You can join the team and risk doing poorly or not join and spend the time on your schoolwork. How would you decide?
5. Your parents go out of town for a week List five new responsibilities you will have while you are home that week alone.

For Further Study

1. Look through a magazine that is geared to teenagers, paying close attention to the advertisements. Choose one advertisement and bring it in to class. With your classmates, discuss the ways in which the advertisement might affect an adolescent's body image and self-concept.
2. Interview three adults of your parents' age to find out what they remember most about their adolescent years.
3. Write a short essay about the qualities that you believe are important in a friendship. In your essay, include how your concept of friendship has changed over the years.

15

As you read, think about

▶ how you are preparing to take on the responsibilities of young adulthood.

▶ how your middle adult years can be a time of opportunity.

▶ how to remain active and healthy during your older adult years.

▶ why dying should be a time for loving and sharing rather than despair.

Adulthood, Aging, and Death

I t's been snowing all night, and school has been canceled. The sun is out, and a hush covers the city as you make your rounds, shoveling walks and driveways.

Suddenly, you hear laughter close by. Toni's grandparents are building a snowman! They are hard at work, rolling a huge head for their creation. You can see what a good time they're having, and it makes you think. You never imagined Mr. and Mrs. Rowe having fun like that without their grandchildren. All at once, you feel better about getting older. You see yourself building snowmen with your friends, your children, your grandchildren—and just for your own enjoyment—throughout your life.

In this chapter, you'll learn about the aging process and about staying healthy and productive through all the stages of your life.

Adulthood is a time to work toward goals, to form and strengthen relationships, and to enjoy life.

1. YOUNG ADULTHOOD

During the next few years, you will begin the transition from adolescence to adulthood. Some of you may have begun this change already. At what point do you become an adult? On a certain birthday? When you are financially independent? When you marry? When you finally become physically mature?

In general, Americans are considered to be adults legally at the age of 18 for some activities and 21 for others. From a physical and mental standpoint, it is difficult to say when adulthood begins. Change is an ongoing process from childhood to adolescence to young adulthood, and it continues throughout your life as an adult. To give you some guideline, young adulthood will be defined as the period between the ages of 20 and 40.

Physical Maturity

If you look up the term *adult* in the dictionary, you will find the definition "fully developed and mature." Certainly, most people reach **maturity** (muh **tyoor** ih tee), the state of being full grown in the physical sense, by adolescence or by their early twenties. By this time, all of your body systems are fully developed, and you are as tall as you will ever be.

If you have been healthy and have received adequate nutrition and exercise, you are likely to reach your **physical peak** during young adulthood. Physical peak means your weight is at a healthy level and your physical abilities are at their maximum levels. Measures of your physical abilities include strength, speed, and breathing and heart capacity.

The image of a peak implies that all other changes will be downhill. Once you reach your maximum physical development, however, you can maintain your physical strengths for many years to come. You can do this by maintaining a healthy diet, getting adequate rest, exercising, and avoiding tobacco, alcohol, and other drugs.

Although you can remain at your physical peak for years, aging is a normal biological process. As your body ages, changes occur. The rate at which these changes occur is influenced by many factors. Some of these factors are listed in Figure 15-1. For some people, physical aging may begin to be noticeable during young adulthood. As you age, your body gradually begins to slow and lose strength. Other early signs of aging include gray hair, balding, and wrinkles.

Emotional Maturity

What does acting like a mature adult mean? It means being independent, yet at the same time having close, loving relationships. It means expressing your feelings in a healthy way. It means being able to cope with stress or seeking help when you need it. It means enjoying life and continuing to change and learn new things. It means maintaining a positive image of yourself in spite of setbacks.

Your success in meeting all the tasks of adulthood depends on your self-concept, the physical and mental picture you have of yourself and your place in the world. If you have a strong, positive self-concept, you will be able to take your setbacks, as well as your successes, in stride. Divorce, separation from a loved one, and loss of a job are not unusual occurrences for adult Americans. You may well have to deal with one of these stressful situations at some point during your adulthood. Knowing who you are—your skills, strengths, weaknesses, values, and beliefs—can help you to handle situations like these. It can also aid you in seeking help when a problem is too much to handle alone.

No one acts in a mature, adult way all the time. Everyone has ups and downs, successes and defeats. Change is a basic element in every stage of life, including adulthood. How you adjust to the changes in your life determines how happy and healthy an adult you will be.

Relationships

Young adulthood is characterized by several major psychological and social milestones. Perhaps one of the most important of these is the establishment of close, loving relationships with others outside your family. As you may remember from Chapter 2, the American psychologist Erik Erikson identified the search for intimacy versus a retreat into isolation as the central issue for young adults.

Factors That Affect Physical Aging

- Heredity
- Healthful behaviors
- Availability of good medical care
- Positive attitude
- Avoidance of diseases, accidents, and hazardous situations

Figure 15-1. Which of these factors can you control?

◀ **Figure 15-2. Many people maintain their physical peak well beyond young adulthood. Pete Rose was a star baseball player until he retired at 45.**

FAMILY RELATIONSHIPS   Young adults may live at home or away from home. Either way, parents and children must shift from a dependent child–parent relationship to a more independent, adult–adult relationship. Young adults living away from home need to adjust to the separation from their families. Both young adults and their families may experience a sense of loss because of their physical separation. Telephoning, writing, and getting together for special occasions can help ease the separation.

Once you have moved away from home, you must assume responsibility for your own behavior and health. You must, for example, budget your money and do your own laundry. Without some earlier experience, all of your responsibilities can seem overwhelming to you. Adolescence provides you with an opportunity to practice many of the independent, responsible, healthful behaviors that you will need as a young adult.

FRIENDSHIPS   You are more likely to form lasting friendships during young adulthood than during adolescence. Why? Because, as a young adult, you have a better sense of who you are. Young adults tend to choose friends who share similar interests and values.

Friends provide you with companionship, entertainment, emotional support, and feedback about yourself. Friends are an important source of **validation** (val ih **day** shun). Through validation, you reassure a person that his or her feelings, ideas, or decisions are reasonable. Suppose, for example, that a friend of yours has decided not to go to college, despite his parents' pressures. You might validate your friend's decision by telling him that his reasons make sense to you. In explaining why you agree with him, you

Friends sometimes can reassure you that your ideas, feelings, or decisions are reasonable.

may help your friend better understand the reasons behind his decision. If, however, you do not believe that his decision is best for him, you owe it to your friend to tell him so.

Although validation is important at every stage of life, it is especially important during young adulthood. This is because young adulthood is a time when you make many lifelong decisions—decisions about marriage, children, and career. Although you must make these important decisions yourself, it helps to have friends who can help you honestly assess them.

INTIMACY   Having a clear idea of who you are and trusting others are the basis for emotional intimacy. **Emotional intimacy** is the ability to share your innermost feelings with someone else and have a caring, loving relationship. A loving relationship means that you sometimes place another person's well-being and needs before your own. If you are in love with someone, you should be willing to compromise and make some sacrifices for that person.

If you have a clear sense of self, you will be able to be giving and share your thoughts and feelings with someone else. You will not need to pretend to be someone else in order to have a relationship. You also will recognize that others have separate identities and that you cannot control their thoughts or actions.

MARRIAGE AND PARENTHOOD   Nine out of ten Americans marry at least once. Most of these marriages occur during young adulthood. At least one study has indicated that Americans consider marriage the most important factor

▲
Figure 15-4. Having a friend's support and reassurance is important during young adulthood.

◀ **Figure 15-5. Before you marry, it is important to have a clear idea of who you are.**

Figure 15-6. Having a satisfying career is a major concern of most young adults.

Young adults are concerned about finding a career in which they are effective, productive, and satisfied.

in determining happiness during adulthood. People usually select marriage partners who are similar in age, education, and social background to themselves. Both men and women rate kindness, understanding, and intelligence as more important than physical attractiveness in selecting a mate.

You need to know yourself fairly well before you select a marriage partner. You need to know what your goals are and how you are going to achieve them. You need to know what is important to you. Some people continue their search for identity well into their 20s and 30s, and, for some, even beyond these years. These adults may not feel ready for marriage. For other people, young adulthood not only is a time for marriage but also a time to become parents. The relationship between parent and child is critical to the development of a healthy child. In addition to food and shelter, children need loving care and attention. Young adults who become parents must be financially and emotionally ready to take on the responsibilities of parenthood.

CAREER Another major concern of young adults is to find a career at which they are effective, productive, and satisfied. During adolescence, you think, plan, and prepare for your life's work. During young adulthood, you must make decisions and take actions. You must consider the salary you need to earn to be self-supporting. If you are continuing your education, you need to know what courses are necessary to achieve your goal. If you are married and have children, you need to juggle your work or school responsibilities with the needs of your family.

Although work can be rewarding, it also can be a source of stress. You may feel that you have no control over the kind of work you do; you may be fearful of being fired; your work may prevent you from spending time with your family or friends. Using coping skills, such as those described in Chapter 3, can help you deal with the stress of work. An overly stressful job, however, may require a career change.

Section Review

1. How would you define young adulthood?
2. Describe two major issues that every young adult must resolve.
3. What is emotional intimacy?
4. Name three characteristics that are typical of emotionally mature adults.

What Do You Think?
5. Relate a recent conversation in which you gave or received validation.

2. MIDDLE ADULTHOOD

Middle adulthood is the period from about the age of 41 to the age of 64. Although you are years away from middle adulthood, you probably know people who are in this stage of life. What are your impressions of middle adulthood? Do you look forward to being middle-aged?

Physical Changes

By middle adulthood, external signs of aging are more evident than they were in young adulthood. Graying and thinning hair, wrinkles, extra weight, and impaired vision and hearing are likely to affect all middle-aged people at some point. During these years, hormonal changes also are occurring within the body.

During middle adulthood, the production of sex hormones in both men and women gradually slows. This gradual change in hormone production, called **climacteric** (kly **mak** tur ik), takes place over a period of three to eight years. For women, the result of climacteric is menopause, which is the end of menstruation. After menopause, women no longer produce mature eggs and, therefore, cannot become pregnant. For some men, climacteric is marked by reduced sexual activity, although men continue to produce sperm throughout their adult lives.

Concerns and Relationships

Middle adulthood is a time to share, apply, and benefit from the experiences you gained during young adulthood. For many people, middle adulthood is a time of peak professional ability and creativity.

Signs of aging are more evident in middle adulthood than in young adulthood.

◀ **Figure 15-7. Although all of these people are in middle adulthood, they show varying degrees of aging.**

Figure 15-8. Middle adulthood is a time when interests shift to the welfare of others.

GENERATIVITY Erik Erikson identifies the central task of middle adulthood as **generativity** (jen ur ah **tiv** ih tee). Generativity means that people shift their concern from themselves in the present to the welfare of others in the future. Generativity is the ability to care for other generations, to direct your energy toward the welfare of others, while maintaining your own self-esteem and personal identity. During middle adulthood, you may take care of children or aging parents, or both. By voting and participating in community projects, you may work to improve your community. You may become politically active outside of your community. You may share your knowledge and experience with others. During this time, you find a balance between meeting your own needs and contributing to the welfare of others. The reward of generativity is the knowledge that you have done your best to make the world a better place.

SELF-EVALUATION It is common for people in middle adulthood to go through a period during which they evaluate their lives. This period of self-evaluation often occurs because adults realize that they are not going to live forever and they may not achieve all of their goals. During this period, people may compare the dreams they had during young adulthood with their actual accomplishments. They may ask themselves questions such as:

- Have I accomplished what I set out to do?
- Is my marriage satisfying? Does my spouse really love and understand me?
- What do I want to do that I haven't already done?
- Have I done anything to make the world a better place?

During middle adulthood, people may begin to evaluate their lives.

Because questions like these can create anxiety, this period of self-evaluation sometimes is called the "mid-life crisis." It is through these types of questions, however, that people begin to monitor and evaluate their lives. For some, mid-life crises lead to change. A person may decide to take a new direction—change careers, return to school, or travel. For others, mid-life crises are times to appreciate what they have and to make their goals more realistic.

The likelihood of experiencing a mid-life crisis depends on your expectations, your sense of control, and your financial, social, and emotional resources. Do you expect your adulthood to be characterized by few changes or do you understand that change is an element in all stages of the life cycle? Do you feel in control of your life, or do you think there is nothing you can do to direct your life? Are you able to overcome setbacks? Do you have family and friends on whom you can rely? If you realize that change is a part of life, and if you have the resources to deal with change, you probably will experience only a healthy period of questioning and reevaluation. Instead of a cause for crisis, the changes

that occur during middle adulthood can be viewed as opportunities for growth and as challenges that you can meet with optimism.

RELATIONSHIPS The need for close relationships in middle adulthood is the same as it is in young adulthood. You do not outgrow your need for romance, close friends, or caring family relationships. Now, however, you may be concerned with your grandchildren and responsible for the care of your elderly parents.

One myth of middle adulthood is the "empty nest" feeling—feelings of sadness and worthlessness when children move out of the house to live on their own. How much difficulty do parents have adjusting to their children leaving home? Although research has indicated that parents do experience a period of adjustment when their children leave home, many view this period as a time of opportunity. Some adults experience a renewed sense of romantic love within their marriage and begin to participate more in their favorite activities or hobbies.

O━━x
When children leave home, most middle-aged adults enjoy their new freedom.

Section Review

1. Describe the effects of climacteric on both sexes.
2. What is generativity?
3. Explain how self-evaluation during middle adulthood can affect people in a positive or negative way.

What Do You Think?

4. How can you help a parent or other close adult who is going through a mid-life crisis?

3. OLDER ADULTHOOD

Older adulthood, the period from age 65 on, now lasts longer than ever before. Your great-grandparents could only expect to live about 47 years. You can expect to live about 75 years. You also can look forward to being healthier and more active than older adults in the past.

Despite the longer life span and the improved state of health of older adults, many people still view this stage of life negatively. Figure 15-10 summarizes some myths and facts about older adults. Which facts are new to you?

Physical Changes

Physical changes continue in older adulthood. These changes include wrinkling and the loss of skin **elasticity** (ih la **stis** ih tee). Elasticity refers to how well your skin molds to your body or snaps back into place when pulled. New signs of aging, such as age spots, or darkened areas of the skin, may appear on the hands, face, and scalp. For men, a receding hairline and thinning hair may occur. For both men and women, the hair turns gray or white and loses some of its luster. As blood vessels weaken, older adults may bruise

Figure 15-10. From your own experience with the elderly, which myths are false?

Myths and Facts About Older Adults

1. **Myth:** Old people complain a lot about their physical ailments.
   Fact: Most elderly people report that they feel well and healthy most of the time despite the effects of aging.
2. **Myth:** Most older adults live in nursing homes and cannot get around by themselves.
   Fact: Only about 5 percent of the elderly live in nursing homes and fewer than 20 percent of the elderly are unable to get around by themselves.
3. **Myth:** Older adults do little more than sit around and watch television and sleep.
   Fact: Senior citizens have many interests and sleep fewer hours per day than most younger adults.
4. **Myth:** A large majority of people over the age of 65 regret being retired.
   Fact: Most people over 65 say they are enjoying their retirement years.
5. **Myth:** Older adults who continue to work are inefficient and miss many work days due to illness.
   Fact: Senior citizens are extremely productive workers and seldom are late to or absent from work.
6. **Myth:** Older people are forgetful and they have trouble learning new things.
   Fact: Aging has little effect on people's mental capabilities; older people are not unusually forgetful nor do they have trouble learning new things.
7. **Myth:** Old people tend to be lonely and often feel depressed.
   Fact: The majority of older adults are content with their lives and are not lonely.
8. **Myth:** Most people over 65 have a physical disease or disorder that limits their freedom to do what they wish.
   Fact: Most elderly people are healthy and physically active.
9. **Myth:** Older adults normally have no interest in members of the opposite sex.
   Fact: The need for intimacy and loving relationships with members of the opposite sex does not diminish with age.
10. **Myth:** Older people are obsessed with dying and fear death more than any other age group.
    Fact: Although older adults know that they will not live forever, the majority fear death less than any other age group.

more easily and heal more slowly. As hormone production decreases, height and weight may decline. The senses of sight, taste, hearing, and touch gradually become less acute.

Aging also occurs inside the body. Many of the body systems slow down and become less efficient. Nevertheless, most older adults retain the ability to meet the demands of everyday life. Some continue to work, travel, and pursue strenuous sports, such as running or bicycling. The key to coping with the aging process is accepting the changes in your body and making the most of your capabilities.

PHYSICAL DISEASES   One of the body systems weakened by the aging process is the **immune system,** which is the disease-fighting system of the human body. As a result, common infectious diseases, such as pneumonia and flu, are more threatening to an older adult. Older adults should take preventative measures, such as getting flu shots, to reduce their risk of death from infectious diseases.

A serious illness, called **Parkinson's disease,** strikes 1 out of every 100 people over the age of 60. Parkinson's disease is characterized by a progressive loss of normal muscle function. The muscles become stiff, causing shaky, crippled movements. Although the cause is not understood, it is known that Parkinson's disease is related to the lack of normal functioning of certain parts of the brain. Another major crippler of older adults is **arthritis** (ar **thry** tis). Arthritis attacks the joints of the body, making simple tasks, such as holding a pencil or climbing stairs, extremely painful.

The most common diseases among older adults are heart disease, cancer, stroke, and lung disease. Many of these diseases are related to the health behaviors practiced during earlier life stages. Although some of these diseases can be treated in older adulthood, most cannot. To reduce these health risks as you age, you should practice healthful behaviors throughout your life.

ACCIDENTS   The bones of older people tend to be brittle; they break easily and heal slowly. The brittleness is due to a condition called **osteoporosis** (**ahs** tee oh pur oh sis), or thinning of the bones. This is caused by a loss of bone calcium, the substance that makes bones strong and hard. Exercise and a diet high in calcium-rich foods help prevent osteoporosis. Once it occurs, preventative measures, such as installing railings along stairs and bathtubs, can reduce the chances of falls.

Concerns and Relationships

Older adulthood is Erikson's eighth and final stage of psychological and social development. According to Erikson, this is a time for people to pause and reflect upon their lives.

Transplants Aid Parkinson's Patients

Parkinson's disease is a disorder that gradually destroys particular brain cells. Victims first suffer tremors and finally are completely disabled. While the cause of the disease is unknown, there is an encouraging new treatment: transplanting tissue from a person's adrenal glands into the brain.

Although some transplants have been successful, experts admit they don't know exactly why. They do know that adrenal tissue and brain tissue originate in the same embryo cells. Researchers speculate that adrenal tissue has the ability to change into brain tissue and to make new nerve connections when it is transplanted into the brain. Then it may also begin to produce dopamine, a brain hormone that is lacking in Parkinson's patients.

There is no clear evidence that adrenal tissue actually performs these functions—only remarkable improvement in those who have had transplants. Researchers hope that similar operations may be useful in treating Alzheimer's, strokes, and spinal and head injuries.

Can transplants cure Parkinson's disease?

What have they accomplished? What do they still wish to do? Have they had a positive effect on other people in their lives? What wisdom have they acquired? A positive outcome of this self-evaluation leads to a sense of wholeness, acceptance, and optimism. A negative outcome leads to a sense of despair and hopelessness.

INTEGRITY   Erikson says that the chief task of older adults is the achievement of **integrity,** the stage of feeling complete. This means reviewing your life and accepting the good and the bad without regrets. In short, achieving integrity means you feel content and are unafraid of death.

Older adults are likely to achieve integrity if they continue to be psychologically intimate with others or committed to something, such as family, friends, religion, or career, that gives meaning to their lives. Being part of a family or group and feeling confident and optimistic about their lives are other measures of integrity for older adults. Adults who achieve integrity are not only able to accept death, they are also able to enjoy the time they have left.

INTELLECTUAL SKILLS   Although there are some changes in mental functioning during older adulthood, these changes usually have little effect on thinking, learning, or long-term memory storage. There is evidence that suggests the aging process can be slowed by keeping the mind active and challenged. Most older adults are fully capable of continuing stimulating intellectual work. Some choose to continue working; others decide to develop new interests or extend their educations.

Achieving integrity in older adulthood means feeling contented and unafraid of death.

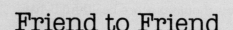

Friend to Friend

Mark:
Sue, what's wrong? You seem so down.

Sue:
I am. I just visited my grandmother in the nursing home. She has Alzheimer's disease. It's gotten so bad that she doesn't even know who I am anymore. I had to keep telling her my name. And then she kept yelling at me.

Mark:
Oh, that must feel terrible.

About 10 percent of older adults suffer from **dementia** (di **men** shuh), a disorder characterized by mental confusion and an irreversible loss of brain function. This condition sometimes has been called **senility** (sih **nil** ih tee). Dementia may be caused by a variety of factors, including a diet lacking in some important nutrients, a physical injury to the brain, or a disease such as stroke.

One type of dementia that can strike someone under the age of 60 is **Alzheimer's** (**Ahlts** hy murz) **disease.** There is no known cure for Alzheimer's disease. The first sign of the disease is forgetfulness. Later, a sense of mental confusion and helplessness sets in. Gradually, the person loses the ability to function mentally or physically. When this happens the patient needs constant care and attention. People who have Alzheimer's disease usually die within ten years of showing the first symptoms of the disease.

Alzheimer's disease is as hard for the families of patients as it is for the patients themselves. Because of the emotional strain of caring for an Alzheimer's patient, often a decision must be made to place the patient in a health-care facility. Many communities have patient-care support groups for the family members of Alzheimer's patients.

RETIREMENT   Although some people continue to work after the age of 65, many people retire. Retirement often involves many adjustments. For example, the person who retires must adjust to being separated from fellow workers who also may be close friends. The retired person may have to adjust to less income or may have to find new activities to fill each day.

▲ **Figure 15-11. Many adults remain active and alert throughout their lives.**

Sue:

It does. I feel like she's gone, but she's still there. It hurts so much. We used to have such great times when we were together.

Mark:

It's as if the person you knew has died. That is sad. If you'd like to talk about it, I'd love to hear about the special times you had with your grandmother.

Sue:

Would you? I'd love to relive some of the wonderful memories I have.

357

Figure 15-12. Retirement gives older adults an opportunity to spend more time with loved ones.

The need for loving relationships continues into old age.

Although retirement is a stressful time for many, it need not be. People who think of retirement not as an end, but as a beginning, will find it a challenging time of renewed growth. Many retired people use the time to start new careers, expand their schooling, learn new hobbies, or spend more time with family and friends.

RELATIONSHIPS Like all adults, older adults need close and loving relationships with family members and friends. It may require additional effort and adaptability on the part of older adults, however, to meet these needs.

Because women tend to live longer than men in this country, it is likely that a woman will be widowed before a man. Either way, the loss of a mate can be a major setback. The older adult must prepare for this by making an effort to maintain close relationships with others. It is not uncommon for a widowed person to start a new relationship with someone of the opposite sex. Loving relationships do not stop with the onset of old age.

To maintain loving family ties, both older adults and their children and grandchildren need to make an effort to see one another and to share experiences. The rewards of this effort can be great. Grandparents may have the time to take special outings with grandchildren or teach them skills they enjoy such as fishing or cooking. For older people who lack grandchildren, the Foster Grandparents program puts older people in touch with younger people.

Many other opportunities for social contact exist for the older person. Some communities have clubs to bring together older adults. A shared hobby can be a source of new friends. Some colleges and universities provide reduced tuition programs for people over 65. The Elder Hostel program arranges travel at low rates. Many schools and cultural institutions encourage older adults to work as volunteers. In fact, older adulthood can be a most rewarding time of life.

Section Review

1. List three health problems that older adults may face.
2. What is meant by achieving integrity?
3. Why does retirement require both social and psychological adjustments for older adults?
4. Describe three ways older adults can make the last stage of the life cycle challenging and rewarding.

What Do You Think?

5. Think of two ways that you could make the time you spend with an older person, such as a grandparent, more enjoyable and memorable.

4. DEATH AND DYING

Death is part of the normal cycle of all living things, including humans. No amount of fame, money, or love prevents death. While death marks the end of life, dying is a part of living.

Death with Dignity

As strange as it sounds, the process of dying has changed since the time of your great-grandparents. Chances are you will not die in the same manner as they did. The medical advances that have lengthened the average life span have also given doctors the ability to prolong the life of a dying person. This has created a concern for appropriate death. An **appropriate death** is one that fulfills a person's expectations and ideals. Should a dying person's life be prolonged indefinitely, even when the person's mental and social life has ceased? Because of questions like this one, many adults find that they fear the process of dying more than they fear death itself.

A program that provides physical, emotional, and spiritual care for dying people and support for their families is called **hospice** (**hahs** pis). To make hospice affordable, most of the workers, except for medical personnel, are trained volunteers. Hospice workers visit the dying in hospitals, nursing homes, or at home. Some hospice programs have their own facilities where dying patients can be given round-the-clock care by hospice workers. Hospice workers help patients and their families to accept death and to enjoy the time that is left as much as possible.

Because medical advances can now prolong life, many people are concerned about dying with dignity.

◀ **Figure 15-13. Hospice workers encourage terminally ill patients to enjoy the time they have left.**

The Stages of Dying

A **terminal illness** is one that results in death. The way people cope with terminal illness depends on their expectations, their psychological strengths, and the reactions of loved ones. Elisabeth Kubler-Ross, a psychiatrist, has studied the reactions of terminally ill people and their families to dying and death. Dr. Kubler-Ross has found the following pattern of reactions:

- First, denial: "Oh, no, not me."
- Second, anger and envy of healthy people: "Why me? Why not someone else?"
- Third, a tendency to bargain or try to postpone death: "If I am good and give up drinking and cigarettes, I'll get better and live."
- Fourth, depression or a sense of loss: "I can't work, I can't care for my children, I hurt all the time. I feel worthless. What's the use?"
- Fifth, acceptance: "Soon this will be over. I'm ready. I've said all my good-byes."

Other research has shown that not everyone reacts toward death in the same way. Some people do not experience all five of the stages of dying; others may experience the stages in a different order.

Coping with a Dying Loved One

Suppose your grandparent, parent, or friend is dying. You may find yourself going through some of the same emotional stages that the dying experience: "Oh, no, it can't be her turn to die! It's all a mistake." "Why him? Why couldn't it be someone else?" "If I am really good, maybe I can prevent her from dying." "Oh, I can't stand to see him suffer so much. Maybe it will be better when it is over and death finally comes."

Most people are uncomfortable with death and dying. Some may try to cover up their grief by false cheer. Others may keep away. Silence or absence helps neither the family nor the dying person.

What should you do? Focus your energies on the dying loved one. Visit the person as often as you can. Talk about your plans and hopes, even though that person will not be there to share the future with you. Listen to what the dying person has to say. Let him or her talk about the past.

Most dying people want to talk about what is happening to them. Do not be shy about discussion of death. If death frightens you, think of the dying person as someone who is about to set out on a long journey. You want to share your feelings of loss before a loved one goes. You may want to ask about the journey.

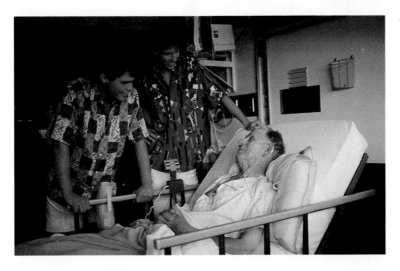

What if the dying person is in a coma? Does it matter whether you visit? Some people who have survived comas say they remember some events that occurred while they were in the coma. Touching and talking can help you, and perhaps the person can feel your touch and hear the words you speak.

Dealing with your own grief is not easy. There is no quick solution. You must not become so overwhelmed you forget to take care of yourself, but at the same time, you should not deny how you feel. Talk about your loss with family and friends. Describe how you will miss the dying person. Think of how you would like to remember the person. Continue your usual routine as much as possible and include visits with the dying person. Also allow yourself some time to let go and grieve.

Your love for another person is a great tribute to that person. When a person is dying, your time to express your love is limited; you should use it well. Say all the loving, sad, and funny things you can think to say while you still have the opportunity. Make dying a time for loving and sharing, not loneliness and despair.

Friends and family can be a support to the dying person and to each other.

Section Review

1. What is an appropriate death?
2. What are the advantages of a hospice program?
3. Briefly describe the five stages that people may experience after they find out that their illness is terminal.

What Do You Think?
4. Suppose you have been told that you have only six months to live. Describe how you would like your family and friends to treat you.

Setting Goals

Now that Mario is a senior in high school, everyone is asking him about his goals. When his uncle tells him to consider "where he'll be in ten years," his father complains Mario doesn't know where he'll be next week. At school, Mario's advisor wants him to choose his courses in light of his college goals, and his girlfriend is concerned over whether or not he's going away to school. His best friend Joe keeps saying this year is their last chance to party before they have to act like adults.

Mario knows he should start looking ahead, but how far into the future? He's always said he wants to be a doctor, but he's never done anything about it. His attention and energies seem to skip from one thing to another.

The following guidelines could help Mario focus his energies on achievable goals. You can use them, too, to help set your own realistic and reachable goals.

1. Know Yourself

Before deciding on specific goals, jot down what you know about yourself. What are your long-term interests? What activities do you enjoy? What are your abilities? What are the most important things in your life? Goals that correspond to your interests and values will be more desirable. Goals tied to your abilities will be easier to reach.

2. Make Goals Clear, Specific, and Positive

A clear, specific, positive goal accurately describes what you want to be doing when you achieve it. It describes an observable, measurable behavior. "I want to get all Bs this term" is clearer than "I want to do better in school." It allows you to measure your success by counting the number of Bs you receive. How do you measure "doing better"?

Getting all Bs is also more specific than the negative "I don't want any Fs this term." It is future-oriented, giving you something to strive for. Positive goals are like signposts ahead. You are able to measure your progress toward them, and each one is an achievement when you finally reach it.

3. Include Deadlines

Set a reasonable time limit for your goal. Deadlines make goals more specific, add a sense of urgency, and provide a good way to measure success. If you cannot meet the deadline, you may need to consider a more realistic time limit. For example, if you were able to raise four out of five grades to B this term, this would be good progress, not failure. The goal of earning all Bs should be rescheduled for next term.

4. Break Long-term Goals into Small Steps

Long-term goals, such as running the marathon, should be broken into smaller, more manageable and measurable steps. Future marathoners begin their training with short distances. Only when they have built the speed and endurance necessary for long distances do they go on to run the full marathon course.

5. Keep Written Goals Visible

Write your goals down. Then, tape them to your closet door, mirror, notebook, or other place you look at frequently. This repeated reinforcement of a goal will keep you focused on achieving it.

6. Evaluate Your Progress

At times, stop and ask yourself if you are making progress toward your goal. If so, good. If not, how can you get on track?

Setting goals helps you work toward achieving them.

APPLY THE SKILL

1. Review Mario's situation. How could he use the steps above to help set some long-term and short-term goals? How could he use a career goal to focus his energies during his senior year?

2. What is wrong with each of the goals below? Rewrite each example as one (or several) clear, specific, positive goals. Include realistic deadlines.
(a) I don't want to gain any more weight.
(b) I want to be a professional tennis player.
(c) I want to stop fighting with my parents so much.
(d) I want to eat better.
(e) I want to be happy.

3. Think about a time when you set a goal and tried to reach it. Did you use any of the steps described above? Explain. Did you reach your goal? Why or why not?

4. Get to know yourself better by listing your interests, abilities, and values.

Keeping that list in mind, write two clear, specific, positive goals you want to achieve by:
(a) the end of the school year.
(b) the end of high school.
(c) the end of ten years.
Then break your goal down into manageable subgoals.

5. Review the list of your personal qualities from question 4. Using the guidelines above, set a goal with a realistic deadline of two weeks or less. Use subgoals if necessary. After two weeks, evaluate your success. How did the guidelines help make your goal achievable?

15 | Chapter Review

Chapter Summary

- As with the other stages of the life cycle, the adult years are marked by many changes. Physically, the body shows gradual signs of aging, such as gray hair and wrinkles; socially and emotionally, the person faces new concerns and responsibilities.
- A strong personal identity helps adults of all ages cope successfully with the changes they face.
- During young adulthood, a person reaches his or her physical peak.
- Forming close, loving relationships and finding productive work are the two major tasks of young adults.
- The central task of middle adulthood is generativity, which is the concern for the welfare of other generations.
- The likelihood of a person experiencing a mid-life crisis during middle adulthood depends on the person's expectations, sense of control, and financial, social, and psychological resources.
- Many older adults are healthy, mentally alert, and capable of productive work to an advanced age.
- The development of integrity is the chief task of older adulthood. If older adults feel content with the life they have lived, they will be able to accept death and enjoy the time remaining.
- Death is a part of the normal cycle of all living things. People with terminal illnesses often go through a specific pattern of reactions: denial, anger, bargaining, depression, and acceptance.
- Dying should be a time for loving and sharing, not loneliness and despair. It is best to spend the time you have with a dying loved one talking honestly about the feelings the two of you have.

Vocabulary Review

Listed below are some of the important terms in this chapter. Choose the term that best matches the phrase in the exercise that follows.

Alzheimer's disease	elasticity	integrity	senility
appropriate death	emotional intimacy	maturity	terminal illness
arthritis	generativity	Parkinson's disease	validation
climacteric	hospice	physical peak	
dementia	immune system	osteoporosis	

1. reassuring a person that his or her feelings, ideas, or opinions are reasonable

2. the ability to share innermost feelings with someone else and to engage in a caring, loving relationship

3. the gradual reduction in the production of certain hormones in men and women during middle adulthood

4. a program that provides care and support for dying people and their families

5. the shift of concern from oneself to the welfare of other generations

6. an illness characterized by a progressive loss of normal muscle function

7. the loss of calcium from the bones during older adulthood

8. one leading cause of dementia among people under age 60

9. an end to life that fulfills a person's expectations and ideals

10. the time during which a person's physical abilities are at a maximum

What Have You Learned?

1. Why does age not necessarily reflect physical, emotional, and social maturity?
2. During what stage of the life cycle do you reach your physical peak?
3. How are emotional intimacy, productive work, and self-concept interrelated?
4. What external and internal physical changes occur during middle adulthood?
5. List three ways a person might express generativity during middle adulthood.
6. Why do some middle-aged people never experience a mid-life crisis?

7. List five habits an older adult can follow to prolong life and good health.
8. What does Erik Erikson consider to be the key issue for older adults to resolve?
9. How are the concerns of older adults like those of young and middle-aged adults?
10. Why are some people more afraid of the process of dying than they are of death itself?
11. Describe three behaviors that help you handle the terminal illness of a loved one.
12. Why is it helpful to think of a dying person as someone about to take a journey?

What Do You Think?

1. What steps can you take to ensure a smooth transition into adulthood?
2. Emotionally and socially, what do you think parents need from their children during a mid-life crisis?
3. Imagine that identical twins lose track of each other at age 20 and are reunited at age

40. Is it likely that their adult lives have been as similar as their childhoods?
4. Describe yourself as you would like to be during young, middle, and older adulthood.
5. Why is a strong identity necessary for achieving intimacy in young adulthood and integrity in older adulthood?

What Would You Do?

1. List four behaviors that will help you remain at your physical peak in adulthood.
2. List some benefits and risks of emotional intimacy. Do the benefits outweigh the risks?
3. Imagine that your parents are close to retirement age. They want to move to a small town where mostly older adults live. They

want your opinion about the move. What would you say?
4. How would you maintain a strong relationship with a grandparent in a nursing home?
5. A friend is terribly depressed about her father's death. How would you comfort her and help bring her out of her depression?

For Further Study

1. Interview some adults, making sure to include one from each of the three age groups. Ask them about the type of advice they would offer to teenagers about to enter adulthood. Compare the responses of the people you interviewed. What did you learn about adulthood from the interviews?
2. During a favorite TV program, jot down the kinds of advertisements that appear between segments of the program. How many young, middle-aged, and older adults appear? What impressions do the ads give of adults in each age group? Do you think the impressions are accurate? Why or why not?

Rita gave me this pamphlet. Signing doesn't look that hard. What do you say we take the class Juan took? Then, we could be in on the conversation, too.

U N I T

5

Diseases and Disorders

16
Infectious Diseases

17
AIDS and Other Sexually Transmitted Diseases

18
Noninfectious Diseases and Physical Disabilities

16

As you read, think about

▶ the causes of infectious diseases and how they are spread.

▶ how your body defends itself against infectious diseases.

▶ the stages of an infectious disease.

▶ the ways to treat and prevent infectious diseases.

Infectious Diseases

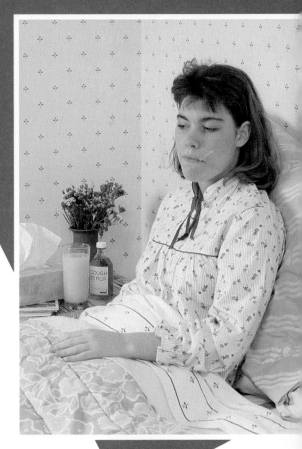

T he tickle in your nose increases. With a tissue in hand, you wait. "Ah-ah-ah-CHEW!" Then comes another sneeze and another. It all adds up—sore throat, runny nose, and now sneezing. You have just caught a cold, the most common infectious disease.

Fortunately, your cold is not a serious illness, and you know how to take care of yourself while you have it. Still, it's no fun having to stay in bed and keep away from your friends. Between sneezes, you wish someone would find a cure for the common cold.

In this chapter, you'll learn about infectious diseases, their causes, and how they are spread. You'll find out how your body defends itself against them and how your family can reduce the risk of infection through correct hygiene and a healthy life style. Finally, you'll learn how medication and other therapies are used to fight influenza, pneumonia, mononucleosis, and other infectious diseases.

Avoid infectious diseases when you can, but when you do get sick, be sure to get proper care.

369

1. THE NATURE OF INFECTIOUS DISEASES

For as long as there have been humans, there have been **infectious** (in **fek** shus) **diseases.** Infectious diseases, also known as communicable diseases, are caused by organisms that enter and then live within the human body. Most of these organisms are so small that they can be seen only through a microscope. When organisms are this small, they are called **microorganisms.**

Spread of Infectious Diseases

Organisms that cause disease in plants or animals, including humans, are called **pathogens** (**path** uh junz). Most pathogens are microorganisms. How do they get into the body? Some are breathed in with air, and some are swallowed. Others enter the body through large or small breaks in the skin or in the moist linings of the eyes, ears, nose, mouth, or other parts of your body. People usually get infectious diseases in one of four ways.

CONTACT WITH ANOTHER PERSON Most infectious diseases are spread through contact with a person who has the disease. Diseases that spread from one person to another, like a cold, are called **contagious** (kun **tay** jes), and people who have these pathogens are said to be contagious. The pathogens can be spread by direct physical contact with an area of infection on another person's body or by tiny droplets of moisture sneezed or coughed into the air and then inhaled by a noninfected person. The common cold, flu, and chicken pox often are spread this way. Most sexually transmitted diseases are spread by direct physical contact.

CONTACT WITH AN ANIMAL There are some serious infectious diseases that are transmitted to humans through the bites of animals, including birds and insects. For example, a person can develop rabies, a deadly disease of the nervous system, if he or she is bitten by an infected dog or other animal, such as a raccoon. Malaria, a disease that is common in the tropics, is spread from person to person through mosquito bites.

CONTACT WITH A CONTAMINATED OBJECT Although most pathogens cannot live for long outside the body, some can live for short periods of time on objects. These pathogens are transmitted from one person to another through shared objects, such as eating utensils, toothbrushes, or needles used by drug abusers. Larger organisms, like lice, can spread from person to person on hairbrushes and combs.

Sometimes when you handle objects that have been sneezed on, coughed on, or somehow infected with a pathogen, you transfer the pathogen to yourself when you touch your eyes, your mouth, or your food. This is why it is a good idea to wash your hands before eating.

CONTACT WITH ENVIRONMENTAL SOURCES

Food, water, or soil that have been infected with pathogens are sources of infectious diseases. These are known as environmental sources. **Legionnaires'** (lee juh **nairz**) **disease,** a serious respiratory infection, for example, is thought to be spread by the air in buildings that have contaminated air conditioning systems. As people inhale the air, the pathogens enter the body. Another example of an environmental source is food poisoning. Food poisoning is caused by microorganisms that grow in foods not refrigerated or cooked properly. A person who eats this food develops nausea, vomiting, and abdominal pain. Although the blood used for transfusions is screened carefully before it is used, it can be another environmental source of disease. Even the drinking water in places where sanitation is poor or flooding has occurred may be contaminated by pathogens. Sometimes, pathogens live and grow in soil and cause disease when they enter the body.

Figure 16-2. Mosquitoes and other animals can transmit infectious diseases.

Figure 16-3. Bacteria can be spherical, rod-shaped, or spiral-shaped.

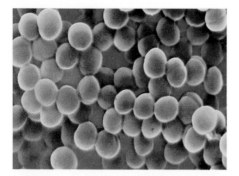

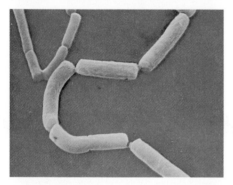

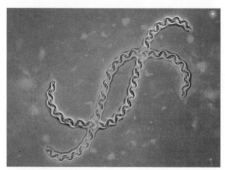

Causes of Infectious Diseases

Not all microorganisms that enter the body are pathogens. In fact, there are many microorganisms present in the body at all times. These microorganisms are called **resident microorganisms.** They are found in the mouth, on the skin, and in the digestive tract. Most of them are harmless as long as they stay where they belong. Some of them actually help with normal bodily functions.

Pathogens, however, are different. They are organisms that do not belong in the body, and if they enter and multiply, they cause disease. Most pathogens are parasites. A **parasite** (**pa** ruh syt) is an organism that lives on or inside a living thing and takes its food from that living thing.

BACTERIA Single-celled microorganisms that can live almost anywhere are called **bacteria** (bak **teer** ee uh). Bacteria can live in air, in soil, in food, and in human bodies. Bacteria even have been found in the freezing waters of the Arctic and in the boiling waters of hot springs.

Some bacteria damage healthy cells when they enter them. However, most bacteria injure cells by giving off poisons called **toxins** (**tahk** sins). Food poisoning, for example, is caused by toxins given off by bacteria in food. Another type of bacteria found in soil and on objects produces **tetanus** (**tet** un us) **toxin.** This type of bacteria can cause an infection whenever there is a deep wound, especially one that does not drain. Tetanus toxin damages the nervous system, causing uncontrollable muscle contractions and paralysis.

VIRUSES The simplest type of parasites, **viruses,** are about 100 times smaller than most bacteria. Viruses cannot multiply unless they enter living cells and take over their reproductive mechanisms, which damages or kills the cells.

Different types of viruses invade different types of human cells and cause disease in different parts of the body. For example, several dozen different viruses can cause the

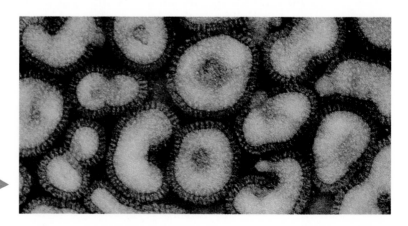

Figure 16-4. A human virus displays a particular form and structure when looked at closely.

Examples of Other Pathogens

Pathogen	Characteristics	Means of Spread	Diseases
Rickettsia	microorganisms that grow inside cells	bites of body lice, ticks, and fleas	Rocky Mountain spotted fever; typhus
Mycoplasma	smallest microorganisms; can be free-living	contact with an infected person	pneumonia; ear infections
Trichinella	parasitic worms	contaminated meat from infected animals	trichinosis (invasion of muscles)
Toxoplasma	single-celled parasites	cats, to water or food, to humans	toxoplasmosis (birth defects if mother infected while pregnant)
Schistosoma	small parasitic worms	fresh-water snails to drinking water	schistosomiasis (invasion of liver, intestines, kidney, brain)
Tapeworm	flat, parasitic worm up to several feet long	contaminated meat	tapeworm (invasion of the intestines)

common cold. Still other viruses cause mumps, chicken pox, cold sores, and liver infections. Viruses cause many other infectious diseases, too many to list here.

Figure 16-5. Infectious diseases are caused by a wide variety of organisms. Which of these might be found in food?

FUNGI Small simple organisms that grow either as parasites in living organisms or in the remains of dead organisms are known as **fungi** (fuhn jy). Although yeasts, mushrooms, and molds are fungi, there are some fungi that cause infections. Fungi grow best in warm, dark, moist areas. Ringworm, a skin infection that forms a circle just under the skin's surface, and athlete's foot are two typical fungal infections. Some other types of pathogens are listed in Figure 16-5.

Section Review

1. What is the difference between an infectious disease and a noninfectious disease?
2. Name two ways that infectious diseases are spread.
3. Where do resident microorganisms live?
4. How do viruses multiply?

What Do You Think?
5. When did you last have a cold? Where do you think the pathogen came from?

2. THE BODY'S DEFENSES AGAINST INFECTION

Since pathogens are everywhere, and your body comes in contact with many every day, why are you not always sick? When you do get sick, what keeps the pathogens from multiplying and growing until they take over your body? The answer to both of these questions is that your body knows how to defend itself.

Physical and Chemical Barriers

Your body's first line of defense is its protective coverings. Your skin, for example, is a physical barrier to pathogens. The surface cells of your skin are hard and have no gaps between them. Your skin also has chemical barriers, such as sweat. Sweat contains acids that kill many bacteria. Finally, your skin constantly sheds old cells, and the pathogens on these cells are shed, too. In fact, microorganisms cannot get through skin unless the skin has a cut, scrape, burn, or other injury.

The entrances to the body, such as the mouth, eyes, or nose, have their own physical and chemical barriers. These entrances have moist linings called **mucous (myoo** kus) **membranes.** Mucous membranes are covered with a layer of sticky mucus which, can trap many pathogens and wash them away. Your saliva and tears can also trap or wash away pathogens. After the pathogens have been trapped, certain chemicals and specialized cells in mucus, saliva, and tears attack them. Some of the pathogens are killed. Others are kept from reproducing or getting food. These attacks can keep pathogens from getting into the body to cause disease.

If a pathogen gets beyond the body's entrance points, surface membranes, chemicals, and special cells along the airways, digestive tract, and urinary tract prevent entry into the body. These systems also can expel pathogens physically. Inhaled pathogens that reach the windpipe, for example, may be trapped by mucus and moved toward the mouth by **cilia (sil** ee uh), tiny hairlike structures that beat rhythmically to move mucus upward. The pathogens are removed along with mucus when you cough or blow your nose, or they can be attacked by the chemicals in saliva and swallowed.

Acids and other chemicals in the digestive tract make life difficult or impossible for many pathogens. The normal motions of the digestive tract not only move food through your system but also move pathogens out. Resident bacteria compete with pathogens for food and space. These bacteria also give off substances that kill invading bacteria. Pathogens in the urinary tract are always washed by the flow of urine, which is usually acid enough to kill bacteria.

Pathogens that enter the body's passageways meet physical and chemical barriers.

Inflammation

If a pathogen gets through the physical and chemical barriers presented by your body and begins to injure cells, your body is ready with its second line of defense: inflammation. **Inflammation** (in fluh **may** shun) is the body's response to all kinds of injury, from cuts and scrapes to internal damage caused by infectious diseases. Inflammation is needed for healing.

Inflammation starts within seconds of damage by anything—a burn, a cut or scrape, a splinter or dirt, or a pathogen. The damaged cells release chemicals that cause several responses, all of which help fight the damage. Tiny blood vessels in the injured area dilate, or widen, which allows more blood to flow to the injured areas. Fluids leak out of the dilated vessels along with some white blood cells known as **phagocytes** (**fag** uh syts), or eater cells. The phagocytes begin to "eat up" any pathogens that may be present. At the same time, other phagocytes are attracted to the injury from nearby tissues. As all these rescuers crowd into the area, the injury becomes red, swollen, tender, and sore; in other words, **inflamed.** The phagocytes and chemicals continue to kill pathogens and clean up the damage. The phagocytes surround and digest pathogens, dead cells, and tiny bits of wreckage. They also give off substances that cause healing to begin.

The Immune System

The **immune** (ih **myoon**) **system** is the body's last and most complicated line of defense against pathogens. Unlike the phagocytes and chemicals that kill any pathogen found in an injury, the immune system recognizes, seeks out, and destroys specific pathogens throughout the body. The immune system can even "remember" some pathogens that have previously invaded the body. If these pathogens enter the body again, they are killed before they can cause disease. When this happens, the body is said to be immune to that disease, or to have **immunity.**

Pathogens that enter the body for the first time often cause disease. This is because the immune system does not attack them as quickly as it does pathogens it has encountered before and developed immunity to. As the immune system works to fight against the new pathogens, they are killed, and the body gradually recovers. At the same time, inflammation is working to heal injured tissues.

The immune system's weapons are a class of white blood cells known as **lymphocytes** (**lim** fuh syts). Lymphocytes live in the blood and in the **lymphatic** (lim **fat** ik) **system,** illustrated in Figure 16-7. The lymphatic system is a network of vessels that collects fluid and cells from tissues and delivers

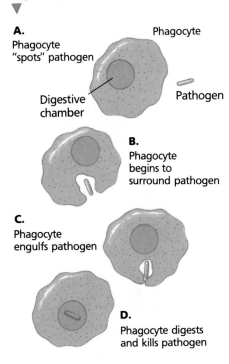

Figure 16-6. A phagocyte attacks and kills a pathogen by surrounding and digesting it.

A.
Phagocyte "spots" pathogen

Phagocyte

Digestive chamber

Pathogen

B.
Phagocyte begins to surround pathogen

C.
Phagocyte engulfs pathogen

D.
Phagocyte digests and kills pathogen

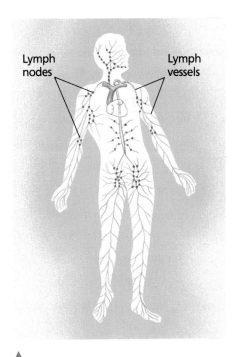

Lymph nodes

Lymph vessels

Figure 16-7. A complex network of vessels and nodes makes up your lymphatic system.

them to the bloodstream. The lymphatic vessels have hundreds of small stations, called **lymph nodes (limf nohdz)**, or lymph glands that filter the lymphatic fluid. This fluid is known as **lymph.** The lymphocytes and certain phagocytes wait in the lymph nodes and attack pathogens as they pass through. Other lymphocytes attack pathogens in the blood or in the tissues.

There are two types of lymphocytes—B lymphocytes and T lymphocytes. The B lymphocytes, or **B cells,** produce antibodies. **Antibodies (an** tee bahd eez) are proteins that "tie up" pathogens by attaching to their surfaces. This action keeps the pathogens from harming the body. It also helps phagocytes to find and consume the pathogens. Different B cells produce different antibodies designed to attack different pathogens or toxins, as shown in Figure 16-8. Once they have done this, the B cells do not forget how to produce these antibodies. The B cells circulate in the bloodstream for years, ready to produce antibodies the minute the pathogen reappears. The B cells, then, are the memory part of the immune system. Some B cells live and produce antibodies on the mucous membranes. These cells are an important part of the body's outer defenses.

T lymphocytes, or **T cells,** have many different functions in the body. Unlike B cells, T cells do not produce antibodies. Instead, these cells produce other substances that regulate all of the functions of the immune system. In addition, some T cells kill pathogens directly.

Figure 16-8. Different B cells produce different antibodies, each specific to a specific pathogen.

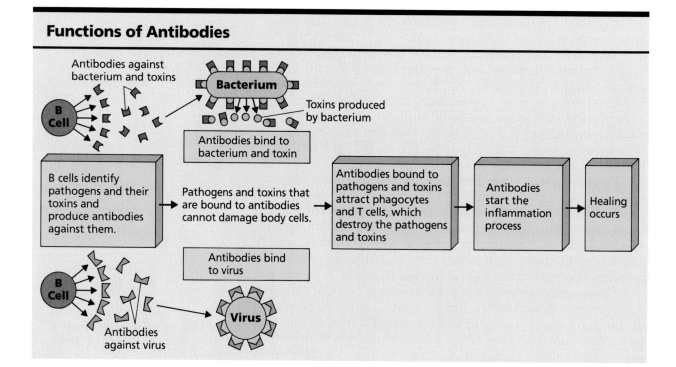

Functions of Antibodies

Antibodies against bacterium and toxins

Bacterium

B Cell

Toxins produced by bacterium

Antibodies bind to bacterium and toxin

B cells identify pathogens and their toxins and produce antibodies against them.

Pathogens and toxins that are bound to antibodies cannot damage body cells.

Antibodies bound to pathogens and toxins attract phagocytes and T cells, which destroy the pathogens and toxins

Antibodies start the inflammation process

Healing occurs

B Cell

Antibodies bind to virus

Virus

Antibodies against virus

The Three Lines of Defense Against Infection

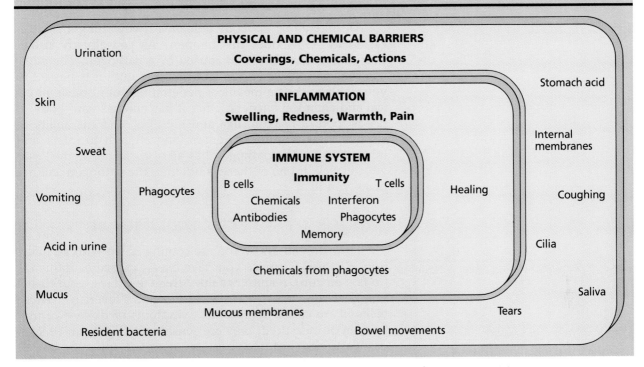

PHYSICAL AND CHEMICAL BARRIERS
Coverings, Chemicals, Actions

Urination

Skin

Sweat

Vomiting

Acid in urine

Mucus

Stomach acid

Internal membranes

Coughing

Cilia

Saliva

INFLAMMATION
Swelling, Redness, Warmth, Pain

Phagocytes

Healing

IMMUNE SYSTEM
Immunity

B cells   T cells
Chemicals   Interferon
Antibodies   Phagocytes
Memory

Chemicals from phagocytes

Mucous membranes   Tears

Resident bacteria   Bowel movements

▲
Figure 16-9. Can you explain how the body's three lines of defense work against infection?

T cells live in the blood, in the lymphatic system, and in tissues. When T cells discover any pathogens in tissues, some of the T cells produce interferon. **Interferon** (in tur **feer** ahn) is a substance that warns healthy cells that pathogens are near. The healthy cells then produce substances that prevent the pathogens, particularly viruses, from living and multiplying inside them. Sometimes some cells release interferon if they are invaded by a pathogen. This warns the cells' neighbors to fight the pathogen. Figure 16-9 summarizes the body's three lines of defense.

Section Review

1. Name two of the body's protective coverings.
2. Describe two ways the body can expel pathogens.
3. Where does inflammation occur?
4. Which type of white blood cell is responsible for maintaining immunity?

What Do You Think?
5. Young children get a greater number of infectious diseases per year than older children and adults. Why do you think this is so?

3. DEVELOPMENT OF INFECTIOUS DISEASE

Despite all of the body's defenses, you still get sick occasionally. How does this happen? As you already know, every infectious disease is caused by a pathogen. The pathogen needs a place to live and multiply until it is passed to you. It also needs a means of penetrating your body's physical and chemical barriers. Once it has entered your body, it needs food, a place to live and multiply, and the ability to survive your immune defenses long enough to infect and injure tissues. If a pathogen has all of these needs met, you will get sick. If one of these is not met, the pathogen will not make you ill.

Stages of Infectious Disease

How do you know you are coming down with an infectious disease? Suppose you have been exposed to **influenza** (in floo **en** zuh), respiratory flu. After a few days, your throat may feel sore, or you may feel hot and "feverish." These feelings are called **symptoms.** Symptoms of disease cannot be seen or measured; they are sensations. **Signs** can be seen or measured. Your doctor can see your red, inflamed throat. You can measure your temperature with a thermometer. These are signs of disease.

Before you begin to feel ill, the influenza virus enters your body, invades cells in your respiratory system, and multiplies. The time between entry of the virus, or pathogen, and the development of signs and symptoms is called the **incubation** (in kyoo **bay** shun) **period.** You still feel fine even though the pathogen is multiplying.

Pathogens that enter the body and multiply before the immune system can attack cause disease.

Figure 16-10. Once you have entered the recovery stage, you may feel well enough for visitors.

As your throat begins to feel sore, and you start to feel tired and cranky for no particular reason, you enter the **prodromal** (proh **drohm** ul) **period** of illness. During the prodromal period, you may be contagious; that is, you can pass the flu virus on to others. Your immune system discovers that a pathogen has entered your body.

Soon your head aches, your muscles feel sore, and you are sneezing and coughing. You take your temperature and discover you have a fever of 102°F. **Fever,** a body temperature above 98.6°F, is a common sign of most infectious diseases. It occurs because infection causes the body's cells to release **pyrogens** (**py** ruh junz), chemicals that signal the brain to raise body temperature. No one is quite sure what purpose a fever serves in infection. It is possible higher body temperatures harm some pathogens.

You go to bed early and stay home from school for the next two days. This stage of your illness, "full-blown flu," is called the **acute stage.** Your tissues are inflamed, and your immune system is entering the fight.

Two days later you wake up feeling a little better. Your fever is down to 99.8°F, and you decide to get up for breakfast. You have begun the **recovery stage.** You may stay home for the rest of the week, but your immune system is winning!

By the end of the week, your aches and pains have disappeared, and your temperature is normal. Your immune system has won, but you do not feel as energetic as usual, and you still have a cough. This period, between the end of infection and feeling really well, is called **convalescence** (kahn vuh **les** ens). If you do not take care of yourself during convalescence, you may have a **relapse.** A relapse is the return of disease during or soon after convalescence. As you can see in Figure 16-11, you go through five stages as you move from illness to wellness.

Fever is a common sign of many infectious diseases.

Figure 16-11. An infectious disease like chicken pox develops in stages. How long does fever usually last?

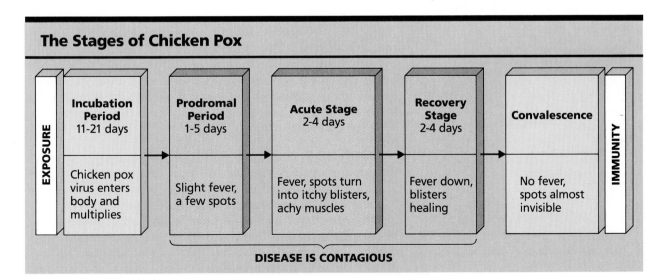

The Stages of Chicken Pox

EXPOSURE	Incubation Period 11-21 days	Prodromal Period 1-5 days	Acute Stage 2-4 days	Recovery Stage 2-4 days	Convalescence	IMMUNITY
	Chicken pox virus enters body and multiplies	Slight fever, a few spots	Fever, spots turn into itchy blisters, achy muscles	Fever down, blisters healing	No fever, spots almost invisible	

DISEASE IS CONTAGIOUS

Fending Off the Common Cold

Some time in the future you may be able to protect yourself from the common cold. Researchers have found a nasal spray that can prevent colds from spreading among family members. The spray contains interferon, which is a protein manufactured by body cells when they are attacked by viruses.

In recent studies, volunteer families used the interferon spray every day for a week whenever one family member showed signs of a cold. The spray prevented the spread of most colds that were caused by rhinoviruses. This was good news because rhinoviral colds account for almost half of all common colds.

The interferon spray is not a cure-all. It did not protect family members from other types of colds, and it caused nosebleeds in some of the volunteers. Many more studies need to be done before interferon nasal spray can be approved for use by the general public.

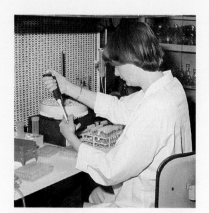

Can interferon spray cure colds?

Common Infectious Diseases

There are thousands of kinds of infectious diseases. Some are common in one part of the world but rare or absent in other places. In the United States, over 40 kinds of infectious disease commonly occur. Colds and flu are among the most common.

THE COMMON COLD AND FLU The **common cold** is really a group of symptoms and signs caused by a variety of viruses. One or two days after exposure, infected people develop sneezing, sore throats, runny noses, coughing, chest congestion, fever, headaches, and muscle aches. A person with a cold is most contagious during the first day or two of symptoms. Colds are spread by hand contact and inhaling droplets from sneezes and coughs.

Unfortunately, there is no cure for the common cold. Even so, many products (over $500 million worth every year) are sold to reduce its symptoms. Some of these products may hide the symptoms of more serious disease. Most colds last three to seven days. The best way to treat a cold is to stay home, rest, eat well-balanced meals, and drink plenty of fluids. You should stay home to avoid giving your cold to others. If you develop any of the signs and symptoms listed at the end of the chapter, see your doctor.

Influenza also is spread by airborne droplets and contact with contaminated objects. Influenza viruses can cause more serious illness than cold viruses, even though many of the symptoms are the same. Some types of influenza can be prevented by flu shots, injections that stimulate immunity.

In people who are elderly or who have heart disease or breathing problems, flu may develop into **pneumonia** (noo **mohn** yuh), a serious infection of the lungs. Many people die each year from pneumonia, which can be caused by viruses, bacteria, or even fungi.

RUBELLA German measles, or **rubella** (roo **bel** uh), is caused by a virus. The signs of rubella include a rash, coughing, sneezing, sore throat, swollen glands in the back of the neck, and chest congestion. Rubella causes birth defects in babies whose mothers have been exposed to the virus during the first few months of pregnancy. Rubella can be prevented by injections that stimulate immunity.

INFECTIOUS MONONUCLEOSIS "Mono," or **infectious mononucleosis** (mahn oh noo klee **oh** sis), is a viral infection that causes the lymph nodes, tonsils, and spleen to become swollen and tender. The infected person has a fever and a sore throat and feels tired all the time. Because the virus usually enters the body in the saliva of the infected person, it is sometimes called the "kissing disease." Many people develop mononucleosis during their teenage years.

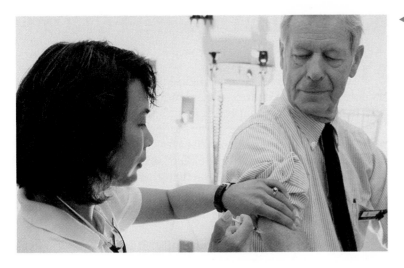

Figure 16-12. Flu shots can prevent the spread of influenza.

Usually, the infection disappears in three to six weeks. Treatment consists of plenty of rest and well-balanced meals. After infection, the virus remains in the body for life.

HEPATITIS A viral disease of the liver is **hepatitis** (hep uh **ty** tis). Because the liver is important to many bodily functions, hepatitis is a serious disease.

There are two types of hepatitis. **Hepatitis A,** a milder form, is transmitted in human wastes, contaminated food, especially shellfish, and contaminated water. Illness begins three to six weeks after exposure, and recovery takes several weeks. **Hepatitis B** is transmitted in blood, on dirty needles shared by drug abusers, and by sexual contact. Serious illness develops six to twelve weeks after exposure. Healing takes a long time. Even after healing, the virus can remain in the body for years and be passed to others.

Both types of hepatitis cause fever, nausea, pain in the abdomen, tiredness, and **jaundice** (**jawn** dis), or yellowing of the skin. Sometimes it causes the urine to turn brown. People who have hepatitis need a doctor's care.

Persons with hepatitis need to be treated by a doctor.

Section Review

1. Name two of the four things a pathogen needs to cause disease.
2. How are symptoms and signs different?
3. How do you feel during the incubation period of an infectious disease?
4. Which organ is affected by hepatitis?

What Do You Think?
5. How would you try to lessen the spread of flu infection to other members of your family?

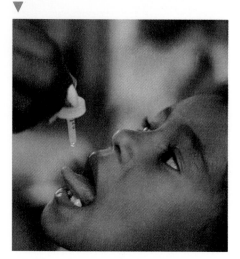

4. PREVENTING INFECTIOUS DISEASES

There are three means of disease prevention. You can try to reduce your chances of contact with pathogens, but as you know from this chapter, it is difficult to avoid some pathogens. You can become immune to some pathogens by receiving injections against a disease. Of course, you also can become immune by having the disease. Finally, you can help your body fight disease by practicing good health habits.

Immunity

There are two types of immunity. Immunity that is created by your own immune system is called **active immunity.** For example, if you have had chicken pox, your body creates antibodies to the chicken pox virus. If you have received a tetanus injection, your body has created antibodies to the tetanus virus.

When you were a baby, you probably received injections to protect you from some infectious diseases, such as diphtheria, pertussis, tetanus (DPT), measles, rubella, mumps, and polio. These injections are called **immunizations** or **vaccinations** (vak suh **nay** shunz). The substance given is a **vaccine** (vak **seen**). Vaccines contain small amounts of dead or altered pathogens or their toxins—just enough to activate your immune system but not enough to make you sick. The vaccine tricks your immune system into making antibodies to the pathogen, as if you had the disease. This creates immunity. After a few years, you may receive a "booster" dose of some vaccines, particularly the vaccines for tetanus and polio, to "remind" your immune system to maintain the body's immunity.

At some time in your life, you may need additional vaccinations. Many people need to be protected against infections because of the work they do, the places to which they travel, or accidental exposure to an unusual pathogen. Influenza vaccines are given to elderly or ill people to protect them from the flu, and during flu epidemics, vaccination is recommended for everyone. Unfortunately, no one has yet developed a vaccine for the common cold.

Another type of immunity is passive immunity. **Passive immunity** is temporary immunity that is acquired by receiving antibodies from another immune system. Suppose you have been bitten by a dog that has rabies. Your doctor will give you injections of antibodies against rabies immediately, so that you do not develop the disease. These antibodies are taken from the blood of animals (usually horses) that have been exposed to the rabies virus. The animal's antibodies are active in your body just long enough to prevent rabies.

Passive immunity occurs naturally in newborn babies who receive antibodies from their mothers before birth. These antibodies, also passed on to the child in the mother's breast milk, protect newborns who are too young to develop active immunity.

Treating Infectious Diseases

Diseases caused by bacteria are often treated with antibiotics, such as penicillin. **Antibiotics** (an tee by **aht** iks) are substances that inhibit or kill living organisms. Some antibiotics attack many types of bacteria; others attack only one type. Antibiotics are effective only on bacteria. They do not kill viruses. At the moment, there is no cure for viral infections. Usually doctors prescribe rest, a well-balanced diet, and plenty of fluids for viral infections. These things help the body fight and recover from the infection. Scientists also are experimenting with some substances, such as interferon, that strengthen the immune system.

Anyone who watches television or visits the local drugstore knows that hundreds of medicines are sold over the counter (without a doctor's order) to treat the discomforts of viral infections. These medicines will not cure an infectious disease, but they may make you feel better while you have it. Taking over-the-counter medicines, however, can cause problems if:

- They make you feel well enough to go about your usual routine when you should be home in bed.
- They hide signs and symptoms that would normally cause you to see your doctor.
- They enable you to go out and spread your illness to other people.

Whether you are taking a drug prescribed by your doctor or an over-the-counter medicine, follow all of the instructions on the container. Never take a drug prescribed for someone else or give yours to another person. Drugs prescribed by doctors are serious medicines.

Staying Healthy

When you are in good health, your body's defenses against diseases are at their best. Here are some guidelines for keeping your body healthy and free of infectious disease:

- Eat well-balanced meals. Choose nutritious foods for snacks. Do not skip meals.
- Get at least eight hours of sleep each night.
- Spend some time every day relaxing.
- Exercise aerobically for at least thirty minutes three or more times a week.

Antibiotics are effective against bacteria but not viruses.

- Avoid stress if you can, and get help to cope if stress cannot be avoided.
- Stay away from people who have an infectious disease.
- Wash your hands before eating, and keep your hands out of your eyes and mouth.
- Do not share a toothbrush, hairbrush, comb, bath towel, eating utensil, drinking straw, or drink container with another person.
- Keep your body clean, and wash your hands several times a day.
- Have regular physical and dental checkups.
- Make sure that your vaccinations against infectious disease are complete and up-to-date.

If you become ill, you can protect others from infectious disease if you stay home for the first day or two of an infectious disease; cover your mouth and nose whenever you cough or sneeze; dispose of used tissues properly; and wash your hands frequently.

Health careers

If a person becomes sick today, a doctor may prescribe a certain medication to treat the illness. This medication, and the hundreds of other medicines that are now available to doctors and their patients, represents years of hard work by **pharmacologists.**

Pharmacologists develop new drugs to treat or prevent human diseases. Pharmacologists work in research laboratories and must understand both chemistry and biology. Their work progresses slowly because the drugs they develop must be tested carefully for effectiveness and safety.

To become a pharmacologist, a person must earn a Ph.D. degree in pharmacology or a related medical field such as toxicology, the study of poisons. Sometimes, a person who has earned a medical degree goes on to specialize in pharmacology.

A **pharmacist** dispenses medicines that have been prescribed by doctors. Pharmacists also advise people on the use of nonprescription medications. To become a pharmacist, a person must earn a degree in pharmacy (usually from a five-year college program) and obtain a state license.

Pharmacologists develop drugs for medical use.

Figure 16-14. When you are ill, do not hesitate to get medical help.

If you do get an infectious disease, you can help your body to recover by going to bed and resting! This treatment and well-balanced meals are all that you need to recover from mild infection. But, what if your infection is not mild? An extremely sore throat, an earache, vomiting or diarrhea, or a temperature of 101°F or more require a doctor if they last more than two days.

You also need to see a doctor if mucus from your nose or cough is thick and yellowish green; if you have difficulty breathing; if you have severe pain anywhere; or if you have a cut or scrape that does not seem to be healing as it should. If your illness lasts longer than usual, or you are worried about your health for any reason, see your doctor and discuss your concerns with him or her.

Practicing good health habits helps you to stay healthy and to recover quickly from a disease.

Section Review

1. How does vaccination prevent disease?
2. Name the two types of immunity.
3. What type of drug is used to treat infectious diseases caused by bacteria?
4. Name one sign and one symptom that are good reasons for seeing your doctor.

What Do You Think?
5. Under what circumstances would an injection for passive immunity be the preferred treatment?

16 | Chapter Review

Chapter Summary

- Infectious diseases are caused by pathogens, such as bacteria, viruses, and fungi.
- Pathogens get into the body by contact with an infected person or animal, a contaminated object, or a contaminated substance.
- Bacteria injure the body by penetrating the cells or by producing toxins. Viruses injure the body by invading cells.
- The body's physical barriers are skin and mucous membranes; its chemical barriers are substances in sweat, mucus, tears, saliva, digestive juices, and urine.
- Inflammation is the body's response to any injury. It is a process that the body uses to attack, clean up, and heal an infection.
- The immune system is the body's last line of defense against pathogens. B lymphocytes (B cells) produce antibodies that attach themselves to pathogens. T lymphocytes (T cells) have many functions, including the regulation of the entire immune system.
- Immunity is defined as the immune system's ability to produce antibodies to pathogens that it has met in the body before and to kill these pathogens before they are able to cause disease.
- Disease cannot develop unless the pathogen has a suitable place to survive, a means of getting into the body, nutrients and space to multiply inside the body, and the ability to survive attacks of the immune system long enough to cause disease.
- Infectious disease has five stages: the incubation period, the prodromal period, the acute stage, the recovery stage, and convalescence. Relapse is the return of disease.
- Vaccination is one means of creating active immunity. Active immunity is also created by having a disease.
- Antibiotics are used to treat bacterial infections but not viral infections. Drugs that stimulate the immune system are being tried to cure some viral infections.
- There are three ways to prevent getting infectious diseases: avoid contact with pathogens in every possible way, be immunized by injection if a vaccine is available, and keep your body healthy.

Vocabulary Review

Listed below are some of the important terms in this chapter. Choose the term that best matches the phrase that follows.

active immunity
acute stage
B cells
cilia
fever
hepatitis

immune system
infectious
　mononucleosis
inflammation
incubation period

lymphatic system
lymphocytes
mucous membranes
passive immunity
pathogen

phagocytes
relapse
symptom
toxins
vaccination

1. eater cells
2. liver infection
3. cells that produce antibodies
4. tiny hairs that beat mucus upward through the air passages
5. a sensation of illness

6. moist, protective coverings
7. period of disease when you feel sickest
8. type of immunity that follows disease
9. the body's response to injury
10. harmful chemical substances that are produced by bacteria

What Have You Learned?

1. List the four ways that pathogens get close enough to the body to enter.
2. How do bacteria injure the body's cells? How do viruses injure the body's cells?
3. What is a resident microorganism? How is it different from a pathogen?
4. Why is skin a barrier to pathogens?
5. How do the mucous membranes protect the body from pathogens?
6. What do phagocytes do?

7. Name two ways that lymphocytes protect the body.
8. How does interferon protect healthy cells?
9. Define the five stages that characterize any infectious disease.
10. How is hepatitis spread?
11. Explain how a vaccination creates immunity in the body.
12. What is the fastest way to get over a viral infection, such as the common cold?

What Do You Think?

1. More people get flu during the winter months than at any other time of year. Why?
2. Why do you think some infectious diseases are more common in young people than in older people?
3. There has been a flood in your town. Why has the department of public health advised

people to boil tap water for five minutes before using it for drinking?
4. You are taking a trip to India. Will you need more vaccinations first? Why or why not?
5. You are not sure whether you have been vaccinated for rubella. Is it important to find out? Why or why not?

What Would You Do?

1. Someone at school asks to borrow your hairbrush. Would you say yes or no? Why?
2. It is Saturday, and you are looking forward to going to the basketball game. But you are getting a headache, and your throat is feeling a little bit sore. Would you take an aspirin and go to the game, or stay home and rest? What is likely to happen as a result of your choice?
3. Your seven-year-old brother has a cold. He is sneezing and coughing at the breakfast

table, and you think he just sneezed right into your cereal! What could you say, besides "Cut it out"? Would you eat the cereal?
4. Your dog gets into a fight with another dog and one of them bites you. Will you tell anyone about the bite? Why?
5. Last night after dinner, you left a chicken casserole on the counter all night. What will you do with the chicken casserole now? Explain your answer.

For Further Study

1. Some diseases are major problems in developing countries where sanitation is poor and the people do not have safe drinking water. Two such diseases are **schistosomiasis** (shis toh sah **my** ah sis) and **trachoma** (trah **koh** mah). Find out about one of these diseases and write a short paper on your findings.
2. Call your doctor's office and ask to see your immunization record—the list of vaccinations you have received in your life. Which diseases have you been vaccinated against? When are you due to receive your next booster doses?

17

As you read, think about

▶ the reasons for the high incidence of STDs in this country.

▶ how STDs can be prevented and how some STDs can be cured.

▶ why AIDS is such a serious STD.

▶ the kinds of personal behaviors that can help prevent the spread of AIDS and other STDs.

AIDS and Other Sexually Transmitted Diseases

S ome problems need everybody's attention. You got up early this morning to join the walk to raise money for AIDS research. It looks as though it will take many years of expensive research to find a cure for this terrible disease that affects so many people. Until then, education and awareness are the best weapons against AIDS, so you hope the march and the pamphlets you're handing out will get a lot of people thinking.

In this chapter, you will learn about AIDS and other sexually transmitted diseases, their causes, symptoms, treatment, and the ways these diseases are transmitted.

It is important to know about AIDS and other sexually transmitted diseases.

Check Your Wellness

How much do you know about AIDS and other sexually transmitted diseases? To test your knowledge, decide whether each of the statements below is true or false.

1. It is possible to have a healthy, caring relationship without having to fear sexually transmitted diseases.
2. Not having sexual contact with another person is the most effective way to avoid sexually transmitted diseases.
3. It takes only one sexual contact with an infected person to get an STD.
4. AIDS is not limited to male homosexuals and hemophiliacs.
5. It is highly unlikely that AIDS can be transmitted through sneezing, coughing, crying, hugging, holding hands, or using the same telephone.
6. The only no-risk sexual behavior with respect to AIDS is abstinence.
7. No one can build up an immunity to STDs.
8. An infected, pregnant woman can pass her STD to her newborn.

1. THE SILENT EPIDEMIC

This chapter discusses a group of infectious diseases that many people are reluctant to talk about. Although you may find it difficult or embarrassing to do so, you should discuss the contents of this chapter with your parents, guardians, or other family members. It is important for you to understand and consider carefully the information that is presented in the following sections.

Education Is the Only Vaccine

The U.S. Public Health Service has said, ''By 1990, every junior and senior high school student in the U.S. should receive accurate, timely education about sexually transmitted diseases.'' It is the goal of this chapter to provide you with the frank, accurate, timely information about **sexually transmitted diseases (STDs)** that you need. STDs are a group of diseases that can endanger your health and, in some cases, your life. They are spread from person to person usually through sexual contact. STDs are also called **venereal** (vuh **neer** ee ul) **diseases,** or **VD,** after the name of the ancient, mythical Roman goddess of love, Venus. Look at Figure 17-1. Have you heard any of these myths about STDs before?

The most deadly of the STDs is *acquired immuno-deficiency* (im myu noh dee **fish** en see) *syndrome,* or **AIDS,** which, as of now, has no known cure or vaccine. For the present, the best defense against AIDS is knowledge. People must use their knowledge to make healthful choices throughout their lives. If they do not, thousands of people may lose their lives unnecessarily.

You may think that AIDS and other STDs have little to do with your life today, but there are teenagers who have STDs, including AIDS. In fact, the Surgeon General, the head of the U.S. Public Health Service, has predicted that as the AIDS epidemic spreads, it will affect more and more people of all ages. Besides the tragedy of lost lives, there is a financial burden that will have to be shared. The Surgeon General has estimated that the cost of caring for AIDS patients could be as high as $16 billion by 1991.

AIDS and other STDs can be prevented. They can be prevented by changes in personal behavior. The most effective preventative behavior is **sexual abstinence** (**ab** stuh nuns), which means not having any kind of sexual contact with another person.

Each person must know the facts about STDs and behave in ways that prevent their spread. Often, schools, religious groups, and community service organizations offer small group discussions to help teenagers arrive at healthful decisions about their styles of living. These decisions are among the most important you will make in your life.

It is possible to have a healthy, caring relationship with another person without having to fear STDs. Millions of people in this country do. For all people, however, this means structuring caring relationships around shared interests and healthful activities that do not include sex or drugs.

The World Around You

All of us are influenced by the people close to us and by what we see happening around us. You may be pressured by your friends to do things that you know are risky. You also may be influenced by some of the behaviors shown on television shows today or in advertisements, videos, movies, books, and magazines. The consequences of these behaviors

Figure 17-1. Is sexual contact the only way to get an STD? Can a person develop an immunity to STDs?

▼

Myths and Facts About STDs

1. **Myth:** Teenagers seldom get STDs.
   Fact: Hundreds of thousands of teenagers get STDs each year.
2. **Myth:** The most common STD in this country today is syphilis.
   Fact: The most common STD in this country today is chlamydia.
3. **Myth:** Sexual contact is the only way for a person to get an STD.
   Fact: Some STDs, such as syphilis and AIDS, can be transmitted through blood-to-blood contact. Although this is common with AIDS, it is highly unlikely with syphilis. Others, such as pubic lice and scabies, can be transferred from infested clothing or bed linens.
4. **Myth:** Using birth control pills prevents STDs.
   Fact: Birth control pills provide no protection against STDs.
5. **Myth:** A person cannot get an STD by having sex only once.
   Fact: It takes only one sexual encounter with an infected person to get an STD.
6. **Myth:** Anyone who has an STD will show signs of it.
   Fact: Many STDs, such as gonorrhea and chlamydia, have no symptoms early in the infection. Others, such as syphilis and genital herpes, have symptoms that come and go. Signs of AIDS may not show up for ten years.
7. **Myth:** If a person gets an STD once, he or she cannot get it again.
   Fact: There is no effective immunity against STDs. People can get STDs again and again with equal severity.

8. **Myth:** To avoid infection, people should stay away from public telephones, swimming pools, hot tubs, and bathrooms.
   Fact: Almost all the organisms that cause STDs die quickly outside of the human body. Therefore, with the exception of lice and scabies, people are highly unlikely to get STDs from nonliving objects, such as telephones, showers, tubs, swimming pools, or toilets. Lice and scabies can be picked up from infested bed linens or clothing.
9. **Myth:** Medicine given to an infected person by a friend can cure an STD.
   Fact: All STDs should be treated with medication prescribed by a doctor. The doctor's instructions must be followed carefully to ensure that the STD is cured. Sharing medication is dangerous and can result in no one being cured.
10. **Myth:** A person cannot get more than one STD at a time.
    Fact: People can have many STDs at the same time. Evidence indicates that some STDs may make people more susceptible to getting AIDS.
11. **Myth:** There are vaccines to prevent STDs.
    Fact: There are no vaccines that prevent STDs, although scientists are trying to develop ones for gonorrhea and AIDS.
12. **Myth:** If the symptoms of an STD go away, a person does not need to see a doctor.
    Fact: Just because the symptoms of an STD disappear, it does not mean that the disease is over. Only a doctor can tell whether a person is still sick or not.

Figure 17-2. Being well-informed about STDs is everyone's responsibility.

If untreated, STDs can cause permanent damage and even death.

can be devastating. Each year, for example, there are an estimated 13 million new cases of STDs in this country alone. When not treated by a doctor, these diseases can cause permanent damage and even death.

Why are there so many cases of STDs? First, today many people become sexually active at a young age. Second, many sexually active people tend to have more than one partner. Third, many people who are sexually active are not taking precautions to prevent infection, either because of ignorance or carelessness. Fourth, some people who are infected not only fail to seek immediate medical treatment, they also fail to avoid sexual activity when they are infectious. Finally, some STDs cannot be cured.

The first step in preventing STDs is to realize that they are a problem. The second step is to learn the facts about STDs. How much do you already know?

Section Review

1. Why is it a good idea to discuss important life-style decisions with parents, guardians, or respected persons in the community?

2. Define STD.

3. What is another term for STD?

4. How can the many cases of STDs in this country today be explained?

What Do You Think?

5. Do you think the media—television, radio, newspapers, magazines, and books—should present more information about STDs? Why or why not?

2. KINDS OF STDs

There are more than 50 different kinds of sexually transmitted diseases. They range from life-threatening diseases to diseases that are merely irritating. Most of these diseases are curable and do not damage the body permanently when they are treated promptly by a doctor.

Only the ten most common STDs, not counting AIDS, will be discussed in this section. AIDS, the most deadly of the STDs, will be treated in a separate section. Should you or any other concerned individual want more information about STDs, it can be obtained from the national VD Hotline. The information operator at 1-800-555-1212 can supply the toll-free number.

There are only two ways to prevent STDs other than AIDS. As you know, one way is sexual abstinence. The other is to practice **sexual fidelity,** which means to have a caring relationship, such as marriage, with only one other person whom you know is uninfected. Uninfected couples who practice sexual fidelity run little or no risk of getting many STDs. An additional precaution must be taken to prevent AIDS. Because AIDS can be passed to another person through shared drug equipment, such as needles or syringes, couples practicing sexual fidelity also must have no history of shared intravenous drug use, the use of drugs injected directly into the blood.

The more sexual partners a person has, the greater the risk of STDs. It takes only one sexual contact with an infected person to get an STD. You should realize that it is impossible to know if people have STDs just by looking at them. Often, people with STDs have no visible signs of disease.

Because the microorganisms that cause most STDs survive only a short time outside of the human body, it is highly unlikely that people can get an STD from nonhuman sources, such as bed linens, clothing, doorknobs, telephones, bathtubs, swimming pools, or toilet facilities. Microorganisms causing STDs also cannot be passed from person to person through insect bites. STDs caused by animals, such as lice or mites, however, can be passed on through contact with certain articles, such as soiled bed linens or clothing.

Serious STDs

The four STDs that are discussed in this section are potentially damaging because people often do not know that they are infected. In some cases, infected persons show no early signs of disease. In other cases, the signs of infection come and go, leading people who are infected to believe they are disease-free when they are not. Even if infected persons show no signs of the diseases, they can spread the diseases to others.

Abstinence and sexual fidelity are the most effective ways to prevent many STDs.

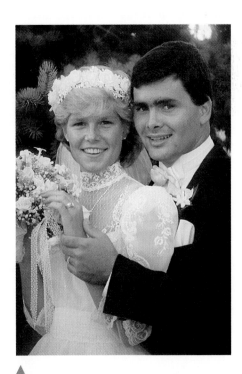

▲
Figure 17-3. A caring, long-term relationship with only one person reduces the risk of STDs.

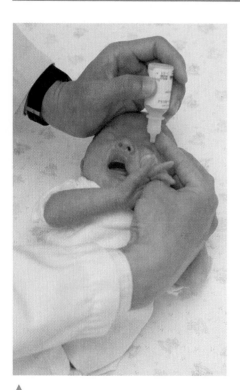

▲
Figure 17-4. Newborn babies are routinely given medicated eyedrops to prevent possible STD infections.

○━━┳

Gonorrhea and chlamydia are the leading causes of pelvic inflammatory disease.

Anyone who is sexually active should have regular checkups by a doctor or nurse. Only a doctor can treat an STD effectively. Confidential, free VD clinics are available throughout the United States and are listed in the telephone directory under Venereal Disease.

Infected mothers can spread sexually transmitted diseases to their babies either before or at the time of birth. This can be prevented by seeking medical care and counseling early in pregnancy.

CHLAMYDIA The most common bacterium-caused STD in this country is **chlamydia** (klam **id** ee uh). Over four million cases of chlamydia occur each year in the United States. The symptoms of the disease are given in Figure 17-5. Unfortunately, infected women usually show no early signs of the disease.

If untreated, chlamydia causes serious, painful infections of the urinary tract in men and infections of the reproductive organs in women. About half the cases of **pelvic inflammatory disease**, or **PID**, are caused by chlamydia. PID is a serious infection of the organs of the pelvic area in women, often involving the ovaries, fallopian tubes, and uterus. These infections can result in **sterility** (stuh **ril** ih tee), the inability to have a biological child.

Chlamydia may also cause infection of the lymph nodes and skin. Permanent injury to the lymphatic system and spread to organs such as the liver can occur if the disease is not treated.

Infected mothers can pass chlamydia to their babies during birth. In the infant, this can result in infections of the lungs and eyes or even in death. Treatment for chlamydia involves antibiotics.

GONORRHEA The bacterium **gonococcus** (gahn uh **kahk** us) causes an STD called **gonorrhea** (gahn uh **ree** uh). These bacteria usually infect the urinary tract in both men and women, as well as the reproductive organs of women. Figure 17-5 lists the symptoms of gonorrhea. Unfortunately, many people do not notice the early signs of gonorrhea and may not even know that they have it.

If untreated, gonorrhea can result in sterility in both sexes. In women, gonorrhea, along with chlamydia, is a leading cause of pelvic inflammatory disease. Gonorrhea can be cured with antibiotics, especially penicillin.

An infected pregnant woman can transmit the bacteria that cause gonorrhea to her baby as it passes through the birth canal. For this reason, in the United States, babies are routinely given special medicated eyedrops at birth to kill the bacteria and prevent the development of any infection. If an infected baby fails to receive medication, the baby can become blind, and the disease can spread to other parts of the baby's body.

Four Common Sexually Transmitted Diseases

Chlamydia **Cause:** Bacterium *(photomicrograph)*	**Transmission:** Sexual contact. *Newborns:* passage through infected birth canal.	**Usual Symptoms:** *Females:* Painful urination, abnormal discharge from the vagina, bleeding between menstrual periods, abdominal pain. Often, no symptoms *Males:* Unusual watery discharge from penis, painful urination *Newborns:* eye and lung infections
	Appearance of First Symptoms: 2-4 weeks after contact *Newborns:* 7-12 days after delivery	**Treatment:** Infected persons and their sexual partners must be tested and treated with antibiotics. Sexual activity must be avoided until the disease is cured.
Genital herpes **Cause:** Virus *(photomicrograph)*	**Transmission:** Contact with blisters or with viruses shed by an infected person with no blisters apparent. *Newborns:* passage through infected birth canal	**Usual Symptoms:** Cluster of tender, painful blisters, swollen glands, fever, achy feeling *Newborns:* varies from mild symptoms to brain damage and death
	Appearance of First Symptoms: Variable, usually 2-10 days after contact; symptoms recur every so often	**Treatment:** Infected persons should avoid sexual activity when blisters are present or when viruses are being shed. Condom use is advised by doctors. Acyclovir makes symptoms less severe. There is no cure.
Gonorrhea **Cause:** Bacterium *(photomicrograph)*	**Transmission:** Sexual contact. *Newborns:* passage through infected birth canal	**Usual Symptoms:** *Females:* Discharge from vagina, or birth canal. Often, no symptoms *Males:* Abnormal pus discharge from penis, painful urination *Newborns:* eye infection
	Appearance of First Symptoms: 1-30 days after contact; on average, 3-5 days after contact	**Treatment:** Infected persons and their sexual partners must be tested and treated with antibiotics. Sexual activity must be avoided until disease is cured.
Syphilis **Cause:** Spirochete bacterium *(photomicrograph)*	**Transmission:** Sexual contact; congenital	**Usual Symptoms:** First stage: painless sore that goes away after about 1-5 weeks Second stage: body rash, hair loss, flu-like symptoms, swollen glands *Newborns:* damaged skin, bones, eyes, teeth, and liver
	Appearance of First Symptoms: 10-90 days after contact. Usually, around 3 weeks after contact.	**Treatment:** Infected persons and their sexual partners must be tested and treated with antibiotics. Sexual activity must be avoided until disease is cured.

Source: Massachusetts Department of Public Health

Figure 17-5. How soon do symptoms of serious STDs first appear? What precautions and treatments are usually recommended?

SYPHILIS A serious, many-stage STD, known as **syphilis** (**sif** uh lis), is caused by a **spirochete** (**spy** ruh keet) bacterium. In the first stage, a small, painless sore, called a **chancre** (**shang** ker), appears. Figure 17-6 shows what a chancre looks like. After about one to five weeks, the chancre heals and leaves a thin scar. At this point, an infected person may think the disease has gone away, but it has not. If untreated by a doctor, the disease progresses to stage two.

Stage two of syphilis is characterized by flulike symptoms: fever, headache, swollen lymph glands, and loss of appetite. Most infected people develop a skin rash, also shown in Figure 17-6, that does not itch. If the disease is still untreated, it progresses to a third stage.

Stage three is the hardest to detect. All symptoms may disappear for years. At any time, however, the spirochete can begin to attack the brain or the circulatory system, causing serious damage and death.

Syphilis is most infectious during the first two stages. During these early stages, a person can become infected by direct contact with the blood or sores of an infected person. If a chancre touches a break in an uninfected person's skin, for example, infection can occur. At any stage of the disease, a pregnant woman will pass the disease to her developing baby. When the disease is passed to a baby in this way, it is called **congenital** (kun **jen** ih tl) **syphilis.**

Untreated syphilis in an adult causes brain damage, paralysis, and heart disease. In its early stages, syphilis is curable with penicillin. If allowed to progress beyond the second stage, the spirochete can be killed, but the damage to the body systems cannot be reversed. Congenital syphilis harms the skin, bones, eyes, teeth, and liver of a newborn baby. Congenital syphilis can be prevented if an infected mother receives treatment during pregnancy.

GENITAL HERPES Unlike the **herpes simplex I virus**, which causes blisters usually around the mouth, **herpes simplex II** causes **genital herpes** (**jen** ih tl **hur** peez). Genital herpes is an incurable condition characterized by clusters of painful blisters, shown in Figure 17-7, that appear periodi-

Figure 17-6. The sign of the first stage of syphilis is a small, painless sore. During the second stage, an itchless skin rash appears.

▼

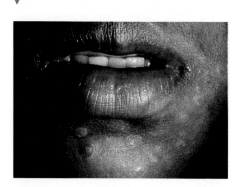

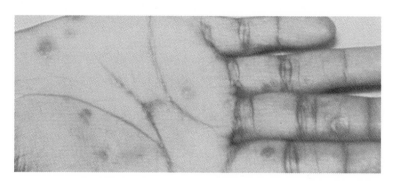

cally on or around the **genitals.** Genitals are the external parts of the reproductive system. Although there is no known cure for genital herpes, a doctor can prescribe medication to reduce the severity of the symptoms.

People can get genital herpes from an infected person, even when the infected person shows no signs of the disease. To prevent infection in newborns, some doctors recommend that pregnant women with genital herpes have their babies by **cesarean** (suh **zer** ee un) **section.** Cesarean section is a method of delivery that surgically removes the baby from the mother rather than allowing the baby to pass through the birth canal.

Genital herpes in women has been linked to cancer of the **cervix** (**sur** vix), the opening to the **uterus,** a hollow, muscular, pear-shaped organ. Therefore, women with genital herpes should receive checkups for signs of cervical cancer at least once a year.

Figure 17-7. Clusters of painful, clear blisters are one symptom of a herpes simplex virus infection.

Other STDs

Chlamydia, gonorrhea, syphilis, and genital herpes are among the most potentially dangerous STDs. Many other common STDs are not as dangerous, but they may cause discomfort. All STDs, however, should be treated promptly to avoid complication and the spread to others.

One common STD is inflammation of the birth canal, or **vagina,** called **vaginitis** (vaj uh **ny** tis). This condition can be caused by a number of sexually transmitted pathogens. One pathogen is *Trichomonas* (trik oh **moh** nis), which is a single-celled organism.

Not all cases of vaginitis are the result of sexual transmission. Another cause may be a yeast infection known as **candidiasis** (kan dih **dy** uh sis). This type of yeast infection is caused by the fungus *Candida.* Sometimes the use of antibiotics can cause candidiasis. This happens when the antibiotics kill the normal bacteria that live in the vagina. When these bacteria are present, they usually prevent the yeast from growing.

When vaginitis is caused by *Trichomonas,* there is a frothy, green discharge from the vagina. When it is caused by *Candida,* there is a white, cheezy discharge. In both cases, there is an itching and burning sensation in the vaginal area. Once its cause is known, vaginitis can be cured easily with drugs prescribed by a doctor. To prevent reinfection, a woman's partner should also be treated.

A bacterial STD with symptoms similar to the first stage of syphilis is **chancroid** (**shang** kroyd). People who have chancroid develop painful open sores around the genitals. The sores are infectious but can be cured with antibiotics.

Warts that are sexually transmitted are known as **genital warts.** The warts, which are caused by a type of virus, may

All STDs should be treated promptly to avoid complications and transmission to others.

Figure 17-8. The itch mite is the organism that causes scabies.

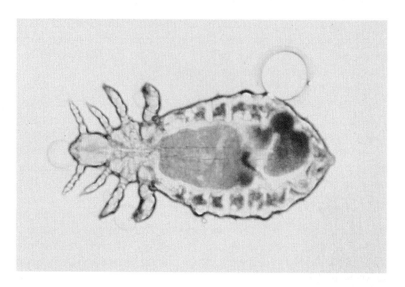

occur around the penis, vagina, or anus. A doctor can treat genital warts in a number of ways, including special ointments, freezing, laser therapy, or surgery. Keeping the skin clean helps prevent the spread of the warts. Because there is evidence that genital warts may be linked with certain cancers, people with a history of genital wart infections should receive regular checkups by a doctor.

Lice that infest the hair in the genital area are called **pubic (pyu** bik) **lice.** The lice, which are a type of insect, and their eggs are visible upon close inspection. They can be killed by using a special medicated lotion or shampoo. Bedding and clothing also should be washed in extremely hot water or ironed with a hot iron.

A tiny animal, called an itch mite, shown in Figure 17-8, causes **scabies (skay** beez), an itchy rash. The mite burrows into the skin to lay its eggs. Scabies can be cured by scrubbing infected areas and applying a medication prescribed by a doctor. As with pubic lice, bedding and clothing also should be washed in hot water.

Section Review

1. List ten common sexually transmitted diseases.
2. Describe in detail four serious, common STDs.
3. Why should STDs be treated by a doctor as quickly as possible?
4. Why should pregnant women who have STDs seek medical care early in their pregnancies?

What Do You Think?
5. Why do you think there are so many common myths about STDs?

3. AIDS

Probably the most talked about STD today is AIDS, acquired immunodeficiency syndrome. *Acquired* means that people get the disease from someone else. *Immunodeficiency* means that the immune system is damaged, or deficient, and cannot fight off many diseases. *Syndrome* refers to the group of signs or symptoms that accompany a disease.

Although there is evidence that there were cases of AIDS in this country before 1981, AIDS was first officially identified here in 1981. Most of the early cases were found among male **homosexuals** (hoh moh **sek** shoo uls), persons who have sexual relations with someone of the same sex. AIDS, however, is not limited to any particular section of the population. Since 1981, the number of cases has increased so rapidly that the disease is now considered an epidemic. Figure 17-9 shows how rapid the increase has been. Because sexual behavior determines the degree of risk for getting AIDS, certain groups of people may run a greater risk of infection than others. These groups include male homosexuals; prostitutes, people who are paid for having sex with someone; sexual partners of prostitutes; and people who have sex with persons of the same sex and with persons of the opposite sex. People who share drug equipment, people married to people at risk for AIDS, and children of infected mothers are also at risk.

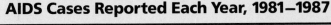

The number of AIDS cases has increased to an epidemic level.

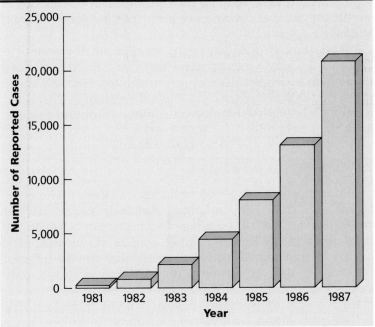

Figure 17-9. Because of the rapid increase in the number of cases, AIDS is now considered an epidemic in the United States.

Figure 17-10. There is no evidence that AIDS is transmitted by casual contact.

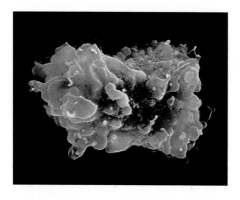

Courtesy of Lennart Nilsson, Boehringer Ingelheim International GmbH

Figure 17-11. Human immuno-deficiency viruses (in blue) are shown coming out of a human T cell (T-lymphocyte). The T-lympho-cyte will die, and the viruses will attack other T-lymphocytes.

AIDS is caused by the **human immunodeficiency virus,** also known as **HIV.** Inside the human body, HIV attacks and disables the T-lymphocytes. T-lymphocytes are shown in Figure 17-11. As you may recall from the last chapter, T-lymphocytes, or T-cells, are a type of white blood cell that helps the body fight off disease.

HIV is passed from one person to another through contact with an infected person's body fluids, usually blood, semen, or vaginal secretions. **Semen** (**see** mun) is the fluid, produced by the male reproductive organs, that carries the male reproductive cells. Anyone who has sexual relations with someone who may be infected or anyone who shares needles or syringes with an infected person places himself or herself at risk.

Even though HIV has been found in small amounts in other body fluids, such as saliva and tears, there have been no known cases of HIV being transmitted through fluids other than blood, semen, and vaginal secretions. Therefore, it is unlikely that HIV can be transmitted through sneezing, coughing, or crying.

Fears and Myths

Many people are afraid to be near a person who is infected with HIV. They are afraid that they can get HIV by casual contact, such as hugging. This fear is not based on the facts as presently known. Unlike cold or flu viruses, HIV cannot be transmitted simply by being near an HIV-infected person. To date, infection with HIV has occurred only through an exchange of blood, semen, or vaginal secretions. For this reason, most experts believe that you cannot get HIV by hugging, sitting nearby, using the same bathroom, holding hands, eating at the same table, using the same telephone, swimming in the same pool, or dancing with an infected person.

Some people are afraid to donate blood because they think the needles used to draw blood may be infected with HIV. This is untrue. Hospitals and organizations such as the American Red Cross take every precaution to be sure that blood donors are protected from infections. The needles used to draw blood are germ-free. They have never been used before. After each use, the needles are thrown away and never used again.

Before reading further, find out how much you really know about AIDS. Study the myths and the facts about AIDS listed in Figure 17-12. How many myths have you heard before? Where did you hear them?

Figure 17-12. How long can HIV remain in the body before symptoms of AIDS appear?

Myths and Facts About AIDS

1. **Myth:** Teenagers cannot get AIDS.
   Fact: Anyone who is sexually active or who shares needles or syringes when using drugs is at risk for getting AIDS.
2. **Myth:** There will soon be a vaccine for AIDS.
   Fact: Because of the many forms of the virus that causes AIDS, a vaccine for AIDS is unlikely in the near future.
3. **Myth:** It is not a good idea to try on bathing suits in a big department store because a person could get AIDS.
   Fact: The virus that causes AIDS dies quickly outside of human body fluids; there are no cases of a person getting HIV from clothing.
4. **Myth:** It is OK to share needles when getting one's ears pierced or getting a tattoo.
   Fact: HIV can be transmitted through blood-to-blood exchange; therefore, only unused, germ-free needles should be used when getting one's ears pierced or getting a tattoo.
5. **Myth:** There are cases of people getting AIDS from a mosquito bite.
   Fact: There are no cases of AIDS transmission through the bite of any insect, including mosquitoes.
6. **Myth:** A pet, such as a dog, cat, or bird, can carry the virus that causes AIDS.
   Fact: No animal, except for a certain kind of monkey, has ever been found to carry or transmit the virus that causes AIDS.
7. **Myth:** Only male homosexuals get AIDS.
   Fact: Men, women, and children get AIDS.

8. **Myth:** It is not a good idea to eat in restaurants, because the people handling the food might have AIDS.
   Fact: There are no cases of AIDS being transmitted through air, water, or food, or by any objects such as eating or cooking utensils.
9. **Myth:** You can tell if a person has the virus that causes AIDS just by the way they look.
   Fact: People can harbor the AIDS virus in their bodies for years and show no signs of illness.
10. **Myth:** If a person does not seem sick, you cannot get the AIDS virus from them.
    Fact: Anyone with HIV can pass it on to another person through the exchange of certain body fluids, such as blood, semen, or vaginal secretions.
11. **Myth:** If you want to be safe, you should not even get near a person infected with the AIDS virus.
    Fact: There are no cases of AIDS ever being transmitted through casual social contact, such as by being in the same classroom or by dancing together.
12. **Myth:** You can get the virus that causes AIDS from blood transfusions during an operation in a hospital.
    Fact: Since 1985, when a blood test for HIV was developed and put into use, the chances of getting HIV from blood transfusions have become extremely small in this country.

Symptoms of HIV Infection

Many people infected with HIV show no symptoms for months or years. Later, these people may develop symptoms that include swollen lymph nodes, fever, diarrhea, weakness, and unexplained weight loss. People with these symptoms were said to have **AIDS-related complex,** or **ARC,** but now these symptoms are considered a form of AIDS. Since the symptoms of ARC are similar to those of many other diseases, a blood test is needed to confirm the presence of HIV.

Persons who are infected with HIV have difficulty defending themselves against certain diseases. The diseases that attack a person whose immune system defenses have been weakened by HIV are known as **opportunistic** (op ur too **nis** tik) **diseases.** These are diseases that use the opportunity of weakened immunity to develop. When persons with HIV develop the symptoms of opportunistic diseases, they are said to have AIDS. One example of an opportunistic disease that afflicts persons with HIV is **pneumocystis carinii** (noo moh sis tis kar **rin** ee), a rare form of pneumonia. AIDS patients usually die from this form of pneumonia.

Another opportunistic disease that afflicts AIDS patients is a rare, deadly kind of cancer, called **Kaposi's sarcoma** (Kuh poh sheez sar **koh** muh), or **KS.** A sarcoma is a kind of cancerous tumor, or growth, that spreads throughout the body, eventually killing the patient.

Friend to Friend

Sondra:
Ellen, look at the great outfit I got for Ling's party. I can hardly wait, but you sure don't look excited. Are you worried about something?

Ellen:
It's about the party ... sort of. I was really looking forward to going with Jack. But I've been hearing all this stuff about AIDS. And now about AIDS and *kissing*.

Sondra:
Getting AIDS from kissing? I've read that you cannot get AIDS from kissing.

Transmission of HIV

Anyone who has HIV has the potential to pass the virus on to someone else through the exchange of blood, semen, or vaginal secretions. People with HIV are infectious whether or not they have symptoms. There are four main ways that HIV can be passed on. These are:

- through sexual relations with an infected person.
- through shared needles or syringes, contaminated with the blood of an infected person.
- through contact with an infected person's blood or blood parts.
- by being the child of a mother who became infected before or during pregnancy.

From 1978 to 1985, it was possible for some people to become infected with HIV through transfusions of contaminated blood or blood parts. **Hemophiliacs** (hee muh **fil** ee aks), people with a blood-clotting disorder, and anyone who lost a great deal of blood due to an injury or a surgical procedure were particularly at risk. Since 1985, all donated blood is tested for the presence of HIV before it is used. In addition, before blood is taken, possible blood donors are carefully screened to exclude high-risk persons.

Because a blood donor may be infected and not know it, and because it takes several weeks or even months for signs of HIV infection to show in the blood, there is unfor-

People with HIV are infectious even if they do not have symptoms.

Ellen:
Mallory told Joanne AIDS is spread that way. And I don't know. I'd really like to get this straight in my mind before the party.

Sondra:
Then let's check with someone who's more of an expert than Mallory! Mr. Philips, my health teacher, is really easy to talk to. I'll come with you.

Ellen:
Would you? I'm not sure I could face asking him on my own.

Sondra:
Sure. I want to get some straight answers, too.

Immune System Boosters

While many scientists search for an AIDS vaccine, others are turning their efforts to treating AIDS patients. One area of research involves lymphokines.

Lymphokines are proteins made naturally by the body. They stimulate the immune system. They are useful in patients whose immune systems become weakened from the side effects of drugs or other therapies being used to treat an illness. Scientists can now make lymphokines in the laboratory. One lymphokine, called GM-CSF, stimulates bone marrow to produce the white blood cells that fight infection.

In one study, AIDS patients with low levels of white blood cells, as a result of being treated with an anti-AIDS drug, were given GM-CSF. It was able to boost the white cell count of the AIDS sufferers.

Scientists predict that lymphokines also will be used in bone marrow transplants and for severe burns.

The use of lymphokines depends on research.

tunately still a small risk of getting HIV from transfused blood. For this reason, some doctors advise patients to donate their own blood before an operation.

People who deal regularly with blood or body secretions should use equipment that can act as a barrier between their skin and any possible HIV infection. Some dentists and dental hygienists, for example, now wear latex gloves and protective face coverings. The gloves and face coverings prevent a patient's blood from entering any tiny openings that may be in the dentist's or hygienist's skin. For the same reason, your school nurse may now wear latex gloves when treating a wound that is bleeding. These precautions are recommended by the Centers for Disease Control.

Treatment

Scientists are working hard to find a cure for AIDS. One approach is to discover a method of boosting the immune system, which then could stop opportunistic diseases. Another way is to find some treatment that can stop HIV from reproducing inside the body. A third way is to develop a vaccine against HIV infections. Thus far, finding a vaccine has proved difficult because HIV has many forms. Under these circumstances, a single vaccine is unlikely to be effective against all the forms of HIV.

People who may have been exposed to HIV should seek medical care and counseling immediately. A blood test for HIV is available at free, confidential clinics throughout the country. This test detects HIV antibodies, the substances produced in the blood to fight HIV. Unfortunately, however, the human body does not produce HIV antibodies right away. On average, HIV antibody production takes three to five months after an individual's exposure to HIV. In some cases, antibodies have not appeared until six months after exposure. This means that in the early weeks or months of infection, a person can have a negative result to the antibody test. Therefore, people in high-risk groups should be retested every few months. New treatments for AIDS are being tried all the time. Although none of the treatments can cure the disease presently, some can slow the disease or ease the individual's discomfort.

Prevention

AIDS is a preventable disease. The key to preventing AIDS is the practice of health-promoting behavior. All actions that put an individual at risk for becoming infected with HIV should be avoided. The only no-risk sexual behavior with respect to AIDS is abstinence. If you, your parents, or other concerned persons want to obtain more information about AIDS, there is a toll-free AIDS Hotline number. Call the toll-

▶ Figure 17-13. The fight against AIDS is helped by events that raise money for AIDS research.

free information operator at 1-800-555-1212 for the AIDS Hotline number.

Keeping informed about AIDS is an important aspect of prevention. Because scientists have been studying AIDS only since 1981, there is still a great deal to learn about the disease. However, much is known about AIDS, and this information is being made available to the public. You can get reliable, up-to-date information on AIDS from health-care professionals such as doctors, from the AIDS Hotline mentioned earlier, and from publications of the U.S. Public Health Service, such as the Surgeon General's reports. While you are learning, help to educate others. Share the facts about AIDS with your friends. Help others guard against the disease.

Keeping well-informed is an important part of preventing AIDS.

Section Review

1. What causes AIDS?

2. What is the difference between AIDS and ARC?

3. How is the AIDS virus transmitted from one person to another person?

4. What steps can be taken to prevent AIDS from spreading?

What Do You Think?

5. If you were asked to babysit a child who was infected with HIV, would you say yes or no? Give at least two reasons for your answer.

4. STDs AND YOUR FUTURE

Most STDs occur among people between the ages of 15 and 30. You and all the other readers of this chapter can curb the spread of STDs. You can do this by your behavior now and in the future. You can do this by acting in ways that protect yourself and others from the risks of STDs.

Low-Risk Behaviors

It is the responsibility of each individual to choose behaviors that safeguard his or her health and the health of others. Young people should consult their parents, guardians, or other concerned adults when trying to decide which behaviors are best and safest for them. If you think this may be awkward or embarrassing, you may want to try role-playing the discussion with your friends before talking to your parents or guardians.

As mentioned earlier, there are only two ways to avoid STDs other than AIDS—sexual abstinence and sexual fidelity among uninfected partners. Abstinence and not sharing intravenous drug equipment are the only no-risk behaviors for avoiding AIDS or HIV infection at present. The sharing of needles or syringes by drug users places a person at high risk for HIV infection.

Preventative Behaviors

For people who are sexually active and not practicing sexual fidelity, the Surgeon General of the United States has recommended certain preventative behaviors. These ways of behaving help reduce the risks of getting STDs.

AVOID EXCHANGE OF BODY FLUIDS Most STDs are transmitted through sexual contact with the mucous membranes of the body. To prevent this, the Surgeon General suggests that males always use **condoms**, latex sheaths that cover the penis, when engaging in any kind of sexual activity. When used properly, condoms can reduce, but not totally eliminate, the chances of infection.

There are additional precautions that must be taken to prevent infection with HIV. All direct contact with the blood or blood-containing secretions of people who may be infected should be avoided.

STAY AWAY FROM RISKY SITUATIONS Individuals should avoid situations in which they feel they may lose control or may be tempted to engage in some type of high-risk behavior. For example, they should stay away from situations in which they may feel pressured to have sex or to use intravenous drugs.

Behaviors for High-Risk Persons

People who have many sexual partners and/or share drug equipment have a high risk of getting one or more STDs, including AIDS; so do their partners. These persons should be tested regularly for STDs. The testing may be done by a private physician or at a VD or an AIDS clinic. Getting an STD once does not prevent a person from getting it again.

High-risk persons should never donate blood, body tissues, or organs. Hospitals and organizations such as the American Red Cross try to screen out potential donors who are members of high-risk groups. The safety of medical blood supplies depends on people behaving responsibly.

People who suspect that they have been exposed to an STD should seek immediate medical treatment. People who are receiving treatment should not share medications with others because the medications may be the wrong ones. They even may be ineffective or dangerous if used improperly.

It is the responsibility of every person with an STD to locate and inform everyone whom they may have exposed to the STD. Local STD clinics or public health departments will assist them. The goal is to stop the spread of STDs, not to judge anyone's behavior. Finally, anyone receiving treatment for an STD must follow the doctor's instructions carefully. If medications are not taken properly, they may not cure the disease. Until the disease is cured, all sexual contact must be avoided to prevent reinfection.

▲ **Figure 17-14. It is important to seek treatment at the first sign of an STD.**

Community Responsibilities

STDs are a potential threat to just about everyone. You can help by behaving responsibly and passing on factual information about STDs to others. If someone you know gets an STD, be supportive. Listen to the person's worries and concerns. Treat the person the same way you would treat anyone who was ill and needed help.

O━┳
People who suspect STD exposure should seek immediate medical attention.

Section and Review

1. In what age group do most STDs occur?
2. What behaviors reduce the chances of getting STDs?
3. What behaviors are suggested for persons who are at high risk for getting STDs?
4. If a person gets an STD, why is it important to follow carefully a doctor's instructions for treatment?

What Do You Think?
5. In the future, more and more people will be needed to care for and counsel AIDS patients. Explain why you would or would not consider this job as a career choice.

17 | Chapter Review

Chapter Summary

- Important decisions about one's style of living should be made with the help and guidance of parents, guardians, family, and respected community leaders.
- Sexually transmitted diseases (STDs) are infectious diseases that are spread mainly by sexual contact.
- The most effective ways to prevent STDs other than AIDS are by practicing sexual abstinence or sexual fidelity. To prevent AIDS, it is also necessary to avoid intravenous drug use and relationships with other past or present drug users.
- The most serious STDs in this country are chlamydia, gonorrhea, syphilis, genital herpes, and AIDS.
- Chlamydia and gonorrhea can cause sterility, infections of the urinary tract, and pelvic inflammatory disease. Both of these STDs can be cured with antibiotics.
- Syphilis has three stages. Penicillin can kill the bacteria at any stage, but after stage two, the damage cannot be reversed.
- Genital herpes and AIDS are incurable.
- The human immunodeficiency virus, HIV, causes AIDS.
- There are four main ways a person can become infected with HIV: having intimate sexual contact with an infected person; using a needle or syringe that is contaminated with the blood of an infected person; coming into direct contact with the blood or blood parts of an infected person; being the child of a mother who was infected before or during pregnancy.
- HIV weakens the immune system. Opportunistic diseases then develop.
- Everyone can help prevent STDs by behaving responsibly, keeping informed, and sharing the facts about STDs with others.

Vocabulary Review

Listed below are some of the important terms in this chapter. Choose the term that best matches the phrase in the exercise that follows.

acquired immuno-
   deficiency syndrome
AIDS-related complex
candidiasis
chancre
chancroid
chlamydia

congenital syphilis
genital herpes
genital warts
gonorrhea
human immuno-
   deficiency virus

opportunistic diseases
pelvic inflammatory
   disease
pubic lice
scabies
sexual abstinence

sexually transmitted
   diseases
syphilis
Trichomonas
vaginitis

1. diseases that attack a person whose immune system is weakened by HIV

2. an incurable STD caused by the herpes simplex II virus

3. a group of symptoms caused by HIV

4. a yeast infection that causes an inflammation of the birth canal

5. a small, painless sore that is one of the first symptoms of syphilis

6. an incurable, deadly STD that damages the body's immune system

7. the most common bacterium-caused STD in this country

8. the cause of AIDS

9. an infection of the organs of the pelvis that can result in sterility

10. a common, curable STD that is caused by the bacterium gonococcus

What Have You Learned?

1. List two myths about STDs. Then list two facts that you learned from this chapter.
2. Give three or more reasons why there are so many cases of STDs in this country.
3. Why is it important to get prompt medical attention for STDs?
4. Distinguish between the diseases gonorrhea, chlamydia, syphilis, and genital herpes.
5. How can gonorrhea, chlamydia, syphilis, and genital herpes affect a newborn?
6. Why do females often not know that they are infected with an STD?
7. Name three curable STDs other than gonorrhea, chlamydia, and syphilis.
8. Name four ways that HIV is spread and four ways that it is not spread.
9. List the high-risk groups for HIV.
10. Explain why someone receiving a blood transfusion before 1985 could get HIV.
11. What behaviors help prevent STDs?
12. Why should someone with an STD follow a doctor's orders carefully?

What Do You Think?

1. The Centers for Disease Control consider education a vital step in the battle to prevent STDs. What do you think? Why?
2. Certain groups, such as the military, are required to take tests for HIV. Many people say that this testing is an invasion of privacy. What do you think? Why?
3. Many states require couples to be screened for some STDs before getting a marriage license. Is this a good idea? Why or why not?
4. Why do pregnant women who have been exposed to STDs need medical counseling?
5. Do you think condom ads should be allowed on TV? Why or why not?

What Would You Do?

1. How would you discuss this chapter with your parents or guardian? Write a short skit to illustrate your discussion.
2. Suppose you went to a party where there was drinking and intravenous drug use. You did not want to risk getting AIDS or another STD. What would you do?
3. The Surgeon General suggests that teenagers say no to sex and drugs. Explain in your own words why this is a good idea.
4. You are asked to write a pamphlet about AIDS for your school. What is the best way to explain AIDS to other students?
5. A student in your class is infected with HIV. Some students are afraid to be with him. What would you say to ease their fears?
6. Hospitals are looking for foster parents for babies with HIV. How would you feel about having a foster brother or sister with HIV? What precautions should be taken?

For Further Study

1. Developments in the treatment of AIDS are occurring rapidly as AIDS research continues. Using newspapers, magazines and other recent sources, write a report on current and proposed methods of treating AIDS. Explain how each method works or would work to improve the patient's health. Select the method that you think is most promising.
2. Find out what resources are available in your community to educate people about STDs. Obtain literature about STDs and organize a health fair to help educate students in your school about STDs.

18

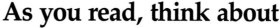

As you read, think about

▶ the various types of and risk factors for noninfectious diseases.

▶ the different kinds of cardiovascular disease and how you can reduce your risk for the disease.

▶ the warning signs of cancer and the ways you can reduce your risk for cancer.

▶ the guidelines for interacting with physically disabled persons.

Noninfectious Diseases and Physical Disabilities

Y ou zoom across the court and catch the ball one-handed. You push hard on your wheels to maneuver into position to shoot. The other team closes in, but you pull to the right and quickly send the ball flying over their heads. Two points!

It takes courage and determination to overcome severe physical disabilities, but many disabled people lead productive, enjoyable lives. In this chapter, you will learn about the causes, the treatment, and preventive measures used against physical disabilities and noninfectious diseases.

People with disabilities can lead full and productive lives.

1. THE NATURE OF NONINFECTIOUS DISEASES

Check Your Wellness

Are your health awareness levels and life-style choices helping to protect you from noninfectious diseases? How many of these can you answer yes to?

1. Do you avoid using tobacco products?
2. Do you avoid high levels of salts, sweets, fried foods, and alcohol?
3. Do you include fiber-rich foods and foods rich in vitamins and minerals in your daily diet?
4. Do you exercise on a regular basis?
5. Do you know your family health history?
6. Do you maintain the correct weight for your age, sex, height, and frame?
7. Do you have routine physical exams and know when to consult a physician?
8. Do you know the warning signs of cancer?
9. Do you know the self-tests for cancer?
10. Are you aware of environmental health hazards at home and at work?
11. Do you include regular quiet or relaxation times in your schedule?

Diseases that are not caused by pathogens are called **noninfectious diseases.** These diseases cannot be transmitted by contact with a person, object, or substance. They are not communicable or contagious. Noninfectious diseases are caused by a variety of factors. As you can see in Figure 18-1, some factors are genetic, or inherited, while others may be environmental or life-style factors. Some factors are certain to cause a disease, while others, called **risk factors,** increase the likelihood of getting a disease. Smoking, for example, increases the chances of lung disease. Many noninfectious diseases are thought to be caused by a combination of different risk factors. Some risk factors are unavoidable, but most risk factors can be avoided once you learn what they are. Two types of noninfectious diseases described in this chapter—cardiovascular disease and cancer—are the leading causes of death in adults in the United States.

Genetic Risk Factors

A risk factor that is inherited—under the control of genes—is a **genetic risk factor. Genes** are the chemicals in your body's cells that determine all of your physical traits. Genes determine your eye color and body height, for example, as well as many other traits and even certain diseases. In some cases, an individual may inherit the gene for a specific genetic disease. Depending on the type of genetic disease inherited, it may be present at birth, a **congenital** (kun **jen** uh tul) **disease,** or it may become evident later in life. Some of these genetic diseases are discussed in Chapter 12 and Chapter 13. Diseases such as these are unavoidable by the individuals who inherit them.

Most genetic risk factors, however, do not cause a disease by themselves. They make it likely, but not certain, that a disease will develop, especially when other risk factors are present. A person who is genetically at risk for a certain disease often can overcome the risk by practicing healthful habits. For example, a person may be genetically at risk to develop high blood pressure. By avoiding smoking and alcohol and by exercising regularly and eating a balanced diet, the person may avoid the disease.

When a disease tends to run in a family, the term **familial disease tendency** is used to describe this type of genetic risk factor. A person's sex also can be a genetic risk factor. This is because some diseases occur more frequently in one sex than in the other.

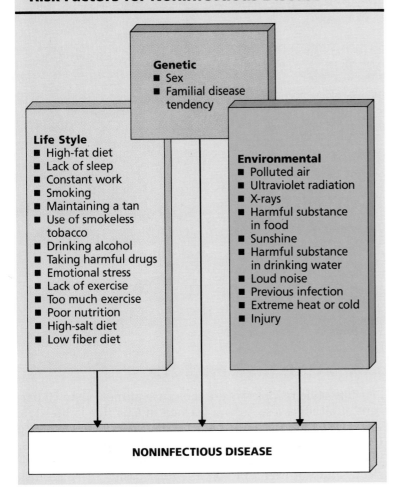

Risk Factors for Noninfectious Disease

Genetic
- Sex
- Familial disease tendency

Life Style
- High-fat diet
- Lack of sleep
- Constant work
- Smoking
- Maintaining a tan
- Use of smokeless tobacco
- Drinking alcohol
- Taking harmful drugs
- Emotional stress
- Lack of exercise
- Too much exercise
- Poor nutrition
- High-salt diet
- Low fiber diet

Environmental
- Polluted air
- Ultraviolet radiation
- X-rays
- Harmful substance in food
- Sunshine
- Harmful substance in drinking water
- Loud noise
- Previous infection
- Extreme heat or cold
- Injury

NONINFECTIOUS DISEASE

◀ **Figure 18-1.** Among the three types of risk factors that lead to disease, which can you most easily avoid?

Environmental Risk Factors

Unlike genetic risk factors, **environmental risk factors** originate in your environment, or surroundings, not in your body. Many can be avoided. Environmental risk factors include harmful substances in the air you breathe or in anything you eat, drink, or touch. For example, polluted air, cigarette smoke, alcohol, unhealthful foods, and toxic fumes are all environmental risk factors.

Other environmental risk factors have to do with your actual physical environment. These include long exposure to extreme heat or cold, loud noise, high altitude, and exposure to radiation, including sunlight.

Even previous infection by a pathogen can be a risk factor for a noninfectious disease. This is possible because some pathogens cause damage that may result in a noninfectious condition later.

Exposure to harmful substances in the environment can contribute to noninfectious diseases.

Figure 18-2. You can reduce risk ▷ factors for disease by practicing healthful habits.

Life-Style Risk Factors

Life-style risk factors are the cause of more than 50 percent of all illnesses. As you learned in Chapter 1, **life-style risk factors** are harmful behaviors or habits, such as using tobacco products, drinking alcohol, taking harmful drugs, overeating, following an unhealthful diet, not getting enough sleep, and not exercising on a regular basis. These are risk factors that you can avoid. Another life-style risk factor is mental and emotional stress. Although you cannot always avoid stress, frequently stress can be reduced by successful coping as explained in Chapter 3.

Life-style risk factors are harmful behaviors or habits that can be avoided.

Section Review

1. Define noninfectious disease.
2. What is a familial disease tendency?
3. Name the three main types of risk factors that increase the likelihood of disease.
4. Can a pathogen ever cause or contribute to a noninfectious disease? How?

What Do You Think?

5. What are some environmental risk factors in your life that you may be able to avoid?

2. CARDIOVASCULAR DISEASES

Diseases of the heart and blood vessels are called **cardiovascular** (kar dee oh **vas** kyuh lur) **diseases.** These diseases kill almost as many people each year as all other causes of death combined. In the United States, almost one out of every two people will develop cardiovascular disease.

Types of Cardiovascular Disease

The heart (*cardio*) and blood vessel (*vascular*) diseases are described together, because whatever affects one affects the other. This is because the cardiovascular system is a closed system, with the heart as the pump and the vessels as a network of flexible tubing throughout the body. When any part of the system develops a problem, the entire system is in danger of overwork and failure.

HIGH BLOOD PRESSURE The force that is made by blood pushing against the walls of the arteries and veins within the body is called **blood pressure.** This pressure is created by the heart as it pumps blood. Each time the heart beats, it pushes blood out into the arteries, which then carry the blood to every part of the body.

Normal blood pressure can vary. It may be low when you sleep but high when you are nervous, excited, or exercising. If blood pressure increases above normal limits and remains high, the result is **high blood pressure,** or **hypertension** (hy pur **ten** shun). Hypertension causes the vessel walls to thicken, forcing blood through a narrower passageway. This makes the heart work harder.

Hypertension is called the "silent killer" because it has no symptoms and frequently goes undetected. High blood pressure cannot be cured, but it can be controlled. Many medications can lower high blood pressure. Some medications, called **diuretics** (dy uh **ret** iks), promote the excretion of excess body fluids and salt in the urine. This decreases pressure by decreasing the amount of fluid (blood) in the vessels. Other medications lower blood pressure by widening narrow blood vessels. You can help prevent or control high blood pressure by eating a low-salt diet, exercising regularly, reducing your level of stress, and maintaining your weight at a normal level.

ARTERIOSCLEROSIS **Arteriosclerosis** (ar teer ee oh skluh **roh** sis), or "hardening of the arteries," is a condition in which the arteries become hard and stiff. At present, it is the most common cause of cardiovascular illness in the United States. Hypertension is a major factor in the development of arteriosclerosis.

Cardiovascular diseases affect the heart and blood vessels.

Weight, diet, activity, and stress can affect your blood pressure.

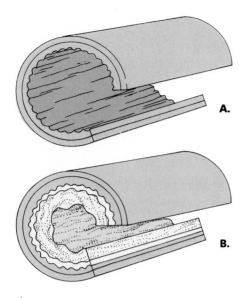

The most common form of arteriosclerosis is **atherosclerosis** (ath uh roh skluh **roh** sis). Atherosclerosis, illustrated in Figure 18-3, is a disease in which fatty deposits narrow or block arteries. Eating foods high in fat and cholesterol is a significant risk factor for atherosclerosis. Another major factor is lack of regular exercise.

HEART ATTACK Each year more than half a million people in the United States are victims of **heart attack.** During a heart attack, the death of some heart tissue occurs. Depending on the extent of tissue death in the heart, a heart attack can be life-threatening, or it can result in some lessening of heart function.

A heart attack is usually caused by coronary heart disease. **Coronary heart disease** refers to a blockage of the coronary arteries—those arteries supplying the tissues of the heart with blood. The blockage may be due to fatty deposits (atherosclerosis) or a blood clot. The heart tissue beyond the blockage soon becomes starved of oxygen and dies. If the blockage is in a large coronary artery, many heart tissue cells die, and the individual suffers a heart attack, or "coronary," which often results in death.

Figure 18-3. A gradual buildup of fatty deposits in the coronary arteries will reduce blood flow to the heart.

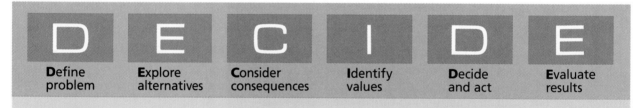

| **D**efine problem | **E**xplore alternatives | **C**onsider consequences | **I**dentify values | **D**ecide and act | **E**valuate results |

CONCERN FOR A FRIEND'S HEALTH

Your friend Dave has high blood pressure. He was keeping it under control by being careful about his diet. But lately he seems to be eating more salt and fatty foods than he should, especially when he is with his friends. Instead of considering his special condition, he just orders what everyone else does.

When you spoke to Dave about cutting down on salt and fat, he got angry and said a real friend wouldn't keep nagging him. But you are concerned that he could be seriously damaging his health, and you want to help.

1. Use the DECIDE process on page 16 to decide what you would do in this situation. Explain your reasons for making this decision.

2. Suppose the action you decided on did not bring the desired results. What would you do next?

3. List some ways that a person can show support for a friend who has a particular physical illness or restriction.

Will a friend with high blood pressure listen to reason?

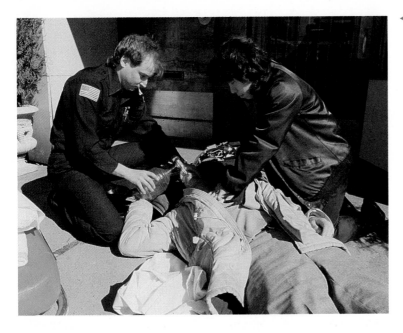

Figure 18-4. Only a trained person should administer CPR to the victim of a heart attack.

The chest pain of coronary heart disease is called **angina pectoris** (an **jy** nuh **pek** tuh ris). It occurs if the heart muscle does not get enough oxygen. Usually the pain occurs during exercise or periods of emotional stress when the heart rate and blood pressure increase, and the heart muscle needs more oxygen than usual. The pain eventually disappears with rest. If, however, the heart muscle continues not to get enough oxygen, the pain persists and a heart attack occurs. Figure 18-5 lists the warning signs of a heart attack.

If **cardiac arrest** occurs, that is, if the heart stops completely, someone trained in basic life support must administer **cardiopulmonary resuscitation** (kar dee oh **pul** muh ner ee rih sus uh **tay** shun) (**CPR**). CPR combines mouth-to-mouth breathing with chest compression to maintain the flow of oxygen-rich blood to the brain while the heart is not working.

HEART FAILURE   Heart failure is not a single event, like heart attack, but a condition in which the heart slowly fails from overwork. Usually, years of arteriosclerosis, atherosclerosis, and high blood pressure are the cause of heart failure. These conditions make the heart work harder than it should. Swelling of the feet and lower legs is one of the symptoms of heart failure.

STROKE   A **stroke** is a sudden disruption of blood flow to a part of the brain. Without the oxygen and nutrients carried by the blood, the brain cells die.

Some strokes occur when an artery supplying blood to one section of the brain is blocked. The block may be caused either by atherosclerosis or by a blood clot, or **thrombus**

Warning Signs of Heart Attack

- Uncomfortable pressure or pain in the center of the chest lasting for two minutes or longer
- Pain spreading to the shoulder, neck, or arms
- One or more of the following: severe pain, dizziness, fainting, sweating, extreme anxiety, nausea, or shortness of breath

  A person experiencing the warning signals of an attack should be kept still and relaxed and taken immediately to a hospital, even if the pain seems to go away.

Figure 18-5. Recognizing these warning signs and acting upon them can help save a life.

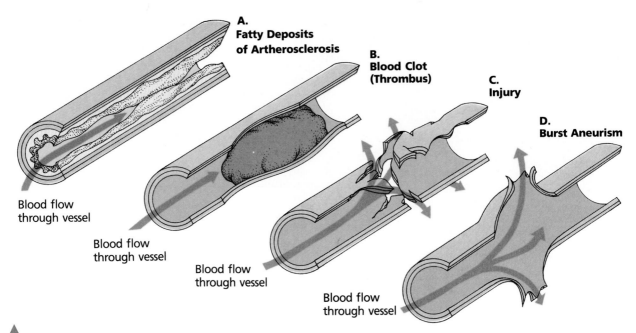

A.
**Fatty Deposits
of Artherosclerosis**

B.
**Blood Clot
(Thrombus)**

C.
Injury

D.
Burst Aneurism

Blood flow
through vessel

Blood flow
through vessel

Blood flow
through vessel

Blood flow
through vessel

Figure 18-6. A blockage (A, B) or break (C, D) in an artery leading to the brain causes a stroke.

Figure 18-7. Any warning signs of stroke, whether mild or severe, should receive prompt medical help.

The Warning Signs and Symptoms of Stroke

- Sudden weakness or numbness of the face, arm, and leg on one side of the body
- Loss of speech, trouble talking, or trouble understanding speech
- Dimness or loss of vision, particularly in one eye
- Unexplained dizziness, nausea, unsteadiness, or sudden falls

Often, strokes are preceded by "little strokes." Little strokes are warnings that a major stroke may occur if blood pressure and stress are not reduced.

(**thrahm** bus), shown in Figure 18-6. Other strokes occur when a defective artery in the brain bursts, flooding the surrounding tissue with blood. The cells that were nourished by the artery are deprived of their blood supply and cannot function. If the bleeding is from an artery in the cerebrum, the main portion of the brain, the stroke is called a **cerebral hemorrhage** (suh **ree** brul **hem** uh rij).

Cerebral hemorrhage may also be caused by a head injury or by an **aneurysm** (**an** yuh riz um) that bursts. An aneurysm is a blood-filled weak spot that balloons out from the artery wall. The weak spot is usually caused by high blood pressure. Aneurysms do not always cause trouble, but when one bursts in the brain, a stroke results. The signs of a stroke are shown in Figure 18-7.

Strokes affect people in different ways, depending on the type of stroke and the area of the brain affected. Brain damage from a stroke can affect the senses, speech, and the ability to understand speech, behavior, thought patterns, and memory. Paralysis on one side of the body is common. If the patient survives, sometimes normal function can be regained with therapy.

OTHER CARDIOVASCULAR DISORDERS Veins are blood vessels that return blood to the heart. As you can see in Figure 18-8, in healthy veins, one-way valves permit blood to flow toward the heart, but not away from it. In a condition termed **varicose** (**va** rih kohs) veins, these valves do not work. As a result, the veins in the legs become inflated from the back pressure of blood. You can easily recognize the disorder. The veins are close to the surface of the skin of the legs and may form a bluish, spiderlike pattern.

Risk factors for varicose veins include familial tendency, female gender, pregnancy, standing for long periods of time, heavy lifting, and obesity.

Varicose veins can usually be helped if the person wears elastic support stockings, maintains normal weight, and avoids standing for long periods. In severe cases, the veins are removed surgically.

Several infectious and noninfectious conditions cause **heart valve disease.** As you learned in Chapter 10, the heart's valves open and close like one-way swinging doors. Heart valve disease prevents the valves from opening and closing as they should.

A common cause of heart valve damage is **rheumatic** (roo **mat** ik) **heart disease.** Rheumatic heart disease is caused by rheumatic fever, an inflammatory disease in which the body's own immune system damages the valves of the heart. Because rheumatic fever is caused by the same bacteria that can cause strep throat, an infectious disease, all sore throats should be treated appropriately.

Another major cause of heart valve disease is a **congenital heart defect.** A congenital heart defect is a structural deformity caused by abnormal development before birth. Most congenital heart defects either obstruct the flow of blood through the heart or cause it to be rerouted. About 25,000 babies are born each year in the United States with heart defects. Most congenital heart defects are discovered in infancy and corrected by surgery.

Irregularities of the heartbeat are called **arrhythmias** (uh **rith** mee uhz). Arrhythmias are caused by abnormalities of the heart's electrical pathways. The heart may beat too slowly or too quickly or with an uneven rhythm. **Fibrillation** (fib ruh **lay** shun) is a life-threatening arrhythmia in which the heart contracts in an uncoordinated fashion.

Some abnormal heartbeats can be controlled by drugs or by artificial pacemakers. An **artificial pacemaker** is a small, battery-operated unit that is surgically implanted in the heart. The unit produces the electrical impulses needed to make the heart pump rhythmically.

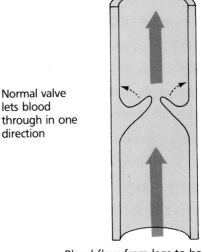

Normal valve lets blood through in one direction

Blood flow from legs to heart

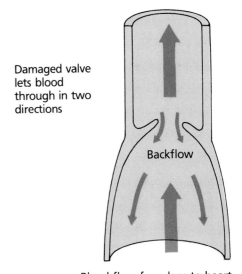

Damaged valve lets blood through in two directions

Backflow

Blood flow from legs to heart

▲ **Figure 18-8. Damaged valves in veins result in varicose veins.**

Detecting and Treating Cardiovascular Disease

Cardiovascular disease cannot be cured, but it can be controlled or prevented from getting worse. For this reason, early detection and treatment are important. Several tests are used to detect cardiovascular disease.

An **electrocardiogram** (ih lek troh **kar** dee uh gram), or **ECG,** is a graph of the heart's electrical activity that can show abnormalities in heart function. The electrical impulses that cause the heart to beat are picked up by electrodes attached

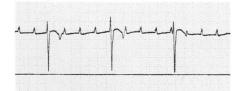

Figure 18-9. An ECG records a pattern of electrical impulses that shows how the heart is performing.

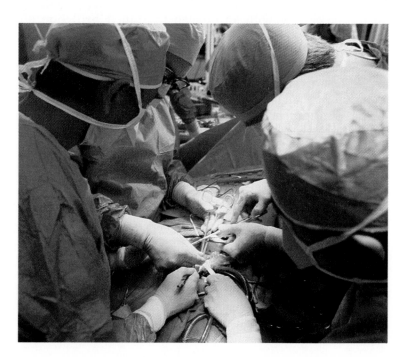

Doctors use x-rays and microphones to detect a narrowing of coronary arteries.

to the patient's skin. The impulses are recorded as a pattern on graph paper, as Figure 18-9 illustrates. Changes from a standard pattern may indicate heart disease. An ECG can be obtained when the patient is at rest or during exercise. When the patient is exercising, the procedure is called a **cardiac stress test.**

Blood flow through the coronary arteries can be detected by an x-ray technique called **coronary angiography** (an jee **ahg** ruh fee). Because blood vessels do not show up well in conventional x-rays, a special x-ray absorbing dye must be released into the coronary arteries. In this procedure, a flexible tube called a catheter is threaded through blood vessels until it reaches the heart. The dye is released from the catheter into the coronary arteries, and x-rays are taken. From the appearance of the dye in the coronary arteries, doctors can tell if blockage or narrowing of the arteries has occurred.

In **phonocardiography** (foh nuh kar dee **ahg** ruh fee) microphones placed on the chest detect sounds made by the heart and turn them into a graphical display. Different defects in the heart produce specific readouts on the display.

Treatment of cardiovascular disease depends on the condition. Surgery is commonly used to improve the blood supply to the heart muscle. Surgeons use a vein (usually taken from the patient's leg) or an artificial vessel to construct a detour around a blocked coronary artery. This procedure is called **coronary bypass surgery.**

If the heart muscle cannot do its work, the heart of a deceased organ donor may be transplanted to take over the job. Although this surgical procedure has saved many lives,

Figure 18-10. Coronary bypass surgery is now a routine procedure.

a heart-transplant patient may die because the immune system attacks and rejects the new heart. Doctors now use drugs that suppress the immune system to lower rejection rates.

Preventing Cardiovascular Disease

"Prevention is the best medicine" is good advice especially when it comes to cardiovascular disease. Establishing good health habits at a young age will greatly reduce your risks of developing diseases of the heart or blood vessels later in life. Some suggestions to help you prevent cardiovascular diseases are listed below:

- Do not smoke tobacco. Smokers have more than twice the risk of heart attack as nonsmokers. Smoking also increases the risk of stroke. The more you smoke, the greater the risk of cardiovascular disease.
- If you do smoke, quit. The risks of heart disease are greatly reduced within two years after quitting. Ten years after quitting, the chances of having a heart attack are about the same as for a nonsmoker.
- Control your blood pressure. It should be checked regularly by a doctor or nurse.
- Reduce the amount of high-cholesterol foods you eat. Too much cholesterol in the blood can cause atherosclerosis. Eat less butter, mayonnaise, and fatty meat.
- Eat more chicken, fish, fresh fruits, and vegetables.
- Cut down on salt. Reducing the amount of salt you eat will help prevent high blood pressure.
- Exercise regularly. Aerobic exercise of 20 minutes duration at least three times a week strengthens the heart and improves blood circulation throughout the body.
- Avoid obesity. If you are overweight, your heart has to work harder than it should.
- Learn to manage stress. Feelings of stress and anxiety can contribute to heart disease.

▲ **Figure 18-11. Maintaining cardiovascular fitness promotes lifelong health.**

Section Review

1. What are four life-style risk factors that can contribute to high blood pressure?

2. What causes atherosclerosis?

3. How does atherosclerosis affect blood flow?

4. What is the major difference between a stroke and a heart attack?

What Do You Think?

5. Are you in a high-risk group for heart disease? How can you change your life style to reduce the risks of heart attack?

3. CANCER

In the United States, the second leading cause of death for adults is cancer. **Cancer** is the name given to the many diseases caused by rapid, uncontrolled growth and spread of abnormal cells.

Cancer cells often form a mass of tissue called a **malignant** (muh **lig** nunt) **tumor.** Because the tumor has no sheath, or membrane, enclosing it, the cancer cells invade the surrounding tissue. A **benign** (bih **nyn**) **tumor,** on the other hand, is a mass of tissue formed from noncancerous cells. The cells in a benign tumor grow more rapidly than normal cells but more slowly than most cancer cells. In addition, a benign tumor is enclosed within a sheath so that it does not spread to nearby tissue.

The danger of cancer is that it invades and destroys normal tissues. This occurs as the cancer cells grow out into neighboring tissues; when they get into blood or lymph, they are carried elsewhere in the body. The spread of cancer from where it first develops to other parts of the body is called **metastasis** (muh **tas** tuh sis).

Many cancers can be cured if they are detected early and promptly treated. Death results if the spread of cancer is not stopped, because cancer cells eventually replace normal, functioning cells.

What Causes Cancer?

There is no single cause for all forms of cancer. Some cancers are caused by specific cancer-causing agents, called **carcinogens** (kar **sin** uh juns). They are often classified into three groups: chemical, physical, and biological.

Some chemical carcinogens are found in the workplace, for example, asbestos and coal tars. Food additives, especially certain artificial colorings, can also produce cancer. Many chemicals in cigarette smoke are carcinogens.

Physical carcinogens include ultraviolet and high-energy radiation, such as x-rays. Prolonged exposure to the ultraviolet rays of the sun or sun lamps can cause skin cancer. Biological carcinogens include a few types of viruses.

Genes that cause cancer when they are stimulated by carcinogens are called **oncogenes** (**ahn** koh jeenz). All human cells contain genes that control cellular reproduction. Recent research has suggested that carcinogens can transform these normal genes into oncogenes.

Types of Cancer

Cancer is usually named for the tissue or organ in which the cells first begin to develop. Cancer can occur in almost any part of the body. Some cancers occur only rarely while

Cancerous tumors invade and destroy normal tissues.

Figure 18-12. People who work with carcinogens should wear protective equipment.

others are more common, as you can see in Figure 18-13. Many cancers grow and spread slowly, while others grow and spread rapidly throughout the body.

SKIN CANCER The ultraviolet rays of sunlight are the principal cause of skin cancer, the most common of all the cancers. There are three types of skin cancer. The two most common types are very slow-growing and almost always curable. The least common type, called a **melanoma** (mel uh **noh** muh), is the most serious. It usually begins in a mole, a dark area on the skin, and spreads very rapidly.

The amount of pigment in your skin determines how vulnerable you may be to the damaging effects of sunlight. People with dark skin are less likely to develop skin cancer than light-skinned people. Any unusual skin change, especially in the size or color of a mole, may indicate skin cancer.

LUNG CANCER Lung cancer is the most common type of life-threatening cancer and the leading cause of cancer deaths among American men and women. Cigarette smoking is the leading cause of lung cancer.

Lung cancer is often difficult to detect early because symptoms do not appear until the disease is quite advanced. Symptoms include a persistent cough, chest pain, and repeated attacks of pneumonia or bronchitis. Surgery is the most common form of treatment.

ORAL CANCER Cancer of the mouth can affect any part of the oral cavity—the lip, tongue, mouth, or throat. It is usually detected in the early stages by a doctor or a dentist. Oral cancer is found most frequently in men over 40 years of age and occurs twice as often in men as in women, although it is beginning to occur more often in younger people, particularly those who use chewing tobacco.

Warning signs include difficulty in chewing, swallowing, or moving the tongue or jaws. Cigarette, cigar, and pipe smoking, chewing tobacco, and excessive use of alcohol increase the risk of oral cancer.

BREAST CANCER Breast cancer is a major threat to women in the United States. Women at high risk include those who are obese, have had few or no children, were first pregnant when they were older than 30, or whose mothers had breast cancer. New research suggests the risks of breast cancer are increased in women who drink alcohol, even in moderate amounts.

Effective treatment depends on early diagnosis. That is why a monthly breast self-examination should be a lifelong habit from the teenage years on. The breast self-examination is described in Chapter 12. X-rays of the breast that detect cancer are called **mammograms** (**mam** uh gramz).

The Yearly Incidence of Some Cancers

Type of Cancer	Males (%)	Females (%)
Skin	3	3
Oral	4	2
Lung	20	11
Breast		27
Colon and rectum	14	16
Pancreas	3	3
Prostate	20	
Ovary		4
Uterus		10
Bladder	10	4
Leukemia and lymph cancers	8	7
All other	18	13

Source: American Cancer Society, Inc., 1987

Figure 18-13. Which type of cancers have the highest incidence among men? Among women?

Women should begin monthly breast self-examinations in their teens.

Seeing Through Bone

The patient's bed is slowly pushed into a six-foot-long tunnel. Inside, a magnetic field scans her body, creating signals that a computer uses to form images of body tissues on a computer screen. Doctors examine the image, looking for problems not visible on x-rays. With this process, called magnetic resonance imaging (MRI), doctors can diagnose and then treat diseases that used to be considered fatal.

MRI creates pictures by causing the water inside the body to give off signals. Since the water content among tissues varies, different tissues can be distinguished from each other. With this method, for example, the spinal cord becomes visible even though it is surrounded by bone. In the past, doctors could see the spinal cord only after injecting it with a substance that shows up on x-rays. This was often painful and risky.

MRI is helping doctors detect tumors and other disorders that otherwise would not be detectable. Also, MRI does not expose the patient to the potential harm of x-rays.

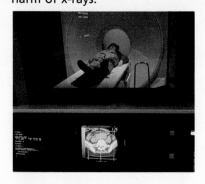

MRI is a diagnostic tool.

REPRODUCTIVE CANCERS   Cancer of the cervix, the ring of tissue at the opening of the uterus, used to be the number one cause of cancer deaths in women. This has changed because of a test that is called the **Pap test.** In this test, a tiny amount of tissue is painlessly removed from the cervix and then examined under a microscope. The Pap test can reveal even the earliest cell changes associated with cancer. Detected early, cervical cancer is curable.

After lung and skin cancers, cancer of the prostate gland is the most common form of cancer in men. Warning signs include painful or burning urination or blood in the urine. A regular rectal examination, especially for men over 40, helps detect prostate cancer.

Cancer of the testes is one of the most common cancers in men 15 to 34 years of age. Young men with undescended testes are at specific risk for testicular cancer. Dull aching in the groin or lower abdomen are symptoms of testicular cancer. Early signs of the disease can be detected with the simple, three-minute testicular self-examination described in Chapter 12.

COLON AND RECTAL CANCER   Cancers of the colon and rectum are the second most common types of fatal cancer, after lung cancer. Warning signs include bleeding from the rectum, blood in the stool, and changes in bowel habits. Evidence suggests that bowel cancer may be linked to diet. A diet high in fat or low in fiber or both may be a significant risk factor.

LEUKEMIA AND HODGKIN'S DISEASE   **Leukemia** (loo **kee** mee uh) is a form of cancer affecting the tissues in which blood is formed, mostly bone marrow. Leukemia causes millions of abnormal, immature white blood cells to be released into the blood system. These nonfunctioning cells weaken the body's immune system. Warning signs of leukemia include weight loss, repeated infections, and anemia, a condition in which there are too few red cells in the blood.

Cancer of the lymph nodes is called **Hodgkin's disease.** This condition is characterized by the painless swelling of the lymph nodes, fever, and weight loss. Hodgkin's disease is more common in men than women and usually occurs between the ages of 15 and 34 or after age 50. If detected early, Hodgkin's disease is curable in about 80 percent of cases.

Detecting and Treating Cancer

The key to cancer cure is early detection and treatment. All of the warning signs of cancer can have causes unrelated to it. It is important, therefore, to *know your body*. The warning signs of cancer apply to unusual changes that do not go away. If you are "tuned in" to your body, you will know when something unusual is the matter. Let your doctor know immediately if you have any of the warning signs listed in Figure 18-14. Notice that together the first letters of the warning signs spell "caution," not "panic."

These methods for early detection of disease are known as **screening tests.** Mammograms, Pap tests, and chest x-rays are screening tests. When the result of a screening test is positive, it must be confirmed by another test. Doctors will often surgically remove a small piece of the tissue in question to examine it under a microscope for signs of cancer. This procedure is called a **biopsy** (**by** ahp see).

Treatment for cancer depends on the type of cancer and its stage of development. Surgery is performed to remove a malignant tumor when there are no signs that it has spread. **Radiation therapy**, the use of high-energy radiation to kill cancer cells, can slow or stop the spread of cancer. Once cancer has spread, however, surgery and radiation are less useful. **Chemotherapy** (kee mo **thehr** uh pee), the use of drugs to attack cancers, reduces the rate of cancer cell reproduction and tumor growth. Over time, it can eventually destroy the tumor or growth.

In another type of treatment called **immunotherapy** (im yuh noh **thehr** uh pee), the body's own disease-fighting system, the immune system, is stimulated to control cancer. Some drugs stimulate the production of white blood cells, which attack cancer cells.

Most cancers are considered to be cured if the patient exhibits no signs of the disease for five years or more after treatment is stopped. The cancer is then said to be in **remission**. Unfortunately for many patients, remission may last only a few years. If the cancer returns after remission it is usually more difficult to treat than the original cancer. The survival rates of some cancers are shown in Figure 18-15.

The Seven Warning Signs of Cancer

- Change in bowel or bladder habits (such as constipation, diarrhea, or incomplete emptying of the bowel)
- A sore that does not heal
- Unusual bleeding or discharge (particularly from the rectum or vagina)
- Thickening or lump in the breast or elsewhere
- Indigestion or difficulty in swallowing
- Obvious change in wart or mole (such as growth, discharge, unusual appearance)
- Nagging cough or hoarseness

Source: American Cancer Society, Inc.

Figure 18-14. Any of these warning signs can alert you to a possible problem.

Source: American Cancer Society, Inc., 1982

Cancer Survival Rates

Type of Cancer	5-Year Survival Rates (percent of patients alive 5 years after treatment)
Lung	13
Leukemia	33
Oral	51
Colon and rectum	52
Cervical and uterine	66
Prostate	70
Breast	74
Hodgkin's disease	80
Melanoma	80
Testicular	89

Figure 18-15. Early detection of cancer greatly increases the chances of survival.

Preventing Cancer

Although the specific cause of most cancers is unknown, certain risk factors have strong associations with certain cancers. Here are a few suggestions that can help you to reduce the risk of cancer.

- Do not use tobacco. Tobacco and tobacco smoke contain carcinogens, and smoking is the greatest preventable cancer risk factor of all. Pregnant women who smoke can harm their unborn babies. Chewing tobacco can cause oral cancer.
- Avoid drinking alcohol. Drinking, especially along with smoking, greatly increases the risks of oral cancer. Alcohol increases the risk of breast cancer in women.
- Respect the sun's ultraviolet rays. Wear protective clothing and use a sunscreen.
- Avoid carcinogens in the workplace. Be sure to have your employer provide you with information about any carcinogens that you work with. By law employers are required to provide special protective clothing or respirators that can protect you.
- Eat high-fiber foods, such as whole-grain bread and cereals, fruit, and vegetables, such as broccoli, carrots, and cauliflower. High-fiber foods reduce the risks of colon and rectal cancers as well as help to reduce blood-cholesterol levels.
- Trim fat from your diet. Avoid fried foods as much as possible. Eat chicken, fish, and lean meats. Choose skim milk instead of whole milk, and reduce your intake of cream (including ice cream), cheese, and eggs.
- Eat foods rich in vitamins A and C, such as fresh vegetables and fruits. These vitamins are thought to help protect against some cancers.
- Exercise regularly and maintain normal weight.
- Avoid unnecessary x-rays, especially during pregnancy.
- Regularly examine breasts or testes and skin for abnormal lumps or growths.

Healthful habits can reduce the risks of getting cancer.

Section Review

1. Describe the two types of tumors.
2. How does cancer spread?
3. What is a carcinogen?
4. Name three methods of cancer detection.

What Do You Think?
5. What would you tell a friend who thinks that there is nothing anyone can do to prevent cancer?

4. Physical Disabilities

A **physical disability** is a condition that prevents normal physical function. A **handicap** is a limitation on what you can accomplish. People who have physical disabilities may or may not be handicapped. Physically disabled people adapt to their physical limitations and are able to lead normal, productive lives.

Types of Physical Disabilities

A physical disability may be caused by a congenital defect, a disease, or an injury. The three most common types of physical disabilities are impaired sight, impaired hearing, and impaired mobility.

IMPAIRED SIGHT One out of every 19 people in the United States suffers from some form of impaired, or restricted, sight. Most of these people can see with the aid of contact lenses or eyeglasses. About 12 percent of those impaired, however, cannot see well enough to read even with glasses, and about 4 percent are blind. Some causes of sight impairment are discussed in Chapter 7.

People with impaired sight use tape recordings of books, texts, and periodicals. They also read material written in braille, a system that uses characters made up of raised dots. Specially marked canes inform others of the person's impairment and are used to detect obstacles, such as curbs. Specially trained seeing-eye dogs ensure mobility for many sight-impaired people. A list of guidelines for interacting with a sight-impaired person are given in Figure 18-16.

Guidelines for Interacting with a Sight-Impaired Person

- Speak right away so that the person will know you are present. Ask if you can help.
- If the person asks to be guided, extend your arm and place the person's hand on it. Do not grab the person by the arm.
- Remember that a seeing-eye dog is a worker, not a pet. Ask the person's permission before you touch or talk to the dog.
- Help the person to become oriented to a new environment by describing where things are and who is present.

Figure 18-16. How could you familiarize a sight-impaired person to a new place?

◀ **Figure 18-17. Stevie Wonder's achievements show what one can do to develop other senses and skills.**

Figure 18-18. Why would a hearing-impaired person watch your mouth?

Figure 18-19. What courtesies should you show a mobility-impaired person?

IMPAIRED HEARING About 13 million people in the United States have some degree of hearing impairment. Of this number, nearly 2 million are totally deaf. The causes of hearing impairment are discussed in Chapter 7.

Hearing aids can often help people who cannot hear well. Those with severe hearing loss make use of anything and everything visual to communicate. Signing, for example, is a language consisting of hand positions and movements. Some hearing-impaired people are very good at lip reading. There are special telephones that amplify sound for the hearing-impaired and systems of lights to take the place of telephone rings and door bells. And, of course, deaf people communicate by writing. Figure 18-18 lists guidelines for conversing with hearing-impaired persons.

IMPAIRED MOBILITY The ability to move normally can be impaired by nervous system and muscle disorders, joint diseases, or the absence of a limb. Canes, walkers, wheelchairs, crutches, braces, or artificial limbs often are used to assist people with impaired mobility. In children, the number one cause of impaired mobility is **cerebral palsy** (suh **ree** brul **pawl** zee). Cerebral palsy is a disability in which there is lack of muscular coordination and possible speech difficulty. It is often caused by complications during pregnancy or at birth, resulting in damage to the nervous system. If a mother is exposed to measles or mumps during pregnancy, the risk of cerebral palsy increases. Alcohol consumption and radiation exposure during pregnancy also increase the risk. Although there is no cure for cerebral palsy, children with this disorder can be helped with physical and speech therapy and sometimes with surgery. Improvements in health care during pregnancy and in delivery procedures can help prevent some cases of cerebral palsy.

The absence of a limb (arm or leg) or of a foot or hand can be congenital or caused by accidental injury. It could also be the result of surgical **amputation** (surgical removal). Automobile and motorcycle accidents are common causes of accidental amputations. Surgical amputation may be done to remove an injured part that is beyond saving, to remove a bone affected by cancer, or to remove tissue that has died from lack of circulation. Tissue can die because of frostbite or because of long-term blockage of vessels that supply the tissue with blood.

Fortunately, advances in medical technology are helping many people with impaired mobility. Artificial devices that replace missing body parts are becoming more and more sophisticated and useful. For people who are paralyzed, research on nerve cell function holds great promise. Scientists are now exploring ways to make damaged nerves grow and repair themselves. Figure 18-19 gives guidelines for interacting with mobility-impaired persons.

Living with Physical Disabilities

Do you have a physical disability, or do you know someone who does? If you do, you know that the key to living with physical disability is adaptation. People adapt to physical disabilities in different ways, depending on the disability, their feelings about it, the amount of support they receive from others, and the success of therapy and special equipment. Many organizations help people to deal with specific disabilities. Laws have been passed to ensure that wheelchair ramps and special bathroom facilities are present in public buildings. Some disabled people become activists who work to improve attitudes toward the disabled and help disabled people live normal lives.

How can you help a physically disabled person? The best way is to let the disabled person take the lead. You can do this by being patient and waiting for the person to perform the activity independently or to ask for your assistance. Most people with physical disabilities want to function independently. Your role is to help them do things for themselves and to respect their independence.

The second guideline is not to assume that a physically disabled person is mentally disabled as well. This should be obvious, but it is often overlooked. Be careful what you say. Many people with impaired muscular coordination, such as that caused by most forms of cerebral palsy, have normal intelligence, hearing, and sight. People in wheelchairs are not out of hearing range just because you are standing and they are sitting! People who cannot see can hear every word you say; and those who cannot hear are very tuned in to attitudes expressed by your face and posture.

Perhaps the first two guidelines can be summed up by a third one: do not underestimate a physically disabled person. Your positive attitude about the person's abilities is the best way of preventing the disability from developing into a handicap.

▲
Figure 18-20. Physically disabled people can participate in many exercises or sports to stay fit.

Never limit disabled people with your sense of what they can hear, think, or do.

Section Review

1. What is the difference between a physical disability and a handicap?
2. What causes cerebral palsy?
3. Name one reason for surgical amputation.
4. State two guidelines to keep in mind when you are with a physically disabled person.

What Do You Think?

5. How would you want to be treated by others if you had a physical disability?

Evaluating Health Information

Imagine you have just been offered a summer job of life-guarding at a local beach, when you read an article stating that people who spend a lot of time in the sun risk skin cancer and premature wrinkling.

Now, what do you do? First, you should attempt to verify the article's facts. In the rapidly changing fields of health and medicine, new studies sometimes contradict old studies, and experts often disagree about the significance of new results. This makes it difficult to report research findings. Thus, news stories may contain misleading or even false information.

How can you sort all this out? When reviewing new health information, keep an open, yet critical, mind. Use the following questions to evaluate health reports.

1. Who Is the Author?

If possible, determine who wrote the article and what the person's credentials are. Usually, health professionals (physicians and medical researchers) are the best qualified authors. Health information experts (writers trained to interpret health information) are also well-qualified, but they lack the specialized training of health professionals. General reporters and people who write advertisements may not be well qualified to interpret health information.

2. Is the Source Trustworthy?

Reliability depends on more than just the author. It is important to consider where the information appears. The most reliable sources are medical and science journals. The least reliable sources are advertisements and publications funded by firms with financial interests in the field (for example, a booklet funded by a vitamin manufacturer). These sources are apt to be weighted in favor of one viewpoint.

3. Is the Evidence Convincing?

It is important to assess the quality of the evidence upon which the news is based. Some signs of weak evidence are:

- the use of vague statements that lack supporting information, such as "Doctors recommend . . ." or "In all probability . . . ."
- phrases like "In animals . . . ," "Of that age group . . . ," or "In laboratory tests . . . ." These indicate the findings are based on studies done on a limited basis.
- lack of information about a key aspect of the topic.

4. Has the Information Been Verified?

The most reliable information is based on evidence that has been tested. When different researchers arrive at similar results by independent means, the results are more accurate. Thus, the best way to assess new health information is to compare it with other sources.

Knowing how to evaluate health information can help you make the right decision.

Unfortunately, verifying information is not always a simple or foolproof method. Often experts disagree about the conclusions that can be drawn from research findings. By becoming familiar with all the views on an issue, however, you can be confident of making a more informed decision.

APPLY THE SKILL

1. Read the article entitled "Fish Oils and Heart Disease" on page 204. Do you believe it is accurate? Why or why not? Make a list of any additional information you would need to assess its accuracy.

2. Suppose you were asked to promote fish oil capsules. Write a convincing advertisement for the product. It must be based on facts, but your goal is to sell the product.

3. Suppose you were a consumer who had just read the advertisement for fish oil capsules. List the steps you would take to decide if the product offers any health benefits.

4. Choose a health news item from a recent newspaper or magazine. Write a report evaluating the article using the guidelines outlined above.

18 | Chapter Review

Chapter Summary

- Noninfectious diseases are caused by risk factors, not pathogens. They are diseases that cannot be passed on by people, objects, or substances.
- Risk factors are factors that increase the likelihood of getting a disease.
- Genetic risk factors are inherited, and they cannot be avoided. They include sex and the tendency to develop a disease.
- Environmental risk factors are substances or conditions in the environment. These include polluted air, loud noise, radiation, and extreme heat or cold. Most of these risk factors can be avoided.
- Life-style risk factors can be avoided usually. They include unhealthful diet; use of tobacco, alcohol, and other drugs; too little sleep, and lack of regular exercise.
- Diseases of the arteries include high blood pressure, arteriosclerosis, and atherosclerosis. All of these conditions cause vessel narrowing and make the heart work harder than it should.
- Diseases of the heart include heart attack, heart failure, arrhythmias, and diseases of the heart valves.

- Different types of cancer affect different tissues. Cancer may begin in cells where genes that control cellular reproduction are transformed by carcinogens into oncogenes.
- Carcinogens often are classified into chemical, physical, and biological groups. Chemical carcinogens can be found in the workplace, in foods, and in tobacco products. Physical carcinogens include ultraviolet and high-energy radiation. Biological carcinogens include some viruses.
- Many types of cancer and heart disease can be prevented by avoiding environmental and life-style risk factors. Early detection and treatment can control cardiovascular disease and cure many forms of cancer.
- Physical disabilities are conditions of impaired physical function. They include impairment of mobility, of hearing, and of sight. Many people with physical disabilities adapt to them and are able to lead independent, productive lives.
- In interacting with people who have physical disabilities, it is important to let them set the pace, to respect their independence, and to ask them how you can help.

Vocabulary Review

Listed below are some of the important terms in this chapter. Choose the term that best matches the phrase in the exercise that follows.

angina pectoris	coronary heart disease	malignant tumor	remission
aneurysm	electrocardiogram	mammogram	risk factor
arrhythmia	genetic risk factor	metastasis	stroke
arteriosclerosis	heart attack	oncogene	thrombus
carcinogen	hypertension	Pap test	varicose veins

1. high blood pressure
2. "hardening of the arteries"
3. chest pain of coronary heart disease
4. a mass of cancerous cells
5. detects cervical cancer

6. a blood clot
7. death of heart muscle
8. irregular heart beat
9. bleeding in the brain
10. a cancer-causing substance

What Have You Learned?

1. Which life-style risk factors cause the greatest number of deaths from cancer and cardiovascular disease?
2. Why is hypertension sometimes called the "silent killer"?
3. What is the difference between a heart attack and heart failure?
4. In what ways are a heart attack and a stroke similar to each other?
5. Name two risk factors for varicose veins.

6. Identify three of the seven warning signs of cancer.
7. In what ways does immunotherapy fight cancer?
8. Name three factors that increase the risk of having a child with cerebral palsy.
9. How can you best help a physically disabled person?
10. What is the most important key to living with a physical disability?

What Do You Think?

1. What type of sports do you think help you to maintain a healthy heart? Name some of those sports. Why are they effective?
2. Why do you think that noninfectious diseases have replaced the infectious diseases as the leading causes of death?
3. Many public places now ban smoking in common areas. Do you think that the health

benefits to society justify this restriction? What about the rights of the individual?
4. What do you think the psychological effects of a physical disability might be?
5. What do you think causes people who have physical disabilities to become activists who work for better opportunities for all disabled individuals in our society?

What Would You Do?

1. Your elderly next-door neighbor is shoveling snow. Suddenly, he sits down, clutching his chest. What should you do?
2. Your mother's job requires that she stand a lot. You've noticed that her legs are developing varicose veins. What advice can you give her?
3. You and some friends are going to the beach on a hot summer day. What will you do to protect yourself?

4. As you are shopping at your local supermarket, you happen to notice that the ceilings of the building contain asbestos, a carcinogen. What would you do?
5. Imagine that you are standing at a crosswalk beside a blind person who is waiting to cross the street. The person has a red-and-white cane but does not have a seeing-eye dog. What should you do?

For Further Study

1. Research suggests that people with so-called type A personality are prone to heart disease. What sort of traits characterize the type A personality?
2. Researchers have found that drinking alcohol is linked to breast cancer. How serious a threat is alcohol to women? Write a one-page report based on the best information you can find on this question.
3. Draw a map of your school building and trace a safe route that a person in a wheelchair could use to get to his or her classes, the gym, and the cafeteria.

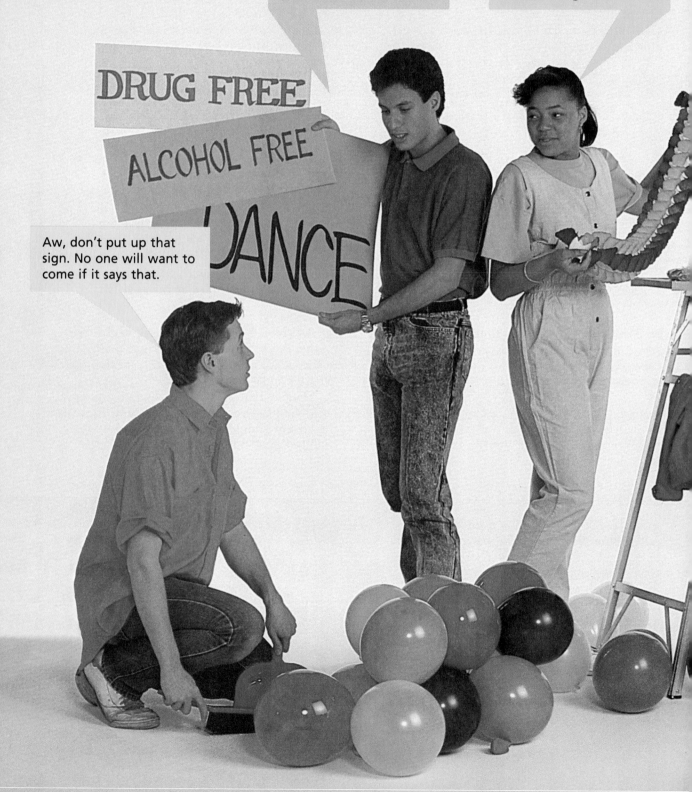

Hey, give your friends some credit. Lots of kids I know think for themselves and stick with their decisions. After all, no one wants to end up like Dom!

IN MEMORY OF

DOM LAFATTA

A MEMORIAL SCHOLARSHIP FUND DANCE

UNIT

6

Drugs, Alcohol, and Tobacco

19

As you read, think about

▶ what drugs are and how they affect your body.

▶ what drug abuse is and what its risks are.

▶ the many kinds of drugs and their effects.

▶ how you can help yourself and others stay away from drug abuse.

Drug Use and Abuse

All eyes are on you as you first begin your talk. This junior-high-school class is anxious to know about drugs from the viewpoint of a high-school student. They ask all kinds of questions, and you are glad you had those 30 hours of training as a peer leader. You have the facts about the dangers of drug abuse. You can assure the students that everybody does not use drugs at high school. You can help them role-play ways of saying no effectively. This Peer Leadership Program is one of the most rewarding things you have ever done.

There are lots of ways to have fun, express yourself, and be a leader. You can focus on the arts or sports or participate in a program that allows you to help others.

Unfortunately, some teenagers turn to drugs to take their minds off their troubles or to make themselves feel important. In this chapter, you will learn about how drugs affect the mind and body as well as ways to avoid using drugs.

Being well-informed about the dangers of drugs makes it easier to say no.

1. DRUGS AND THEIR USE

Is there such a thing as appropriate drug use? How do
people misuse drugs? When does drug use become abuse?
To begin to answer these questions, you need to understand
what a drug is and how it affects the body.

What Is a Drug?

A **drug** is any substance that alters the way cells and
tissues function. For instance, aspirin can reduce the pain of
a pulled muscle by changing the way in which some nerves
send pain impulses to the brain. Aspirin prevents the impulses from reaching your brain, so you feel less pain. Drugs,
like aspirin, that are used to treat medical conditions are
called **medicines.** We can classify medicines into two groups,
prescription drugs and over-the-counter drugs.

Prescription (prih **skrip** shun) **drugs** usually are strong
drugs that are safe to use only under the direction of a doctor.
Doctors use prescription drugs to treat diseases or to control
conditions like high blood pressure. There are other drugs
that do not require a doctor's prescription and may be purchased by anyone. These drugs are called **over-the-counter
(OTC) drugs.** Common over-the-counter drugs are aspirin,
cold remedies, and antacids.

Illegal drugs, or "street drugs," are sold for a purpose
that is against the law. Prescription drugs can be illegal if
they are sold without a prescription. Others have no medical
use and must be produced illegally before they can be sold.
Illegal drugs are often known by street names, or slang
expressions that describe what they look like or what they
do to the user. For example, "red devils" are red pills that
cause calm and drowsiness. They are among the drugs sometimes referred to as "downers."

**Figure 19-1. Numerous over-the-
counter drugs are available to
consumers.** ▶

How Does Your Body React to Drugs?

Drugs act on your body's functions in a particular way. What a drug does to your body is called the drug's **action.** What you feel is the drug's **effect,** or the physical and mental response to the action of the drug. The same drug may affect different people in different ways. A person's age, height, weight, body type, sex, heart rate, and breathing rate are factors that account for some of these differences. These same factors are used by a doctor to establish the **dosage (doh sij),** or the proper amount of a drug. In general, the larger your body, the higher the dosage of a prescribed drug. If you are built like a professional football player, your doctor may prescribe a higher-than-usual dosage. If you have the build of a jockey, a smaller-than-normal dosage may be sufficient. Even over-the-counter drugs have recommended dosages.

While a drug's effect may help you to feel better, drugs can produce **side effects.** Side effects are effects in addition to the desired effects. Usually these are undesirable effects such as nausea, headaches, dizziness, or drowsiness. Cold remedies, for example, often cause drowsiness. Checking the labels of drugs tells you what side effects they may cause.

DRUG ALLERGIES Occasionally, people develop **drug allergies.** Drug allergies are side effects that occur because your body tries to reject the drug. Some drug allergies occur quickly; others develop more slowly.

Common allergic reactions are rash, runny nose, stressed breathing, or rapid heartbeat. You should contact your doctor if these or other unusual symptoms appear after you have taken a drug. Severe drug allergies can cause serious problems and even death.

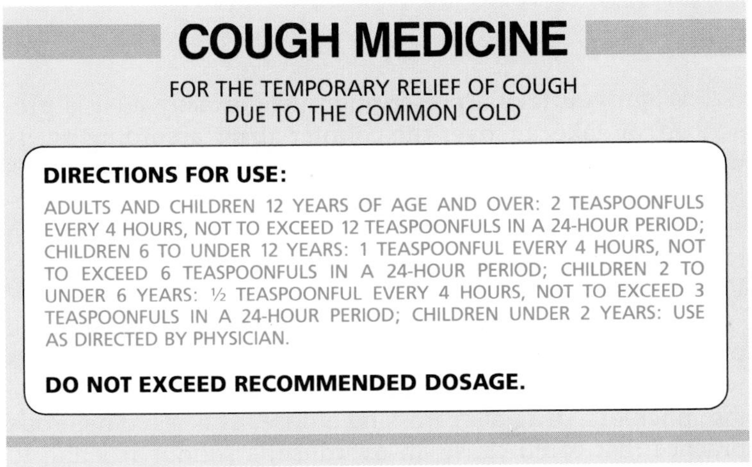

A drug may affect different people in different ways.

COUGH MEDICINE

FOR THE TEMPORARY RELIEF OF COUGH
DUE TO THE COMMON COLD

DIRECTIONS FOR USE:

ADULTS AND CHILDREN 12 YEARS OF AGE AND OVER: 2 TEASPOONFULS EVERY 4 HOURS, NOT TO EXCEED 12 TEASPOONFULS IN A 24-HOUR PERIOD; CHILDREN 6 TO UNDER 12 YEARS: 1 TEASPOONFUL EVERY 4 HOURS, NOT TO EXCEED 6 TEASPOONFULS IN A 24-HOUR PERIOD; CHILDREN 2 TO UNDER 6 YEARS: ½ TEASPOONFUL EVERY 4 HOURS, NOT TO EXCEED 3 TEASPOONFULS IN A 24-HOUR PERIOD; CHILDREN UNDER 2 YEARS: USE AS DIRECTED BY PHYSICIAN.

DO NOT EXCEED RECOMMENDED DOSAGE.

◀ **Figure 19-2. Age is one factor used to determine the dosage of a drug.**

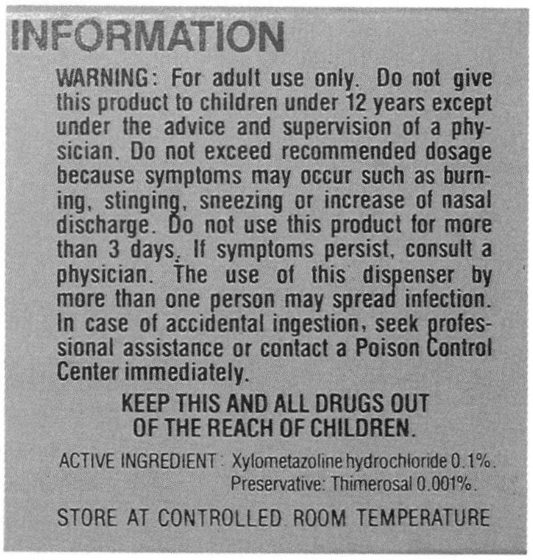

▲
Figure 19-3. Drug container labels warn of possible side effects and precautions you need to take.

Drugs can interact, or change each other's effects, when they are taken together. When drugs are combined, a number of interactions may occur. One type of interaction is called an **antagonistic** (an tag uh **nis** tik) **interaction.** In an antagonistic interaction, each drug's effect is cancelled out by the other, or the action of both is reduced so that neither one has the predicted result.

People taking drugs to lower their blood pressure, for example, are warned that caffeine will have an antagonistic interaction with their medication. If they drink large amounts of caffeine-containing beverages, such as coffee, tea, or some colas, the caffeine may cancel out the beneficial effect of the drugs because caffeine ordinarily causes a rise in blood pressure.

Another type of interaction occurs when certain drugs taken together combine their actions. When two drugs work together in a positive way an **additive interaction** occurs. The result is an effect about twice as great as either one of the drugs alone. Certain drugs may interact to produce effects that are many times greater than either drug would produce by itself. This increased interaction is called a **synergistic** (sin ur **jis** tic) **reaction.** A synergistic reaction can be life-threatening when it causes drastic changes in your body. For example, some drugs reduce the activity of the central nervous system and slow body functions. These drugs are often prescribed to treat emotional and psychological conditions such as anxiety, tension, and nervousness. If they are combined with alcohol, the effects of the drugs are more than doubled and can lead to coma or death.

Sometimes even eating certain foods while taking prescription drugs can cause dangerous results or interfere with the drug's intended medical effect. For example, the antibiotic drug **tetracycline** (tet ra **sy** kleen) cannot be taken at the same time as dairy products because the drug will not work properly.

What Are Drug Misuse and Drug Abuse?

When you take a prescription drug exactly as it is prescribed or take an over-the-counter drug according to its directions, you are engaging in **drug use.** This type of use is legal and expected. Unfortunately, many people use prescription or over-the-counter drugs incorrectly, often through ignorance. The improper use of drugs is called **drug misuse.** Drug misuse can be dangerous.

Sometimes people misuse drugs by taking more than the prescribed amount. They may believe mistakenly that this will speed their recovery from an illness. Other people take too much of a drug after missing a dose. This is a dangerous practice that could cause an **overdose,** a serious reaction to

⚓ Drug misuse occurs when people do not use drugs according to directions.

the drug that can sometimes result in death. Still another form of drug misuse is taking drugs prescribed for someone else. People sometimes make the mistake of assuming that a drug prescribed for a friend or family member is safe to take simply because a doctor has prescribed it. Another person's prescription drug, however, has been chosen for that particular person and condition, and it may be useless or even dangerous for you.

Other forms of drug misuse include taking drugs with the wrong foods or liquids or taking them at the wrong time of day. Health-care professionals, such as nurses or doctors, can explain the procedures to follow with every drug. In fact, usually the labels on prescription or OTC drugs say how much to take, how often to take it, and how long to continue taking it.

Another way people misuse certain drugs is to stop taking them too soon. Drugs for some infections must be taken for several days after you stop feeling ill. If you stop taking the drug too soon, some bacteria can survive, and the infection can return.

Drug misuse is not restricted to prescription drugs. Some people misuse over-the-counter drugs. Drugs that have been on the shelf for too long a time can become old and not work as well as they should. All have an **expiration** (ek spuh **ray** shun) **date** marked on the container. The expiration date is the date after which a medicine may not be effective. After the expiration date, the drugs may not be effective and should be thrown away. Reading the labels on the containers is important for the proper use of both over-the-counter drugs and prescription drugs.

When people intentionally misuse drugs for nonmedical purposes, they are engaging in **drug abuse.** Some drugs that can be prescribed by doctors as medicines are abused. Other abused drugs are illegal drugs, which have little, if any, value as medicines and are unlawful because of their dangerous, often unpredictable effects. Because drugs are chemicals that can produce powerful changes in your body, drug abuse is dangerous.

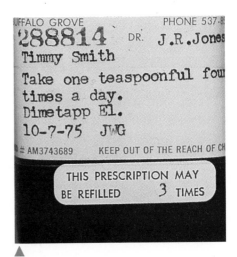

Figure 19-4. A prescription drug label specifies the amount to take and when to take it.

Using drugs for nonmedical purposes is called drug abuse.

Section Review

1. What are the similarities and differences between drugs and medicines?

2. Why are prescriptions required for some drugs?

3. What are drug use, misuse, and abuse?

4. What are some ways in which people misuse drugs?

What Do You Think?

5. How can you avoid dangerous drug interactions?

2. DRUG ABUSE

Why do people use drugs? Life is not easy for anyone. Some people, however, turn to drugs as a way of coping with life's problems. Other people attempt to change their mental or physical capabilities with drugs. Still others use drugs to try to feel good or get "high." Unfortunately, the desired effects are often followed by harmful and unpleasant side effects.

Patterns of Drug Abuse

People of all ages abuse drugs. Some are aware that they are abusing drugs. Others are not aware or deny their abuse. The age group with the highest percentage of drug abuse includes people between the ages of 18 and 25. Most of these people report that they were first introduced to illegal drugs in their high-school years.

DRUG ABUSE AMONG TEENAGERS   Mike is a 15-year-old high school student who has been smoking marijuana (mar uh **wah** nuh) almost every day for two years. Mike says that he can stop using it at any time. He says that he continues to use it because he enjoys its effects and enjoys smoking it with his friends.

Mike's reasons for smoking marijuana are like those of many teenagers. They start to abuse drugs because they want to be accepted. Most drug abusers report that their friends or peers introduced them to drugs.

○══➤

The people with the highest percentage of drug abuse are between the ages of 18 and 25.

Figure 19-5. When you are feeling depressed, drugs will not solve your problems.   ▶

Teenagers also can be influenced by advertisements for alcohol, tobacco, and over-the-counter drugs. Because the models in these ads appear happy, healthy, and popular, the underlying message is that these drugs can improve your life and solve your problems.

Curiosity is still another reason that some abuse drugs. Teenagers especially hear so much information and misinformation about drugs that they become curious about them. Many doubt that drug abuse is as dangerous as they have been told.

For some young people, trying drugs is a way of rebelling against parents or society in general. These abusers may want to call attention to themselves or appear different from others. They may also want to escape the pressures and problems of family and school.

DRUG ABUSE AMONG ADULTS Kathy is a 40-year-old woman who began taking diet pills with a doctor's prescription five years ago to control her weight. She changes doctors every few months so that she can ask for a new prescription and continue taking the drug. Kathy does not consider herself a drug abuser. She plans to stop taking diet pills as soon as she has more time to exercise.

Some adults like Kathy either do not realize that they are drug abusers or deny their abuse to themselves and to others. Other adults have abused either illegal or legal drugs since they were teenagers. Using drugs has become a way of life, and they do not consider drug use unusual.

DRUG ABUSE AMONG THE ELDERLY Jack is an 80-year-old man who lives alone. He has been taking sleeping pills almost every evening since his wife died two years ago. At first a doctor prescribed the drug for him. Now, Jack buys similar pills from a neighbor. He is afraid that the neighbor is a "drug pusher," but he has come to rely on having a drug to help him sleep.

Studies have indicated that people over the age of 65 use more prescription drugs than any other age group in this country. Unfortunately, elderly people often have problems with misuse. Often they have several medical problems and have more than one drug prescribed for them by a doctor. Often they see more than one doctor, which increases the risks of confusion and misuse. They may confuse or misread instructions and take pills at the wrong times, take too many pills, or skip medications entirely. Any of these actions can cause serious health consequences.

An older person may tend to use many over-the-counter drugs for minor health complaints. Although most over-the-counter drugs are safe when they are used as directed, some of them can interact with prescription drugs and cause dangerous results.

Peer pressure, curiosity, the urge to rebel against authority, and the desire to escape problems are reasons some teenagers turn to drugs.

Figure 19-6. Elderly people can have problems with drug misuse.

Drug Testing

Because drug use can affect a person's performance on the job, some employers feel that drug testing is necessary, especially when the safety and security of others is at stake.

Urinalysis, one common testing method, identifies drug residues in a person's urine. Traces of most drugs show up in the urine for up to two or three days after being taken. Though effective, urinalysis is limited. A person can foil the test by substituting someone else's urine for their own. Furthermore, urinalysis only detects recent drug use.

A new test solves these problems by using hair samples. Like urine, hair carries traces of the drugs a person takes. The advantage, however, is that each strand of hair records a person's drug use for as long as it remains in the scalp. Washing the hair does not affect the process. The test, called radio-immunoassay of hair (RIAH), requires about fifty strands of hair. Drug residues farthest from the hair root represent drugs taken longest ago.

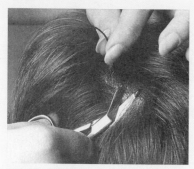

Hair can be used to detect drug use.

DRUG ABUSE AMONG ATHLETES Jim sprained his ankle before the try-outs for the basketball team. He wants to try out, but his ankle hurts. A friend has offered him some "pain pills" and has told him that professional athletes take painkillers all the time.

Jim's friend is wrong, but Jim's problem is not unusual. Although most professional and amateur athletes consult their doctors or trainers about aching muscles, sprains, or other complaints, a few athletes do use drugs unwisely. Some may use drugs to relieve pain. This can lead to more serious injuries that can end their careers. Others think that the drugs will help them to concentrate on the game. Still others abuse drugs to help build their muscles.

As many of these athletes have discovered, drug use can result in lifelong or life-threatening disorders. In fact, most organizers of athletic events forbid athletes to use drugs during competitions.

Risks of Drug Abuse

Your body makes both immediate and gradual changes to accommodate the action and effects of any chemical substance. When you take a drug, your body immediately changes its internal functioning. Over time, your body also changes its response to the drug.

TOLERANCE When drugs are repeatedly used or abused, the body may develop a **tolerance** (**tahl** ur uns) for the drug, or a resistance to the drug. Tolerance causes your body to need increasingly larger doses of drugs to achieve the effect that was originally produced.

Many drugs can produce tolerance. Many pain relievers, for example, may not relieve pain after the prescribed dosage has been taken for a while. It may take two or three pills, instead of only one, to get the same effect. Tolerance can cause some people to take too much of a drug—a problem that can lead to overdose and even death.

A related problem is **reverse tolerance.** Reverse tolerance is a state in which less and less of a drug is needed to experience the drug's effects. This can mean that even a small dose can lead to overdose and death.

DEPENDENCE Some drugs produce **dependence,** a state in which a person becomes incapable of controlling drug use. Dependence can be physical, psychological, or both psychological and physical. Either type of dependence changes the way the body functions and can seriously damage health.

When the body becomes adjusted to a drug and requires the drug to function normally, **physical dependence** occurs. Physical dependence takes time to develop and often occurs as tolerance builds. Physical dependence can sometimes be seen as **addiction** (uh **dik** shun). When a drug's use is specifically limited by law because it can cause dependence, the drug is classified as a **controlled substance.** Doctors and hospitals must keep careful records of controlled substances.

A physically dependent person who stops taking a drug will suffer from **withdrawal symptoms.** These symptoms are the body's way of reacting to not having the drug. The symptoms are unpleasant and can include nausea, vomiting, fever, headaches, dizziness, body aches, depression, and cramps.

Some withdrawal symptoms are life-threatening. Some people may experience **seizures,** attacks during which the person may lose consciousness and experience convulsions. Other people may suffer from **hallucinations** (huh loo suh **nay** shuns), imaginary sights and sounds. People who are hallucinating are out of touch with reality and can be a threat to themselves and others.

In fact, withdrawal from certain drugs, especially if the user has developed a high tolerance, can be dangerous. In these cases, doctors must develop a treatment plan to withdraw the drug slowly or to replace it so that the person's body is not shocked by the abrupt absence of the drug.

A strong desire or need to continue using a drug is called **psychological** (sy kuh **lahj** ih kul) **dependence.** When people become psychologically dependent on a drug, they associate the drug with specific feelings or moods. When the drug's effect wears off, so does the feeling. A psychological need for a drug is difficult to overcome because abusers want to experience the feeling or mood they associate with the drug. Drug abusers who are psychologically, but not physically, dependent often believe that they can stop using the drug if they want to. This is because they do not experience physical withdrawal symptoms. But, stopping drug abuse is not easy once a person has become psychologically dependent.

RISKS TO UNBORN CHILDREN AND NEWBORNS

A woman who uses or abuses any drug during pregnancy risks harming herself and her baby. Some drugs may cause a baby to be born with physical or mental disorders or even physically dependent on drugs. During pregnancy certain chemicals can pass from the mother's bloodstream into the baby's. At certain stages in a baby's development, exposure to drugs can damage the baby's development. Even if the mother has taken only a small amount of a drug, it can still be enough to affect the developing baby.

Doctors warn expectant mothers to be careful throughout a pregnancy but especially during the first several weeks of pregnancy. A woman who suspects or knows she is pregnant should check with her doctor before using any prescription or over-the-counter product.

Mothers who breast-feed their babies must still take precautions when using any form of drug. Many substances can

○━┳
Drug abuse can lead to physical and psychological dependence.

Figure 19-7. Women who are pregnant should avoid taking any drug.
▼

pass from the mother to her child through her milk. These women should always check with their doctors before using any medications.

LEGAL RISKS   Federal and state laws specify what drugs and drug-associated activities are illegal and the penalties for violating these laws. The penalties for individuals who manufacture or sell drugs illegally can include long prison terms and heavy fines. In some states, just possession of some drugs can result in imprisonment and a fine. Even when a jail term or fine is not imposed, the individual will be on record as a drug violator. Many drug abusers commit other crimes, such as shoplifting and robbery, to support their drug habits. The legal penalties for these and other drug-related crimes can include imprisonment.

Many companies and government agencies will not hire persons convicted of violating drug laws. Medical, dental, and law schools can deny admission to applicants who have been convicted of drug violations. The armed services and certain branches of the government will not employ individuals who have been involved with drugs.

The fact is that people place their careers and their health in jeopardy whenever they become involved with drugs.

Penalties for drug-associated crimes can include long prison terms and heavy fines.

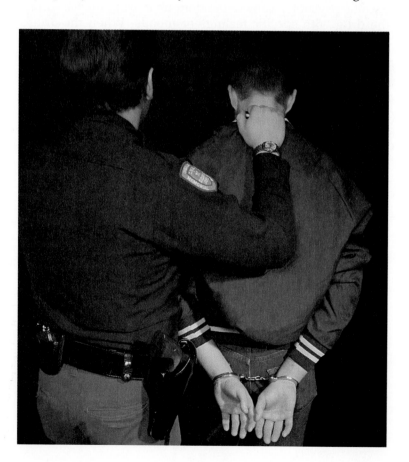

Figure 19-8. Drug abuse is a legal offense that carries with it severe penalties. ▶

Effects on Families

When a family member abuses drugs, all members of the family are affected. The relationships within the family become strained as the behavior and personality of the abuser changes. The abuser may behave unpredictably. He or she may have wild mood swings or become withdrawn and disinterested in family relationships and responsibilities. Other family members may experience anger, fear, resentment, or frustration, particularly when they are not aware that drugs are the cause of the abuser's abnormal behavior. If the drug abuse problem continues, the family can reach a crisis as the members struggle to cope with the stress that continues to build. Once the problem is recognized as a drug problem, steps can be taken. Fortunately, programs to help abusers and their families are available. In fact, therapy for drug abusers is most effective when it also involves the whole family. Understanding the underlying cause for the drug abuse and enlisting the support of the other family members can restore and reinforce the family's stability.

Drug abuse by one person in a family affects all members of a family.

Section Review

1. What are four reasons why people abuse drugs?
2. What are three negative effects of drug abuse?
3. What is tolerance?
4. Why should women who are pregnant or who suspect they are pregnant check with their doctors before taking any type of drug?

What Do You Think?

5. What would you suggest as a long-term solution for drug abuse problems in the United States?

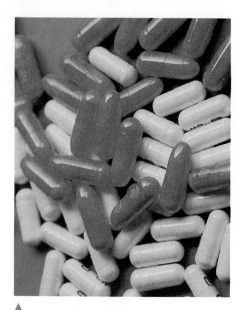

Figure 19-10. Barbiturates are prescription drugs that are sometimes sold illegally.

Depressants are the most misused and abused category of drugs.

3. DRUGS OF ABUSE

Drugs are divided into categories according to their chemical properties and according to their actions and effects. Drugs in the same category are often abused in the same way.

Depressants

Drugs used to slow down the body's functions are called **depressants** (dih **pres** unts). Depressants relieve tension, relax muscles, and slow processes like heart rate, respiration, and reflexes. Depressants are misused and abused more than any other category of drug.

There are many subcategories of depressants. One such category, the **sedative-hypnotics,** include drugs used to relax a person and to induce sleep. Barbiturates (bar **bich** ur its) are a type of sedative-hypnotic. They are usually prescribed for people with sleep disturbances. Barbiturates are also useful in treating **epilepsy** (**ep** uh lep see), a disorder of the nervous system that causes convulsions, and in preparing people for some types of surgery.

When they are abused, barbiturates can produce physical and psychological dependence. People who abuse barbiturates can develop tolerance quickly and soon need the drug before they can sleep. As tolerance increases, their bodies begin to slow down. They walk slowly and slur their speech. They react more slowly to the external environment. Some abusers complain that they cannot see clearly. Withdrawal symptoms can be severe and in some cases lead to death or symptoms of mental illness.

Another category of depressants are the **anti-anxiety drugs,** also known as **minor tranquilizers** (tran kwuh lyz urz). These drugs are prescribed to relieve tension, reduce anxiety, and cause drowsiness.

Another drug, **methaqualone** (meth uh **kway** lohn), is a tranquilizer similar to the barbiturates, but it is no longer used as a medicine. Its effects range from a sense of calm to extreme happiness to dizziness. Abusers become both physically and psychologically dependent. They may experience headaches, numbness, nosebleeds, diarrhea, and pain in their arms and legs. Once dependence develops, abusers often put up with these symptoms to avoid the pain of withdrawal symptoms. When taken with alcohol, methaqualone can cause death.

Antipsychotics (an tee sy **kaht** iks), or **major tranquilizers,** are depressants used to treat severe mental or emotional illnesses. Doctors prescribe antipsychotics only for severely ill patients because they are powerful drugs with many side effects. Both anti-anxiety drugs and antipsychotics can cause severe physical and psychological dependence.

Narcotics

A **narcotic** is any depressant drug made from or chemically similar to **opium** (**oh** pee um). Opium is a drug obtained from the opium poppy plant. Other natural narcotics, such as **morphine** (**mor** feen), **codeine** (**koh** deen), and **heroin** are also made from the opium poppy plant. Narcotics act in small doses to dull the senses, relieve pain, and induce sleep. Morphine and codeine, for example, are used in prescription medications for severe pain. Some prescription cough medicines contain codeine because it acts to suppress coughing. Both morphine and codeine build tolerance and lead to dependence. Although morphine is the stronger of the two, both drugs cause the user to lose appetite and feel drowsy.

Opium is often abused when it is mixed with tobacco and smoked. Like other narcotics, opium decreases appetite and causes sleep. Users often describe dreams filled with color and a sense of peaceful relaxation. Abuse, however, leads quickly to physical and psychological dependence. Withdrawal symptoms can be severe.

One of the most frequently abused narcotics in the United States is heroin. It creates a sense of well-being by dulling the senses. Users no longer feel pain or fear. They appear dazed. Heroin abusers develop dependence quickly, sometimes after only a week or two of regular use. Withdrawal symptoms are severe.

If heroin is mixed with other narcotics or depressants, an overdose may occur. Overdose can cause loss of consciousness, coma, and death. Illegal drugs like heroin are especially dangerous because the purity of the drug is different each time. Dealers of illegal drugs often "cut" the drugs they sell by adding other substances, which can also be dangerous. Some common additives are powdered laxatives, cleansing powder, and rat poison.

Abusers cannot predict what these added substances are or what effects they will have on their bodies. Heroin abusers who inject the drug also can transmit or become infected with diseases if they share or use dirty needles.

A narcotic that acts somewhat like heroin in the body is **methadone** (**meth** uh dohn). Methadone is sometimes used as a substitute for heroin in treatment programs for heroin abusers. Its use keeps the abuser from experiencing severe withdrawal symptoms. Like heroin, methadone is an addictive drug, but unlike heroin, it does not produce a "high" feeling that leads to continued use of the drug.

Two other narcotics that do not occur naturally but are created by chemists are **meperidine** (muh **pehr** ih deen) and **propoxyphene** (proh **pahks** uh feen). At their usual dosages, these synthetic drugs are weaker than morphine. When an abuser takes a large dose, however, the effects can be similar.

Figure 19-11. The poppy plant is the source of opium and other drugs.

Opium, morphine, codeine, and heroin are all types of narcotics.

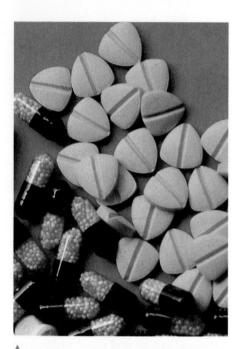

Figure 19-12. Amphetamines are stimulants that can produce tolerance and serious side effects.

Stimulants

Drugs that speed up the body's activity are called **stimulants.** They increase heart rate and blood pressure and make the abuser feel more excited and alert. With most stimulant drugs, the abuser develops tolerance as well as physical and psychological dependence.

Stimulants are sometimes prescribed as medicines to help people lose weight. They are also used to treat certain childhood behavioral disorders. Stimulant drug abuse, however, poses serious health risks. Because the heart rate, respiration rate, and blood pressure are raised, the abuser can suffer heart damage. Continued abuse results in an inability to sleep, hallucinations, weight loss, nervousness, confusion, and psychological problems.

Caffeine is a natural stimulant found in coffee, tea, some soft drinks, and chocolate. Some over-the-counter drugs sold to help people stay awake also contain caffeine. Caffeine can make you feel jittery, nervous, tense, and unable to sleep.

One group of synthetic stimulants are the **amphetamines** (am **fet** uh meens). Amphetamines are prescription drugs. Like many other drugs, they are sometimes sold illegally. These drugs cause a sense of pleasure, but the effect wears off quickly, often leaving the abuser depressed. The depression then leads the abuser to take more of the drug.

When they are "high," abusers appear energetic. They might also be aggressive or irritable. Amphetamine abuse leads to psychological dependence. Unpleasant side effects include blurred vision, headache, and dizziness.

Another drug that produces strong stimulant effects is **cocaine.** Although it is legally classified as a narcotic, cocaine's effects are so different from other narcotics that it is medically classified as a stimulant. When used illegally, cocaine is often inhaled through the nose or injected into a vein.

Cocaine is strongly addictive. Tolerance develops rapidly, causing abusers to need larger and larger amounts. When the drug wears off, the abuser often experiences depression, sometimes called a "crash." The depression can be severe. Cocaine abusers also may suffer from damage to the membranes lining the nose. Cocaine abuse can cause death because it interferes with the brain's control over heart function and respiration. Occasionally a person dies from cocaine after just one use of the drug.

A process called "free-basing" changes cocaine into a concentrated, smokable form known as **crack.** Crack, also called "rock," is the most potent form of cocaine. Because of its strength, the short but powerful effects produced by crack occur within seconds after it is smoked. These effects lead many people to believe, mistakenly, that crack is purer than other forms of cocaine. The effects, however, are a result of the free-basing process, not the drug purity.

Crack, the most potent form of cocaine, is strongly addictive.

Studies have shown that at least 25 million Americans have tried cocaine at least once, and over 6 million use it once a month or more. The National Cocaine Hotline (1-800-COCAINE), which provides information about cocaine abuse and treatment, has received over 2 million calls since 1983.

Psychedelics

Drugs that distort the senses are called **psychedelics** (sy kih **del** iks) or **hallucinogens** (huh **loo** suh nuh juns). Psychedelic drugs change a person's mental state. They often cause feelings of pleasure and sometimes make abusers feel they have special powers. Abusers of psychedelic drugs cannot tell what is real and what is an illusion. In extreme cases, people have even leaped from buildings in the belief that they could fly.

Psychedelic drugs can produce frightening and unpredictable mood swings. Abuse of psychedelic drugs can change a person's personality. Abusers may experience memory loss, be unable to perform normal activities, or lose track of time and their surroundings.

All psychedelic drugs are illegal. The strongest psychedelic drug is **lysergic** (ly **sur** jik) **acid diethylamide** (dy eth ul **am** id), or **LSD.** LSD's effects are unpredictable—it can either stimulate or depress the body. A common reaction is that the abuser sees colorful pictures. Some abusers feel that they have great creative powers and brilliant ideas, but LSD can also cause unpleasant side effects, such as shaking, nausea, and chills.

LSD use can lead to frightening episodes known as "bad trips." Some abusers become so frightened that they put themselves in real danger. LSD has another unpredictable effect called a **flashback.** A flashback is an unexpected return to a bad trip that may occur long after the drug was taken. Flashbacks can happen at any time without warning, causing accidents and even prompting suicides.

Another psychedelic drug, **phenocyclidine** (fen noh **sy** kluh deen), **PCP,** or "angel dust," was originally developed for use as an anesthetic in animals. PCP is usually sprinkled on cigarettes or mixed with marijuana for smoking. It also may be injected, sniffed, or eaten. Like LSD, PCP produces unpredictable effects. It can act as a stimulant, depressant, or psychedelic. Abusers of PCP have committed suicide and engaged in violent acts. Some abusers also have shown signs of severe mental illness.

Two psychedelic drugs, **peyote** (pay **oh** tee) and **mescaline** (**mes** kuh leen), are made from the peyote cactus, which grows in the southwestern United States and Mexico. Like users of LSD, users of peyote see imaginary shapes and colors. Users often experience unpleasant effects as well, including vomiting and stomach cramps.

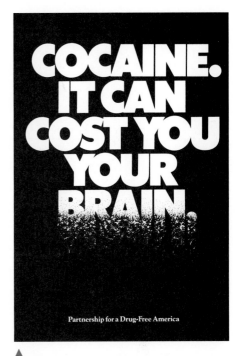

Figure 19-13. Cocaine abuse can be deadly.

Under the influence of psychedelic drugs, a person cannot tell what is real and what is an illusion.

Another psychedelic drug, **psilocybin** (sil uh **sy** bin), is made from a Mexican mushroom. Psilocybin is much like LSD, but its effects are milder. Continued use of psilocybin can cause psychological dependence.

Marijuana and Other Related Drugs

Marijuana is an illegal drug made from the flowers and leaves of the Indian hemp plant. It is a psychedelic drug, although its effects are not as severe as some of the effects of other psychedelic drugs. Today, marijuana is one of the most frequently abused drugs.

Marijuana is also known as "pot," "grass," or "weed." Generally, marijuana leaves and stems are smoked in a pipe or in a handmade cigarette called a "joint" or "reefer." Smoking marijuana can depress the body's functioning. It usually makes the user feel relaxed, lightheaded, and calm. It can also cause confusion, sudden mood changes, memory problems, and loss of coordination. Some abusers become withdrawn. Most feel an urge to eat.

Because marijuana can affect movement and speech, users may not act normally. They may panic at sudden noises or be unable to remember things. Driving a car or operating machinery is especially dangerous because vision and reflexes are impaired.

🔑

Marijuana is a psychedelic drug that can act as a depressant.

Long-term use of marijuana carries some of the same risks as smoking tobacco, including lung damage, chronic coughing, and an increased risk of cancer. In fact, more cancer-causing agents are found in marijuana smoke than in tobacco smoke.

Marijuana causes psychological dependence. Users who claim that they can easily quit often find this hard to do. Marijuana also causes reverse tolerance, so that abusers find themselves experiencing more severe effects when they use less of the drug.

Marijuana has been shown to decrease sperm production in men. Long-term use contributes to chronic difficulty in carrying out daily activities. People who use marijuana tend to forget details such as where they left important objects or when they made appointments. Over time, they become less interested in work, family, and friends.

The Indian hemp plant is also the source of the illegal drug **hashish** (**hash** eesh). Hashish, or "hash," is often sold as tiny brown cubes that are smoked. It is sometimes boiled to make an even stronger drug called **hashish oil.** This oil is mixed with tobacco and smoked. Both forms of hashish produce the same short-term and long-term effects as marijuana, but they are more likely than marijuana to cause an altered mental state.

The effects of both marijuana and hashish are due to the chemical **THC.** Scientists are testing THC for medical use in cancer patients because it appears to relieve nausea during chemotherapy. Marijuana may have another medical use in the treatment of some eye diseases.

Some researchers have suggested that THC may cause birth defects. Long-term abuse of drugs containing THC produces psychological dependence and can lead to a physical dependence. Withdrawal symptoms include sleep difficulties, anxiety, and vomiting.

Inhalants

Drugs that are inhaled for a desired effect are called **inhalants** (in **hay** lunts). Inhalants quickly affect the body because they are able to enter the bloodstream directly through the lungs.

Some people unknowingly misuse or abuse inhalants. Have you ever used a cleaning product or a paint to find that the fumes made you cough or made your eyes water? Chances are the directions instructed you to to use the product in an open, well-ventilated area.

Commercial solvents like paint thinner, cleaning fluid, nail polish remover, and spray paints all give off dangerous fumes. One way to prevent inhalant misuse is to educate people who buy and use these products. Consumers should work with chemicals in large, airy spaces, sometimes with

▲

Figure 19-15. Marijuana, hashish, and hashish oil are illegal drugs that come from the Indian hemp plant.

the windows open. Chemical containers should be closed to avoid accidental inhalation.

Some people abuse inhalants to achieve brief feelings of excitement or giddiness. **Glue sniffing,** in which glue fumes are inhaled, is a form of inhalant abuse. After the effects of the fumes are over, the abuser often experiences headaches, dizziness, nausea, blurred vision, and loss of coordination. Some inhalants cause permanent damage to the liver, lungs, brain, and kidneys. Continued abuse may lead to unconsciousness and even death.

Another inhalant is **nitrous oxide,** better known as "laughing gas." Nitrous oxide is used by dentists as a painkiller because it causes relaxation. Long-term abuse can cause psychological dependence and damage to the kidneys, liver, and bone marrow.

Two other inhaled drugs are **amyl nitrite** (**am** ul **ny** tryt) and **butyl nitrite** (**byoot** l **ny** tryt). Both of these drugs cause relaxation, light-headedness, and a burst of energy. Amyl nitrite is used as a medicine for some heart patients. Both drugs can cause psychological dependence and problems of the heart and circulatory system. Although cocaine is commonly inhaled, it is usually not classified as an inhalant.

Steroids

The category of drugs that are abused mostly by athletes are **anabolic steroids** (an uh **bahl** ik **ster** oyds). Steroids are chemically related to the male hormone **testosterone** (tes **tahs** tuh rohn). They are used to boost muscle size and to raise

Figure 19-16. Be sure there is adequate ventilation when using certain chemicals that may give off harmful fumes.

Figure 19-17. Athletes who turn to steroids risk permanent damage to their bodies.

tolerance to pain. Some weightlifters, body builders, and football players use steroids for these reasons, but the consequences of taking such drugs can be harmful.

Steroids can damage your liver and heart and raise your blood pressure dangerously high. Steroid abuse can alter appearance by stimulating overgrowth of the skull and facial bones and enlarging hands and feet. Steroids are especially dangerous for teenaged athletes whose bodies are still developing. Many athletic competitions disqualify athletes who use steroids.

Designer Drugs and Look-Alike Drugs

The most commonly abused drugs are controlled by law. Less common, however, are so-called designer drugs. **Designer drugs** are drugs that are chemically similar to some illegal drugs. Designer drugs are dangerous. They can cause dependence and severe side effects. Eventually, making drugs that act like controlled substances may become illegal.

Drugs that are sold on the street and made to look like commonly abused drugs are called **look-alike drugs.** These drugs may contain any kind of substance. A drug abuser expecting to buy an amphetamine may be buying instead a cold remedy. Many look-alike drugs contain caffeine. Others contain more dangerous substances.

Look-alike drugs contain unknown substances.

People who take look-alike drugs take additional risks if they mix the look-alikes with other drugs or with alcohol. Because they do not know what the look-alike drug contains, they can easily create serious drug interactions. If the effects are life-threatening, medical personnel may not be able to treat the abuser successfully without knowing what drug has been taken.

Section Review

1. Name one category of drugs and explain their general effects.

2. What are three medicines that are also abused as illegal drugs? Why is each of these drugs abused?

3. Explain why using psychedelic drugs can be dangerous to both the users and anyone around them.

4. What steps can you take to avoid accidentally inhaling fumes from household chemicals?

What Do You Think?

5. Why do you think 11- to 13-year olds are more likely to turn to marijuana than to cocaine, for example, for their first illegal drug experience?

4. CHOOSING TO BE DRUG FREE

You may already know about the pressures to experiment with drugs. How can you help yourself and others stay away from substance abuse? What can you do to help someone who is abusing drugs?

Recognizing Drug Abuse

How do you know that a friend is abusing drugs? Do your friend's moods change abruptly? Sudden changes in mood are one clue to drug abuse. Has your friend begun to do poorly in school? Drug abusers often neglect their school work as they focus their attention and energy on finding and taking drugs. Has your friend's appearance changed? Some drug abusers neglect their appearance and personal hygiene.

Figure 19-18 offers some typical signs of drug abuse. Some drugs cause specific effects and therefore provide clues about their abuse.

Help for Drug Abusers

Before drug abusers can be helped, they need to recognize their problem. Unfortunately, this may be difficult for them. Many abusers deny their behavior; others deny the problems that led them to drug abuse.

Once drug abusers have recognized their problems, there are many options available to them. Many organizations counsel people about drug problems. Community hospitals usually have outpatient clinics or programs that provide low-cost or volunteer counseling for teenagers and adults. Local schools and governments also schedule parent meetings, peer group counseling, and drug-free programs. National and local telephone hotlines can tell you where to call for drug information and treatment referral in your area. For these numbers, call 1-800-555-1212, or check the telephone book under Drug Abuse and Addiction.

There are at least three types of programs for drug abuse. One treatment program is called a detoxification program. A **detoxification** (dee tahk suh fih **kay** shun) **program** involves a gradual but complete withdrawal from the abused drug. People who enter detoxification programs usually receive medical treatment and supervision in a hospital. Drug abusers may stop taking the drug all at once, or doctors may reduce the drug dosage slowly to avoid painful withdrawal symptoms. Detoxification programs always include counseling to help them deal with drug abuse and to cope constructively with the problems that led to it.

Signs of Drug Abuse

- Major changes in behavior
- Sudden changes in mood
- New friends who are suspected of abusing drugs
- Poor school performance
- Changes in appearance
- Irresponsible decision-making
- Aggressiveness
- Lying, cheating
- Forgetfulness, withdrawn attitude
- Loss of memory
- Poor coordination
- Slurred speech
- Attention-getting behavior
- Denial of any problems

▲

Figure 19-18. Learning to recognize the signs of drug abuse can make a difference.

Recognizing that a problem exists is a drug abuser's first step to becoming drug-free.

Another type of treatment is the **therapeutic** (ther uh **pyoo** tik) **community.** Therapeutic communities are residential treatment centers where drug abusers can live and learn to adjust to drug-free lives. Often drug abusers are required to undergo detoxification before becoming a part of the community. Residents are closely supervised to prevent any drug use. These communities provide medical advice and counseling to help abusers develop a sense of personal and social worth. The staff of therapeutic communities usually consists of health-care professionals and former drug abusers.

A third type of treatment, called **methadone maintenance,** can be used to help heroin abusers. Because methadone produces effects similar to heroin, this treatment involves substituting methadone for heroin. Small, regular doses of methadone prevent withdrawal symptoms and block the effects of any heroin taken by the abuser. This treatment is intended to eliminate the desire for the drug.

Since methadone can cause physical dependence, treatment must be monitored carefully by a trained professional. Long-term use of methadone may cause such side effects as liver damage. Methadone is not a cure for heroin addiction, but it can be a first step.

Therapeutic communities offer medical support and counseling to drug abusers.

Choosing a Healthy Life Style

You make decisions every day. You decide what to eat, whom to share a joke with, which clothes to wear, and how much exercise to do. You also may be making decisions about drugs. Making the right decision can be the most important one in your life.

Deciding not to take drugs can be a difficult decision when you are faced with the pressure to take them. There are ways to avoid drugs in your life. One way is to say no when you are offered drugs. At the end of this chapter, there are guidelines that will help you to say no to drugs. Another way to avoid drugs is to manage the stress in your life and to get help when you need it.

Sometimes you may feel that your problems are overwhelming. Drugs often appeal to people because they seem to be an easy way to escape the problems and stresses that are part of everyone's life. To avoid drugs you need to realize that no drug will solve a problem. Drugs make problems worse and create new problems. The only way to solve a problem, or at least cope with it, is to develop and use your problem-solving and stress management skills to the best of your ability. This is not easy for anyone, but it becomes easier with practice and the realization that you must control your life. Overcoming the pressures that can lead to drug use does not have to be and should not be a solitary effort on your part. You can talk to your parents, school counselors, teachers, trusted friends, or close relatives for help. Seeking advice and weighing possible choices when faced with a problem is

Problem-solving and stress-management skills are the only positive ways to cope with troubles.

Health careers

Counseling drug abusers requires special interpersonal skills.

To overcome a drug abuse problem, a person may need help from someone outside his or her circle of family and friends. **Drug counselors** are trained to help people overcome the difficult problem of drug abuse.

Drug counselors work in one-on-one situations and with groups. They can work for special clinics and hospitals with drug treatment programs or for companies with employee drug programs. Some may work for telephone hotlines while others may run private offices. Drug counselors often work with the abuser's family as well as the abuser.

Compassion and an ability to gain someone's trust are important for this career. These counselors must also be good listeners.

Since no certification or license is required to become a drug counselor, drug counselors have a wide range of backgrounds and experience. One- and two-year master's degrees are offered at various colleges, although a high-school diploma alone is enough to enter the field.

a healthy approach to solving problems. If you are depressed, angry, hurt, or sad, you can choose from many healthful activities that will help you feel better. Talking with a friend, starting a hobby, going to a movie, listening to music, reading a book, playing sports, or writing a letter are all possibilities. Doing something constructive will lift your mood and make you feel good about yourself.

Abusing drugs cannot relieve the pressures in your life. It can only postpone decision-making and create more problems. Imagine how you would feel if you had to tell lies, hide your physical condition, worry about police, and deal with drug side effects. People who become dependent on drugs spend almost all of their time thinking about drugs, taking drugs, getting the money for drugs, and looking for drugs. Drugs end up controlling their lives.

O—📏

Seeking help and choosing healthful alternatives to drugs can help you cope with problems.

Section Review

1. What are four clues that might warn you someone is abusing drugs?
2. What are two ways in which a drug abuser can be helped to quit?
3. Why is methadone used as a treatment for heroin addiction? Are there drawbacks to its use?

What Do You Think?
4. Suppose you were at a party where drugs were being used. What would you do?

Saying No

Two of the teenagers below are trying to coax their friend into smoking marijuana with them. The friend, however, does not believe in using drugs. Even so, she worries about what her friends will think if she refuses.

Perhaps you have felt this way about saying no to your friends. Maybe you worried that if you said no, your friends would be disappointed or think you were "uncool." You might even have decided to go along with your friends just to avoid the discomfort of saying no.

Saying no to friends is never easy. Nevertheless, being true to yourself and honest with friends are two values that help you develop a sense of your own identity.

To refuse an offer convincingly, you must do more than say no. The following guidelines can help you learn to say no in a way that tells others you mean it.

1. Give a Reason for Your Refusal

Don't say no without presenting your personal reason(s) for not going along with the suggestion. Be honest—do not supply phony reasons. Honest answers are more easily accepted by other people. Some answers might be:

"No thanks, . . . I don't want to start a bad habit."

. . . I don't need it to have a good time."

. . . I want to keep a clear head."

. . . My parents would be upset if they knew."

. . . I could get suspended from the team."

. . . I don't do drugs."

2. Demonstrate Your Concern for Others

Express your concern for those trying to persuade you. You might say things like:

"I couldn't stand it if you hurt yourself doing that."

"Your parents would ground you for months if they ever found out."

"Some people have died from doing drugs."

"I'm worried about the amount you drink."

"You're only hurting yourself by doing drugs."

"Once you hurt yourself, it's too late."

3. Provide Alternatives

Try to persuade your friends to do something safer or more comfortable. Here are some suggestions:

"Let's leave this party and go back to my house."

"This is boring. Let's rent a movie and watch it at my place."

"Doesn't anybody feel like going to the gym instead of doing this?"

4. Use Eye Contact to Reinforce What You Say

Your body language can either strenghten or weaken your message. To make it clear that you mean no when you say it, you should look your friends in the eyes when presenting your feelings. Try to avoid staring at the ground or glancing away. Lack of eye contact indicates anxiety and nervousness. Do not give power to your persuader by looking away.

5. Take a Definite Action

If your friends persist in trying to persuade you after you have made your feelings clear to them, it is wise not to continue rehashing the point. Instead, you should try to take a definite action that removes you from the situation and makes it clear that you cannot be persuaded to change your mind.

Here are some examples of specific actions that you can take to remove yourself from potentially harmful situations: Call for help rather than drive home with a drunk driver. Get up and leave a party. Widen your circle of friends. Call other friends and do something else.

Saying no and choosing what you want to do can make you feel good about yourself.

APPLY THE SKILL

1. Imagine that you are studying for a test with one of your friends when he or she asks you to sit close by during the test and share your answers. Describe how this request would make you feel and some possible ways in which you might respond to the request. If you were to say no, what honest reason could you give and how would you express it? What do you think would be some of the possible consequences of your saying no? What would be some of the possible consequences of saying yes?

2. Describe two situations from your past in which you said no to others who were trying to convince you to do something you did not want to do. Explain how you felt in each situation. List the things that allowed you to say no in each of these cases. In which situation was it more difficult to say no? Why? Did you use any of the steps presented in this skill when you said no? If so, describe the steps and how effective they were.

3. Choose a situation from your own life in which you did not say no but wished you had. What were the consequences of not saying no? What did you learn from this experience? Using the steps presented here, describe a plan that you could have used in that particular case. Do you expect to be in a situation where you will be pressured to say yes but will want to say no? How will you prepare yourself to say no?

19 | Chapter Review

Chapter Summary

- Drugs alter normal body functioning.
- Prescription drugs are ordered by a doctor. Over-the-counter drugs are available in drugstores. Illegal drugs may or may not have a legal, medical use.
- Drug actions and effects may vary from person to person. Certain drugs used together can produce dangerous effects.
- Improper use of drugs for medical purposes is drug misuse. Intentional drug use for nonmedical purposes is drug abuse.
- People may misuse or abuse drugs to avoid personal problems, to change their mood, to relieve pain, or to join their peers.
- Continued drug abuse can produce tolerance and physical or psychological dependence.
- For pregnant women, drug abuse can cause damage to their unborn children. Pregnant women and breast-feeding mothers should not take drugs without a doctor's advice.
- Drug abuse is against the law and can result in heavy fines and prison terms. Drug abusers can be barred from medical, dental, and law school as well as the armed services and some branches of the government.
- Drug abuse can cause problems for the abuser's family.
- Marijuana use can lead to loss of interest in daily activities.
- Inhalants are drugs that are breathed in through the nose.
- Some athletes abuse anabolic steroids in attempts to build their bodies.
- Drugs obtained illegally may contain additional poisonous ingredients.
- Designer drugs and look-alike drugs are especially dangerous because, if their effects are life-threatening, medical personnel cannot identify their chemical make-up.
- Drug abusers can turn to a variety of local programs for help.
- You can cope with your personal problems in positive ways that will make it easier for you to say no when offered drugs.

Vocabulary Review

Listed below are some of the important terms from this chapter. Choose the term that best matches the phrase in the exercise that follows.

abuse
cocaine
codeine
depressant
detoxification program
drug

drug interaction
effect
inhalant
misuse
medicine

narcotic
over-the-counter drug
physical dependence
prescription
psychedelic

psychological dependence
stimulant
tolerance
withdrawal symptoms

1. any chemical that alters the structure or function of body systems

2. category of drugs that speed the body's functions

3. using a drug in a way that harms the body

4. doctor's written order for a drug

5. category of drugs that slow down the body's function

6. medical treatment for withdrawal from drug dependence

7. category of drugs that distort the senses

8. possible effects of mixing chemical substances

9. uncomfortable feelings abusers suffer when they stop taking certain drugs

10. dependence formed when a person believes the drug is needed to feel good

What Have You Learned?

1. List three examples of drug misuse.
2. Can the same drug make you feel different each time you use it? Explain your answer.
3. Name and briefly describe three types of drug interactions.
4. In what ways have advertising and the media influenced drug abuse in America?
5. What effect does tolerance have on drug abuse patterns?
6. What causes withdrawal symptoms to occur in the drug abuser?

7. How can anabolic steroids be harmful to an individual's health?
8. Describe the effects of anti-anxiety drugs.
9. What effects can caffeine produce in the body? How can you avoid misusing this drug?
10. What role does methadone play in treating heroin dependence?
11. How might you tell a friend that you suspect that he or she is abusing drugs?
12. List several ways a high-school student can respond to pressure to take illegal drugs.

What Do You Think?

1. Which type of dependence do you think is harder to break—physical or psychological dependence? Give your reasons.
2. In what ways are drug abuse and criminal acts linked together?
3. Some people do not approve of methadone treatment programs because they say it is substituting one drug dependence for another. Do you agree? Explain your answer.
4. Studies show that students who regularly use illegal drugs tend to get lower grades in school, do not participate in organized sports activities, and are more likely to lie or steal. Why do you think this is true?

What Would You Do?

1. What precautions would you take to lessen your exposure if you were working with a chemical solvent like paint thinner?
2. Your younger sister has been invited to a party. She confides in you that she has heard there will be a lot of drugs there and she is curious. What advice can you give her?
3. How could you help a friend who confides in you about her drug problem? Give at least two suggestions.

4. If you were a newspaper editor, would you print a story about a movie star who overdoses on illegal drugs? Explain your answer.
5. Imagine you are a parent. What measures could you take to discourage your child from experimenting with drugs?
6. If you were a doctor, what would you need to know before you prescribe medicine for a patient? What would you tell this patient about the medicine you prescribe?

For Further Study

1. Invite a local law enforcement official to your school to find out about illegal drug activity in your area. How do these officers conduct their investigations? What special problems and dangers do they face in the course of these investigations?
2. Find out what rehabilitation and counseling services are available in your community for people who are abusing drugs. Call five of these facilities to find out what services they provide. Make a poster listing the facilities, their telephone numbers, and the services offered.

20

As you read, think about

▶ what alcohol is and how it affects the body.

▶ why people choose to drink or not to drink, and what the risks of alcohol abuse are.

▶ what it means to be responsible about alcohol.

Alcohol

A ll that scrubbing and polishing was worth it. There are still two hours to go, and you've almost reached the goal. You and your friends are washing cars to raise money for SADD, Students Against Driving Drunk. You're shining bumpers and buffing hoods to promote your stand against a dangerous combination—alcohol and driving. You know that alcohol-related accidents are the greatest health hazard facing teens today.

What effect does alcohol have on the mind and body? What are the long-term effects of heavy drinking? Why do people use alcohol? Why do they abuse it? In this chapter, you'll find answers to these questions. You'll also learn about the disease of alcoholism and how it affects not only the alcoholic but also his or her family and friends. Finally, you'll look at groups, such as SADD, Alcoholics Anonymous, Al-Anon, and Alateen, that help people struggling with the problems of alcohol dependency, and you'll learn about ways to combat alcohol abuse.

Alcohol abuse is a threat to everyone. Groups of all ages can work in the fight against it.

1. ALCOHOL AS A DRUG

Did you know that alcohol is a drug? In the body, it acts as a powerful depressant. Like other depressants you learned about in Chapter 19, the alcohol in beer, wine, and liquor slows the body's reactions and functions. It causes confusion, decreased alertness, poor coordination, blurred vision, drowsiness, and even death when it is taken quickly and in large amounts.

How Alcohol Is Made

The alcohol used in alcoholic beverages is ethyl alcohol, or **ethanol** (**eth** uh nawl). Ethanol is a byproduct that is produced when yeast use some form of sugar to grow. The process by which yeast produce ethanol from sugar is called **fermentation** (fur men **tay** shun). Just about any kind of sugar- or starch-containing food can act as a source of sugar for yeast. The sugar for beer-making, for example, comes from malted barley. The sugar for wine-making comes from grapes, berries, or other fruits.

Different kinds of alcoholic beverages contain different amounts of alcohol. When fermentation is the only process used, the alcohol in the beverage is not more than 14 percent because the yeast stop growing at this point. Beer and wine are two examples of alcoholic drinks that use only fermentation. Most beers have an alcohol content between 4 and 6 percent. The alcohol content of most wines is about 12 percent. Other alcoholic beverages have much higher levels of alcohol. To produce levels above 14 percent, an additional process, called **distillation** (dis tuh **lay** shun), is used. In the distillation process, the fermented liquid is heated, causing the alcohol to boil off, or vaporize, leaving most of the water behind. The alcohol-containing vapor is collected and cooled back to a liquid called **liquor** (**lik** ur). The process of distillation is shown in Figure 20-1.

Liquor can be made by distilling fermented grains, fruits, potatoes, sugar cane, or molasses. Whiskey, for example, is a liquor made from fermented grains, such as corn, rye, or barley. Rum is a liquor distilled from fermented sugar-cane juice or molasses. Liquor usually contains 40 to 50 percent alcohol. To indicate the amount of alcohol in a liquor, manufacturers list its proof on the label. **Proof** is a measure of the percent of a given volume of a beverage that is made up of alcohol. The proof is equal to twice the percentage of alcohol. Thus, 100-proof whiskey contains 50 percent alcohol.

After distillation, the liquor is aged in wooden barrels, and different flavors are added. It is the aging process and the addition of different flavors that give each type and brand of liquor its particular flavor.

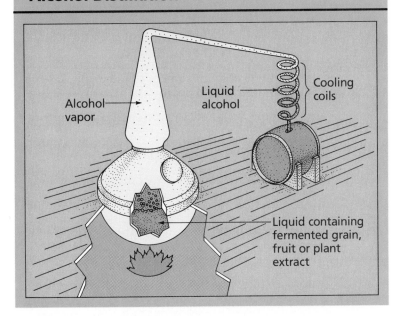

Alcohol Distillation

Alcohol vapor

Liquid alcohol

Cooling coils

Liquid containing fermented grain, fruit or plant extract

Absorption of Alcohol

Unlike food, alcohol does not need to be digested. Some alcohol, in fact, is absorbed directly through the stomach wall into the bloodstream. If the stomach is empty, the alcohol is absorbed quickly, and the drinker feels its effects right away. If the stomach contains food, the alcohol is absorbed more slowly. As the alcohol leaves the stomach and enters the small intestine, more of it is absorbed. Although the drinker may feel the effects of the alcohol more gradually this way, the effects still occur.

After alcohol is absorbed, it travels through the blood to all parts of the body. The amount of alcohol in a person's body is expressed by the **blood alcohol concentration (BAC).** The BAC is the amount of ethanol, in milligrams, present in a given volume of blood in milliliters. The BAC is expressed as a percentage. For example, a BAC of 0.1 percent means that 0.001, or 1/1000 of the fluid in the blood, is alcohol. A BAC of 0.1 percent reduces muscle coordination, perception, and judgment. In most states, a BAC of 0.1 percent is considered legally drunk. At this BAC, the ability to drive is greatly reduced.

A variety of factors can affect the BAC of a person. These factors include the person's body weight, the amount of food in the stomach, the rate of alcohol consumption, and the rate at which the person "burns" the alcohol. Someone who has three drinks in the last 45 minutes of a four-hour party will become more intoxicated than someone who drinks the same amount over the four-hour period. Figure 20-3 shows the rise

Figure 20-2. Wine, which is aged in wooden casks, is an alcoholic drink that is made without distillation.

Blood Alcohol Concentration: Effect on Behavior

Approximate Blood Alcohol Concentration (BAC)	Number of Drinks in a One-Hour Period	Effects on a 120-Pound Person
0.028	1	mild change and impairment of judgment, feeling of warmth, and well-being
0.038	1.5	motor skills impaired, slight trembling of hands
0.05	2	behavior less controlled; driver's attitude fluctuating from uncaring to impulsive
0.08	3	loss of coordination and self-control; speech and hearing somewhat affected
0.10	4	legally drunk at this level; substantial impairment of muscle coordination, perception, and judgment; walking; speaking, and hearing affected
0.16	6	unmistakably drunk; all body coordination seriously affected; vision blurred and speech slurred and unclear
0.20	8	intoxication strong; loss of ability to stand and no control over thoughts and perceptions
0.25	10	extremely intoxicated; body enters into a state of total confusion
0.30	12	severe intoxication, loss of consciousness; coma or death possible
0.40 to 0.50	16	breathing and heart action can stop; coma and death probable

Figure 20-3. How does the rate of drinking affect the level of blood alcohol concentration?

in the BAC with increased alcohol consumption, and the effects this has on body functions and behavior. The type of alcohol a person drinks also affects the BAC. Usually, the higher the percentage of alcohol, or the proof, the more rapid the rate of **intoxication** (in tahk sih **kay** shun), the set of negative effects alcohol has on the body, ranging from a mild loss of judgment to a loss of consciousness. Remember, however, people drink different amounts of different types of alcoholic beverages. For example, one 12-ounce (341-milliliter) can of beer, one 5-ounce (142-milliliter) glass of wine, and one 1.5-ounce (43-milliliter) glass of 80-proof liquor all contain about the same amount of alcohol and all can make a person equally intoxicated.

After alcohol has been consumed and absorbed into the blood, it is metabolized. **Metabolism** (muh **tab** uh liz um), as you learned in Chapter 10, is the total of chemical reactions that occur within the body. Metabolism changes a substance chemically so that it can be used by or removed from the body. The process of alcohol metabolism occurs in the liver where alcohol is changed to carbon dioxide and water. The carbon dioxide is released from the body in the lungs and the water passes out of the body as breath vapor, perspiration, or urine.

As alcohol is metabolized, the BAC decreases and the effects of alcohol slowly diminish, provided the person is not drinking. As reflexes and coordination return to normal, an intoxicated person slowly becomes steadier. Many people refer to this process as "becoming sober" or "sobering up."

While there are differences from one person to another, the liver metabolizes about 0.5 ounces (14.8 milliliters) of alcohol in one hour. Although many people believe that cold showers, exercise, fresh air, or coffee will speed up the sobering process, nothing can speed the rate of alcohol metabolism. Coffee, fresh air, exercise, or cold showers may help to keep a person awake, but they do not eliminate the intoxicating effects of alcohol.

How Alcohol Affects the Body

Alcohol changes the way parts of the brain work. It changes the way a person feels. It interferes with coordination by affecting the muscles that help to support the body. The degree of these effects depends on the amount of alcohol consumed. People who think that intoxication can be enjoyable fail to realize that intoxication is a form of poisoning. They also fail to realize that intoxication can begin with only one drink.

A person who drinks may notice first a loss of sensation. Vision, hearing, and other senses also lose their sharpness. Nerves are not as quick to pick up sensations of pain and transmit them to the brain as they are when alcohol is not present. Because alcohol lessens sensations of pain, it was one of the first painkillers used in medicine.

As alcohol takes effect, the drinker begins to lose judgment and self-control. At the same time, the person begins to feel relaxed and unafraid. When these two effects are combined, the person's **inhibitions** (in hih **bish** unz), or the controls that people put on their emotions, are reduced. Once inhibitions are reduced, people may behave in ways they would normally never consider. For example, a person under the influence of alcohol may express anger in violent or destructive ways.

When alcohol depresses the central nervous system, it slows the speed with which the body reacts to danger. Under the influence of alcohol, a driver who sees an oncoming car will not respond as quickly as usual. The few seconds difference between the driver's normal reaction time and the driver's reaction time with alcohol can be the difference between a safe ride home and a tragic accident.

▲
Figure 20-4. The different quantities of beer, wine, and liquor shown above have approximately the same alcohol content.

Alcohol depresses the nervous system, slowing the body's reaction time to danger.

Alcohol also affects sleep. Alcohol in the blood reduces the time spent dreaming, and dreaming is important in helping you to think clearly and to concentrate during the day. When alcohol disturbs a person's dreams, clear thinking becomes more difficult. In addition, the lack of restful sleep usually makes the person anxious, tired, and irritable.

Drinking heavily often causes a person to wake up with a hangover. A **hangover** is one or more physical symptoms such as nausea, upset stomach, headache, and a sensitivity to noise that result from drinking too much alcohol. The exact cause of a hangover is not known. The only way a person can prevent one is to avoid alcohol altogether or to drink slowly while eating food. Food in the stomach slows the rate at which alcohol is absorbed into the bloodstream. This allows the body time to metabolize the alcohol.

Alcohol also affects the water content of the body by increasing urine output. Part of this increased output is due to the water in alcoholic beverages. The other cause is the

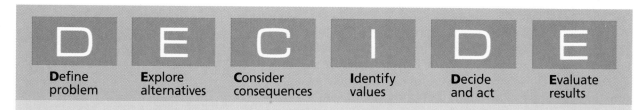

| **D**efine problem | **E**xplore alternatives | **C**onsider consequences | **I**dentify values | **D**ecide and act | **E**valuate results |

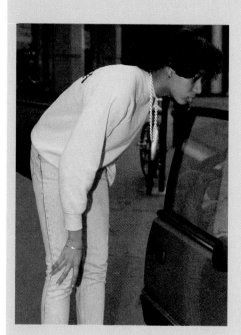

Should Linda ride home with a friend who may be drunk?

DRINKING AND DRIVING?

Linda has been at a party with some of her friends. She was planning to get a ride home with Dave but she has seen him drink four beers since he arrived. Dave was acting a little differently, and Linda was not sure if he should drive. Unfortunately, she did not know anyone else at the party who could give her a ride, and she knew that her parents had gone out with some friends for the evening. Besides, three of her friends were taking a ride from Dave.

"I'm probably getting worried for nothing," thought Linda. "What could happen in the few miles to my house, anyway?"

1. Use the DECIDE process described on page 16 to decide what you would do if you were in Linda's position. Explain your decision.

2. What role might peer pressure play in influencing Linda's decision? List some decisions that you have made where peer pressure played a role.

3. Suggest a realistic plan that you and your friends could put into effect to avoid situations like the one described above.

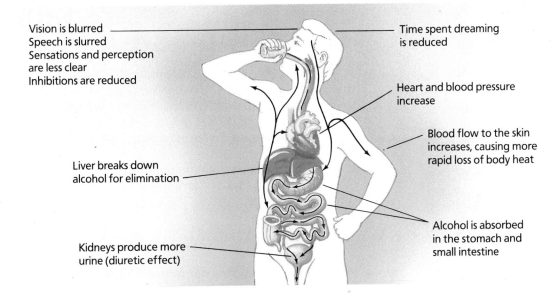

Vision is blurred
Speech is slurred
Sensations and perception
are less clear
Inhibitions are reduced

Time spent dreaming
is reduced

Heart and blood pressure
increase

Blood flow to the skin
increases, causing more
rapid loss of body heat

Liver breaks down
alcohol for elimination

Alcohol is absorbed
in the stomach and
small intestine

Kidneys produce more
urine (diuretic effect)

▲
**Figure 20-5. Alcohol has many
harmful effects on the body
including loss of vision, hearing,
muscle coordination, and
consciousness.**

⌐━━×

Alcohol causes a drinker to lose more
water than usual.

effect alcohol has on the body chemicals that regulate kidney function. When alcohol is present in the body, the kidneys cannot concentrate urine as much as usual. This effect, called the **diuretic** (dy uh **ret** ik) **effect** of alcohol, causes the person who drinks to lose more water than usual. This can lead to **dehydration** (dee hy **dray** shun), a severe loss of water from the tissues of the body. The effects of alcohol on the body are summarized in Figure 20-5.

Some people believe that alcohol acts as a kind of love potion, but this is a myth. Alcohol has only an indirect effect on sexuality. In small amounts, it decreases inhibitions and increases relaxation, making sexual behavior easier for some people. As alcohol intake increases, however, it reduces sexual interest. Long-term use of alcohol in men can cause impotence, or the inability to have sexual relations.

Section Review

1. Describe what happens during the fermentation and distillation processes.
2. What percentage of alcohol does 88-proof Scotch contain? How does this percentage differ from the percentage in wine and beer?
3. What are the intoxicating effects of alcohol?
4. What factors influence how intoxicated someone will become after drinking alcohol?

What Do You Think?
5. Why do you think a person's mood can be affected by alcohol?

2. PATTERNS OF ALCOHOL USE AND ABUSE

Alcohol consumption in the United States varies from one group to another. Usually men drink more frequently than women, although this pattern is changing. People 50 years old and older do not drink as much as younger adults. Rural regions have a lower percentage of drinkers than have metropolitan areas. Professional and business people are more frequent drinkers than manual laborers. Thus, age, sex, education, occupation, and many other factors play a role in drinking behavior.

Why People Choose Not to Drink

People may choose not to drink for a variety of reasons. For some people, alcohol is unpleasant. They may dislike the taste of it or react unfavorably to it during or after drinking. Persons with certain medical conditions or taking certain drugs cannot drink alcohol because of the dangers of drug interaction. For people who are weight conscious, alcohol is not desirable because of its high calorie content. Some people avoid alcohol because of its harmful effects on the body or because they do not want to lessen alertness or judgment. Other people may avoid alcohol for religious reasons. No matter what the reason or reasons for choosing not to drink,

There are many reasons why people choose not to drink alcohol.

Figure 20-6. It is always appropriate not to drink.

that decision is a healthful one. Choosing not to drink eliminates the chance of alcohol abuse. Abuse of alcohol, like the abuse of any drug, is a destructive behavior.

People who choose not to drink may have to resist pressure from those who are drinking. It is important for the nondrinker to feel comfortable with his or her decision. A person should not need to defend his or her choice not to drink. If anyone asks the reasons for not drinking, the best reply is usually a truthful one.

Why People Choose to Drink

People drink for a variety of reasons. Some like the taste of alcoholic beverages. Some people choose to drink only when celebrating social, cultural, or religious events. Others believe that drinking goes with eating. They may feel, for example, that wine enhances the taste of food or that drinking with meals helps them relax and enjoy their companions. Others simply like the effect alcohol has on them.

Drinking occasionally with others in these relaxed, pleasant circumstances is known as **social drinking.** In social drinking, alcohol is used to enhance or complement the enjoyment of the occasion. For many people, social drinking is their only form of alcohol use, and it may involve using small amounts of alcohol with meals and at special occasions.

Social drinking can become too frequent or involve excessive amounts of alcohol. If this starts to happen, the drinking behavior may become **problem drinking.** Problem drinking can include a range of behaviors. Usually, however, problem drinking occurs when drinking alcohol becomes a person's routine way of dealing with stress. Alcohol ceases to be an occasional and enjoyable experience and becomes an escape from unpleasant realities. In problem drinking, the person often drinks alone and cannot choose not to drink, because he or she has become psychologically dependent on alcohol. As you know, psychological dependence is an emotional need for a drug, a need that is often associated with specific routines and events.

How can you tell the difference between social drinking and problem drinking? Social drinkers consume alcohol without creating problems for themselves, their families, or society. They can control their drinking, and alcohol does not influence how they live. Problem drinkers create difficulties for themselves and those around them. Alcohol affects all aspects of their lives—their relationships, their health, and their work. Fortunately, people who are psychologically dependent on alcohol can with help stop drinking if they are strongly motivated to do so. Unfortunately, this often occurs only after problem drinkers have already hurt themselves or others. A simple self-test to determine whether or not someone is a problem drinker is shown in Figure 20-7.

Figure 20-7. One or two "yes" answers to any of these questions may indicate a drinking problem.

▼

A Problem Drinker's Self-Test

- Do you drink to avoid facing problems or when you are angry?
- Do you prefer to drink by yourself rather than with others?
- Do you try to stop drinking but fail?
- Do you lie to others about how often or how much you drink?
- Do you ever forget whole blocks of time when you are drinking?
- Do you get drunk even when you do not intend to do so?
- Are your school grades dropping?
- Do you drink in the morning?
- Do you get into trouble when you drink?
- Is it important to you to show others that you can drink alcohol?

Source: A. A. World Services, Inc., "A Message to Teenagers," New York, 1980.

Alcoholism

For the person who is a problem drinker there is the additional risk of developing alcoholism. **Alcoholism** is a progressive, incurable disease in which a person is physically and psychologically dependent on alcohol. Its cause is usually the result of many factors acting in combination. A person who has the disease is called an alcoholic. Psychologically, alcoholics consider alcohol a regular, essential part of coping with daily life. Physically, an alcoholic's body requires alcohol to function. Without alcohol, alcoholics suffer withdrawal symptoms. Alcoholism affects an estimated 4 percent of the American population.

Alcoholics may suffer some of the same withdrawal symptoms that other drug abusers suffer. These include shakiness, sleep problems, irritability, rapid heartbeat, and sweating. About one-quarter of the alcoholics in this country experience hallucinations during withdrawal. In cases of advanced alcoholism, suddenly stopping the use of alcohol can cause **delirium tremens** (dih **leer** ee um **tree** munz), sometimes called DTs. Delirium tremens includes uncontrollable shaking of the entire body, hallucinations, and insomnia. It is a reaction of the central nervous system to the absence of alcohol. Delirium tremens can be fatal.

Today, many researchers and health professionals consider alcoholism a disease. They believe that alcoholics continue to have this disease even after they have stopped drinking. To avoid the effects of alcoholism, alcoholics must avoid drinking alcohol altogether. Even one drink may cause the alcoholic to lose control and begin to drink again.

Alcoholics are physically and psychologically dependent on alcohol.

Friend to Friend

David:
I don't know how to say this, but I'm worried about your drinking.

Greg:
What are you talking about?

David:
Well, for one thing, I've noticed that you've gotten drunk every weekend for the past two months.

Greg:
So I have a few too many. Who cares?

According to these researchers, an alcoholic progresses through early, middle, and late stages of alcoholism. Each stage can take weeks, months, or years. Teenage alcoholics tend to go through the stages faster than adult alcoholics.

In the early stage, the drinker begins to drink more often and tends to be preoccupied with drinking. Sometimes this type of drinker is known as a problem drinker. The main motivation for drinking is the feeling the alcohol brings about, or the easing of problems that seem too painful to face. The most important evidence of this developing alcoholism is the blackout. **Blackouts** are periods of time that a person who has been drinking cannot remember. Occasional blackouts are a sure sign that the drinker is changing psychologically as well as physically.

During the middle stage, the alcoholic's physical dependence on alcohol becomes complete. Family, social, and business relationships worsen. The alcoholic in this stage may practice denial, refusing to see the problem or to get help. As you know, denial can be a negative coping strategy.

During the late, or chronic, stage, the alcoholic falls apart mentally, emotionally, and physically. He or she lives for drinking and experiences reverse tolerance for alcohol—less and less alcohol causes intoxication. Chronic alcoholics become isolated from society because all their efforts are directed toward getting alcohol. Serious health problems, which can include malnutrition, hallucinations, tremors, and viral and bacterial diseases, become frequent complaints.

There are many theories about the causes of alcoholism. Some scientists have studied physical, nutritional, and genetic factors to explain alcohol addiction. They have found

In the early stage of alcoholism, blackouts are evidence that the disease is developing.

David:
I do, and I'm worried. Last weekend you insulted your girlfriend in front of me, and you put a dent in your dad's car. Is that really what you want to do?

Greg:
Not really. I don't mean to drink that much. I just get carried away.

David:
Maybe it would help to talk to a counselor. If you want, I'll go with you.

that alcoholism occurs more frequently in children of alcoholics, which suggests that the disease may be inherited. They have also noted, however, that children who are not raised by their alcoholic parents are less likely to show signs of alcoholism. For this reason, some people believe that alcoholism is at least partly related to environmental factors.

Risks of Alcohol Abuse

Alcohol abuse leads to a wide range of serious problems that harm the alcohol abuser as well as everyone around the abuser. These problems include physical and mental health problems, the breakdown of personal relationships, harm to an unborn child, and disabling and fatal accidents.

According to the American Health Foundation, alcohol is the leading drug abused by high school students. Alcohol abuse is a problem for nearly 3.5 million teenagers. Drinking among teenagers often results in poor grades, drunken driving, dropping out of school, and the use of other drugs. Twenty-five percent of all deaths between the ages of 14 and 17 are alcohol-related.

LONG-TERM HEALTH RISKS People who use alcohol in moderation and only occasionally usually do not risk developing the health problems that are related to alcohol. Problem drinkers and alcoholics can develop a variety of disorders of the digestive system, liver, and heart with the long-term use of alcohol. Certain forms of cancer, nervous system and mental disorders, and nutritional deficiencies also are related to heavy alcohol use. Prolonged alcohol use can lead to stomach ulcers, liver damage, and an increased risk of cancer of the mouth, esophagus, throat, and voice box. Heavy drinkers are likely to develop **hepatitis** (hep uh **ty** tis), or inflammation of the liver. As you know, hepatitis causes jaundice, or yellowing of the skin, weakness, fever, and death. Prolonged use of alcohol also causes **cirrhosis** (sih **roh** sis) of the liver in which scar tissue replaces normal liver tissue. Scar tissue interferes with the liver's ability to carry out its normal functions, including the metabolism of alcohol. Cirrhosis, which is illustrated in Figure 20-8, causes the death of about 13 thousand Americans each year.

Alcohol causes fat to be deposited in heart muscle. This causes the heart to pump blood through the body less efficiently. Over time, alcohol abuse contributes to many cases of heart disease, our country's leading cause of death.

Still another effect of long-term alcohol abuse is the death of nerve cells in the brain. Nerve cells can never be replaced. The loss of many nerve cells causes forgetfulness, inability to concentrate, and poor judgment.

Problem drinkers and alcoholics often substitute alcohol for food, which can result in malnutrition, especially vitamin

Alcohol abuse harms not only the alcoholic but many others as well.

▲
Figure 20-8. How does the liver with cirrhosis (top) differ from a normal liver (bottom)?

B deficiency. Lack of vitamin B, for example, can lead to heart failure. Even though alcoholics may be malnourished, many are overweight because of alcohol's high calorie content.

SAFETY RISKS   Because alcohol affects judgment, coordination, and vision, alcohol abuse creates serious safety hazards. For example, alcohol is frequently involved in accidents. Almost half of the fatal driving accidents and about two-thirds of all driving accidents involving personal injury are related to alcohol use. Eighty percent of all pedestrian accidents involve alcohol. Estimates suggest that about 60 percent of all drownings and 85 percent of all deaths from fires are alcohol-related. Alcohol is also involved in 45 percent of all arrests for homicide, theft, assault, rape, child abuse, and disorderly conduct.

INTERACTIONS WITH OTHER DRUGS   Certain drugs interact dangerously with alcohol. Barbiturates, for example, can be especially dangerous with alcohol. Taken together, these two drugs increase the effect of each other. They may cause a dangerous slowing of the heart rate and respiration. In extreme cases, the heart can stop.

When alcohol is mixed with antibiotics, the effectiveness of the antibiotic is lessened. When alcohol is taken with antihistamines, body functions slow down. As a general rule, alcohol should not be taken with other drugs.

FETAL ALCOHOL SYNDROME   A pregnant woman who drinks risks giving birth to a child with a set of birth defects that make up **fetal alcohol syndrome (FAS).** This happens when alcohol enters the bloodstream of the developing fetus from the bloodstream of the mother, causing changes in fetal development. Babies born with FAS often

Alcohol abuse is involved in about one-half of all fatal driving accidents.

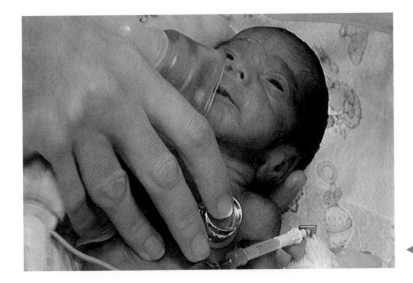

◀ **Figure 20-9. Fetal alcohol syndrome is a preventable disorder.**

Cars That Say No to Drunk Drivers

Judges in several states are taking an interesting step to keep drunk drivers off the road. In addition to requiring attendance at an alcohol education program, some judges are ordering drunk-driving offenders to install a new device in their cars. The device, called the ignition interlock system (IIS), prevents a car from starting when the driver is drunk.

The IIS is connected to the ignition under the car's dashboard. Before the driver starts the car, he or she must breathe into a mouthpiece for five seconds. The IIS determines the alcohol content of the person's blood. When it is too high, the car will not start.

The device is hard to fool. After passing the "breath" test, IIS users must blow a series of "breath pulses" into the mouthpiece. Drunk people find it hard to teach this code to someone else, so they cannot ask their friends to help start the car. Also, the IIS shuts off a car that is left idling after five minutes. This prevents a driver from leaving the car's engine on while buying a drink.

The IIS can stop drunk driving.

suffer from mental retardation, heart defects, malformed faces, or delayed growth.

Fetal alcohol syndrome is a completely preventable disorder. Since no one knows exactly how much alcohol causes FAS or less noticeable defects, the best advice for a woman is not to drink *any* alcohol when she is pregnant or when she thinks she might be pregnant.

FAMILY DISRUPTION Laura's father is an alcoholic, and she knows how alcoholism can affect a family. Her father sometimes spent the grocery money on alcohol. He often missed work, and he once was fired because he was drunk. Her family lost its health insurance and could not pay the doctor's bills when her sister was sick.

When anyone at home tried to talk to her father about getting help, he became defensive and angry. He reacted by drinking more heavily and yelling as he denied the problem. Laura never asked friends to visit her because she was afraid and ashamed of her father. The situation in Laura's family became worse and worse as her father's alcoholism worsened. Eventually, Laura's mother decided that she had to end her marriage to save herself and her children from emotional damage. Laura and her sister now live with their mother while their parents proceed with a divorce.

Although all families that face alcoholism are not the same as Laura's, many of the problems Laura faced are common. When a parent is drinking, the family resources may be spent on alcohol. Other family members often live in fear of the alcoholic's changes in mood and possibly violent outbursts. They live each day with uncertainty and fear about what new problems will arise.

When an alcoholic family member displays wild or unpredictable behavior in public, others in the family frequently are embarrassed. If the family structure falls apart because of divorce, family members may feel they could have done more to help the alcoholic. They may even blame each other for allowing the alcoholic to break up the family. Whatever the outcome of the family's experience with alcoholism, all the members go through an emotional ordeal.

Teenage alcoholics also disrupt their families. Most teenagers who drink try to hide their behavior from their parents. The first sign of their drinking is often poor performance at school. If their parents ignore their problems or accept excuses, the problems will worsen. Teenage alcohol abuse carries all the same risks that affect adult alcohol abusers.

LEGAL RISKS In most states, a person must be 21 years old to buy alcohol. Selling alcohol to someone under the legal drinking age is a criminal offense for both the seller and the buyer. Even at a private party, giving alcohol to someone under the legal drinking age is against the law in many cases.

Figure 20-10. A "breathalyzer" test can determine if a person is legally drunk.

The law requires people who are old enough to drink legally to behave responsibly. **Driving while intoxicated**, also called **DWI**, is against the law in every state. Drivers who cause accidents are usually tested to determine their BAC. BAC can be measured by testing a person's blood, urine, breath, or saliva. If a driver is found to have a BAC above the legal limit, the person's driver's license may be suspended and he or she may face other penalties as well. In most states, it is illegal to drive a vehicle if you have a BAC of 0.1 percent or higher. Signs of intoxication can appear at a BAC of 0.03 percent or lower. Therefore, a person who has had even one drink should not attempt to drive.

Driving while intoxicated is against the law in every state.

Section Review

1. What are some of the reasons that many people choose not to drink?
2. Differentiate between social drinking, problem drinking, and alcoholism.
3. Describe the three stages of alcoholism.
4. Describe four risks of alcohol abuse.

What Do You Think?
5. What information about alcohol will most influence your future decisions about drinking? Why is this information important to you?

3. BEING RESPONSIBLE ABOUT ALCOHOL

While many problems would be solved if everyone chose not to use alcohol, the reality is that a majority of people in the United States drink alcohol. If you decide to use alcohol when you reach the legal age, you are responsible for using it safely and appropriately. Using alcohol does not have to be a problem; it is a problem when alcohol use becomes abuse. When alcohol is used appropriately, it is used only occasionally, in moderation, and in social rather than solitary settings. Remember that even moderate use of alcohol causes a reduction in coordination and judgment. If you choose to use alcohol when you are of legal age, you must not place yourself or others at risk by driving.

For some people, using alcohol even once can be a problem. These people behave responsibly when they recognize that they cannot use alcohol at all.

Saying No to Alcohol

Deciding not to drink requires thinking about your reasons for not drinking and determining how you will say no in a situation where people are drinking. Planning will help you do this. If you make your decision in advance, you will find it easier to say no when the time comes.

To make your decision about alcohol when you reach the legal drinking age, you may want to ask yourself the following questions:

- Are my friends pressuring me into drinking?
- Am I considering drinking to impress others?
- Am I concerned about what others think?
- What might happen if I get drunk? Will someone get hurt? Will I get into trouble?

You may discover that some people will not accept your decision not to drink. Many people who drink want to have their actions reinforced by other people. You never need to apologize for not drinking; you need only say no. You do not need to give your reason, but you can if you wish.

People who respect your decision will accept whatever you say, especially if you are positive in your response. If asked, "Would you like a beer or something else to drink?" there are several positive ways you can say no:

- "No, I don't like the taste."
- "No, I don't drink."
- "Yes, I'd like a soft drink."
- "I'm not old enough to drink, I'll just have a glass of orange juice, thanks."

People who decide to use alcohol must be responsible for using it legally, safely, and appropriately.

▲
Figure 20-11. Saying no to alcohol is easier if you think through your reasons in advance.

The answer you give is up to you. Deciding now and practicing what you want to say when the time comes will make your response easier. Avoiding these situations will make it easier still.

Take responsibility for planning activities that do not involve drinking. You may want to go swimming or skiing or camping. Perhaps you would prefer to go to the movies, to a play, or to a dance. Some people find helping an organization raise money or organizing a school activity far more fun than situations that involve drinking. Getting a job, starting a small business, playing a sport are all activities that allow you to socialize without drinking.

Controlling the Use of Alcohol

Learning to be responsible about alcohol means not using alcohol until you have reached the legal drinking age and controlling situations in which social drinking occurs. Being responsible involves managing the amount of alcohol you drink, determining the times and settings in which you will drink, never driving after drinking, and never riding with an intoxicated driver. People who drink responsibly decide when, where, and how much they will drink. They are always able to control their use of alcohol, and they cannot be pressured to drink more than they want.

Your feelings and mood can determine the way alcohol affects you. Alcohol seems to intensify a person's mood. A person who is depressed will often become more so when drinking. Someone who is angry tends to become angrier. Times when you are depressed, angry, or worried are not appropriate times to drink.

Social drinking is safest when people are having fun. Alcohol is not an effective way to cope with stress. In social situations the host needs to be responsible about serving alcohol. For example, the host should always provide beverages without alcohol so guests can make their own choices. The host should also serve food with alcohol to help slow its effects. Insisting that guests not drive home while they are still feeling the effects of alcohol is also part of being responsible. The ultimate responsibility, however, rests with the drinker. He or she must never drive after drinking.

Because a person who is intoxicated is an unsafe driver, you should never get into a car with a drunk or drinking driver. The driver may be a friend, a relative, or the parent of a child for whom you were babysitting, but a driver who has been drinking, even after one or two drinks, risks an accident. This is not a risk you need to take.

If you go places where there is drinking, make arrangements for your ride home before you go. Talk with your parents about taxis, buses, trains, or car pools. If you find yourself in a situation with a drunk driver, ask for help.

Figure 20-12. A responsible host provides alternatives to alcohol.

Never drive after drinking and never get into a car with a drunk or drinking driver—no matter who they are.

▶

CONTRACT FOR LIFE

**A Contract for Life
Between Parent and Teenager**

Teenager   I agree to call you for advice and/or transportation at any hour, from any place, if I am ever in a situation where I have been drinking or a friend or date who is driving me has been drinking.

_____
Signature

Parent   I agree to come and get you at any hour, any place, no questions asked and no argument at that time, or I will pay for a taxi to bring you home safely. I expect we would discuss this issue at a later time.

I agree to seek safe, sober transportation home if I am ever in a situation where I have had too much to drink or a friend who is driving me has had too much to drink.

_____
Signature

_____
Date

© Copyright 1987
This Contract may not be duplicated

S.A.D.D. does not condone drinking by those below the legal drinking age. S.A.D.D. encourages all young people to obey the laws of their state, including laws relating to the legal drinking age.

Distributed by S.A.D.D., "Students Against Driving Drunk"

⊶

There is no such thing as responsible use of alcohol if it is consumed by those under the legal age.

You might think about making an agreement with your parents. Agree that you will never drink illegally, never drink and drive, and never get into a car with a driver who has been drinking. You will call if you need a ride home. In return, your parents agree to arrange a ride for you, no questions asked. One group, Students Against Driving Drunk (S.A.D.D.), has developed a contract for students and their parents. The contract, shown in Figure 20-13, is designed to make it easier for teenagers to call for help to avoid a DWI situation. It also gives teenagers a chance to discuss the problem of alcohol use and abuse with their parents.

Treatment for Alcoholism

A person who is an alcoholic is an alcoholic for life. With appropriate treatment, however, the progress of the disease can be stopped. By completely avoiding alcohol, alcoholics can lead productive, normal, happy lives. The first step in treatment is to acknowledge the condition and to want help. Many alcoholics deny their problem. For some, the shock of losing a job, being arrested, or being left by their families causes alcoholics to enter treatment programs.

The second step in treatment is detoxification, or the elimination of alcohol. During detoxification, the alcoholic experiences the symptoms of withdrawal, which last about three to seven days. Sometimes drugs can make these symptoms easier to manage. Severe withdrawal symptoms can be extremely dangerous and require medical care.

As alcohol is withdrawn, the alcoholic receives care for the malnutrition and other health problems caused by drinking. Eventually, the alcoholic begins **rehabilitation** (ree huh bil ih **tay** shun), the process of long-term improvement. Learning to cope with the stress of everyday living and learning to avoid alcohol are the goals of rehabilitation. Alcoholics receive counseling to help them understand both their disease and their behavior. Some alcoholics also receive a drug called **disulfiram** (dy **sul** fur am). Disulfiram causes severe nausea and vomiting if the person taking it drinks alcohol.

Community, religious, and health organizations often sponsor support groups for alcoholics. One of the most successful such groups is **Alcoholics Anonymous (AA).** In AA, the alcoholic is helped by other recovering alcoholics. The group's goal is to help its members remain alcohol-free.

Because the problems of the alcoholic seriously affect other family members, two other organizations, Al-Anon and Alateen, are designed to help them. **Al-Anon** helps the other family members understand the alcoholic and maintain their own mental health. **Alateen** provides help for teenagers who live with an alcoholic. Al-Anon and Alateen use the same self-help group process as AA does. At meetings, family members share their common experiences of living and coping with an alcoholic. You can find the phone numbers for AA, Al-Anon, and Alateen in your local phone book.

Figure 20-14. The message is clear—never drink and drive.

Alcoholics Anonymous is one of the most successful alcoholic rehabilitation groups.

Section Review

1. Name two ways in which a person can be responsible about alcohol.
2. What are the steps in the treatment of alcoholism?
3. What are some of the ways in which you can say no to alcohol?
4. How can a person control the use of alcohol?

What Do You Think?
5. What kinds of school or community programs do you think would help teenagers avoid alcohol abuse?

Intervening to Help a Friend

Jen had been concerned about her friend Christina's drinking for some time, but last night was the final straw. Jen and Christina were to meet at a friend's party, but Christina showed up an hour late and drunk. Rather than let Christina drive home drunk, Jen drove her home. The next day, Christina denied everything and insisted she did not have a drinking problem.

Other friends are giving up on Christina. But Jen still cares about Christina and fears her friend may be in serious trouble. She wants to help, but how can she when Christina is so out of touch with reality?

Intervening to help an alcohol- or drug-dependent friend is difficult. You fear you may lose the friend. But your friend's behavior may cause that loss in a fatal way. Use these guidelines to help save your friendship.

1. Stop "Enabling" Behaviors

"Enabling" behaviors are actions *you* take that allow, or enable, someone else to continue to behave dangerously without facing the consequences. By making it more difficult for people to behave dangerously, you make them rethink what they are doing.

Tell your friend you are going to stop:

- **Covering up**—such as saying your friend is at your house when he or she is not.
- **Giving second chances**—such as repeatedly lending money when your friend has not paid back previous loans.
- **Making excuses**—such as "That's OK, everyone's late sometimes."

2. Talk to Your Friend

Talking to your friend about his or her dangerous behavior will not be easy, but it is worthwhile if you:

- **Express your concern** Say you are intervening because you are worried about his or her well-being.

- **Help your friend face the facts about his or her destructive behavior**
  Present specific evidence of the problem. Describe behaviors accurately and simply, using dates and times when possible.
- **Describe your feelings**
  Tell how your friend's behavior affects you. For example, Jen might say to Christina, "I was worried something had happened to you when you were late. And when you showed up so drunk you couldn't walk straight, it hurt me."
- **Don't criticize or argue**
  Resist the temptation to be judgmental. You are objecting to the behavior, not the person. Do not get drawn into No-I-didn't, Yes-you-did arguments. Expect your friend to deny chemical dependency or other destructive patterns of behavior. If your friend argues, say "I just want you to know how *I* feel" and leave.
- **Offer specific help and support**
  Prepare a list of resources that your friend can go to for help. Include names, addresses, and phone numbers. Offer to go with your friend to the school counselor, social service center, member of the clergy, health professional, or other resource.

3. Ask Another Friend to Help

The more people speaking the truth and offering support, the better. Be sure to discuss your concerns and the guidelines

A friend may need your help to overcome an alcohol problem.

for intervening with the second friend. Work together.

4. Follow Through

Do what you said you would do, and stop doing what you said you would not do any more. Be sure your friend knows that your determination to stop "enabling" is firm and that your offers of support can be counted on.

5. In Extreme Cases, Seek Adult or Professional Help

If you think your friend is in a life-threatening or similarly serious situation, find a more experienced person to intervene directly.

Remember, you can only be responsible for yourself. You cannot *make* another person get help or change behavior. If you have done the above, you have done all you can, and you are a good friend.

APPLY THE SKILL

1. Review Jen's situation.
(a) What were Jen's "enabling" behaviors? Explain.
(b) Write a dialogue between Jen and Christina reflecting the guidelines presented in step 2.
(c) Under what circumstances do you think Jen should consider asking for adult or professional help? Explain.

2. Give two specific examples of "enabling" behaviors often used by (a) parents, (b) teachers, and (c) friends of a chemically dependent person. For each, explain how "being understanding" in that way really causes the situation to become worse.

3. Prepare a list of local resources for alcoholism, drug dependency, eating disorders, and depression. Include addresses, phone numbers, and hours the resource is available.

20 | Chapter Review

Chapter Summary

- Alcohol acts as a depressant, affecting judgment, self-control, and muscle action.
- Intoxication can occur after only a small amount of alcohol is drunk.
- The amount of alcohol in a person's body is measured by the blood alcohol concentration (BAC). As the BAC rises, a person's coordination, judgment, and control diminish. A person is legally drunk with a BAC of 0.1 or higher.
- BAC is affected by body weight, amount of food in the stomach, type of alcohol consumed, and rate of alcohol consumption.
- The liver breaks down alcohol slowly. Nothing can speed the sobering process.
- Intoxication causes loss of sensation, loss of inhibitions, blurred vision, slowed reflexes, increased urine output, dehydration, and increased blood pressure.
- Social drinkers use alcohol in moderation without letting it affect their lives.
- Problem drinkers are psychologically dependent on alcohol. They often drink alone

and usually as a way of coping with stress.
- Alcoholism is a disease in which the drinker becomes both physically and psychologically dependent on alcohol.
- Alcoholics move through three stages of alcoholism, from problem drinking to physical dependence to chronic alcoholism.
- A serious risk of alcohol abuse is accidents caused by intoxicated drivers.
- Long-term drinking can cause heart disease, cancer, and malnutrition.
- The problem drinker has an effect on the entire family.
- The disease of alcoholism cannot be cured, but alcoholics can learn to avoid drinking.
- Treatment for alcoholism involves detoxification, medical care for health problems, and support groups like Alcoholics Anonymous.
- Deciding not to drink is the safest decision you can make about alcohol.
- People who drink must be responsible for managing the amount of alcohol consumed and avoiding driving.

Vocabulary Review

Listed below are some of the important terms in this chapter. Choose the term that best matches the phrase in the exercise that follows.

Al-Anon
Alateen
alcohol
Alcoholics Anonymous
alcoholism
blackout

blood alcohol
  concentration
cirrhosis
distillation
ethanol

fermentation
fetal alcohol syndrome
hangover
hepatitis
intoxication

liquor
metabolism
problem drinker
proof
social drinker

1. the type of alcohol people can drink

2. condition in which scar tissue replaces healthy liver cells

3. periods of time that a drinker forgets

4. organization that helps children who have an alcoholic in the family

5. the condition of some children born to pregnant women who drink during pregnancy

6. a set of physical symptoms, such as nausea and headache, that frequently occur the day after drinking

7. disease of uncontrolled drinking

8. measure of alcohol in the blood

9. a self-help organization that works to keep member alcoholics from drinking

10. process used to concentrate alcohol

What Have You Learned?

1. What are the differences in alcohol content among wine, beer, and liquor?
2. A bottle of 85-proof vodka has what percentage alcohol by volume?
3. Alcohol is a depressant. Explain this.
4. What are the physical effects of alcohol?
5. How is alcohol eliminated from the body?
6. What are some signs that a person may have a drinking problem?
7. What are some reasons people choose not to drink?
8. How can alcohol affect an unborn child?
9. Describe the symptoms of alcoholism.
10. How do Alcoholics Anonymous, Alateen, and Al-Anon help alcoholics and their families?
11. Why is driving after drinking a problem?
12. How would you determine whether someone is a social or a problem drinker?

What Do You Think?

1. Do you feel that restrictions should be placed on the sale of alcoholic beverages? If so, what type of restrictions? If not, why not?
2. Research shows that children of alcoholics are more likely to become alcoholic themselves. Why do you think this is true?
3. Do you think a warning label should be placed on bottles containing alcohol, i.e., "This drink may lead to drunk driving and the disease of alcoholism"? How effective do you think this warning would be?
4. Studies have shown that students who use alcohol regularly are more likely than non-drinking students to get lower grades, drop out of school, and use other drugs. How would you explain this?
5. Why do teenagers drink? How are their reasons different from adults'?

What Would You Do?

1. What advice would you give someone whose parents are alcoholics? Be specific.
2. What kind of program would you begin to help prevent alcohol abuse by local teens?
3. What would you do if you had the authority to change laws that regulate alcohol use?
4. You notice that a friend constantly has the smell of alcohol on his breath and is behaving differently. What would you do or say? How would he respond?
5. Three members of the football team were suspended from playing for the rest of the season because they were caught at a drinking party. Write a letter to the editor of the school newspaper giving your personal opinion about this situation.
6. Your 16-year-old sister has a date with her boyfriend. He is driving. When he arrives you find that he is obviously intoxicated. What would you do?

For Further Study

1. Organize a role-playing skit for your class. In the skit you and two other class members can act out a discussion between a teenager and his or her parents. The discussion can be about any alcohol-related topic, such as going to a party where alcohol is going to be served.
2. What services exist in your community to help the problem drinker or alcoholic and his or her family? Are these services known and available to students in your school? What is a way to inform students about them?

21

As you read, think about

▶ why people choose not to use tobacco.

▶ why people start to use tobacco.

▶ the chemicals in tobacco and their harmful effect on the body.

▶ why there is no safe way to use tobacco.

Tobacco and Your Health

Y ou are focusing on your rhythm and stride as your feet pound the track. This is the point in the race where you usually get tired, and many runners pass you. But you're in better condition now, and you think you can win. There's only one runner in front of you, and he seems to be slowing down. Do you have the kick left to beat him? Your heart pounds with the effort and the excitement. It's the last lap. You'll give it all you've got. . . .

Smokers do not have the conditioning and stamina to run long-distance races, and this chapter will tell you why. You will see how smoking injures the lungs and restricts the supply of blood to the muscles. You will also learn how smoking contributes to heart attacks, respiratory diseases, and other serious illnesses. Most important, after looking at the reasons some people use tobacco, you will learn how you can avoid the deadly habit of smoking.

By not using tobacco, your body can function at its peak.

1. PEOPLE AND TOBACCO

Can you remember the first time you saw someone use tobacco? How about the most recent time? Many people may answer no to both of these questions. This is because tobacco use has always been a popular and socially accepted practice in this country.

Today, however, more and more people are beginning to notice tobacco use. In addition, people understand more about tobacco today than ever before. Because they do, they are avoiding its use in ever-increasing numbers, as shown in Figure 21-1. If you were to ask a young child why you should not use tobacco, he or she probably would give you a good reason. If you were to ask yourself the same question, you probably could come up with five or ten good reasons. Why do you think tobacco use is still so common today, despite what we now know about its dangers? Do you think it is possible to curb tobacco use? Keep these questions in mind as you read this chapter.

Why People Do Not Use Tobacco

If you do not use tobacco, you may have chosen not to for a number of reasons. The most important reason probably has to do with your health. Since childhood, you have heard about the damage tobacco does to the body. You also have heard how easy it is to get "hooked" on tobacco. This may

Check Your Wellness

If you do not use tobacco:
How strong is your commitment to a tobacco-free life style? Can you answer yes to the questions below?

1. Do you feel good about not using tobacco?
2. Is it easy for you to refuse tobacco?
3. Do you ask for nonsmoking sections in restaurants?
4. Do you support friends and relatives who are trying to quit tobacco?

If you use tobacco:
Is your tobacco habit out of control? See how many questions you answer yes to.

1. Do you want to light up whenever you feel upset, tense, or uncomfortable?
2. Does your use increase when you are with other people who use tobacco?
3. Do you use tobacco without being aware of it?
4. Do you feel more at ease with a cigarette?
5. If you wanted to stop using tobacco, do you know where to get help?

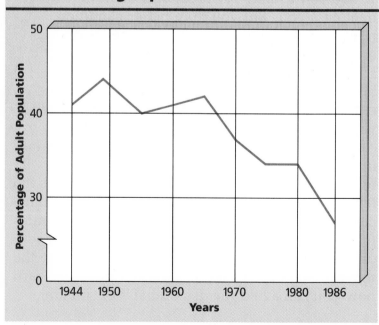

Source: Center for Disease Control, *Morbidity and Mortality Report*, 1987

Figure 21-1. Smoking is declining in America. What percent of the population has quit smoking since 1950?

have prompted you to stay away from it. You may participate in athletics, play a musical instrument, or be involved in other activities with which tobacco use would interfere. You may dislike some of tobacco's other effects—bad breath, poor complexion, discolored teeth, sore throat, and watery eyes.

Social pressures also may have influenced your decision not to use tobacco. These pressures usually come from three major sources—family members, friends, and the media. If you think back to your childhood, you may remember some early family influences. Your parents, whether they use tobacco or not, may have made you aware of tobacco's health effects. They may have offered advice on how to avoid tobacco use. Other relatives, such as older brothers or sisters, may have served as role models for you.

If your friends do not use tobacco, it is likely that you have helped one another in the decision not to use tobacco. Since most people who use tobacco start during their teens, a teenager's friends are an important influence. Have you ever been in a position where you were tempted to use tobacco? Many teenagers who have been in this position credit their friends with helping them to resist the temptation.

Newspapers, television, advertisements, and other media also may have influenced your decision. By publicizing scientific studies on tobacco, the media have kept the public informed about tobacco's dangers. You probably have read or heard much about tobacco through the media. You may have seen antitobacco advertisements like the one shown in Figure 21-3. Many of these advertisements are aimed at teenagers. Why are these advertisements effective?

Figure 21-3. Antitobacco posters warn people of the health hazards involved in using tobacco.

Why People Start to Use Tobacco

If you do use tobacco, take a minute to think about the factors that influenced you to start. Like many tobacco users, it may be difficult for you to pinpoint the reason why you started. It may surprise you to learn that some of the factors tobacco users point to are the same ones nonusers say led them to the opposite decision.

The strongest factors that influence tobacco users to start are usually social pressures—family members, friends, and the media. Studies have shown that children of tobacco users are much more likely to develop the habit than are children of nonusers. When both parents use tobacco, the chances are even greater the child will. This is true even if the parents try to discourage tobacco use. The reasons for this are complex. Children of tobacco users may grow up simply assuming they will use tobacco. Tobacco use is a behavior they are familiar with and one that the adults they know seem to enjoy. These children may think of tobacco use as a behavior that signals adulthood and maturity. While growing up, they may have imitated this adult behavior by "smoking" candy cigarettes or pretzels. These factors make it more likely that they will use tobacco too.

If your friends use tobacco, it is more likely that you will. Using tobacco when friends are using it makes a person feel like part of the group. It is difficult to say no to friends who ask you to join in. Furthermore, if your friends use tobacco, tobacco products are easily available to you. It is not easy to resist the temptation to smoke when a friend's pack of cigarettes is nearby.

Tobacco advertisements on billboards and in newspapers and magazines show young, attractive, popular people using tobacco. They present an image of tobacco use that is healthy and glamorous. This image may have been reinforced in movies where the "hero" often smokes. It is this image that antitobacco posters attempt to destroy. These images also may have influenced the person who uses tobacco.

For tobacco users, the social pressures seem to outweigh the dangers of tobacco use. When asked why they ignored the health hazards, some tobacco users said the dangers did not seem real to them. They did not see any evidence of poor health in friends and relatives who use tobacco. Others thought that tobacco would not become a habit with them. Still others said their curiosity was too strong. These people tried tobacco despite its dangers.

Social pressures—family, friends, and the media—can influence people to try tobacco.

Section Review

1. Why is tobacco use becoming less socially accepted?
2. Give two reasons why people do not use tobacco.
3. Name two reasons why people start to use tobacco.

What Do You Think?
4. What factors do you think influenced your decision about tobacco use?

2. TOBACCO AND ITS CHEMICALS

Fiona was at a party with some friends who were smoking cigarettes. Although she had never used tobacco, Fiona accepted a cigarette when John offered it to her. As she smoked, Fiona began to feel dizzy and ill. Her eyes started to tear, and she began to cough. "Don't worry," said John, "It happens to everyone when they start. If you just give it a chance, you will begin to enjoy it."

Most first-time tobacco users experience reactions similar to Fiona's. For some, this negative reaction is enough to convince them to stay away from tobacco. For others, it is not. People who use tobacco find that their bodies adjust to its negative effects. In fact, after they have used tobacco for a time, they may feel sick when they go without it. This is how a tobacco "habit" develops. The reasons why the habit develops can be traced to the chemicals in tobacco.

The Chemicals in Tobacco Smoke

Picture a typical cigarette, cigar, or pipe. Would it surprise you to learn that when tobacco is smoked, the smoker inhales over 4,000 different chemicals? Of these 4,000 chemicals, at least 1,000 are known to be dangerous. Figure 21-4 lists some of the harmful chemicals found in cigarette smoke. Some of these chemicals, such as **formaldehyde** (for **mal** duh hyd) and **benzopyrene** (ben zoh **py** reen) have been found to cause cancer. Ammonia and hydrogen cyanide, two other chemicals in tobacco smoke, are known to be poisonous. Among all the other dangerous chemicals, nicotine, tar, and carbon monoxide can be singled out as the most deadly found in tobacco smoke.

NICOTINE   **Nicotine** is an addictive, or habit-forming drug, found in tobacco. In its purified form, nicotine is one of the strongest poisons known. At one time, it was used in insecticides because it kills plant pests so effectively. Although the nicotine in tobacco does not cause instant death, its effects on the body over long periods of time are numerous and severe.

As you will see in Figure 21-5, nicotine affects the whole body. When tobacco is smoked, nicotine enters the lungs where it is immediately absorbed into the bloodstream. Eight seconds later, the nicotine reaches the brain. Chemical changes begin to take place. Nicotine causes the heart to beat faster, skin temperature to drop, and blood pressure to rise. The degree of reaction varies from person to person, depending on their tolerance, or resistance, to nicotine. Tolerance increases with use. First-time tobacco users have

Some Harmful Chemicals in Tobacco Smoke

acetaldehyde
acetone
acetonitrile
acrolein
acrylonitrile
ammonia
aniline
benzene
benzopyrene
2,3 butadione
butylamine
carbon monoxide
dimethylamine
dimethylnitrosamine
ethylamine
formaldehyde
hydrocyanic acid
hydrogen cyanide
hydrogen sulfide
methacrolein
methyl alcohol
methylamine
methylfuran
methylnaphthalene
nicotine
nitric oxide
nitrogen dioxide
phenol
pyridine
toluene

Figure 21-4. Tobacco smoke contains many harmful chemicals. Which of these did you already know were poisonous?

Nicotine's Effects on the Body

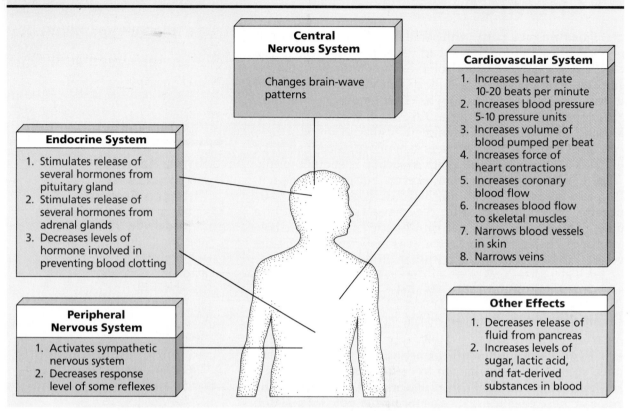

Central Nervous System
Changes brain-wave patterns

Cardiovascular System
1. Increases heart rate 10-20 beats per minute
2. Increases blood pressure 5-10 pressure units
3. Increases volume of blood pumped per beat
4. Increases force of heart contractions
5. Increases coronary blood flow
6. Increases blood flow to skeletal muscles
7. Narrows blood vessels in skin
8. Narrows veins

Endocrine System
1. Stimulates release of several hormones from pituitary gland
2. Stimulates release of several hormones from adrenal glands
3. Decreases levels of hormone involved in preventing blood clotting

Peripheral Nervous System
1. Activates sympathetic nervous system
2. Decreases response level of some reflexes

Other Effects
1. Decreases release of fluid from pancreas
2. Increases levels of sugar, lactic acid, and fat-derived substances in blood

▲
Figure 21-5. Nicotine affects the body in many ways. How does it affect the heart rate and blood circulation?

O━┳

The use of tobacco leads to physical and psychological dependence.

no tolerance to nicotine. In these people, nicotine causes unpleasant reactions, such as a racing heart, sweating, nausea, and dizziness. If tobacco use continues, tolerance starts to develop, and the user begins to experience a "lift," a physical reaction to the chemicals. As tolerance builds, however, the user may need more and more tobacco in order to get the same feeling.

In a short time, tobacco users develop a physical dependence, or addiction, to nicotine. Their bodies must have the drug to function comfortably. A tobacco user who goes without tobacco for a short while may show signs of **nicotine withdrawal**, a reaction to the lack of nicotine in the body. These signs include headache, irritability, restlessness, and a feeling of illness.

Tobacco users also develop a psychological dependence, which means that they feel emotionally and mentally uncomfortable without tobacco. By using tobacco at certain times, when under stress, for example, a person actually trains his or her brain to depend on tobacco whenever stressful situations arise. When the person goes without tobacco, he or she may feel unable to handle stress. Many tobacco users train themselves to "need" tobacco at particular times of the day, such as when they awake or after they have finished meals. Others become dependent on tobacco in social or work situations, such as parties or meetings.

TAR Tar is a dark, sticky mixture of chemicals that is formed when tobacco burns. Smokers can see evidence of this substance on their fingers and teeth, which turn brown when tars stick to them. The tars also stick to the cells of the respiratory system. These tars damage the delicate cells that line the respiratory tract. The cells contain tiny hairs, or **cilia** (**sil** ee uh), shown in Figure 21-6. The cilia beat back and forth and sweep dust, microorganisms, and other foreign particles away from the lungs. If the cilia are damaged, foreign particles enter the lungs, leading to disease.

It is now known that the tar in tobacco smoke contains hundreds of chemical **carcinogens** (kar **sin** uh junz), or cancer-causing agents. Cancer of the lungs, throat, and mouth have been linked to the inhalation of tar in tobacco smoke.

CARBON MONOXIDE Carbon monoxide is a poisonous, colorless, odorless gas that is found in cigarette smoke. You may be familiar with the dangers of carbon monoxide. Deaths that result from leaving a car engine running in a closed area are caused by carbon monoxide poisoning.

When carbon monoxide is inhaled, it attaches to the hemoglobin in your red blood cells. **Hemoglobin** (**hee** muh gloh bun) is a substance in red blood cells that carries oxygen to all parts of the body. As Figure 21-7 illustrates, when car-

▲
Figure 21-6. Cilia line the respiratory tract. How does smoking affect their function?

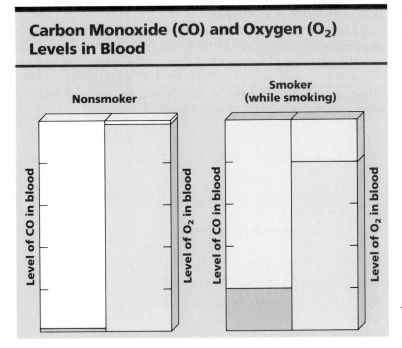

Carbon Monoxide (CO) and Oxygen (O₂) Levels in Blood

Nonsmoker

Level of CO in blood

Level of O₂ in blood

Smoker (while smoking)

Level of CO in blood

Level of O₂ in blood

◀ **Figure 21-7. What effect does smoking have on the blood's oxygen and carbon monoxide levels?**

Smokers often experience shortness of breath as a result of the carbon monoxide in tobacco smoke.

bon monoxide is present, it prevents oxygen from joining with hemoglobin. The more carbon monoxide present in the blood, the less oxygen in the blood. This is because the attraction of carbon monoxide for hemoglobin is more than 200 times greater than the attraction of oxygen for hemoglobin. This results in **anoxia** (an **ahk** see uh), a decreased oxygen level in the body. Because their blood contains too little oxygen to function properly, smokers often experience shortness of breath when they are at all active.

Chemicals in Smokeless Tobacco

While the majority of tobacco users smoke cigarettes, cigars, or pipes, there has been an increase in the use of smokeless tobacco. People who use smokeless tobacco may tell you that the products are safe because no smoke is produced or inhaled. What they may not realize is that smokeless tobacco still contains many of the same harmful chemicals found in tobacco smoke, including nicotine. Figure 21-8 lists some of the various harmful chemicals in smokeless tobacco products.

Carcinogens in Smokeless Tobacco
N-nitrosamines
polonium-210
polycyclic aromatic hydrocarbons (PAH)
arsenic compounds
cadmium compounds
nickel compounds
formaldehyde
coumarin

▲
Figure 21-8. Smokeless tobacco contains carcinogens. What harmful effects can these chemicals have?

There are two kinds of smokeless tobacco products. **Chewing tobacco**, made from poor-quality tobacco leaves, is placed between the cheek and gums and then chewed. **Snuff**, finely ground tobacco, is either inhaled through the nose or held between the cheek and gums. The nicotine in chewing tobacco enters the bloodstream through the membranes of the mouth. The nicotine in snuff gets into the body through the membranes of either the mouth or the nose. Once it has entered the body, nicotine has the same effect as it does when it is smoked.

There are other additional dangers associated with smokeless tobacco use. Most smokeless tobacco products contain particles of sand and grit, which destroy the surface of the teeth, and sugars, which lead to dental cavities. Because the tobacco is held in the mouth for long periods of time, users risk cancers of the mouth.

Section Review

1. Name two of the chemicals in tobacco smoke that can cause cancer.
2. What is the addictive drug in tobacco?
3. How does carbon monoxide cause anoxia?
4. Why is smokeless tobacco harmful?

What Do You Think?

5. How would you explain to a friend that tobacco use is harmful?

3. HEALTH AND TOBACCO

You probably know that tobacco causes bad breath, hacking coughs, poor complexions, stained teeth and fingers, and shortness of breath. You may know that tobacco dulls taste buds, decreases appetite, and destroys vitamins in the body. You may have seen some of these health effects in the tobacco users you know. What you may not see are the more serious diseases that are developing. Tobacco users, especially teenagers, may appear healthy. Each time they use tobacco, however, they increase their chances of developing certain deadly diseases.

The Long-Term Effects of Tobacco

In this country, it is estimated that 350,000 people die each year from tobacco-related diseases. Tobacco use continues despite the warnings that all tobacco products are required to carry by the government. Look at the warnings shown in Figure 21-10. They point out the number of serious diseases that may be caused by tobacco use. Are there any warnings that you would like to add?

CARDIOVASCULAR DISEASE Cardiovascular diseases, diseases of the heart and blood vessels, kill over 125,000 tobacco users in this country each year. The following statistics will give you an idea of the health problems tobacco users face:

Figure 21-9. Not smoking allows you to enjoy the taste of foods.

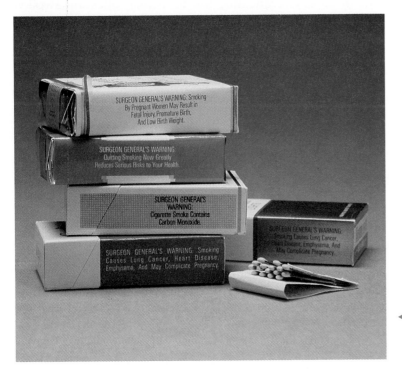

Figure 21-10. The Surgeon General's warnings on tobacco-product labels caution people about the dangers of tobacco use.

- A tobacco user is three times more likely to suffer a heart attack than a nonuser.
- A heart attack is five to ten times more likely to kill a tobacco user than a nonuser.

These statistics really are not surprising when you think about the damage that nicotine and carbon monoxide do to the cardiovascular system. These chemicals force the heart to work harder to deliver oxygen to the cells of the body. Blood vessels become weaker due to the increased force of the blood pushing against the blood vessels' walls. Blood vessel damage can lead to **atherosclerosis** (ath uh roh skluh **roh** sis), the buildup of fatty material on the walls of blood vessels, and to high blood pressure. These conditions increase the chances that a blood vessel near the heart will break or become blocked, resulting in a heart attack. If a blood vessel in the brain breaks or becomes blocked, a stroke may result.

RESPIRATORY DISEASE The dry or hacking cough that affects many smokers is one sign of serious damage to the respiratory system. What causes this cough? As tars destroy the cilia that line the respiratory tract, dust particles and **mucus** accumulate in the air passages. Coughing is the body's attempt to clear air passages of this material.

As a person continues to smoke, coughing no longer keeps the air passages clear. Mucus fills the smoker's **bronci** or bronchial tubes, which are the tubes leading from the trachea, or windpipe, to the lungs. In time, this condition may lead to a condition known as **chronic bronchitis** (brahng **ky** tis). In chronic bronchitis, the bronchial tubes are swollen and clogged with mucus. People with chronic bronchitis find it difficult to fill their lungs with air. Simple activities, such as climbing stairs, may leave them gasping for breath, and they are unable to participate in many sports. Unfortunately, there is no cure for chronic bronchitis. Doctors usually prescribe medications that temporarily open the bronchial tubes to make breathing easier.

Smoking can lead to a more serious disease of the respiratory system, **emphysema** (em fuh **see** muh). Emphysema is a breathing disorder in which the small air sacs in the lungs lose their elasticity. As you read in Chapter 10, oxygen passes through the air sacs into the bloodstream while carbon dioxide passes through the air sacs out of the body. When a person has emphysema, the damaged air sacs lose their ability to expand and contract. Instead, the air sacs resemble tiny balloons that no amount of puffing will blow up. The person with emphysema cannot get enough oxygen into the body or rid the body of carbon dioxide. He or she is always short of breath. For some, even blowing out a match is difficult.

The damage done to the lungs by emphysema cannot be undone. Even if an emphysema victim were to quit smoking, the condition would not improve.

The risk of heart attack increases for tobacco users.

Figure 21-11. A person who smokes will be out of breath during strenuous activity.

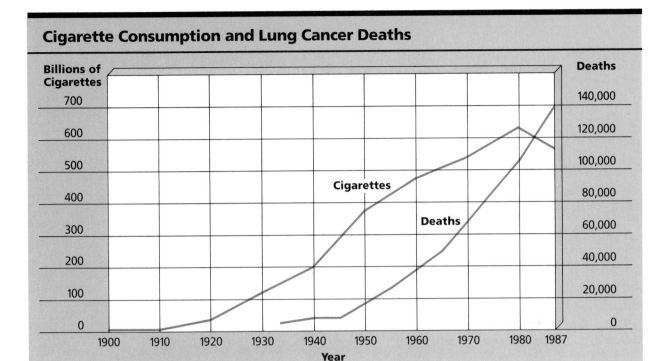

Cigarette Consumption and Lung Cancer Deaths

Billions of Cigarettes		Deaths
700		140,000
600		120,000
500		100,000
400	Cigarettes	80,000
300	Deaths	60,000
200		40,000
100		20,000
0		0

Year: 1900 1910 1920 1930 1940 1950 1960 1970 1980 1987

Source: American Cancer Society, Inc., 1988

CANCER Tobacco is also a major factor in the development of certain types of cancers. Cancer is an area of uncontrolled cell growth that invades the surrounding tissue and destroys it. Cancers can begin anywhere in the body and travel to other sites. In the United States today, lung cancer is the most deadly form of cancer. Scientists estimate that 80 percent of the deaths caused by lung cancer are related to smoking.

Unfortunately, lung cancer is difficult to detect early, which is when treatment would be most effective. By the time most cases of lung cancer have been detected, it is too late for successful treatment. For this reason, lung cancers are often fatal. In the United States, lung cancer is now the leading cause of cancer deaths in women. It is also one of the leading causes of death from cancer in men. As shown in Figure 21-12, cigarette consumption in the United States has started to decline, but the rate of lung cancer deaths continues to rise. This is because lung cancer caused by smoking takes at least 15 to 20 years to develop.

You have already read that smokeless tobacco users risk developing cancer of the mouth. At first, hard, white patches or sores, known as **leukoplakia** (lu koh **play** kee uh) form on the inside of the mouth. In time, leukoplakia may develop into cancer. Cancers of the mouth and throat are common in smokers, especially among cigar and pipe users. If a smoker also uses alcohol, the risk of these cancers increases.

▲
Figure 21-12. Most lung cancers are caused by tobacco. Can you predict when lung cancer rates will start to decline?

Cancers of the lung, mouth, and throat are common in smokers.

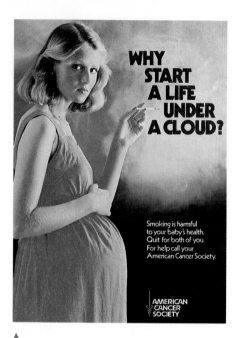

WHY START A LIFE UNDER A CLOUD?

Smoking is harmful to your baby's health. Quit for both of you. For help call your American Cancer Society.

AMERICAN CANCER SOCIETY

▲ Figure 21-13. Smoking exposes both the pregnant mother and her developing baby to harmful chemicals.

TOBACCO USE AND PREGNANCY Based on our knowledge today, it can be said that pregnant women are "breathing for two." This is why doctors recommend that pregnant women do not smoke. The antitobacco poster in Figure 21-13 is an attempt to discourage pregnant women from smoking.

Many of the harmful chemicals in tobacco smoke pass directly from the mother to the developing baby. Tobacco smoke increases the baby's heart rate, reduces its oxygen supply, and slows cell growth. Babies born to mothers who smoke weigh, on average, about seven ounces (200 grams) less than the babies of nonsmokers. These babies also have higher rates of other problems, such as poorly formed organs and slowed mental development. Women who smoke also have higher rates of premature births, miscarriages, and still-births than women who do not.

OTHER PHYSICAL EFFECTS OF TOBACCO Smoking increases an individual's chance of developing a **peptic ulcer**, an open sore in the lining of the stomach or nearby part of the digestive system. Peptic ulcers are difficult to treat in smokers because smoke continually irritates the sores. In this country, peptic ulcers and other diseases of the digestive system kill about 14,000 tobacco users each year.

Fire is another health hazard posed by tobacco use. Fires caused by careless smokers kill and injure thousands of people, both smokers and nonsmokers, each year.

In general, people who use tobacco are in poorer health than those who do not. Illnesses such as colds, allergies, gum disease, influenza, and pneumonia are more common in tobacco users. Some tobacco users have constant runny noses, sore throats, and headaches. These are signs of **sinusitis**, a swelling and reddening of the sinuses. An estimated 50 billion dollars are spent each year in this country treating tobacco-related illnesses.

Passive Smoking

Not everyone who experiences the harmful effects of tobacco smoke has chosen to smoke. Many people are **passive**, or involuntary, **smokers**. You are a passive smoker whenever you breathe **environmental tobacco smoke**, the smoke in the air from other people's cigars, pipes, or cigarettes. If you have ever been in a smoke-filled room or near a person who was smoking, you were a passive smoker. If one or both of your parents smoke, you have probably been a passive smoker all your life. Passive smoking is something that many nonsmokers find unpleasant and annoying. It can irritate the nose and throat and cause the eyes to burn, itch, and water. What is more significant, however, is that passive smoking is harmful to your health.

○━☰ Smoke created by other people's tobacco use can have a harmful effect on you.

THE DANGERS OF PASSIVE SMOKING Passive smokers are exposed to the same harmful chemicals as regular smokers. Nicotine, tar, carbon monoxide, and all the other chemicals present in tobacco smoke are inhaled by passive smokers. Not surprisingly, studies have shown that passive smoking increases the risk of certain diseases in nonsmokers. The children of parents who smoke suffer more respiratory infections than children of parents who do not smoke. Asthma and other allergies are often made worse in the presence of tobacco smoke. In fact, long-term exposure to environmental tobacco smoke increases your risk of heart disease and lung cancer.

Passive smoking increases the risk of certain diseases in nonsmokers.

WHAT TO DO ABOUT PASSIVE SMOKING Although passive smoking is still a serious problem, great progress is being made to eliminate it. Federal, state, and local regulations, laws, and ordinances now prohibit or restrict smoking in many areas. Smoking is prohibited or restricted in hospitals, other health-care facilities, buses, planes, and trains. Many employers have discovered that

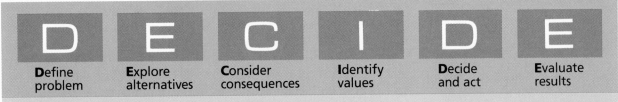

| **D**efine problem | **E**xplore alternatives | **C**onsider consequences | **I**dentify values | **D**ecide and act | **E**valuate results |

A SMOKY VACATION?

Your vacation is finally here! For months, you have been looking forward to going on a vacation with your friend and his family. But, when they arrive to pick you up, you find out that your friend's aunt is going with you. Your friend's aunt smokes three packs of cigarettes a day, one right after another, and another, and another.

You can't stand breathing cigarette smoke, especially in cars or other enclosed places. The smoke makes your eyes tear, your throat sore, and your nose run. The thought of an eight-hour car ride under these conditions is unbearable. As you open the door and get into the car, you are surrounded by a cloud of smoke.

1. Use the DECIDE process described on page 16 to decide what you would do in this situation. Explain the reasons for your decision.

2. How would you put your decision into action? Write out what you would say or do.

3. Suppose the action you took did not bring about the results you wanted. What would you do next?

Will a chain-smoker ruin your vacation?

Figure 21-14. Nonsmoking signs in ▶ **more and more places reflect a growing awareness of the dangers of tobacco smoke.**

Issues in Health

Should Smoking Be Banned in Public Places?

Some people feel that cigarette smoking should not be allowed in public places. They claim that smoking jeopardizes the health and ignores the constitutional rights of nonsmokers. Smoke in the air is more than just an annoyance. Recent studies link secondhand smoke to lung cancer, pneumonia, asthma, bronchitis, and heart disease in nonsmokers. These people claim a ban is needed to protect the nonsmokers' rights.

Other people feel that a ban on public smoking would make smokers a persecuted minority. They believe that smoking is a personal freedom that must be protected. These people claim that the scientific evidence about secondhand smoke is inconclusive. The tobacco industry points out that a smoking ban would have a negative impact on our economy. A ban would result in increased unemployment and a huge loss of tax revenue.

Do you think that smoking should be banned in public places? Why or why not?

prohibiting smoking in the workplace leads to better health among their employees. Most restaurants now have no-smoking areas. Many antismoking organizations, such as the American Lung Association, the American Cancer Society, and the American Medical Association, as well as private citizens' groups, are continuing to press for more restrictions. As smoking becomes less and less socially acceptable, smoking in public will become less common.

Restrictions on smoking in public will not completely eliminate passive smoking. As a nonsmoker, however, you can take certain actions to protect your own health. In some cases, you can avoid inhaling smoke by sitting in nonsmoking areas or avoiding areas where people are smoking. In other cases, asking people politely not to smoke may be the best solution. In situations where you cannot avoid environmental tobacco smoke, let smokers know, politely, that it bothers you. Many smokers will not smoke if they know the smoke is bothering other people. In any case, use your best judgment for each situation when deciding which strategy to use to minimize your exposure to tobacco smoke.

Section Review

1. What are five physical symptoms that a smoker may exhibit over time?
2. How can smoking lead to a heart attack?
3. Name two respiratory diseases caused by smoking.
4. Why is passive smoking hazardous to health?

What Do You Think?
5. What would you do if you worked in an area where there was environmental tobacco smoke?

4. CHOOSING A HEALTHY LIFE STYLE

Despite the dangers of tobacco use, many people believe that "low tar" and "low nicotine" cigarettes are safe, or at least safer, than regular cigarettes. Others believe that pipes and tobacco are safer than cigarettes, that smokeless tobacco is safe to use, or that herbal cigarettes are a safe alternative to tobacco. All of these beliefs are myths, or misconceptions. They are simply not true.

Myths can be dangerous when they lead people to behaviors that are harmful. Understanding why myths about tobacco products are untrue can help to prevent a nonuser from trying tobacco. It can also help a tobacco user give up his or her tobacco habit.

There is no safe way to use tobacco.

Tobacco Myths

Myth 1: *Low tar, low nicotine cigarettes are safe.*

Smokers of low tar, low nicotine cigarettes inhale the same harmful chemicals as smokers of regular cigarettes. Although these cigarettes may contain less nicotine and produce less tar than regular cigarettes, the levels of many chemicals, such as carbon monoxide, are not reduced. In fact, some smokers who switch to low tar, low nicotine cigarettes end up smoking more puffs per cigarette, smoking more frequently, or inhaling more deeply to satisfy the nicotine levels they are accustomed to.

Myth 2: *Smoking pipes or cigars is safer than smoking any type of cigarette.*

This myth is based on the idea that pipe and cigar smokers are less exposed to the dangers of tobacco because they inhale less than cigarette smokers. The fact is that cigars and pipes produce more tar and other harmful chemicals than cigarettes produce. As a result, pipe and cigar smokers have a high incidence of cancer of the lip, mouth, and throat. Former cigarette smokers who switch to cigars or pipes run an additional risk: because they tend to inhale smoke more deeply than pipe and cigar smokers do, they run the serious risk of developing lung cancer.

Myth 3: *Smokeless tobacco is a safe form of tobacco.*

Smokeless tobacco contains many harmful chemicals, including nicotine and heavy metals. Studies have shown a definite connection between smokeless tobacco use and a high incidence of diseases, including cancer, of the nose, mouth, throat, voice box, and esophagus. Furthermore, the nicotine absorbed into the body from smokeless tobacco produces the same harmful effects as nicotine absorbed from tobacco smoke.

Smokeless Cigarettes

Over the years, there have been many kinds of cigarettes on the market. In the past, cigarettes were little more than tobacco and paper. Then, filter-tipped cigarettes were developed. Some years later, low-tar cigarettes were introduced. Now, a new type of cigarette, a smokeless cigarette, has been developed. Unlike other cigarettes, the tobacco in smokeless cigarettes does not burn.

When a smokeless cigarette is lit, a small charcoal-like chunk in its tip ignites. Air tavels across this chunk each time a smoker inhales. The heated air is drawn through a short section of tobacco and past a "flavor capsule," where it picks up a tobacco taste. The cigarette does not burn down, and no ashes are produced.

Although filters in the smokeless cigarette remove some harmful chemicals before they reach the smoker, carbon monoxide and nicotine are not removed. Puff for puff, smokeless cigarettes contain as much of these chemicals as do low-tar brands. This fact supports what health experts have always said: There is *no* way to make a safe cigarette.

Smokeless cigarettes may not produce this kind of smoke, but they are still harmful.

Myth 4: *Nontobacco or herbal cigarettes are safe.*

Cigarettes made from material other than tobacco are no less harmful than regular cigarettes. Smoking is always harmful, since a cigarette made from any plant material will produce tar and carbon monoxide when burned. Some herbal cigarettes are not really tobacco-free. Clove cigarettes, for example, contain tobacco and ground cloves. The absence of nicotine does not make a cigarette safe, since other damaging chemicals may be present in the herbs. The chemicals present in cloves, for example, have caused severe reactions in some clove cigarette smokers.

Quitting the Tobacco Habit

Quitting tobacco use is not easy. It involves breaking both the physical and psychological dependence on nicotine that a user has developed. Knowing what the benefits of quitting will be, however, can make the process easier.

WHAT TO EXPECT   The tobacco user who quits can expect many immediate, as well as long-term, benefits. Immediate benefits include a reduction in blood pressure and a decrease in pulse rate. In addition, as carbon monoxide levels drop off, oxygen levels in the blood will quickly return to normal.

Gradually, the cilia that line air passages will begin to grow back and resume their normal functions. Breathing will become easier as the lungs and air passages begin to clear themselves. The smoker's raspy voice and cough eventually disappear along with the frequent colds and congestion. The senses of taste and smell become stronger again, and the complexion improves. As the time without tobacco lengthens, the risk of developing some tobacco-related diseases decreases. Figure 21-15 summarizes the changes that occur in a smoker's body after quitting.

Along with these physical changes, there are psychological benefits. People who have quit usually feel more confident about themselves. They sense they are controlling their lives rather than being controlled by tobacco.

Many people do not give up tobacco because they fear they will gain weight or become irritable when they stop. In reality, most people who quit do not gain weight. Some may even lose weight. Since tobacco users are often underweight, however, the weight gain they may experience usually is not significant. Exercise has helped many former tobacco users to control weight changes after giving up tobacco.

Some tobacco users may become irritable when they stop using tobacco. It is part of the user's normal response to the stress of breaking the habit. Seeking the support of family and friends and using positive stress management techniques can be especially useful during this time.

Changes in a Smoker's Body After Quitting

Within 20 minutes of last cigarette:
- Blood pressure and pulse rate return to normal levels.
- Body temperature of hands and feet increases to normal.

8 hours:
- Carbon monoxide level in blood drops to normal.
- Oxygen level in blood increases to normal.

1 day:
- Chance of heart attack decreases.

2 days:
- Ability to smell and taste improves.

3 days:
- Bronchial tubes relax.
- Lung capacity increases.

2 weeks to 3 months:
- Circulation improves.
- Walking becomes easier.
- Lung function increases up to 30%.

1 to 9 months:
- Coughing, sinus congestion, fatigue, shortness of breath decrease.
- Cilia regrow, increasing ability to handle mucus, thus reducing risk of infection.
- Body's overall energy level increases.

5 years:
- Risk of developing lung cancer or coronary heart disease decreases dramatically.

10 years:
- Precancerous cells are replaced.
- Risk of developing lung cancer is nearly the same as for a nonsmoker.

Sources: USDA, 1988; American Cancer Society, Inc., 1988

TIPS FOR QUITTING Quitting the tobacco habit is not easy, but it is possible. Millions of people have done it. Most people quit on their own. Others use hypnosis, attend classes or seek other professional help. Many people who have quit found that quitting abruptly, or going "cold turkey," worked for them. Others have been able to quit by gradually reducing their use of tobacco over an extended period of time. There is no one single method that works best for everyone. The single most important element, however, in successfully quitting is a strong personal commitment to quitting.

If you use tobacco and want to quit, be sure to enlist the support of your friends and family members. People who have quit claim that encouragement and support from other people is a great help in breaking the habit. Sometimes it helps to determine when you are most likely to use tobacco and to substitute some other positive activity for the tobacco habit. If you smoke just after eating, for example, you might try calling a friend or going for a walk after your meals. Try to break your routine use of tobacco. For many people, tobacco use provides a way of dealing with stress. If you find that you use tobacco during times of stress, try to develop positive coping techniques, such as exercise and meditation.

You can lessen the difficulties of quitting by reminding yourself of the health benefits you will receive. Think about how the quality of your life will improve: foods will smell and taste better; your breathing capacity will increase; you will look and feel better physically and psychologically; and you will save money. Remind yourself, the sooner you quit, the sooner you gain the benefits of being tobacco-free.

▲
Figure 21-15. The health benefits of quitting smoking begin immediately and continue throughout life.

O—⊤

Although it may be difficult to quit smoking, resources are available to help.

Tips for Quitting Tobacco Use

- Try to quit together with a friend or friends.
- Solicit support from family and friends.
- Remind yourself of the benefits of quitting—physical, mental, financial.
- During the first week drink milk or water instead of coffee or tea and avoid chocolate.
- Take a warm, not a hot, shower or bath in the morning and at night for the first 4 to 5 days.
- Try doing vigorous exercise to reduce the craving for tobacco.
- Substitute other activities for tobacco. Eat carrot or celery sticks, go for a walk.
- Avoid being around people who are smoking.
- Change the routine associated with the times you use tobacco.
- Use positive coping techniques to relieve stress— exercise, meditation, stretching, deep breathing.
- Put aside money or reward yourself when you do not use tobacco.
- Tell yourself the sooner you quit the sooner you will feel better.

▲

Figure 21-16. What activities can help reduce the craving for tobacco?

If you have tried to quit but have not been successful, do not get discouraged. It only means you did not use a method that works for you. Each time you try, you gain more experience in how to quit, and you improve your chances of success. Figure 21-16 offers some basic tips to help you in quitting the tobacco habit.

GETTING HELP There a number of resources available to tobacco users who are trying to quit. For people quitting on their own, booklets and pamphlets containing tips and other helpful information can be obtained from various health organizations, including the American Lung Association and the American Cancer Society. People who feel they need professional help may want to attend local workshops, classes, or support groups. Many of these groups are advertised on radio, in local newspapers, and on community bulletin boards. Local hospitals and other health-care facilities frequently offer programs for helping tobacco users. Your doctor also can help you to set up a program or advise you where to go for help.

Some tobacco smokers have such a strong physical dependence on nicotine that they seem unable to give up smoking. These people may be able to quit now if they use a newly developed product, a chewing gum that contains nicotine. This product is available only with a doctor's prescription. Although the gum allows a person to quit smoking tobacco without experiencing withdrawal symptoms, the user is still exposed to the harmful effects of nicotine. Therefore, the gum is used as only the first of several steps in a program to break the nicotine habit completely.

Figure 21-17. Much literature is available to help people give up tobacco use. ▶

The Tobacco-Free Life Style

Tobacco is the single most preventable cause of death and illness in the United States. Choosing not to use tobacco can be the single most important decision that you will make.

If you have chosen not to use tobacco, your decision will be reinforced by your awareness of how avoiding tobacco will enhance the quality of your life. In fact, it is possible that your example may encourage others to avoid using tobacco. As a nonuser, you will be a part of the growing majority of teenagers and adults who do not use tobacco.

If you have chosen to use tobacco, you have two options. You can decide to quit, or you can continue to use tobacco and live with the consequences. Remember, deciding to quit tobacco use does not limit your choices—it expands them. Living without tobacco frees you to enjoy the full potential of a healthy body.

Do you think it is possible to curb tobacco use? This was a question asked at the beginning of this chapter. The answer depends upon your personal decisions about tobacco and on how strongly you encourage others not to use tobacco.

A growing majority of teens and adults do not use tobacco.

Section Review

1. Why are low tar, low nicotine cigarettes unsafe?
2. What are the risks of smoking pipes or cigars?
3. What are four benefits of quitting the use of tobacco?
4. How can exercise help someone quit using tobacco?

What Do You Think?

5. What would you do to help a friend who is trying to quit using tobacco?

Being Assertive

While Joe and some of his friends were eating lunch in the no-smoking section of a local restaurant, cigarette smoke began wafting over from the next booth. At first, Joe tried to ignore the smoke, but he soon decided that the "No Smoking" sign entitled him to a smoke-free meal. Joe politely asked them to observe the no-smoking rule.

Joe behaved assertively when he stood up for his rights as a nonsmoker. Could you be assertive in a similar situation? If not, you are not alone. Assertiveness is a skill that many people find difficult to master.

Being assertive means expressing your feelings honestly in a way that respects your rights and the rights of others. Acting assertively can help you to feel more self-confident. You will feel good that you can express your needs and stand up for yourself without hurting others.

The stepwise process outlined below will help you master the skill of assertiveness. The process is especially helpful in situations where you would like to act assertively but find it difficult to do so.

1. Evaluate Your Current Behavior

To understand what kept you from acting assertively in a particular situation, ask yourself these questions:

- What outcome did I desire?
- What outcome did I get?
- What negative thoughts kept me from acting assertively in this situation?
- What was I afraid might have happened if I had acted assertively?

2. Observe a Role Model in Action

Identify a person who is able to act assertively in difficult situations. Observe the person as he or she handles a situation in an assertive manner. Pay attention to the words, tone of voice, and body language the person uses.

Afterwards, think about other ways in which you could act assertively in the same situation. What else could you say? How else could you say it?

3. Conduct a Mental Rehearsal

Conducting a mental rehearsal is like running a movie in your mind. Try to imagine yourself being assertive in a situation you expect to be involved in shortly. Mental rehearsal helps you think in detail about how you will look, act, and feel in the actual situation. It also helps you plan for any difficulties you might face.

4. Take Action

Now, you are ready to act assertively. When the situation you have rehearsed actually presents itself, put your plan into action. Keep the following pointers in mind:

Verbal Behavior

- Ask for what you want by using "I" messages (begin statements by saying "I feel" or "I want") instead of blaming or demanding things of others (do not say "You should . . ." or "You did . . .").
- Be specific about your thoughts and feelings. Try not to speak in terms that are too general.
- Be direct and unapologetic when you are facing the other person (for example, say "I believe I was ahead of you."). Do not assume that the other person did something on purpose; it may have been accidental.
- When speaking, talk calmly and clearly. Take time to think things through. When listening, pay full attention to the other person.

Nonverbal Behavior

- Pay attention to your body language. Be sure to use gestures and facial expressions that match your message.
- Look at the other person when speaking. Make direct eye contact.

Being assertive can help you resolve problems that might cause you frustration.

- Stand a comfortable distance from the person you are speaking to. Standing too close may seem threatening to some people.

5. Evaluate Yourself

After the encounter, ask yourself these questions:

- Did I really say what I intended to say?
- Was I direct and unapologetic, yet considerate?
- Did I stand up for myself without becoming defensive or infringing on the other person's rights?
- Was my body language assertive?
- Did I feel good about myself after the encounter?
- Do I think the other person felt comfortable with my interaction?

Questions that you answered no to indicate things you should work to improve for future encounters.

APPLY THE SKILL

1. Think of a situation you would find difficult to handle assertively. Some possible situations are: saying no to a friend who asks you for a favor or returning a defective product to a store. How would you typically handle the situation? Why would you have trouble acting assertively?

2. Think of a person you know who acts assertively. Describe how he or she might handle the situation above.

3. Visualize yourself acting assertively in the situation chosen above. Write out what you would do and say. Anticipate the other person's response and your reaction.

4. Imagine you are returning a defective record album. Saying "I bought this record here last week and it has a defect," demonstrate how your nonverbal behavior can influence your message.

21 | Chapter Review

Chapter Summary

- Knowledge of tobacco's harmful health effects has caused an increased awareness of tobacco use.
- People are influenced not to use tobacco by family members, friends, the media, and by knowing the dangers of tobacco use.
- People start to use tobacco because of pressure from family members, friends, and the media.
- Tobacco smoke contains over 4,000 different chemicals, many of which are harmful.
- Nicotine, tar, and carbon monoxide are the major toxic chemicals in tobacco smoke.
- Smokeless tobacco contains many harmful chemicals, including nicotine.
- Tobacco use dulls the senses of taste and smell; decreases appetite; causes bad breath; hacking coughs, and shortness of breath.
- Long-term effects of tobacco use include cardiovascular disease; respiratory diseases, such as chronic bronchitis, emphysema and lung cancer; and other forms of cancer.
- Smoking during pregnancy is harmful to the baby's development.

- The use of tobacco is associated with many disorders, including peptic ulcers, low resistance to infections, allergies, gum disease, and sinusitis.
- Fires caused by smoking account for thousands of deaths and injuries every year.
- Passive smoking by nonsmokers increases their risk of tobacco-related diseases.
- Many federal, state, and local laws prohibit or restrict smoking in many areas.
- Smoking in any form is harmful, and tobacco use in any form is harmful.
- A person who quits using tobacco can expect to look and feel better physically and mentally and to reduce dramatically chances of having a tobacco-related disease.
- Quitting the use of tobacco requires a strong personal desire to quit. Support from friends and family members helps. Substituting other activities or using positive coping strategies also is helpful.
- Choosing not to use tobacco can be the single most important health decision in your life.

Vocabulary Review

Listed below are some of the important terms in this chapter. Choose the term that best matches the phrase in the exercise that follows.

anoxia
atherosclerosis
benzopyrene
bronchi
carbon monoxide
carcinogen

cardiovascular diseases
chewing tobacco
chronic bronchitis
cilia
emphysema

environmental tobacco
  smoke
hemoglobin
leukoplakia
nicotine

nicotine withdrawal
passive smoker
sinusitis
snuff
tar

1. anything that causes cancer
2. a decreased oxygen level in the body
3. a chemical carcinogen
4. a form of smokeless tobacco
5. swelling of the bronchi
6. combines with hemoglobin

7. a condition caused by the use of chewing tobacco
8. dark sticky mixture of chemicals in tobacco smoke
9. a hairlike structure
10. what a passive smoker breathes

What Have You Learned?

1. How can you convince others not to smoke?
2. How do tobacco ads persuade?
3. How do tobacco users become psychologically dependent on tobacco?
4. Why does tar in tobacco smoke cause respiratory problems?
5. Why is carbon monoxide harmful?
6. What problems are caused by the use of smokeless tobacco?

7. How does smoking cause some types of cardiovascular disease?
8. Distinguish between the diseases of bronchitis and emphysema.
9. Why does smoking during pregnancy affect a developing baby?
10. Why are herbal cigarettes unsafe?
11. What are the risks of pipes and cigars?
12. What is the most important factor for a person who is trying to quit tobacco use?

What Do You Think?

1. Why do you think some baseball players use chewing tobacco? How might an athlete's use of chewing tobacco influence young people who see him?
2. Do you think there should be more or fewer restrictions on the advertising and sale of tobacco products? Explain.

3. Why do you think the number of female smokers has increased over the past decade?
4. What do you think are the most effective ways to protect nonsmokers from environmental tobacco smoke? Explain.
5. What would you suggest to an ex-smoker to help him or her not resume smoking?

What Would You Do?

1. You are sitting in a "No Smoking" section of a restaurant. A person near you lights a cigarette. How would you handle the situation?
2. Recently you saw your 10-year-old sister smoking with some older friends. Later, you talk to her alone. What would you say?
3. Your favorite uncle has come to visit in your home. He knows that no one in your household smokes, but he asks you for an ashtray. What would you do?

4. Your community is considering a law that bans smoking in public. What arguments could be used for or against such laws?
5. Suppose you are a doctor and one of your patients is a smoker with high blood pressure. What advice would you give and why?
6. You are selling advertisements for a school paper, and a tobacco shop wants to buy space for an ad. Would you accept the ad? Why or why not?

For Further Study

1. Interview some people who have quit smoking. Ask them how they stopped smoking, how difficult it was, and how their lives have been changed. Write a report on your findings.
2. Calculate the cost of smoking one pack of cigarettes a day for one week, one month, and one year. List ways to spend this money if it were not used for cigarettes.
3. Design a poster that you feel would help teenagers choose not to use tobacco. You might emphasize the dangers and drawbacks of tobacco use, the joys of a tobacco-free life, or a combination of the two.

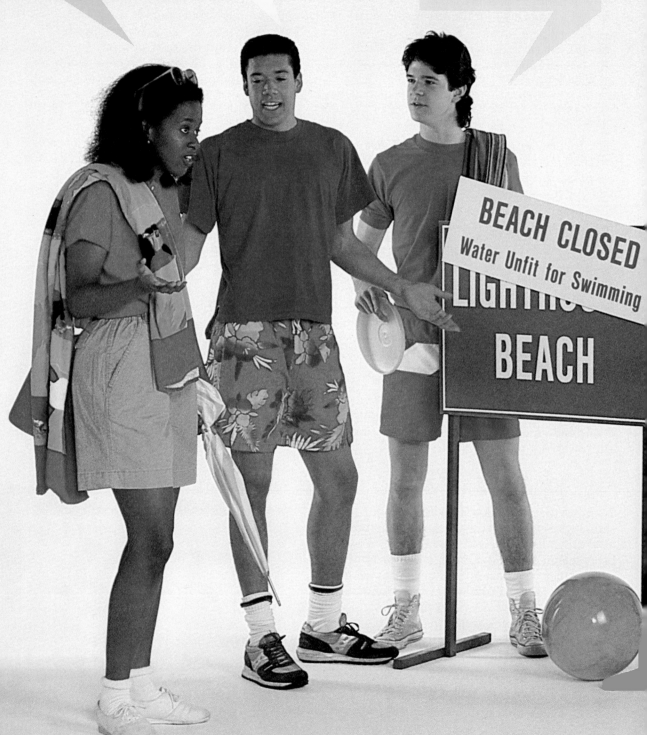

You know, my brother belongs to an environmental action group. I am going to ask him if he knows anything about this. Maybe there is something we could do.

22

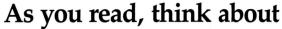

As you read, think about

▶ how pollution affects everything in the environment.

▶ the causes and dangers of air pollution and what can be done to prevent it.

▶ the sources of water pollution and the methods of controlling it.

▶ the problem created by land disposal of solid and hazardous wastes.

▶ what you can do to minimize your exposure to radiation and noise pollution.

A Healthy Environment

The air blows fresh against your face as your horse carries you along at a steady gallop. You love this empty desert landscape! In the clean air, the line of hills along the horizon is as sharply defined as the lines of an etching. The sagebrush casts sharp blue shadows against the barren, yellow desert floor.

Unfortunately, beautiful wilderness areas like this are threatened by pollution. So are areas where millions of people live and farmland where much of our food is grown. City and countryside alike are endangered by air, water, and ground pollution. Hazardous waste and nuclear energy create other environmental problems. In many cases, your own health is at risk. In this chapter, you will learn about the hazards of pollution and what you can do to keep the environment healthy.

We all share the environment. Taking care of it is everyone's responsibility.

1. THE ENVIRONMENT—YOUR HOME

Check Your Wellness

Are you doing your part to protect the environment from pollution? See if you can answer yes to the questions below.

1. Do you walk, bicycle, or use a carpool whenever possible?

2. Do you turn off lights and appliances when not in use?

3. Do you save newspapers, cans, and bottles for recycling?

4. Do you avoid littering, and do you clean up litter that has been thrown away improperly?

5. Does your family keep your stereo and TV at a moderate volume level?

6. Does your family store paints, batteries, cleansers, and other toxic products until they can be disposed of safely?

7. Do you avoid buying products with excessive packaging, especially plastic containers?

8. Are you active in local groups that work to keep the environment clean?

Have you ever thrown a plastic container in the trash or poured an unwanted liquid down a drain? Of course you have. Have you ever thought about where these things end up? Throwing away **wastes**—things that we no longer need, want, or can use—can affect your health and the health of others. Some wastes created by people can harm the **environment** (en **vy** run munt). The environment is everything that makes up your surroundings—the physical world and the living things that inhabit it.

When wastes enter the environment, **pollution** occurs. The wastes that enter the environment are known as **pollutants.** Because all living things depend on the environment for air, water, and the minerals in soil and rocks, pollution affects all living things. When any part of the environment is polluted, all the organisms in the environment, including humans, are harmed.

Since you and everyone else share the same environment—the earth—you have a responsibility to keep the environment healthy. When pollution is not controlled, the air you breathe, the water you drink, and even the food you eat become polluted. You cannot completely avoid producing waste and therefore pollution, but you can reduce the amount of waste you contribute.

Figure 22-1. You can do your part to keep the environment clean. ▶

Biodegradable Wastes

All living things produce wastes as part of living. When living things die, their remains become a form of waste. Usually, bacteria and other organisms use natural wastes as food, breaking them down into simpler substances. The organisms that break down, or decompose, wastes are called **decomposers.** Wastes that can be broken down and used are called **biodegradable** (by oh dih **gray** duh bul) **wastes.**

Biodegradable wastes do not present a problem unless they are put into the environment faster than they can be decomposed. For example, although raw, or untreated, sewage is a rich food supply for some microorganisms, when there is too much of it in water, these microorganisms become too abundant. They use up the oxygen in the water. Without oxygen, other organisms in the water, like fish, die.

While pollution from biodegradable sources can be serious, there are solutions. Sewage treatment plants, septic tanks, and cesspools are designed to treat biodegradable wastes. They allow wastes to be decomposed rapidly before they are released into the environment.

Nonbiodegradable Wastes

The most serious forms of pollution come from wastes created by human activities. Many of these wastes are the result of industries that produce goods used by our society. The processes used in these industries often result in wastes that can kill or injure living things. Often, these wastes are not biodegradable, or they decompose only slowly over a long time. Industries, however, are not the only producers of pollution. Fuels such as oil, gas, and coal, which are used to power cars, buses, homes, and factories, also add to the pollution of the environment. Our standard of living causes us to depend on sources of energy and products that directly or indirectly pollute the environment.

Figure 22-2. Sewage treatment plants decompose biodegradable wastes and return them to the environment.

▼

Section Review

1. What is the environment?
2. Why do you have a responsibility to prevent pollution whenever possible?
3. What are nonbiodegradable wastes?
4. Why do the wastes produced by organisms other than man usually not cause pollution?

What Do You Think?
5. In what ways could you reduce the amount of pollution you generate?

2. AIR QUALITY AND HEALTH

In 1967, a major snow storm in Chicago, Illinois, halted traffic and most of the city's normal activities. When the snow ended, the pollution usually in the air had been washed to earth with the falling snow. The air was crystal clear. Then, as snowplows cleared the streets, cars and buses began to move again. The level of pollutants in the city's air increased once again.

People once thought that air pollution could be controlled by natural processes, like rain and snow. Air pollution happens all the time, however, while major storms happen rarely. Natural processes simply cannot handle all the pollution that is produced.

Air pollution affects your health and the health of the environment. You breathe in air and all of the materials that are contained in air. Some of these materials can damage the delicate tissues of your respiratory system. The same air pollutants that are harmful to you also can damage plants and animals in the environment.

Gases That Pollute

The air you breathe every day is a mixture of gases and small particles. The one gas you need, oxygen, makes up about 20 percent of the air. The remaining 80 percent of the air consists of nitrogen and other naturally occurring gases, including carbon dioxide and argon. When other gases and particles enter the air, the air becomes polluted.

Most of the gases that pollute the air are produced by burning. Whenever coal, oil, natural gas, wood, and other materials are burned, harmful waste gases are produced. Other harmful gases are released into the air when some liquids evaporate or when gases escape from machinery or even from natural sources such as erupting volcanoes.

One dangerous gas produced when fuels are burned is **carbon monoxide,** a colorless, odorless gas. The more incomplete the burning, the more carbon monoxide produced. Carbon monoxide is dangerous because it combines with **hemoglobin** (**hee** muh gloh bun), the substance in the body's red blood cells that carries oxygen to all the cells of the body. When carbon monoxide is present, it binds to hemoglobin and prevents the hemoglobin from carrying oxygen. As a result, your body does not get enough oxygen. The exhaust gases from engines that burn petroleum fuels, such as cars and trucks, contain large amounts of carbon monoxide.

Another waste gas given off during burning is **carbon dioxide.** Unlike carbon monoxide, carbon dioxide is not poisonous. In fact, you produce carbon dioxide in your cells

O——x
Natural processes, like rain and snow, cannot control pollution.

Figure 22-3. Exhaust gases from cars and trucks are a major source of air pollution.
▼

when you "burn" food to generate energy. Unfortunately, the widespread use of coal and petroleum as fuels has caused a rise in the level of carbon dioxide in the atmosphere. Carbon dioxide in the atmosphere slows the rate at which the earth loses heat, which may cause an increase in the earth's temperature. Many scientists believe this effect, called the **greenhouse effect,** will lead to serious global weather changes. That could result in melting of the polar ice caps, which in turn would cause flooding in many coastal areas.

Other gases formed when fuels are burned include nitrogen oxides and sulfur oxides. These gases may cause your eyes to burn and tear. They also can damage lung tissues and worsen other respiratory problems. When these gases mix with water in the air, **nitric (ny** trik) **acid** and **sulfuric** (suhl **fyoor** ik) **acid** are formed, as you can see in Figure 22-4. When rain contains one or both of these acids, it is called **acid rain.** Snow, sleet, and fog also can contain these acids. Acid rain, snow, sleet, or fog dissolve stone, corrode metals, and damage plants. They increase the acidity of lakes, ponds, and streams thus killing or preventing the growth of many water-dwelling plants and animals. This form of pollution is also causing severe damage to trees in many parts of the world, including the eastern United States.

Natural gas, incompletely burned fuel, and fuels and certain solvents that evaporate are sources of **hydrocarbons** (hy druh **kar** bunz). Hydrocarbons are substances made up of hydrogen and carbon. Many hydrocarbons are poisonous, and some can cause cancers. When hydrocarbons react with nitric oxide in the presence of light, they form a brownish haze called **smog.** Many of the substances in smog are harmful to plants as well as animals.

The carbon dioxide produced by burning coal and petroleum have long-term effects on the atmosphere.

Figure 22-4. Acid rain, resulting from the burning of fuels, can cause widespread damage to trees.

Acid Rain Pollution

Sun

Sulfur dioxide and nitrogen oxides → Plus sunlight and water droplets → Produce sulfuric acid and nitric acid mixed with water in the form of:

Snow

Rain

Fog

Run off

Factories, vehicles, and homes

Sea

Run off

Lake

Figure 22-5. Air pollution in cities can reach dangerous levels.

Chemicals called **fluorocarbons** (floor oh **kar** bunz) also contribute to air pollution. These are chemicals that contain fluorine and carbon. Fluorocarbons can damage the ozone layer. The **ozone layer** is a thin layer of the upper atmosphere, which is made up of a form of oxygen called **ozone.** Ozone absorbs most of the sun's harmful ultraviolet light. When fluorocarbons destroy some of the ozone in the ozone layer, more ultraviolet light reaches the earth's surface. Ultraviolet light can cause skin cancer in humans and may damage other organisms.

Fluorocarbons are used in refrigeration and air conditioning equipment. At one time they also were used in aerosol cans, but this use of fluorocarbons has been banned in the United States. Many fluorocarbons are commonly known as **freon.**

Particle Forms of Air Pollution

Some pollutants exist as small or microscopic solid or liquid particles in the air. If you take a clean, white rag and run it along a windowsill, you will find evidence of air pollution. Particles of dust, soot, and mold spores are everywhere. Many of these particles, or **particulates** (pur **tik** yuh lits), are produced by burning. Others are produced from natural sources. Particle pollution enters your breathing system with the air you breathe. The tiny hairs, or **cilia** (**sil** ee uh) that line your breathing passages trap many of these particles before they reach your lungs, but they still can damage your body.

One type of particle pollutant that can cause serious harm is lead. Lead can poison the liver, kidneys, and nervous system. Lead poisoning in babies and young children often results in slow mental development.

Particles of lead are discharged into the air from the exhaust gases of engines that burn leaded gasoline. For many years, people were not aware of the effects of lead particulates. Lead was added to gasoline to improve the performance of engines. As people became more aware of the problem, unleaded gasoline came into use, and the levels of lead in people have dropped dramatically. Although some leaded gas is still being sold, it has only a small amount of lead. Eventually, no gasoline will be allowed to contain lead.

Particles of lead can enter the air from another source— lead paint. Lead used to be an ingredient in most paints. As old lead paint flakes off or is removed, the surrounding air picks up particles of lead. People in areas where lead paint is being removed should wear breathing filters to avoid inhaling paint dust.

Another particle pollutant in the air is **asbestos** (as **bes** tus). Asbestos is a mineral that occurs in the form of fibers. When asbestos fibers are inhaled into the lungs, they damage

Lead and asbestos are particle pollutants that cause serious damage to the body.

the cells of the lungs, causing a disease called **asbestosis** (as bes **toh** sis). In many cases, people who have worked with asbestos, especially if they also smoke, have high rates of certain types of cancer.

Because asbestos does not burn, shingles, floor tiles, and ceiling material were once made of it. The steel girders of buildings were coated with asbestos to prevent damage to them by heat during a fire. In certain areas, asbestos insulation was wrapped around steam pipes to keep heat in. Asbestos is still used in brake linings and brake pads, but alternative materials are beginning to replace it.

Weather and Air Pollution

Although the weather does not cause air pollution, it can affect it. As you may already know, warm air rises. When the air close to the earth's surface is warmer than air at higher elevations, which is usually the case, air pollutants are carried upward. This prevents air pollution levels from building up near the ground. When a **temperature inversion** occurs, however, a layer of cool air near the ground is trapped under a layer of warm air, as shown in Figure 22-6. As a result, pollutants are not carried away and build up to dangerously high levels. People who have respiratory problems usually are advised to stay indoors and to avoid physical activity during periods of severe air pollution.

A temperature inversion can cause pollutants to build up dangerously.

A Temperature Inversion

Cold air

Warm air

Cooler, polluted air

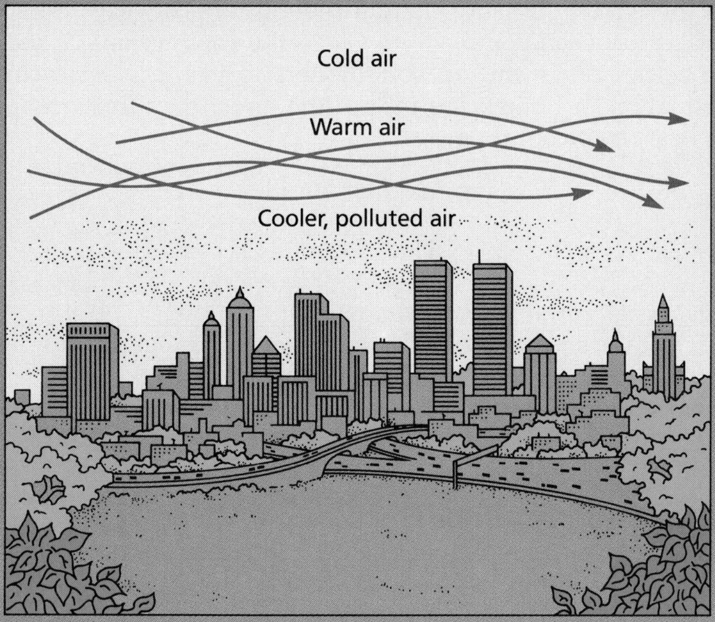

◀ **Figure 22-6. A temperature inversion traps air pollutants in a cool layer of air near the earth's surface.**

Figure 22-7. Keeping a car engine well-tuned reduces pollution and helps to save money.

What Can Be Done

Technology, which has caused many of our air pollution problems, also has helped solve some of them. Catalytic converters on cars have dramatically reduced the amount of pollutants in automobile exhausts. Many states now require that motor vehicles pass annual emission control inspections. "Scrubbers," or filters, on factory and power-plant smokestacks remove particles and some harmful gases before they can be released into the air. More efficient ways of burning oil, coal, and gas have helped to reduce the amount of pollution from these sources as well. As you know, fluorocarbons have been banned in aerosol cans, and scientists are looking into different chemicals for refrigeration units. The use of asbestos is severely limited and banned entirely in construction. Much of this progress has occurred because new laws were passed when people became aware of the dangers of air pollution.

Even with this progress, air pollution continues to be a serious problem. There are many ways in which you, as a private citizen, can help. If you see sources of air pollution, report them to the state agency that enforces air pollution regulations. Support state and federal legislation that favors strict air quality standards.

In your own day-to-day activities, too, you can develop habits that will reduce air pollution. Whenever you can, ride a train or bus instead of driving, or ride a bicycle instead of using a motor vehicle. If you drive, be sure the vehicle is well tuned. A well-tuned engine produces less pollution than a poorly tuned one and saves you money. Turn off lights and appliances that are not being used and lower your thermostat in the winter. Be sure that all fuel-burning devices are adjusted for clean combustion. Clean the cooling fans or coils on refrigerators and air conditioners to use less electricity. Insulation in homes can reduce the amount of fuel needed to heat or to cool them.

Section Review

1. What is the source of most air pollution?
2. How can the use of fluorocarbons be dangerous to the environment?
3. How does asbestos endanger human health?
4. How does a temperature inversion layer affect the air pollution below it?

What Do You Think?

5. If you were a member of your state legislature, what new air pollution regulations would you support?

3. WATER POLLUTION AND HEALTH

Clean, available, fresh water is something most of us take for granted until there is a crisis—a severe drought, for example. More and more people, however, have become concerned about our water resources. Thousands of public and private water supplies in the United States have been shut down because of pollution. In fact, water pollution has become a major environmental health concern.

Types of Water Pollution

Some water pollutants are biodegradable. Sewage, as you know, is a biodegradable waste. If sewage is released into the environment too rapidly, however, it builds up. It can make water foul-smelling and unable to support life. Sewage can also contain bacteria and viruses that cause disease. Hepatitis, for example, is spread when shellfish are harvested from waters contaminated with human sewage.

Other water pollutants are not biodegradable. Many industrial wastes contain acids, metals, solvents, and other toxic chemicals. If these pollutants get into the ground and run into water or are dumped into any body of water, they contaminate the organisms that live in or drink the water.

Salt, used to melt ice and snow on roads, is a serious source of water pollution. Road salt eventually runs into streams and water under the ground. High levels of salt in water kill many organisms that live in water and make the water unfit for human use.

Unfortunately, many of the chemicals in the pesticides, herbicides, and fertilizers used by farmers wash into streams, ponds, and lakes when it rains. They can also seep into the

Figure 22-8. Fresh, clean, unpolluted water is something no one should take for granted.

Figure 22-9. Agricultural chemicals and industrial wastes can be major sources of water pollution.

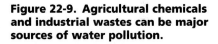

Figure 22-10. Fertilizers that enter bodies of water cause the overgrowth of algae.

water under ground. People who drink water contaminated with pesticides and herbicides suffer harmful effects. In fact, fish living in water contaminated with these chemicals pass the contamination on to people who consume the fish.

Fertilizers cause the type of pollution that you read about earlier. Most fertilizers contain nitrates and phosphates, minerals that plants need in order to grow. When these minerals are washed into streams, rivers, and lakes, they cause small water plants, called **algae** (**al** jee), to grow rapidly. When the algae die, they serve as food for a huge population of decomposers. The decomposers use all the oxygen in the water. Without oxygen, most of the water-dwelling organisms die, and the water becomes foul-smelling and unfit for use. This process of overproduction followed by decay and lack of oxygen is called **eutrophication** (yoo trohf ih **kay** shun).

Industries that take cool water from a river, lake, or ocean and pump it through their machines to cool them create a different kind of water pollution problem. As the cool water passes through the machinery and absorbs heat, it becomes warmer. When the water is returned to the river, lake, or ocean, it raises the temperature of the water. This warming of water is called **thermal pollution.** It causes problems because most water animals can live only within a narrow range of temperatures. The heated water can kill these animals.

Health careers

Medical writers express technical information in simple, everyday language.

It is important that people understand the many complex environmental issues we face today. **Medical writers** help make this information easy to understand.

Medical writers usually prepare articles for newspapers and magazines, but some write books or scripts for radio and television programs. Many medical writers are self-employed, while others work on the staffs of newspapers, magazines, research institutions, and hospitals.

Medical writers must have a knack for writing plainly about technical subjects. For this career, you need a bachelor's degree from a four-year college and a background in journalism, English, or science.

Biological photographers communicate information through visual images. They may photograph a new surgical procedure, bacteria under a microscope, or the effects of acid rain on a lake. Several two- and four-year colleges offer training in biological photography.

What Can Be Done

There are many federal and state laws that are designed to prevent water pollution. Since water pollution still occurs, however, preventing it is everyone's responsibility.

There are things you can do. The simplest thing is to conserve water. When you do not waste water, you reduce the volume of sewage. This allows the septic system or sewage treatment plant in your area to handle the wastes more effectively. Look for sources of water pollution. Many cases of water pollution have been stopped by citizens reporting the violation to state or federal officials.

Do not dump dangerous chemicals, such as oil, solvents, or pesticides, into a drain. These chemicals cannot be handled by a septic or sewage treatment system. Most communities have waste collection centers to which these chemicals can be taken for safe disposal. If you have a question about how to dispose of dangerous chemicals safely, you can call your local board of health or state agency for environmental protection.

○━━┳

You can reduce water pollution by conserving water and properly disposing of toxic chemicals.

Section Review

1. In what two ways can agriculture add to the problem of water pollution?
2. How does underground water become polluted?
3. Why is thermal pollution a concern?

What Do You Think?
4. What are some practical ways you can conserve water every day?

4. LAND POLLUTION AND HEALTH

The amount of waste material produced in the United States every year is staggering—over 300 million tons. Much of the waste material is solid or liquid waste, which is buried in areas called landfills. A **landfill** is an area where trash, garbage, and other wastes are left and covered with soil.

Much of what is placed in landfills is biodegradable. Much of it, however, is not. Many of the nonbiodegradable wastes that are produced every day are potential sources of air and water pollution.

Land Disposal of Wastes

Some types of trash and garbage, such as paper, wood, and leather, are biodegradable. This type of trash may be disagreeable to look at or smell, but it is not dangerous to human health or the environment. Other types of trash, such as glass, plastic, ceramics, and metals are not biodegradable. Although some of these may not be harmful, they remain on the land almost forever.

Some land pollutants are dangerous to human health or safety. The Environmental Protection Agency (EPA) calls substances **hazardous wastes** if they are flammable, explosive, corrosive, or toxic to human or other life. Each year, more than 250 million tons of hazardous wastes are produced in the United States alone. According to the federal government, many of these wastes are disposed of in unsafe ways. A landfill not sealed to prevent leakage of wastes into underground water, shown in Figure 22-12, is an example of unsafe disposal. A sealed landfill, also shown in Figure 22-12, is an example of safe disposal.

Much of the waste produced today in the United States is nonbiodegradable and a source of pollution.

Figure 22-12. Landfills can be designed to prevent pollution.
▼

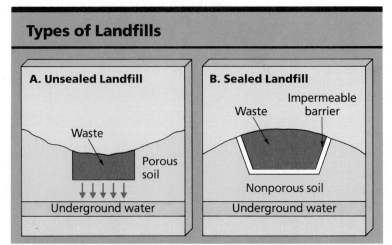

Types of Landfills

A. Unsealed Landfill

Waste

Porous soil

↓↓↓↓↓

Underground water

B. Sealed Landfill

Impermeable barrier

Waste

Nonporous soil

Underground water

▲
Figure 22-13. Hazardous wastes are a serious health threat.

The EPA has identified over 20,000 dumps in the United States that contain hazardous substances. Of these, more than 800 have been placed on a list of dumps to be cleaned up quickly because they are dangerous to public health and the health of the environment.

Most of the hazardous substances that have been dumped are the result of industry and technology. Many of the substances were dumped before their dangers were even known. For example, between 1946 and 1958, one chemical company dumped chemical wastes including benzene, lindane, and dioxin, three toxic chemicals, into the ground around Love Canal in upstate New York. Later, many homes were constructed in the area. In fact, a school was built over the dump site.

In 1976, when heavy rains flooded basements in the Love Canal area, oily liquids, as well as rain water, entered the basements. These oily liquids were chemicals that were leaking out of the dump site.

Studies showed an increase of disease in the area which was linked to the chemicals underneath the homes and schools. Because of this strong evidence, the state government evacuated the people from their homes. Today, the area is unpopulated because of the toxic materials in the soil.

You may have seen pictures of people who clean up toxic dump sites. Their bodies are completely covered by suits that prevent them from coming into contact with any substances. Because some substances can give off toxic fumes, people who clean up toxic dump sites must wear face masks as well as protective suits. Some of the substances they may have to deal with are **carcinogens,** or cancer-causing substances. For example, benzene, a liquid used in many industrial processes, is now known to be a carcinogen.

Chemical Cleanup Using Bacteria

To some bacteria, a chemical spill or dump looks like lunch. These bacteria digest hazardous compounds and change them into safer substances. Recently, scientists have found ways to speed up the bacteria's activities.

Environmental engineers can speed the cleanup process by adding nutrients and water to the waste site. This helps the bacteria work more rapidly. Researchers may also take samples of the bacteria to the lab, where they select the best waste-eaters. Only these bacteria are grown, and barrels of their offspring are returned to the waste site.

Although bacteria cannot break down all wastes, they are the best method in some situations. Their use is often faster, less costly, and less upsetting to a site than are other methods.

You might wonder what happens once the hazardous compounds have all been broken down. With nothing left to eat, the bacteria simply die.

Lab-grown bacteria feed on hazardous wastes.

Other substances are known to be **mutagens** (**myoo** tuh junz). Mutagens are chemicals that cause changes in a cell's genetic material. Genetic material is responsible for passing on traits to the next generation. Often, these changes caused by mutagens are harmful, and the offspring produced are damaged. Other pollutants may damage the nervous system, lungs, or kidneys. In some cases, the damage may be fatal.

What Can Be Done?

Many sites where hazardous wastes have been dumped legally or illegally have been identified and are scheduled for cleanup. Other sites have not been identified. If you suspect hazardous chemicals have been dumped at a site, you should notify your local board of health.

New legislation makes it difficult for industries to dump wastes illegally. Legal dump sites for hazardous chemicals are designed to prevent the escape of wastes into the air or water under ground. In addition, many companies are reducing the amount of wastes they generate or recycling their wastes. New technologies for destroying hazardous chemicals, such as high temperature burning, may provide a way of eliminating large volumes of wastes. Many states have laws that require recycling metal and plastic containers, and some communities have recycling centers.

You can help reduce the problems associated with land disposal of wastes. Support programs that call for the recycling of glass, metal, and paper. If nondisposable containers or consumer goods are available, use them in place of disposable, nonbiodegradable ones. Do not put hazardous materials, such as pesticides, oil, and batteries, into your trash. Save these for special hazardous waste collection centers in your local community. If you have questions about disposing hazardous materials, check with your local board of health or state agency for environmental protection.

▲
Figure 22-14. Recycling containers saves energy and reduces the volume of solid wastes.

Section Review

1. What is a sanitary landfill?
2. How do nonbiodegradable waste products affect the environment?
3. How can land pollution affect human health?
4. What is a mutagen?

What Do You Think?
5. Suppose you were put in charge of designing a new packaging method for a fast-food chain. How could your design protect your products and yet have little effect on the environment?

5. RADIATION AND NOISE POLLUTION

Radiation and noise are two forms of pollution that seem to be getting worse rather than better. **Radiation,** as the term is used here, is a form of high energy that can damage living things. Radiation includes ultraviolet light, x-rays, cosmic rays, and the energy that is given off by certain substances, such as uranium. Substances that give off radiation are said to be **radioactive.**

Sounds tell you something about your surroundings, but loud sound, noise, is a nuisance that can harm your health. Noise seems to be a fact of life. Airplanes, trains, motor vehicles, appliances, television, radio, stereo equipment, and machinery all produce levels of sound that can become noise and endanger your health.

Radiation and Health

Radiation is not new, nor is it something created by humans. There are many forms of natural radiation. Ultraviolet light from the sun, cosmic rays from space, and radiation from naturally occurring radioactive substances in the air, water, and soil make up natural, or **background,** radiation. Background radiation is something that all living organisms are exposed to.

However, not all radiation comes from natural sources. Some sources of radiation are artificial. **Artificial sources** are the result of the technological uses of radiation. For example, you are exposed to radiation every time you have an x-ray taken of your teeth or bones.

Radiation pollution is caused by the activities of humans. It results in exposure to higher-than-background levels of radiation. Exposure to these levels of radiation can result in a disease known as **radiation sickness** or in death. In some cases, the body's immune system is damaged by radiation. The **immune system** recognizes foreign substances in the body, such as bacteria and viruses, and destroys them. A person with a damaged immune system may be affected by diseases that would not affect someone with a properly working immune system.

Radiation can also act as a mutagen. Sometimes the cells with damaged genetic material become cancerous and begin to divide uncontrollably. In fact, even small amounts of radiation can be harmful. For example, there is some evidence to show that even one severe sunburn, caused by overexposure to ultraviolet radiation, can cause some people to develop skin cancers. The effects of radiation exposure add up over time. Each little bit of radiation you receive adds to your total level of exposure.

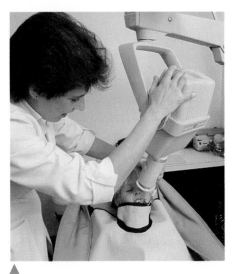

Figure 22-15. Medical and dental x-rays are one form of radiation exposure.

Radiation pollution can damage the immune system, as well as cause disease, cancer, and death.

Figure 22-16. Nuclear power plants are sources of radiation in the environment.

In the past, radiation was added to the air when atomic weapons were tested. Wind carried air-borne radioactivity over the earth. Eventually, the radioactive material fell to earth or was carried to the ground by rain or snow. Radioactivity that falls to earth in this manner is called **fallout.**

Nuclear power plants use radioactive substances. It is possible that a nuclear power plant will malfunction at some point and release a great deal of radiation. Because accidents are possible, nuclear power plants are highly regulated and have many safety systems built into their operation. Generating electricity with nuclear power does have the benefit of not producing the kind of air pollution released from oil or coal-burning power plants.

Other radioactive materials in the environment are the results of the wastes produced by nuclear power plants and by the medical uses of radioactive materials. Since these wastes will give off radiation for years to come, they present a long-term danger to people.

The radioactive gas, radon is estimated to cause 5,000 to 20,000 deaths from lung cancer each year. Radon is produced by radium, a radioactive material, found naturally underground. Radon becomes a problem when it leaks from the ground into the foundations of buildings and builds up to dangerous levels.

Noise and Health

You may already know about the damage loud sounds can do to your hearing. You may have noticed some hearing loss shortly after you have left a loud concert or an area where there was loud machinery. Often, your hearing returns to normal after several hours. Prolonged exposure to loud noise damages the cells in the inner ear. Over time and

Figure 22-17. Noise from any source can be harmful to your health.

a continued exposure to noise, these cells do not recover. Hearing loss then becomes permanent. The louder the sound and the longer the period of exposure to the sound, the greater the risk of hearing loss. Sound levels are measured in units called **decibels.** The loudness of a sound doubles for each ten-decibel increase. Hearing loss begins to occur around 80 decibels, which is the level of sound from a vacuum cleaner. Fifty decibels of sound can interfere with sleep.

A firm connection between noise and disease, except for hearing loss, has not been established. It is believed, however, that noise contributes to stress and stress-related diseases, such as hypertension and peptic ulcers. Certainly, we have all felt the tension that occurs when we are exposed to loud noises.

What Can Be Done

Radiation and noise pollution cannot be avoided completely. They are part of our daily lives. However, many doctors suggest that you limit your exposure to the sun. Heavy exposure to ultraviolet radiation may cause skin cancers. Doctors also suggest that you limit your exposure to x-rays, although you should not be afraid to get an x-ray when it is medically needed. The risk involved in a single exposure is small, and the medical benefits of a correct diagnosis are great. Remember, the effects of exposure to all forms of radiation add up.

Many experts now believe that you should test your home for radon. There are testing kits available for this purpose. Some state environmental agencies also provide these tests. If a radon problem exists, improving ventilation and sealing cracks in foundation walls and floors are recommended procedures.

Limit your exposure to loud noises. Listening to loud music, especially with headphones, is a major cause of permanent hearing loss in teenagers. Avoid areas where noise levels are high. If you cannot avoid them, wear special ear covers or plugs when you are in a noisy environment.

Over time, prolonged exposure to loud noise can cause permanent hearing loss.

▲
Figure 22-18. Radon-detecting devices are available for home use.

Section Review

1. What are some of the sources of radiation in your particular environment?
2. How is radiation a danger to human health?
3. How do loud sounds and noise affect your health?

What Do You Think?
4. What would you do if you learned that a nuclear power plant was going to be built a few miles from your home?

22 | Chapter Review

Chapter Summary

- The environment is the physical world and the living things that inhabit it.
- Pollution, which occurs when wastes enter the environment, affects all living things.
- Wastes are either biodegradable or nonbiodegradable. Biodegradable wastes are broken down into simpler substances by the actions of decomposers.
- Many pollution problems are a result of our standard of living.
- Most air pollution is a result of burning.
- Major air pollutants include carbon monoxide, carbon dioxide, oxides of nitrogen and sulfur, hydrocarbons, fluorocarbons, lead, and asbestos.
- By conserving energy and using public transportation, everyone can help to reduce some of today's air pollution.
- Water pollution is caused by sewage, industrial wastes, agricultural chemicals, and road salt.
- Hazardous wastes that pollute the land pose a danger to human health and the health of the environment.

- Thermal pollution occurs when cooling water from industries raises the temperature of streams, lakes, or ocean areas above the range suitable for water-dwelling organisms.
- Everyone can help reduce water pollution by conserving water and by properly disposing of dangerous chemicals.
- Some hazardous chemicals can damage the body; other hazardous chemicals act as carcinogens or mutagens.
- There are hundreds of dump sites across the United States that pose an immediate threat to the public or the environment.
- Individuals can help reduce land pollution by recycling wastes and by properly disposing of hazardous chemicals.
- Higher-than-background levels of radiation occur in medical and dental x-rays, medical uses of radioactive substances, nuclear weapons tests, nuclear reactors, and radon.
- Loud noise can cause permanent hearing loss. Individuals should avoid areas where there is loud noise or else wear protective ear equipment.

Vocabulary Review

Listed below are some of the important terms in this chapter. Choose the term that best matches the phrase in the exercise that follows.

acid rain	carbon monoxide	hazardous waste	radiation
asbestos	carcinogen	landfill	radon
background radiation	environment	mutagen	temperature inversion
biodegradable waste	eutrophication	ozone layer	thermal pollution
carbon dioxide	fluorocarbon	pollutants	waste

1. a site where wastes are covered with soil
2. a part of the atmosphere that absorbs ultraviolet light
3. a form of waste that is flammable, explosive, corrosive, or toxic
4. the physical world and the living things that inhabit it

5. a substance that destroys ozone
6. wastes that enter the environment
7. when cold air is trapped below warm air
8. a waste gas that causes the gradual warming of the earth
9. a radioactive gas
10. a gas that combines with hemoglobin

What Have You Learned?

1. How are living things dependent on the physical environment?
2. What happens to natural wastes when they are in the environment?
3. Why is carbon monoxide dangerous?
4. Why is the level of carbon dioxide in the atmosphere increasing?
5. What is smog?
6. Why are fluorocarbons considered a problem in the environment?

7. What are two common particle forms of air pollution?
8. Name three sources of water pollution.
9. How can a landfill cause water pollution? Why does thermal pollution endanger plant and animal life in water?
10. When is a substance considered to be hazardous to life?
11. What is an artificial source of radiation?
12. Why is loud noise harmful?

What Do You Think?

1. How could toxic, nonbiodegradable substances dumped into the ocean affect you?
2. How do you think technology has helped humans to be aware of pollution?
3. Some people claim nuclear power plants are a clean source of energy. What do you think they mean by this, and why might other people disagree with this view?
4. What do you think are the advantages and disadvantages of burning trash?
5. Why are people more concerned about pollution now than they were 50 years ago?

What Would You Do?

1. Suppose that you know a factory is polluting a small stream. Reporting the pollution may mean that the factory will close. Would you risk making this report to the authorities? Why?
2. Your family has purchased a house. In a backyard shed you discover a large metal barrel filled with liquid that is beginning to leak. What would you do?
3. You are offered two jobs after graduation. One job pays well, but the office you will work in is noisy and unattractive. The other job pays less, but the office is attractive and quiet. Which job would you choose? Why?
4. You recently learned that a friend has been dumping used engine oil into the town sewer system. What would you do to discourage him from this activity?
5. A friend of yours suggests that the actions of a single person have little effect on the environment. What arguments could you give to your friend?

For Further Study

1. Rachel Carson was one of the first persons to notice the harmful effects of certain chemicals on the environment. Find out more about this scientist's work. You might want to read *Silent Spring*, a book that is regarded by many people as the first to call attention to the problems of polluting the environment.
2. Find out what kinds of treatment facilities are available to deal with wastes in your town or city. You might be able to arrange a visit to a waste treatment facility near you. If you can, you might want to write a report that includes pictures of your visit.

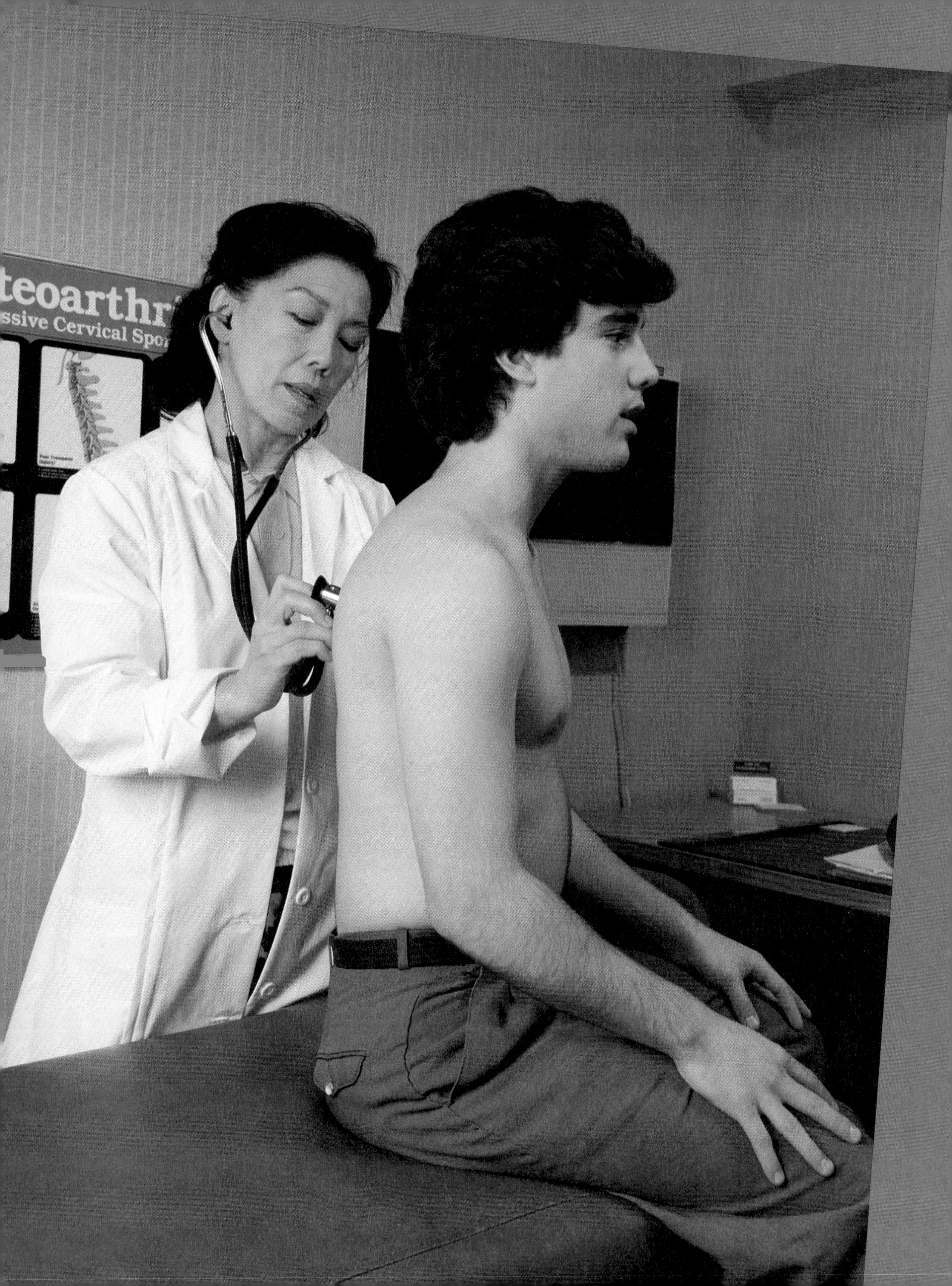

23

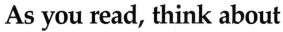

As you read, think about

▶ what kinds of health-care providers and facilities are available to the consumer.

▶ what you can expect during a medical examination.

▶ the difference between private insurance and an HMO.

▶ how to evaluate health-care products and services.

Choosing Health Care

The stethoscope feels cold on your back. As you breathe deeply at the doctor's instructions, you look around the office. There's the blood-pressure cuff and the instruments for examining your eyes, ears, and throat. So far, everything has checked out fine. This is a good time to ask the doctor some questions that have been bothering you. You're glad to get to talk to her now, instead of waiting until you're sick.

Even if you're in top shape, an annual check-up is important. Early detection is vital in many illnesses. It's also important not to wait until a health problem arises to develop a comfortable relationship with a health-care provider you trust. In this chapter, you will learn about your rights and responsibilities as a consumer of medical care and about the many health-care options that are available to you.

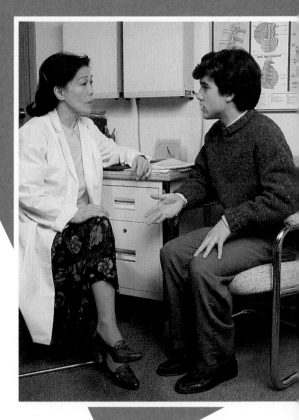

Because your health is so important, you owe it to yourself to choose the best available health care.

Check Your Wellness

Are you a wise consumer of health services and products? See if you can answer yes to the questions below.

1. Are you familiar with the different health-care professionals who can help you with your medical needs?

2. Are you aware of your rights as a patient?

3. Do you ask your doctor to explain things you do not completely understand?

4. Do you know about health insurance?

5. Are you able to resist the efforts of advertisers and salespeople to get you to buy a product you do not really want?

6. Do you try to get reliable information about products and services before you purchase them?

7. Do you follow the instructions on the labels of health-care products and medications?

8. Do you return a product if you are not satisfied with its performance?

1. THE HEALTH-CARE SYSTEM

As you grow older, you will make more and more choices as a consumer of health-care products and services. A **consumer** is anyone who buys goods and services. Obviously, to make wise health-care choices, you will need to be knowledgeable about products, services, and consumer issues in general. Understanding the health-care system is part of being a wise consumer.

When your parents were growing up, doctors were trained to do everything from delivering babies to performing surgery and setting broken bones. Since then, however, health care has become highly specialized. Today, teams of health professionals—from hospital dietitians to laboratory technicians—are available to provide health care.

Health-Care Providers

The health-care professional who takes care of most of your routine medical needs is your primary-care physician. **Primary-care physicians** are medical doctors. A **medical doctor** is a professional who has spent four years in a medical school and has earned the degree of either Doctor of Medicine (M.D.) or Doctor of Osteopathy (D.O.). **Osteopathy** (ahz tee **ahp** uh thee) is a branch of medicine that emphasizes the relationship of the body's muscular and skeletal systems to general health.

To practice medicine, a doctor must spend at least one year as an intern in a hospital and pass the licensing test of the state in which he or she practices. Once licensed, a doctor can make a **diagnosis** (dy ug **noh** sis), provide treatment, and write a prescription for medication. A diagnosis is a doctor's opinion of the nature or cause of a medical condition. A **prescription** is a written order from a doctor to a **pharmacist** (**far** muh sist), specifying the medicine to be given to a patient. A pharmacist is a person trained and licensed to prepare and give out medicines according to the prescriptions of medical doctors.

When you have a medical condition that requires specialized treatment, your primary-care physician will refer you to a medical specialist. A **medical specialist** is a doctor with additional training in a particular branch of medicine and has passed a test that certifies him or her to practice in this specialty. Figure 23-1 lists some of the many medical specialties.

The primary-care physician works with other health-care professionals to bring patients the care they need. These health-care professionals are often called **allied health workers**. They include nurses, dietitians, physical therapists, dental hygienists, and psychologists.

NURSES A nurse is a licensed health-care professional who, working in collaboration with a doctor, provides direct care to patients. Depending on the level of training and experience, a nurse may work closely with a doctor or may function more independently of the doctor.

A **registered nurse (R.N.)** must complete a two-to-four-year nursing program and pass a state licensing examination. R.N.s observe and assess patient symptoms, plan the best approach to promoting recovery, and evaluate progress. They also counsel people of all ages about ways to stay healthy, prevent injury, and live to the fullest capacity.

Licensed practical nurses (L.P.N.s) or **licensed vocational nurses (L.V.N.s)** usually have completed one to two years of training in a program of practical nursing and passed a state licensing test. Because L.P.N.s or L.V.N.s have limited training, they have less responsibility than R.N.s. Many L.P.N.s administer medicines to and treat patients.

Registered nurses who have received additional training in a specialized program may become nurse practitioners. **Nurse practitioners (N.P.s)** are trained to do many of the tasks that only doctors used to perform. For example, N.P.s can take medical histories, perform physical exams, order diagnostic tests, treat routine medical problems, and advise patients on how to prevent disease. N.P.s are fairly independent, usually working with, but not under the supervision of, a doctor.

Other Allied Health Professionals

Doctors are sometimes helped by **physician's assistants**. These are individuals who have received specialized training to perform certain tasks previously done by doctors. These tasks may include taking medical histories and performing physical exams. Unlike nurse practitioners, physician's assistants always work under the close supervision of a doctor.

Persons trained to rehabilitate patients disabled by problems such as back pain, fractures, burns, strokes, sports injuries, and nerve injury are **physical therapists** (fiz ih kul **thehr** uh pists). A physical therapist uses various physical agents, such as exercises and heat, to relieve pain and improve strength and mobility.

A **dietitian** (dy uh **tish** un) is someone who has completed a degree program in foods and nutrition. This training enables the dietitian to set up and supervise food services for institutions such as hospitals. Dietitians may also provide nutritional counseling to patients in a health-care facility or in private practice.

A **dentist** is a health professional who has completed three to four years of training in dental school and has earned the degree of Doctor of Dentistry (D.D.). Dentists examine your mouth, teeth, and gums and fill cavities. Many dentists

---

Medical Specialists

Allergist
treats people who have allergies, or reactions to irritating substances

Cardiologist
specializes in diagnosing and treating heart disease

Geriatric physician
specializes in treating elderly people

Gynecologist
specializes in treating disorders and diseases of the female reproductive system

Neurologist
treats disorders of the nervous system

Obstetrician
concerned with pregnancy, labor, and delivery of a baby

Oncologist
specializes in diagnosing and treating cancerous tumors

Orthopedist
specializes in treating disorders of the bones and joints

Pediatrician
specializes in the development and care of children and in treating diseases of children

Psychiatrist
specializes in diagnosing and treating mental and emotional disorders

Figure 23-1. Among the different medical specialists listed, whose work is concerned primarily with women?

Allied Health Workers

Emergency medical technician (EMT)
provides immediate care to ill or injured patients in an emergency situation
Medical technologist (MT)
performs laboratory tests, such as blood tests
Occupational therapist (OT)
helps disabled people adapt their daily activities and job skills to their particular problems
Pharmacist
makes up and dispenses medicines that are prescribed by a physician
Physician's assistant (PA)
carries out tasks, such as physical examinations, under a physician's supervision
Respiratory therapist
treats respiratory problems under a physician's order

▲
Figure 23-2. Which of these health professionals is skilled in caring for the disabled?

employ a **dental hygienist** (hy **jen** ist), a technician who is trained to clean and x-ray the teeth and to assist the dentist in various procedures. If you have a specific dental problem, your dentist may refer you to a dental specialist. A **dental specialist** is a dentist who has had years of additional training in a particular branch of dentistry and who has been certified to practice in this specialty. An **orthodontist** (or thuh **dahn** tist) is a specialist who has been trained to correct teeth that are out of position, or misaligned. A **periodontist** (pehr ee oh **dahn** tist) is a dentist who specializes in treating various gum diseases.

Treatment for emotional problems is available from a number of different health professionals. A **psychologist** (sy **kahl** uh jist) is a person with two to six years of training beyond college in evaluating and helping people with emotional problems. Psychologists cannot prescribe drugs.

A **psychiatrist** (sy **ky** uh trist) is a medical doctor who has had special training in the treatment of patients with emotional problems. A psychiatrist can prescribe drugs and hospitalize patients who need special treatment. Another type of professional in the mental health field is a social worker. A licensed **social worker** has a master's degree from a school of social work. Social workers are trained to involve the entire family, rather than just the individual, in resolving emotional problems. Nurses with advanced degrees in psychiatric nursing also perform independent psychiatric therapy. Figure 23-2 offers a list of allied health workers.

Health-Care Facilities

During the course of your life you will probably have different kinds of medical needs. Depending on what those needs are, you can seek medical care at private doctors' offices, clinics, hospitals, or specialized health centers.

Perhaps the most frequently used facility is the doctor's private office, which can be in a hospital or in a private building. Here, doctors, nurse practitioners, or physician's assistants do routine examinations as well as tests to diagnose and treat minor illnesses and injuries. Minor surgery, such as removal of a wart, may also be done in the office.

If a medical test or surgical procedure is more complex, doctors may ask their patients to have the test or procedure done at an outpatient clinic. A **clinic** is a facility in which primary-health care is provided by one or more doctors and other allied health workers. A clinic may be an independent facility or part of a hospital. An **outpatient** is a person admitted to a hospital or clinic for tests or treatments that do not require an overnight stay. Many tests involving x-rays are performed at outpatient clinics, as are certain surgical procedures. For example, **cataract** (**kat** uh rakt) **surgery**, surgery to remove a cloudy lens from the eye, can be performed on an outpatient basis. Outpatient care is less costly than a hospital stay because there is no expense for a hospital room, meals, or nursing services.

HOSPITALS   Treatment for a serious disorder, such as a heart attack, requires a period of hospitalization. A patient who is required to stay in a hospital for overnight or longer is called an **inpatient**. Health care given to a patient in a hospital is called secondary health care. The doctor visits the patient every day to note progress and make any necessary adjustments in the patient's care.

In the United States, there are about 7,000 hospitals, ranging from small facilities to large medical centers. A hospital may be a general hospital or a specialty hospital. A **general hospital** treats all sorts of patients with various types of illnesses and injuries. A **specialty hospital** specializes in treating one age group or one type of disorder. Some hospitals, as shown in Figure 23-3, are called teaching hospitals. **Teaching hospitals** are located near medical schools whose faculty members are on the hospital staff. Young physicians and allied health workers train at these hospitals. A teaching hospital also provides facilities for staff members to carry out medical research. Because of this research, teaching hospitals often offer advanced medical care.

LONG-TERM CARE FACILITIES   Not all patients need the kinds of services provided by clinics or hospitals. Some patients need a setting that provides basic nursing care over

Serious disorders are treated in a hospital where doctors closely observe a patient's progress.

◀ **Figure 23-3. In a teaching hospital, medical students visit patients and review cases with doctors.**

Rehabilitation centers, nursing homes, and hospices offer special types of long-term or short-term nursing care.

▲
Figure 23-4. Elderly people can receive full-time care at a nursing home.

a long period of time without the costly services of a hospital. Facilities providing this type of care are rehabilitation or convalescent centers and nursing homes. A **rehabilitation** or **convalescent** (kahn vuh **les** unt) **center** provides care for people who are recovering from surgery, an illness, or an injury. These people eventually return to their homes. A **nursing home** is a facility that specializes in providing long-term care for the elderly or the chronically ill who are incapable of caring for themselves.

One special kind of nursing care is available for terminally ill patients. This care can be given either in the home or in a live-in facility called a **hospice** (**hahs** pis). Hospice care is usually short-term and focuses on helping a dying patient live as comfortably as possible.

HEALTH-CARE SERVICES Volunteer agencies offer many kinds of health-care services. The American Red Cross, for example, gives free medical care, housing, food, and small amounts of money during emergencies. The American Cancer Society frequently provides free transportation to local treatment centers and also lends equipment such as walkers and wheelchairs.

Patients also can be given care and treatment in their own homes. Nurses coming into a home are usually less expensive than nursing-home care. Many patients benefit emotionally from in-home care, since they are able to remain in familiar surroundings.

Local and state health departments also provide services at little or no cost. In many communities, public-health nurses visit local schools to give free hearing and vision tests or give immunization injections. Local and state health departments also provide dental care, mental health care, visiting nursing services, and care to pregnant women. To contact your local or state health departments, look in your phone book under Government Listings.

Section Review

1. Distinguish between the role of a primary-care physician and the role of a specialist.
2. List the names of four allied health careers. Describe the type of work done in each of these careers.
3. What are the advantages of outpatient care compared with the advantages of inpatient care?
4. How do convalescent centers and hospices differ?

What Do You Think?
5. What kind of facility would you choose in order to obtain a routine chest x-ray. Why?

2. PARTICIPATING IN YOUR HEALTH CARE

Up to now, your parents have probably made most of the decisions about your health care. As you grow older, however, you will take on these responsibilities for yourself. Knowing something about your health-care choices can help you choose what is best for you.

Choosing Health Care

Deciding where to go or what doctor to see for routine health care deserves careful consideration. After all, you want health care delivered by qualified people in a setting that makes you feel comfortable. Many people prefer to see a doctor in a clinic. A clinic may be part of, or affiliated with, a hospital, or it may be totally independent. Many clinics have a wide range of laboratory and other testing facilities available to the staff. At some clinics you can arrange to see the doctor of your choice. At other clinics, you may see the first available doctor. Some clinics also give you the option of seeing a nurse practitioner.

Rather than seeing a doctor at a clinic, some people prefer to see a doctor who is in private practice, working for himself or herself. Often several doctors in private practice will have their offices together in the same building and work together in a group practice. Although it may be more expensive to see a doctor in private practice than in a clinic, you usually can expect to see the same doctor every time you make an appointment.

Whether you choose a doctor at a clinic or a doctor who is in private practice, you will need to find a doctor suited to your own needs. The best way to begin is by asking for recommendations from family members or friends whose opinions you trust and from other health professionals you know, such as your school nurse.

When you have the names of some recommended doctors, you might check the *American Medical Association Directory* in your local library. This directory lists the names of doctors, the year they received their medical degrees, and their areas of specialization. Once you have this information, you should begin to think about some of your own preferences. Do you want a young doctor or would you prefer an older one? Would you be more comfortable with a male doctor or a female doctor? Do you want a doctor with an outgoing personality or one who is more reserved?

The best time to make your first visit to a doctor is while you are well. Then, if you need a doctor, you will know who to see. Figure 23-5 lists some questions you might ask yourself when choosing a doctor.

Knowing about available health-care choices helps prepare you for health-care decisions when the need arises.

Evaluating Your Doctor

- Does the doctor answer your questions fully in terms you can understand?
- Does the doctor perform a careful and complete physical examination?
- Does the doctor keep accurate written records that he or she refers to?
- Does the doctor explain reasons for medical tests?
- Does the doctor explain reasons for medicines and give clear directions for taking medicines?
- Do you feel the doctor is listening to what you are saying?
- Does the doctor have after-hour and weekend care for emergencies?
- Is the doctor willing to consult with or refer you to other physicians for special health problems?

Source: Jeffrey R. M. Kunz, M.D., *AMA Family Medical Guide*, 1982

Figure 23-5. Ask yourself these questions when you need to evaluate your doctor.

Figure 23-6. Which of these rights do you feel most strongly about?

Your Rights and Responsibilities as a Patient

It is important to realize that you have certain rights as a patient. If, for example, your doctor recommends that you have your appendix removed, you have the right to have each step of the procedure explained to you. You also have the right to know why you need the procedure, what risks are involved, and what the cost will be. If there is something you still do not understand or feel comfortable about, you have the right to a second opinion. A **second opinion** is the diagnosis and advice of another doctor. You also have the right to refuse the suggested treatment, tests, examinations, or medications.

As a patient, you also have certain responsibilities. For example, it is your responsibility to ask your doctor about anything that concerns your health. Asking questions, even awkward ones, can help you understand your body and whatever treatment you may receive. In fact, most doctors expect questions.

It is also your responsibility to answer your doctor's questions honestly. A doctor needs accurate information from you to be able to make a correct diagnosis. Information about symptoms and any activities or behaviors that may affect your health or treatment are important for your doctor to know. A doctor is there to make sure you get the help you need. Refer to the chart in Figure 23-6 for a summary of your rights as a patient.

Like everyone else, doctors and other health-care professionals vary in their abilities and in how they relate to people. If you are not satisfied with the services provided by a clinic

Friend to Friend

Brenda:
This is my first solo trip to a new doctor. How do I know if she's any good?

Hilary:
O.K., pretend I'm the doctor and ask me questions.

Brenda:
Questions? You don't ask doctors questions.

Hilary:
Of course you do. If you were buying a car, you'd ask a lot of questions first.

or a doctor, you do not have to return. Part of having good health care is being satisfied with the personal, as well as the medical, treatment you receive. Remember, you owe it to yourself to select what is best for you.

The Medical Examination

Have you ever put off seeing a doctor because you were afraid of getting an inoculation or because you dreaded getting undressed in the examining room? If so, you are like many other people. It might be helpful, however, to look upon a visit to a doctor as an opportunity to find out more about your body and to get some answers to any important questions you have.

A medical examination consists of a complete medical history, a time to talk with the doctor, and a physical examination. Your **medical history** is a record of your present and past health, as well as the health of members of your family. Usually, you will have to fill out a medical history form, or the doctor will ask you about your past illnesses and current health.

Your medical examination should also include time for you to ask questions and discuss any concerns you may have about your body or any health-related issues in your life. It is a good idea to bring a list of questions to make sure that you cover everything you wanted to talk about.

After you have talked to the doctor, you will have a physical examination. The **physical examination** is a head-to-toe check of your body to identify any medical problems you may have. It usually begins with a measurement of your height and weight, a blood pressure reading, and a body

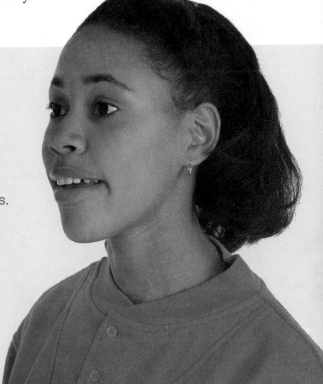

A medical examination helps you and your doctor know the facts about your body and your health.

Brenda:
That's true, but what do I ask?

Hilary:
Anything you want to know—the cost, her qualifications, whether she's available after hours. You'll get a feeling about her as you talk.

Brenda:
O.K., Doc. Let's try it out. I'll write down the questions to use later.

Computer-Assisted Diagnosis

The latest tool in a doctor's medical bag may soon be a computer. Computers soon will assist doctors in diagnosing their patients' ailments.

Using a personal computer, a phone link, and a computer program, doctors can gain access to medical databanks around the country. A doctor simply enters a patient's symptoms, age, sex, and medical history into the computer. The computer then scans the databank and responds with a short list of likely diagnoses.

The computer programs are useful in double-checking a diagnosis. They are especially helpful with rare illnesses a doctor may never have seen before. Because the databanks are updated regularly, they include the most recent information about various diseases and their symptoms.

These programs, however, will never replace a doctor's years of training and experience. The computer's responses are only as good as the information the doctor provides.

Computers offer doctors quick access to medical information.

temperature reading. The doctor may examine your skin, your eyes, ears, nose, throat, and teeth. The doctor may also test your hearing and vision.

During the examination of your upper body, the doctor will listen to your lungs and heart with a stethoscope. A **stethoscope** (**steth** uh skohp) is an instrument used to listen to sounds produced within the body. As the examination continues, the doctor will check your abdominal organs and look for any signs of unusual tissue growth.

An examination of the reproductive organs usually follows. For boys, this includes the external reproductive organs. For girls, the doctor examines the internal reproductive organs for disease or structural problems.

The doctor may then do a rectal examination to check for **hemorrhoids** (**hem** uh roydz) and signs of rectal disease. Hemorrhoids are enlarged veins in the area of the anus.

The doctor may decide to have your blood and urine tested. They may be tested in the office or in a medical laboratory. The doctor will contact you later with the results.

Finally, the doctor checks your muscles, bones, and nervous system. This includes your arms, legs, hands, and feet for signs of joint swelling or bone problems. Your doctor will also check for **scoliosis** (skoh lee **oh** sis), an abnormal curvature of the spine. The doctor also checks your reflexes, coordination, and sensory and motor functions. To check your reflexes, the doctor may use the knee-jerk test. This test involves tapping just below the kneecap with a rubber mallet and observing the action of your leg.

If the doctor finds a medical condition requiring attention, he or she should mention it. The doctor should also explain what the condition means in terms of treatment, additional testing, and possible long-term effects.

Remember that you and your doctor are a team working together; good communication is important. Regardless of how "dumb" you think your questions are, keep asking them. Getting answers to questions about your body will help you participate more fully in your own health care.

Section Review

1. How would you go about getting the information you need to select a doctor?
2. List four rights and two responsibilities that you have as a medical patient.
3. Briefly describe the parts of a medical examination.

What Do You Think?
4. What qualities in a doctor are important to you? How do these qualities affect your choice of a doctor?

3. PAYING FOR HEALTH CARE

At some point in the future, you will be paying for your health care. If you know what choices are available, you can select the method of paying for your health costs that is best for you. One way is for you to pay for each health-care service. This is called out-of-pocket payment. Another way is through health insurance. **Health insurance** is a health-care payment plan that pays for a major part of an individual's medical expenses. Most people buy health insurance because it pays for large medical bills that otherwise would be a financial burden.

There are several types of health-insurance plans that provide coverage for health-related expenses other than medical and hospital expenses. Dental insurance, for example, is becoming increasingly common. Disability insurance provides for the replacement of any income lost during a long recuperation from illness or injury.

Private Health Insurance

Private health insurance may be offered as individual or group plans. Under individual plans, the person who wants insurance coverage pays an annual fee called a **premium** to the insurance company. For the premium, the insurance company guarantees to pay the person's medical expenses

Health-care expenses can be met out-of-pocket or through health and health-related insurance plans.

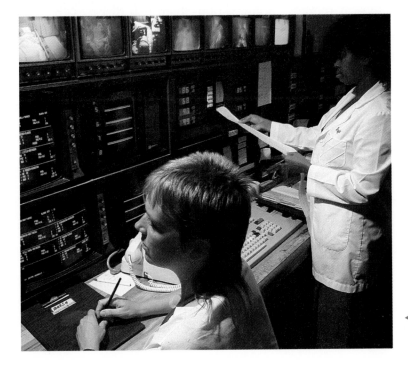

◀ **Figure 23-7. Health insurance can help cover the costs of treatment in an intensive care unit.**

for the year within the limits set in the insurance plan. The premium may be paid at the beginning of the coverage year or in periodic payments throughout the year. Individual plans are much more expensive than group plans. In a group plan, the cost of the insurance is spread among many people. The most common kind of group-insurance plan is one covering the employees of a certain company. The company often pays part or all of the premium as a job benefit. This can be an important benefit for employees whose families are also covered by the insurance plan. People who cannot get employee group-insurance sometimes can obtain it through professional or retirement organizations.

Usually, an insurance plan requires the patient to pay the first part of each year's medical expenses. This first part, which is a fixed amount called the **deductible**, is the portion of the year's medical expenses that the patient must pay before the insurance begins paying. Once the insured person's medical expenses exceed the deductible amount, the insurance company starts to pay for a specified percentage (often 80 percent) of the medical bills. The remaining amount is called the **copayment**, and the insured person is responsible for meeting this expense.

Insurance policies, or agreements, often have limits on the amount they will allow for a medical procedure. If the bill for a procedure exceeds the amount allowed by the policy, the insurance pays only the allowable amount. If the bill is for a procedure that the policy does not cover, no insurance is provided. There are many insurance policies that will not cover certain types of treatments, such as acupuncture or physical therapy. Some serious high-risk diseases that require long-term major medical expense also may not be covered by health insurance.

Medicare and Medicaid

Some people, such as the elderly, the severely disabled, and those with low incomes, may not be able to afford private health insurance. These people often are covered by public, or government, health-insurance programs that are paid for by taxes. The most widely used public health-insurance programs are Medicare and Medicaid.

The federally financed insurance program for elderly people is **Medicare**. Medicare is also available to younger people who are disabled or who have chronic kidney disease.

Medicare comes in two parts. Medicare Part A, which is free, covers all people 65 years old or older who are eligible for Social Security or Railroad Retirement benefits. It carries a deductible and provides 60 days of hospitalization, not including doctors' bills. Medicare Part B, which can be purchased for a small monthly fee, helps to pay doctors' bills, outpatient hospital services, and the costs of some medical services and supplies. Anyone who is 65 years old or older can purchase Medicare Part B whether or not he or she is covered by Social Security.

In addition to Medicare, many older people may be partly covered by Medicaid. **Medicaid** is a state and federal assistance program that pays for the health care of anyone with an income below an established level. Because Medicaid is dependent on tax money from both federal and state sources, its benefits vary from state to state. Anyone can get information about eligibility for Medicaid from the local welfare office or other social-service agency.

Health Maintenance Organizations

A recent concept in providing health care is the health maintenance organization (HMO). A **health maintenance organization** is a group of doctors and allied health workers that provides complete medical services to individuals who are members of the HMO. Individuals and groups who join an HMO pay a predetermined fee, or premium, each month. In return, the HMO covers the cost of all or nearly all needed health services.

Since an HMO's only income is usually the members' monthly payments, it is in the patients' and doctors' interests to keep down costs by keeping members healthy. Therefore, HMOs focus on preventive health practices and regular immunizations, well-baby care, and educating its members in preventive care. These services rarely are covered by private insurance plans. A disadvantage of an HMO is that it usually covers only the costs of health services provided by the HMO staff and affiliated hospitals. If you see a doctor outside of the HMO without your doctor's consent, you must pay separately for the cost of the service. Figure 23-8 lists additional advantages and disadvantages of HMOs.

Advantages and Disadvantages of HMOs

Advantages

- Lower out-of-pocket cost for health care
- No need to pay each time you get health care
- No need to submit claims and wait for reimbursement
- In some HMOs, one-stop shopping for health care, i.e., full range of doctors, testing, and laboratory facilities available at HMO site
- Less time spent in hospital
- Preventative health-care coverage

Disadvantages

- Less choice of health-care providers, such as doctors and hospitals
- For policy coverage, patient requires permission of primary-care physician for each visit to a specialist

▲
Figure 23-8. Do the advantages of HMOs outweigh their disadvantages?

Section Review

1. Why is health insurance an advantage over out-of-pocket payment for medical expenses?

2. In an insurance policy, what does the term *deductible* mean? The term *copayment*?

3. What programs are available to the elderly, the disabled, and those with low incomes? Describe some of these programs.

What Do You Think?

4. You have the choice of joining an HMO or a group-insurance plan, both of which cost the same. How would you go about deciding which plan to join?

4. BEING A WISE CONSUMER

The decisions you will make about health care will range from choosing health-care services and insurance to choosing health-care products. Being a wise consumer means learning about and comparing products or services and being informed about consumer issues. Being a wise consumer helps you get the health-care products and services you need.

Consumers and Advertising

Manufacturers spend millions on advertising because advertising attracts customers to buy their products. All of us are influenced to some extent by advertising.

Advertising can let you know what products are available, but it seldom provides the information you need for wise choices. Sometimes, it is misleading. Advertisers are skilled at making products appeal in ways that have nothing to do with the products. Often, this is done by suggestion, or in ways that we are not even aware of.

One way, called the *image appeal method*, creates a product "image." For example, an advertisement showing young, attractive, healthy people having fun suggests that use of the product makes you like the people in the advertisement. Of course, no product can do this.

As you can see in Figure 23-9, advertisers will also use your trust in a professional group, such as doctors, to sell a product. For example, a medicine may be advertised as con-

Being well-informed helps you to choose wisely from available health-care products and services.

Figure 23-9. Which of these advertising techniques have you seen?

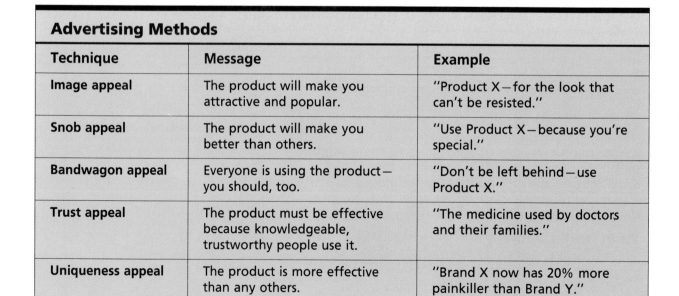

Advertising Methods		
Technique	**Message**	**Example**
Image appeal	The product will make you attractive and popular.	"Product X—for the look that can't be resisted."
Snob appeal	The product will make you better than others.	"Use Product X—because you're special."
Bandwagon appeal	Everyone is using the product— you should, too.	"Don't be left behind—use Product X."
Trust appeal	The product must be effective because knowledgeable, trustworthy people use it.	"The medicine used by doctors and their families."
Uniqueness appeal	The product is more effective than any others.	"Brand X now has 20% more painkiller than Brand Y."

taining the ingredient most doctors recommend. This advertisement might make you think it is the only product containing that ingredient. Chances are, however, many other products have the same ingredient. This type of advertising uses the *trust appeal method*. If you can recognize various methods of advertising, it will help you to make wise consumer choices.

As a consumer you need to base your consumer choices on facts and reliable information not on what advertisements are trying to tell you. To choose health-care products wisely, you should ask for recommendations from health professionals, such as your doctor, pharmacist, or school nurse. Read product labels and other product information. Compare products for their ingredients and cost. Often, products used for the same purpose contain the same ingredients. Taking time to choose will help you be a satisfied consumer.

Consumer choices need to be based on facts and information from reliable sources rather than on advertising.

Choosing Medicines

Many of the health-care products you will choose are medicines. A **medicine** is any substance used to treat a disease, disorder, or injury. The medicines you use are either prescribed by your doctor—**prescription medicines**—or available without a prescription—**over-the-counter (OTC) medicines**.

Prescription medicines are considered safe only when they are used under the supervision of a doctor. Over-the-counter medicines, on the other hand, are considered much safer than prescription drugs, but they should be used only according to the instructions on their containers. At anytime, anyone who wants to use an OTC medicine can purchase one in a store.

With either type of medicine, choices usually are available to you. For example, a prescription medicine often will have a standard or **generic** (jih **nehr** ik) name under which it is sold. Often, several manufacturers will make this medicine. Another manufacturer, usually the one that originally developed the medicine, will make the identical medicine but give it a special or brand name. As an example, *tolazamide* is the generic name of a medicine for the treatment of diabetes. It can be bought at a pharmacy under this name. The same medicine, however, is also sold under the brand name given to it by the manufacturer.

A brand-name product tends to be more expensive than the same product sold under its generic name. Buying generic medicines, therefore, can sometimes save you money. In a brand-name medicine, however, the inactive ingredients, such as coloring, flavoring, fillers, or a protective coating, may differ from those in the generic form. If your doctor prescribes a medicine, you can ask if it is available under a generic name and, if so, if it is the preferred choice.

Figure 23-10. Reading the ingredients label on OTC medicines helps you to compare products wisely.

Over-the-counter medicines include many antiseptics, painkillers, and other drugs that help relieve the symptoms of many common ailments. OTC medicines are sold under company or brand names and under generic names. Many OTC medicines were prescription medicines at one time. Different brands of OTC medicines that are sold for the same purpose often have the same active ingredients. They may differ in the proportion of active ingredients and in the types of inactive ingredients. When you are choosing OTC medicines, you can get the most for your money by reading the ingredient labels and comparing prices.

Using Medicines Wisely

Whether you are using a prescription medicine or OTC medicine, always read the label and any package leaflet information. Use medicines only as instructed and take note of any warnings or precautions. Some medicines cause side effects. **Side effects** are unpleasant responses of your body to the medicine. Although side effects are usually mild, such as a headache or skin rash, they can be severe or even life-threatening. Certain medicines cause side effects when taken in combination with other medicines or certain foods. Ask your doctor about potential side effects of a prescribed drug. Discontinue use of any prescribed medicine that produces side effects until you check with your doctor. If you have questions about any medication, ask your pharmacist. To make sure you do not misuse any medicines, follow the instructions given in Figure 23-11.

Quackery

The selling of useless medical treatments or products is known as **quackery** (**kwak** ur ee). People who are involved in this kind of fraud are known as **quacks**. Quacks often promise that treatments or products will bring about miracle cures or revitalize a person's health. Quacks depend upon people's lack of knowledge and sometimes on the desperate desire of people to be rid of some disease or problem. Of course, quacks are dishonest, and people are cheated by them. The worst consequence of quackery is that it can delay or prevent someone from receiving proper medical care. As long as a person believes a quack remedy is working or might work, he or she will postpone seeing a medical doctor.

Many government agencies will take action against quack products and procedures. Look at Figure 23-13 for a list of federal agencies that investigate claims of deceptive items, practices, or advertising. If you should purchase a deceptive or fraudulent item through the mail, notify your local postmaster. The U.S. Postal Service will investigate and take legal action if necessary. Your state attorney general's office

Rules for Safe Medicine Use

- Tell your doctor about any OTC and prescription medicines that you are taking.
- Tell your doctor about any reactions that you have ever had to any medicines.
- Ask your doctor if the medicine prescribed should be taken with food or on an empty stomach.
- Ask your doctor if you should avoid certain foods, activities, or other medicines while you take the prescribed medicine.
- Ask your doctor how long you should continue to take the medicine.
- Keep all medicines in their original containers.
- Take the medicine in the exact amount prescribed.
- Take the medicine on schedule.
- Never double a dose to make up for a missed dose.
- Report any side effects to your doctor immediately.
- Throw away old medicines.
- Report any signs of tampering with OTC medicines to the pharmacist or store manager.

▲
Figure 23-11. Following these rules helps to make medicines safe and effective.

should also be notified about fraudulent practices within your state. If a local business is involved, you should notify your local Better Business Bureau. You can avoid quackery by carefully evaluating claims made for health-care products. Quackery is likely to be involved when any of the following conditions exist:

- The product is said to be the only possible answer to a medical problem.
- The promised results seem too good to be true.
- The product is claimed to be a cure for a number of different ailments.
- The product offers special secret ingredients that produce a miracle cure.

If you still have doubts about a product, you should ask your doctor about it.

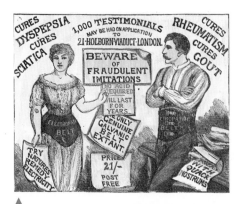

▲ **Figure 23-12. Sometimes medicines and tonics in the early days promised impossible cures.**

Your Rights as a Consumer

Regardless of what services or products you buy, you have certain rights as a consumer. First and foremost is your **right to choose** any product that you want. To be able to make wise choices, you have the **right to information.** You should be able to learn enough about a service or product to make a judgment about it. You also have the **right to safety**. This is the right to expect that any service or product is reasonably safe and will not harm you. When you are dissatisfied as a consumer you have the **right to complain.** Many state and federal laws protect consumers. If you believe a product has not helped you or has been misrepresented, you should complain to the manufacturer and ask for a refund. If you are still not satisfied, you should complain to a consumer protection agency. Remember that knowledge is your best defense against consumer fraud.

Section Review

1. What are some ways advertisers try to influence our consumer choices?
2. What are the differences between the generic and brand-name forms of a medicine?
3. When should you suspect quackery?
4. What are four rights of a consumer?

What Do You Think?

5. You are about to buy a brand-name first-aid spray when you realize that there are other less well-known sprays available. How would you decide which first-aid spray to purchase?

Help for the Consumer

The Food and Drug Administration
5600 Fishers Lane
Rockville, MD 20857
protects the public from the sale of unsafe foods, drugs, and cosmetics

The Federal Trade Commission
6th Street and Pennsylvania Ave. N.W.
Washington, DC 20580
prevents unfair or deceptive advertising

The Consumer Product Safety Commission
5401 Westbard Avenue
Bethesda, MD
(mailing address: Washington, DC 20207)
establishes safety standards for consumer goods and takes dangerous products off the market

▲ **Figure 23-13. Which federal agency would you notify if you were a victim of false advertising?**

23 | Chapter Review

Chapter Summary

- Primary-care physicians work with medical specialists and allied health workers to provide skilled and personalized care for their patients.
- Medical care can be obtained in private offices, clinics, hospitals, and specialized health centers.
- Choosing a clinic or a doctor involves identifying your particular needs and preferences, asking others to recommend the names of clinics or doctors, and doing research to check out the recommendations and narrow your list.
- As a patient, you have certain rights, such as the right to have each step of a treatment explained in terms you can understand. You also have certain responsibilities, such as the responsibility to answer the doctor's questions as honestly as you can.
- A medical examination includes a medical history, a physical examination, and a time to talk with the doctor.
- Health insurance can enable an individual or a family to survive the medical costs of a long illness or injury.
- Health insurance may be private or public. Private health insurance plans may be offered as individual or group plans.
- As a consumer, it is important to be able to evaluate the influence that advertising and health-care literature have on your choices of products and services.
- A medicine may have both a brand name and a generic name.
- Because of possible overdosage or side effects, it is essential to use medicines exactly as prescribed.
- The promotion of useless, and sometimes harmful medical treatments or products is called quackery.

Vocabulary Review

Listed below are some of the important terms in this chapter. Choose the term that best matches the phrase in the exercise that follows.

copayment
deductible
diagnosis
dietitian
health insurance
hospice

licensed practical
  nurse
medical history
Medicare
nurse practitioner

outpatient
over-the-counter
  (OTC) medicine
pharmacist
premium

prescription
quackery
registered nurse
medical specialist
stethoscope

1. the first part of each year's medical bills, paid by the patient

2. a person trained to dispense medicine according to a doctor's order

3. a medical doctor who has received several years of additional training in a particular branch of medicine

4. facility that focuses on helping dying patients live as comfortably as possible

5. record of family members' past illnesses

6. person who receives treatment at a hospital but does not stay overnight

7. person who has studied and received a degree in foods and nutrition

8. health-care payment plan that pays for a major part of an individual's medical costs

9. the annual fee paid to an insurance company for insurance protection

10. the promotion of useless medical products or treatments

What Have You Learned?

1. What are three things that a doctor is licensed to perform?
2. How do L.P.N.s and R.N.s differ?
3. What are the duties of a nurse practitioner?
4. Describe two dental specialties.
5. What are the differences between a psychiatrist and a psychologist?
6. What are some ways you can get information about doctors in your area?

7. What are two responsibilities of a patient?
8. Explain the three parts of a checkup.
9. Why does an HMO focus on preventive health practices and regular checkups?
10. How do manufacturers influence you?
11. What is quackery?
12. What is one advantage to buying a medicine under its generic name? When might buying a particular brand be advantageous?

What Do You Think?

1. Explain why a patient might receive better care at a teaching hospital than at another type of hospital.
2. Why do you think that advertising for health-care products is designed to appeal to your emotions rather than ability to reason?

3. How can you explain that some people continue to buy useless medical products?
4. When might it be desirable to have a health insurance plan with a high deductible?
5. What are some advantages to getting a second medical opinion?

What Would You Do?

1. Family A is a young couple who are expecting a baby and have one pre-school child. Family B is an elderly couple who has a general practitioner who knows them well. What type of insurance would be best for each family? Why?
2. Suppose your grandfather, a widower, lives near you. He does not want to live in your home, but he is careless about eating properly. How could your family help him?
3. You have a choice of two health-insurance plans that have the same benefits. Plan A has an annual deductible of $100; Plan B has

an annual deductible of $1,000. Your employer will pay the premium for Plan B; Plan A will cost you $50 per month. Which would you choose? What must you consider in addition to cost?
4. A small mole on your arm has become larger and has changed texture. You hear of a new skin cream that costs little and produces miraculous results. Would you try the cream before seeing your doctor? Why or why not?
5. You are told to take a prescription medicine for a week. However, after three days you feel fine. What would you do?

For Further Study

1. Choose one medicine from the *Physician's Desk Reference* (PDR), a book that gives information about medicines on the market. What is its generic name? What are its brand names? List its desired effects and side effects.
2. Make a directory of the health-care facilities in your community, such as hospitals, clinics, convalescent centers, and nursing homes. List their special features, such as cardiac fitness clinics or trauma centers. Then, list the name, address, and phone number of each facility.

24

As you read, think about

▶ what public health is and how it affects everyone.

▶ the responsibilities of local and state public health organizations.

▶ how national and international health organizations work to solve worldwide health problems.

Public Health

Today is a brilliant October day with a slight chill in the air. The fallen leaves spatter the park grass with bright yellows and reds. As you rake the leaves into large piles, they give off a pleasant, woodsy smell. This is neighborhood clean-up day, a time when people on your block get together to polish up the neighborhood and share ideas on making it a safer, more healthful, more pleasant place to live.

You have already learned to make many independent decisions that affect your own health. In this chapter, you will see how people work together to protect the health of their own community and other communities around the world. You will discover how local health organizations are involved in the education and care of individuals as well as in the regulation of sewage treatment and restaurant cleanliness. You will also see how national and worldwide health organizations trace and fight communicable diseases, malnutrition, and other threats to public health.

Solving community and worldwide health problems requires everyone's cooperation.

1. SAFEGUARDING THE PUBLIC

Check Your Wellness

Public health organizations have affected your life since you were an infant. How well informed are you about these local and worldwide services?

1. Do you know what kinds of public health services affect you every day?

2. Do you know where to report violations of public health regulations?

3. Do you know which local public health services are available to help people with emotional problems? With alcohol or drug dependency problems?

4. Do you follow public health rules, such as no-smoking and antipollution laws?

5. Can you name three international health organizations and tell what they do?

6. Do you know which government agencies supervise the safety of food and drinking water?

7. Do you keep informed about public health issues in your community?

Imagine what it would be like if you did not have clean water to drink or if a town's garbage was not picked up regularly. What would your life be like if restaurants were not required to prepare foods in a sanitary way or if no one were vaccinated for diseases like smallpox and polio? These are all matters that affect **public health,** the health of people as a group or as a community. You do not usually face any of these problems because there is a public health system in this country. A **public health system** is all the government agencies and private organizations that work to prevent disease and to promote the general health of the public.

Some Background on Public Health

Until the 1800s, few people thought about public health or the need for a public health system. Epidemics of severe or life-threatening diseases were common. An **epidemic** (ep ih **dem** ik) is an outbreak of a disease that strikes many people within a short period of time. In the Middle Ages, for example, as cities grew and sanitary conditions worsened, epidemics of bubonic plague, typhoid fever, and smallpox often occurred. Because the causes of diseases were not understood, most people believed these epidemics were caused by evil forces or demons. As scientists discovered that some diseases were spread by contaminated food and water, laws were passed to improve sanitation.

In 1831, England established the first public health agency ever to combat the spread of **cholera** (**kahl** uh ruh), a disease that causes severe diarrhea, muscular cramps, and vomiting. The agency placed cholera patients in **quarantine** (**kwor** un teen) and then cleaned their homes to prevent spread of the disease. A quarantine is the placing of people who have an **infectious** (in **fek** shus) **disease** in isolation to prevent spread of the disease. An infectious disease is a disease caused by organisms that live in or on the human body.

Although a national board of health was established in 1878 in the United States, state and local governments usually were responsible for public health measures. As the need for a national public health policy grew, the federal government began to develop and fund more public health programs. Today, the Department of Health and Human Services is the federal agency with the widest range of responsibilities for public health. It supports state and local health departments, sponsors health research and education, analyzes health information, sets health standards for food and drugs, and provides programs for the elderly, the mentally ill, drug and alcohol abusers, and the homeless.

The Functions of a Public Health System

The specific tasks of a public health system vary from country to country, depending on the needs of the population and the resources that are available in the country. In the United States, past public health programs have tried to control the spread of infectious diseases. This has been accomplished through many different laws and regulations. Some laws have required communities to provide pure drinking water and proper sewage and garbage disposal. Other laws and regulations have required the inspection of food processing and preparation facilities, vaccinations for children against various infectious diseases, school lunches and other nutrition programs, and programs for health education. All of these measures have contributed to the decline of serious infectious diseases in the United States.

The health problems that affect industrialized countries like the United States are different from the health problems of developing nations. Countries in which poverty, malnutrition, and lack of sanitation are common have a greater number of infectious diseases. These countries do not have the resources to provide vaccinations, sanitation, and health education for everyone. As these countries begin to develop industries and their standards of living improve, new health problems arise. The increased incidence of smoking, high-fat, low-fiber diets, life styles without enough physical activity, and pollution from motor vehicles and industries contribute to rising rates of **noninfectious diseases.** Noninfectious diseases are diseases such as cancer and heart disease, that are not caused by organisms. Mental illness and drug and alcohol abuse also become more common as some

▲
Figure 24-1. People once thought that epidemics were spread by evil demons.

◀ **Figure 24-2. A healthy and productive society is the result of an effective public health system.**

Figure 24-3. In developed countries, noninfectious diseases cause more deaths than infectious diseases. ▶

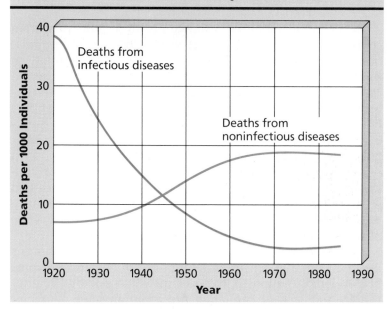

Causes of Death in Developed Countries

Deaths from infectious diseases

Deaths from noninfectious diseases

Deaths per 1000 Individuals

40

30

20

10

0

1920 1930 1940 1950 1960 1970 1980 1990

Year

countries develop. Figure 24-3 shows how the causes of death in countries that are developed have changed during the last 60 years.

For these reasons, public health programs in today's world fight both infectious and noninfectious diseases. Worldwide public health programs educate people about heart disease and cancer. Public health programs also help people with special needs—the elderly, the disabled, the mentally ill, the homeless, and the poor. Frequently, these programs provide treatment for drug and alcohol abusers.

Public Health in Action

Whether it is working to prevent the spread of an infectious disease or helping drug and alcohol abusers, the modern public health system continues to save and to improve the lives of many people. But, how does it do this?

Figure 24-4. Once the cause of a new disease is known, efforts are made to educate the public.
▼

FIGHTING INFECTIOUS AND NONINFECTIOUS DISEASES In 1975, the Connecticut Department of Public Health received reports of 100 times more than the usual number of cases of juvenile rheumatoid arthritis, a rare illness. Sufferers complained of fever, headache, and joint pain and swelling. Some people also had signs of nervous system damage. A public health **epidemiologist** (ep uh dee mee **ahl** uh jist), a scientist who studies unusual outbreaks of disease, suspected that an insect bite was responsible for the disease because all the victims had suffered from a peculiar, spreading rash before the arthritis symptoms appeared. When he interviewed the victims, he found that nine of them remembered being bitten by a tick. Scientists then discovered that a kind of **bacterium** (bac **teer** ee um), or germ, carried by this type of tick caused the same disease, now called Lyme disease, in animals. The health professionals discovered that Lyme disease was passed on to humans through tick bites. They also discovered that the disease can be treated with medication. Public education programs have made people aware of the disease and its cause.

More recently, public health officials have been dealing with the infectious disease **AIDS, acquired immunodeficiency syndrome.** AIDS is discussed in detail in Chapter 17. Since 1981, when the first case of AIDS was diagnosed in the United States, there has been a major public health effort to study the disease. Because no cure or proven vaccine for the disease yet exists, there is an ongoing campaign to educate the public on how to avoid the disease. At the same time, a major research effort is under way in an effort to find a cure for the disease.

Epidemiologists also consult statistics on outbreaks of infectious disease around the world. The statistics are provided by **statisticians** (stat ih **stish** unz), people who collect, analyze, and interpret numerical data. In this way, scientists can predict an epidemic in its early stages and start vaccination and education programs to keep the disease from spreading. You probably have been immunized against **polio,** a disease that causes inflammation of the spinal cord and can result in paralysis. Public health programs led to the development of the vaccine against polio.

Epidemiologists also deal with noninfectious diseases throughout the world. If an unusual number of people in an area have a chronic, noninfectious disease, epidemiologists may look for an environmental cause, such as a chemical contamination of the water supply. Statistical records on noninfectious diseases sometimes indicate possible causes of disease. When the statistics indicated that people who smoke get lung cancer more frequently than those who do not, public health workers used this information to teach other people how to avoid lung cancer.

HELPING SPECIAL-NEEDS PEOPLE Helping substance abusers, the mentally ill, the disabled, the elderly, the poor and homeless, and other people with special needs may not seem as dramatic as fighting a deadly disease, but it is just as important. A large proportion of this country's population depends upon some type of public health service to lead productive lives or to be cared for with dignity. Providing services for each of these groups, however, carries its own set of difficulties. Unlike the straightforward methods used to fight an infectious disease, the approaches to solving many of these public health problems are not always clear.

Power Lines and Cancer

As electricity flows along a wire, it creates a magnetic field. Evidence now suggests that the electromagnetic fields of power lines and appliances may be an environmental health risk.

Recent studies show that living near low-voltage power lines may increase the risk of childhood leukemia. Other studies show that pregnant women who use electric blankets or heated waterbeds are more likely to have miscarriages.

How an electromagnetic field might cause these health problems is not clear. Some experiments show that magnetic fields can change the movement of calcium in and out of cells, which can change basic cell function. But, the magnetic fields created by the electricity around us are hundreds of times weaker than the magnetic field of the earth.

Scientists have not found a clear cause-and-effect tie between electromagnetism and cancer. The early findings simply signal a need for more research.

Can household electricity be a cause of cancer?

Figure 24-5. The public health system helps the elderly and other people with special needs. ▶

Issues in Health

How Can We Solve the Homelessness Problem?

There may be as many as 3 million homeless people on the streets of America today. Most of these "street people" are not drug addicts or mentally ill. They are simply too poor to afford housing.

Many factors have contributed to the homelessness problem. Most important is the shortage of low-income housing. As cities tear down old buildings to construct new offices, hotels, and expensive apartments, little public housing is being built. Displaced people have nowhere to go. In addition, in the 1960s and 1970s, mental hospitals released many of their patients into the communities. Many of them have ended up on the streets. High unemployment rates in the past also contributed to the problem.

No long-term solutions to the homeless problem have been found. Current efforts have focused on immediate solutions such as shelters and soup kitchens. Permanent solutions are desperately needed. These would have to include plans for providing adequate low-income housing and creating more and higher-paying jobs.

What do you think should be done to solve the homelessness problem? Explain.

No matter what the approach, however, the problems of special-needs people require the best efforts of many dedicated public health workers.

The federal government funds and administers many programs to help special-needs people. Although some of these involve research, most of the programs provide services directly to the people in need. The services, which state and local governments administer with federal funds, can range from job training to drug rehabilitation to providing the disabled with easy access to community services. Other programs provide care for the mentally ill in community-based settings or proper nutrition to young children, pregnant mothers, and the elderly. There are many other services provided by federal and state agencies as well as by private public health organizations. All of these attempt to improve the lives of the people they serve. While you may not be aware of it, public health is working every day in your community and throughout the nation to help millions of people and maybe even you.

Section Review

1. What are four types of services that the public health system provides?
2. Which federal agency has the widest range of responsibilities for public health?
3. What does an epidemiologist do?

What Do You Think?

4. Which public health problem—AIDS, mental illness, the elderly, drug abuse—would you like to see receive more funding? Why?

2. PUBLIC HEALTH AT THE LOCAL AND STATE LEVELS

Although the federal government sponsors many public health programs, most public health activities are carried out by local and state governments. Public health programs at this level attempt to prevent disease, to provide health services, and to enforce health laws.

Local Government Health Agencies

At the local level, public health is the responsibility of the town, city, or county board of health. Your local board of health, acting as a branch of the state board of health, enforces health codes that have been established by the state. Board of health members are elected officials, but they often employ a health agent. The health agent is a health professional who carries out inspections and other day-to-day duties. The state health codes that local boards enforce set standards for such things as water quality, restaurant cleanliness, and sewage systems. Local boards of health also record **vital statistics**—the number of births and deaths in a community—and report some diseases to state agencies.

Private Agencies at the Local Level

Private organizations often cover areas of public health that government agencies do not. Some of these organizations receive funds from private donors and government grants. Others are funded only by private donors and may exist only at the local level. Some private national organizations have branches in each community to serve the special

Most public health activities are carried out by local and state governments.

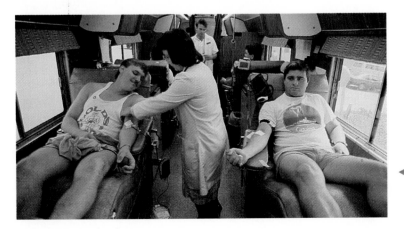

◀ **Figure 24-6. A constant supply of blood depends upon the work of blood donation facilities such as this American Red Cross bloodmobile.**

needs of that particular community. Some examples of these are the March of Dimes, the United Way, the Visiting Nurses Association, and the American Red Cross. The local chapters of the American Red Cross Association, for example, supply hospitals with blood collected from donors. They also conduct health and safety training programs, such as classes in first aid and water rescue, for individuals and for other organizations within the community.

Agencies for the elderly may provide care at home or in centers during the day. They may also provide nutrition counseling, meals, nursing, and transportation to hospitals. Other organizations sponsor hotlines and centers that provide therapy for adolescents with family, drug, or alcohol abuse problems. Some youth organizations work with schools and courts to provide counseling for troubled teens.

State Government Health Agencies

State public health departments uphold state health laws and administer federal funds for health services. These departments administer programs for poor families and for the

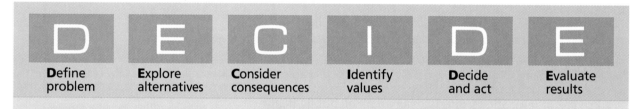

| **D**efine problem | **E**xplore alternatives | **C**onsider consequences | **I**dentify values | **D**ecide and act | **E**valuate results |

AN UNSANITARY RESTAURANT?

William works as a waiter at the town's most popular restaurant. At work yesterday, he noticed two mice chewing through a loaf of bread in the kitchen. This was not the first time that William had seen evidence of mice in the restaurant. When he informed his manager, however, she told him there were no mice in the restaurant. The manager also told William that he should stop spreading these false rumors if he wanted to remain on the job.

William realized that the restaurant was breaking state health codes, but he also knew that a good job like his was hard to find.

1. Use the DECIDE process on page 16 to decide what you would do if you were William. Explain your reasons for making this decision.

2. List the steps you would take to put your decision into effect.

Should William report the health code violation?

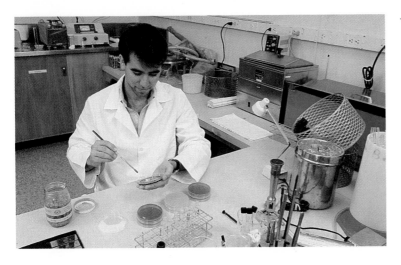

Figure 24-7. State public health laboratories routinely check food for disease-causing agents and chemical contaminants.

elderly, such as Aid to Families with Dependent Children, Medicaid, Medicare, and food stamps.

State health departments are also responsible for the public hospitals and mental-health hospitals owned by the state. State health laboratories test for disease-causing agents and toxic substances in food and water. State health departments collect the vital statistics of local health departments and report the information to the federal government.

State health departments maintain state hospitals and laboratories.

Private Health Agencies at the State Level

Many local organizations are organized at the state and national level to provide better services to their member agencies and to distribute funds and supplies to community branches. Some of these organizations, such as the American Cancer Society and the American Lung Association, focus on one type of disease. Private organizations within a state may also provide hotline counseling for those who need it in their special areas of interest.

Section Review

1. What are the four major areas of public health served by public health agencies?
2. What are two kinds of services that local private agencies may provide?
3. Name two responsibilities that a state health department must fulfill.

What Do You Think?
4. Do you think public health standards are adequate or need to be strengthened?

3. PUBLIC HEALTH AT THE NATIONAL AND INTERNATIONAL LEVELS

Both national and international public health organizations have recognized the need for disease prevention as well as cure. Most countries have national health organizations that provide funds to local agencies, conduct research, and provide a certain level of medical care to the public. Most of these national organizations also work with other countries to solve global health problems. International organizations study serious diseases that can be spread from country to country. They also develop international standards for sanitation as well as the quarantine regulations that are necessary for shipping and travel.

National Public Health

National agencies give financial and administrative aid to state and local health departments. The Department of Health and Human Services (HHS) is the major federal government agency to administer public health funds and programs for the poor, elderly, and disabled. The funds are also used for medical research and educational programs. One of the divisions within the Department of Health and Human Services is the Public Health Service.

THE PUBLIC HEALTH SERVICE The Public Health Service consists of six agencies shown in Figure 24-9. Each agency has its own programs and functions.

- The National Institutes of Health (NIH) directs research on the prevention, detection, and diagnosis of disease through 11 research institutes. The National Cancer Institutes and the National Institute of Environmental Health Sciences, for example, research the causes of cancer and environmental dangers.
- The Centers for Disease Control (CDC) is responsible for preventing contagious diseases throughout the country. All local and state departments of public health must report deaths and some diseases to the CDC. The CDC checks data that can warn of an epidemic or an environmental contamination.
- The Alcohol, Drug Abuse and Mental Health Administration (ADAMHA) supervises the national institutes on alcohol and drug abuse. ADAMHA is also responsible for the operation of National Institutes of Mental Health, which is its research branch.
- The Health Resources and Services Administration (HRSA) is responsible for programs concerning com-

▲

Figure 24-8. Workers at the Centers for Disease Control investigate the causes of new infectious diseases.

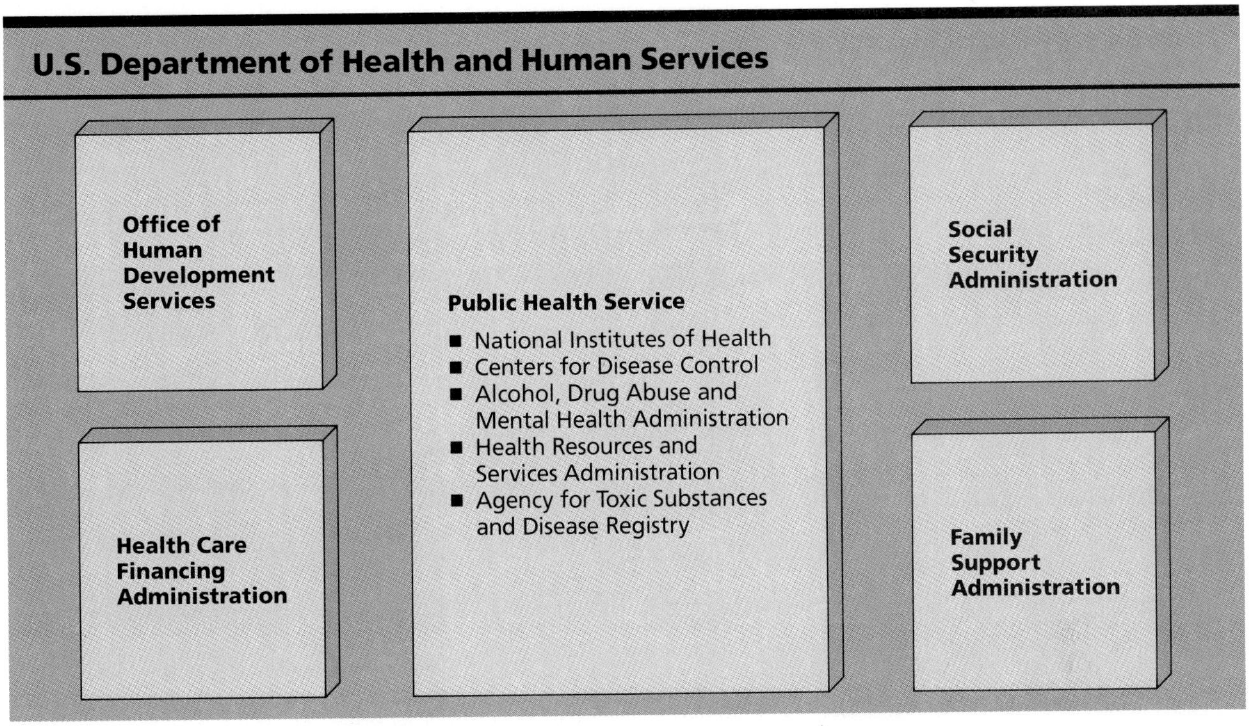

U.S. Department of Health and Human Services

Office of Human Development Services

Health Care Financing Administration

Public Health Service
- National Institutes of Health
- Centers for Disease Control
- Alcohol, Drug Abuse and Mental Health Administration
- Health Resources and Services Administration
- Agency for Toxic Substances and Disease Registry

Social Security Administration

Family Support Administration

Figure 24-9. Each of the agencies of the Public Health Service is responsible for a different area of public health.

munity health and family planning. These programs include maternal and child health-care services. This department also administers the Indian Health Service.

- The Agency for Toxic Substances and Disease Registry (ATSDR) collects, analyzes, and releases information relating to the public health aspects of exposure to hazardous substances.

NATIONAL PRIVATE AGENCIES National voluntary organizations raise and distribute funds for specific health causes. Organizations like the American Cancer Society and the American Heart Association provide money for research into, and education about, heart disease.

International Health Organizations

Major international health organizations are sponsored by the United Nations, by individual governments, and by private organizations. These organizations meet a variety of health needs in different parts of the world.

THE WORLD HEALTH ORGANIZATION The World Health Organization (WHO) is an agency of the United Nations. It provides countries in need with trained professionals in medicine, agriculture, water quality, and other health-related areas to help solve problems such as inadequate food,

The World Health Organization supports and staffs a wide range of programs that provide direct public health aid to countries in need.

Figure 24-10. WHO workers help
provide food and medicine to people
in countries where there is little or
no health care. ▶

epidemics, and water pollution. It sponsors programs for research on epidemics and health education for underpriv-
ileged people in developing countries. WHO maintains
worldwide health statistics to evaluate and predict health
threats. WHO has launched a worldwide attack through education on the spread of AIDS. The United Nation's
Children's Fund (UNICEF) works closely with WHO. It emphasizes services for children, including vaccination
programs, improved nutrition, and health education.

THE AGENCY FOR INTERNATIONAL DEVELOP-
MENT (AID)
The Agency for International Development
was formed by the United States government to distribute
assistance to foreign countries. In 1985, AID provided 1 billion dollars in emergency food for famine-stricken African
countries. **Famine** is a widespread lack of food. AID also
funds programs for immunization, medicines, sanitation,
health-care training, and oral rehydration therapy. **Oral rehydration therapy** is the gradual reintroduction of fluids to
someone who has suffered severe fluid loss. Severe water
loss caused by diarrhea is the major cause of death of children
in many developing countries.

THE PEACE CORPS
The Peace Corps is a U.S. govern-
ment organization that trains volunteers and sends them
abroad to help people in developing nations. Volunteers may
receive training in education, agriculture, or construction.
Peace Corps workers may teach new agricultural techniques,
help improve sanitation and water quality, and provide
health care within the community to which they are sent.

O—⚿

Peace Corps volunteers help people in
developing countries through education
and direct service.

THE INTERNATIONAL RED CROSS (IRC) The International Red Cross is a privately funded organization that was begun in 1859 to aid battlefield victims. Although the IRC still provides aid and services to soldiers, it also organizes medical care, food, and clothing for victims of natural disasters anywhere in the world.

There are many other private organizations that work to solve particular world needs. For example, OXFAM and CARE collect food and money for food to send to famine-stricken areas. Recently, many popular musicians helped raise funds for famine relief in Africa through the private organization called We Are The World. The Heifer Project sends breeding animals abroad so people can develop their own herds and supply food for a community. Can you think of any other world organizations that provide health care?

Many privately funded organizations work to solve particular world needs.

Section Review

1. What is the primary responsibility of the Health Resources and Services Administration?

2. Name three ways in which the World Health Organization promotes world health.

3. How does the Peace Corps contribute to the improvement of world health?

What Do You Think?

4. How do you think international public health services should be funded?

Working in Groups

Gary sat listening as the other student council members argued about how they should raise money for the March of Dimes.

"We should have a walk-a-thon," said Sam.

"No, that's a bad idea," said Sylvia. "Let's have a . . ."

"I say we have a car wash," Tom interrupted.

Finally, Gary stood up and pointed out that no one was listening to anyone else's ideas. "If we're going to get anything accomplished," said Gary, "we have to start working together as a group."

Have you ever wondered why some groups get a lot done and others do not? Group success often depends on group dynamics, how members work together. Since you participate in many groups—your family, friends, a sports team, this class—learning about group dynamics can be helpful. The following guidelines will help you learn to understand and work successfully in groups.

1. Set Goals and Priorities

The first task of a group is to set clear and realistic goals. If there are several purposes, decide which ones are most important. All members should be involved in setting the group's priorities.

2. Choose a Leader

Groups work best when members select a leader. A good leader has the time, interest, and patience to see that things run smoothly. The respect of the other group members is also important.

3. Make a Schedule

As a group, decide what steps are necessary to reach your goals. Which members have special skills or resources for these tasks? Divide activities so that everyone is involved. Finally, work together to set up a realistic schedule for all tasks.

4. Monitor Group Dynamics

People play different roles in groups. Use the examples below to help you identify the roles that people have taken in the groups you have been in.

You can improve group dynamics by encouraging helpful behaviors and discouraging disruptive ones.

Starter: Often begins discussions. Introduces new ideas.

Clarifier: Requests additional information. Restates points so they are clear to all.

Peacemaker: Suggests common ground and compromise when people disagree. Encourages positive group feelings.

Supporter: Is friendly and responsive to others and their ideas. Encourages shy members to join in.

Clown: Uses jokes to attract attention. Disrupts group.

Blocker: Always disagrees with others' ideas or focuses on trivial issues.

Dominator: Tries to control group. Bullies others.

Urge everyone to adopt a positive role. Choose a comfortable meeting place where all of the group members can be seen and heard.

5. Evaluate Group Progress

Are members working together productively? Are tasks being completed on time? If not, the group should discuss the reasons why not. Ask: Were the goals or schedule unrealistic? Were a few people doing all the work? Are there conflicts, and are they being handled well? Was there a communication problem within the group? Remember that a group functions best when *all* members share in the process of helping the group meet its goals.

Knowing how to work in a group is an important and rewarding skill.

APPLY THE SKILL

1. Choose a group you belong to, such as a school club, a sports team, a class group, or even some friends getting together with a specific purpose in mind. Watch the group in action. Use the following questions to analyze how well the group works. Refer to the preceding chart and guidelines for extra help.

2. What are the goals of the group? List them in order of importance. How were the group's priorities decided?

3. Who is the leader? How was that person selected? Does the leader guide the group well or is the leadership too strong or too weak? Explain.

4. Does the group have a schedule for accomplishing its goals? How was it decided? Is it realistic? Do all members have tasks?

5. Identify the roles members play in the group. Who plays positive roles? Negative roles? What roles do you play? Do all members do their share? Are any left out because of "in groups" within the group?

6. Does your meeting place encourage everyone to participate? Is it free of distractions? Is it comfortable?

7. Is your group accomplishing its goals? Do members communicate well and meet deadlines? Is working with your group enjoyable? Why or why not?

8. Look over your answers to the questions above. For each of the questions give your group an overall grade. Where do they do best? Worst? List some suggestions for improving the dynamics and productivity of your group.

24 | Chapter Review

Chapter Summary

- The public health system works through many local, state, national, and international private and governmental agencies and organizations to prevent disease and to promote public health.
- The public health system began in response to the need for government regulation of public sanitation to help curb the spread of infectious disease.
- Health problems vary from country to country, depending on economic development, population, and health resources. The problems faced by a public health system include the spread of disease and the treatment of mental illness, malnutrition, drug and alcohol abuse, and poverty.
- Local boards of health work to ensure public health through enforcement of state health codes that apply to activities affecting food and water contamination.
- Private and volunteer agencies provide funds for medical research and treatment, and organize and administer programs for special needs groups.
- State public health departments enforce state health laws, administer federal funds for health services, and implement support programs for the needy.
- Private state agencies give administrative and financial support to their local branches.
- National public health agencies administer programs that provide health services for the poor, elderly, and disabled.
- The Public Health Service conducts programs for research, disease control, alcohol abuse, and community health.
- International health organizations promote health throughout the world. They work to control malnutrition, water pollution, and the spread of disease.

Vocabulary Review

Listed below are some of the important terms in this chapter. Choose the term that best matches the phrase in the exercise that follows.

epidemic	famine	polio	statistician
cholera	oral rehydration	quarantine	
epidemiologist	therapy		

1. separating a person with an infectious disease from uninfected individuals
2. a scientist who studies outbreaks of disease
3. a bacterial disease causing diarrhea, muscular cramps, and vomiting
4. an outbreak of disease that affects many people in a short period of time

5. a person who collects, analyzes, and interprets numerical data
6. an infectious disease of the brain and spinal cord
7. a widespread lack of food
8. gradual reintroduction of fluid to a person suffering severe fluid loss

What Have You Learned?

1. Why do we have a public health system?
2. How does a public health system ensure community health?
3. Name two private public health agencies.

4. Why did some people believe that epidemics were caused by demons?
5. Name some of the problems that can threaten health in developing countries.

6. How does the public health system control infectious disease?

7. What are some of the public health problems that usually increase as a country becomes industrialized and more prosperous?

8. What government department has the most responsibility for public health?

9. List some areas of public health that are served by local boards of health.

10. Describe two types of programs sponsored by private or volunteer organizations.

11. What are the Centers for Disease Control?

12. How does the World Health Organization promote health?

What Do You Think?

1. Should funding for private health organizations be provided by voluntary donations or by the federal or state government?

2. Some lawmakers believe that people who enter the United States for the first time should be tested for a variety of infectious diseases. Is this a good idea?

3. Suppose the FDA recently approved a new synthetic dye for use as a food coloring. Would you feel safe eating food with this coloring? Why or why not?

4. Should children in the United States be required to have vaccinations for diseases that rarely occur today? Why or why not?

What Would You Do?

1. You notice that the water in your school has begun to have an unpleasant chemical taste, and you are concerned that it could be caused by some harmful substance. What would you do?

2. You are an epidemiologist who has been assigned to determine the source of a dangerous new disease. How would you do it?

3. If you were in charge of deciding which world health problem should be given top priority, what would you decide? Explain.

4. If you were an official in a country where malnutrition was common, how would you approach the problem?

5. How would you help solve the problem of homeless people in this country?

For Further Study

1. Interview a person who works for a public health agency such as the American Red Cross or the American Cancer Society. Ask about the work their organization carries out and the services or programs they offer.

2. Research and report on one of the great epidemics, such as the Black Death. Find out what kind of health care was given to patients, what measures were taken to prevent spread of the disease, how day-to-day life was affected, and what effect it had on history.

3. Talk to a person who has lived in another country about that country's health-care system. Do people have free medical care? Are services provided for the young and the elderly? Do people pay health insurance? Are there public hospitals and clinics? Does the government regulate health care? Report your findings to the class.

Sounds like you were lucky all around, Irv. But do me a favor. Try not to fall off anything else until I get a chance to take that first-aid course!

U N I T

8

Safety and First Aid

25
Personal Safety

26
First Aid

25

As you read, think about
▶ how to prevent accidents at home and in your community.

▶ how to reduce your risk of injury while working or during your leisure time.

▶ why motor vehicle accidents occur and how they can be minimized.

▶ how to protect yourself from crime.

Personal Safety

Sunlight filters down from the ocean surface. A school of tropical fish swims past and you pause, taking the chance to check your pressure gauge. Your tank still holds 20 minutes worth of air. You are alert, warm, and not fatigued. Everything's OK, so you signal this to your diving buddy, who signals back likewise. SCUBA training prepared you for this dive, reducing your risk. You wore the proper gear—mask, fins, wetsuit, regulator and so forth—and checked it all before entering the water. Confident, you now proceed with the dive, flutter-kicking to a colorful rock formation for a little exploration.

Life is full of risks. Knowing what they are, taking the right precautions, and using the proper equipment helps to prevent accidents and injury. In this chapter, you will learn about safety in the home, in the car, in recreational activities, and at school. You will also learn what to do in case of unexpected emergencies or natural disasters.

Whether you are scuba diving or just crossing the street, you should always be concerned about safety.

1. SAFETY AT HOME AND IN YOUR COMMUNITY

By the time you have finished reading this sentence, someone in the United States will have been injured in an accident. An **accident** is an unplanned event that usually results in injury, death, or property damage. Over 8 million accidents occur in this country each year. Figure 25-1 shows the leading causes of accidental death.

How can you prevent accidents or at least lessen injuries due to accidents? One way is to recognize risks to your safety and to practice behaviors that promote your safety. A **risk behavior** is a behavior that increases a person's chances of a harmful outcome. A **safe behavior** protects a person from danger and lessens the effects of a harmful situation. To prevent accidents or lessen the damage they can cause, keep these four factors in mind:

- **Knowledge and awareness:** Recognize risks to your safety, and know what actions to take to reduce the risk of accident. You should know, for example, that it is risky to operate an electric hairdryer when you are wet or near water.
- **Ability:** Realistically judge the ability levels of yourself and others. A child who has just learned to walk, for example, cannot safely climb down a flight of stairs without help.
- **State of mind:** Be aware of your own and others' condition. Anyone who is tired, rushed, distressed, or under the influence of drugs or alcohol is likely to have an accident.
- **Environmental conditions:** Consider the hazards in your environment that might cause an accident. For example, if you have just washed or waxed the floor, do not run across the floor when you hear the telephone ring.

As you read on, think of these four accident-prevention factors and how they apply to each situation.

Hazards in Your Home

One-third of all accidents occur in the home. The leading causes of death from home accidents are falls, fires, poisoning, suffocation, firearms, and drowning. At special risk from these accidents are the very young and the very old.

FALLS Young children are especially likely to be injured in falls. Whenever you put a baby into a crib, make sure that the sides of the crib are in the highest position and are locked into place. Never leave a baby alone on a table or other raised surface. Use safety gates at the top and bottom of stairs to

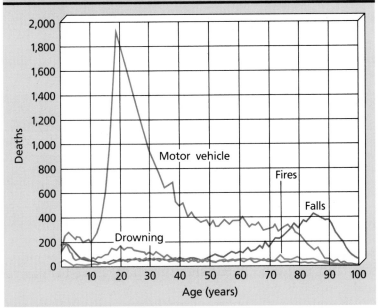

Leading Causes of Accidental Death

Deaths (y-axis): 0, 200, 400, 600, 800, 1,000, 1,200, 1,400, 1,600, 1,800, 2,000

Age (years) (x-axis): 10, 20, 30, 40, 50, 60, 70, 80, 90, 100

Labeled curves: Motor vehicle, Fires, Falls, Drowning

Source: National Safety Council, data for 1984

Figure 25-1. Which age group has the highest death rate from motor vehicle accidents? From falls?

Figure 25-2. How could you reduce the risk of fire in your home?

Reducing Fire Risks at Home

- Install smoke detectors on each floor of your home and outside of all bedrooms.
- Practice a fire escape plan and keep the route clear.
- Have fire extinguishers available in the kitchen, garage, and on each floor of your home.
- Make sure electrical plugs are not overloaded.
- Replace frayed or cracked appliance cords.
- Use the proper fuses in the fuse box.
- Remove extension cords from under rugs or furniture.
- Discourage smokers from smoking in bed or when they are sleepy.
- Keep matches and lighters out of the reach of small children.
- Make sure the pilot lights of gas stoves are working.
- Avoid storing flammable materials in your home or garage, or store them in fireproof, labeled containers.
- Make sure electrical appliances are installed properly and in good repair.
- Use a cover when cooking with oil at high temperatures.
- Keep flammable materials away from heat sources, such as stoves and furnaces.

keep young children from falling downstairs. Do not allow children to sit on window sills or lean against screens. Keep children away from decks or porches that do not have railings. Do not allow a toddler to climb into a highchair alone. Discourage children from playing roughly inside the home.

Hazards in the home can result in a fall for anyone. Falling is especially dangerous for older adults whose bones break easily and heal slowly. To keep falls to a minimum:

- Make sure that all stairways are in good repair and have nonslip treads and strong railings.
- Keep stairs and walkways uncluttered and well lighted.
- Anchor all carpets and rugs firmly.
- Keep floors unslippery and clear of small objects.
- Make sure stepladders are in good repair.
- Equip bathtubs and showers with handrails and nonskid rubber mats or decals.
- Keep outdoor steps and sidewalks in good repair and free of ice, leaves, toys, and other obstacles.

FIRES AND BURNS Household fires kill thousands of people each year. The six most common causes of household fires are careless smoking, faulty or overloaded electrical wiring, unsafe heating units, faulty or improperly used fireplaces, children playing with matches, and improper storage of **flammable materials.** Flammable materials are things that catch fire easily or burn quickly. See Figure 25-2 for some ways to prevent fires in the home.

Figure 25-3. If your clothing catches ▶
fire, stop where you are, drop to the
ground, and roll over and over to
smother the flames.

Stop, Drop and Roll

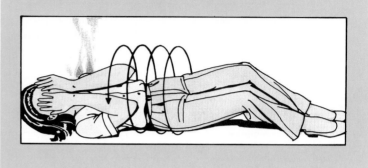

Burns occur often at home. To prevent burns, turn pot handles toward the center of the stove. Teach small children to stay away from the oven or stove when you are using it. Put protective barriers around free-standing stoves or radiators. Test the water in the shower or tub before bathing to make sure it is not too hot.

If your home is on fire, leave immediately. If there is a lot of smoke, cover your face and nose with a wet cloth and crawl along the floor to the nearest exit. Do not pause to telephone anyone or to collect belongings. Once you are outside, do not go back in. Go to a neighbor's or to the nearest fire-alarm box and call the fire department.

If a person catches fire, follow the procedure shown in Figure 25-3. By rolling the person on the ground, in a rug, or heavy coat, you cut off the air the fire needs to keep burning. If a small fire starts on the stove, put it out using a kitchen fire extinguisher. Never use water on a grease fire, since this will cause the fire to spread. If a small fire begins to get out of control, leave immediately and alert other residents to the danger.

POISONING Most poisoning accidents take place in the home and involve children under the age of five who eat or drink poisonous substances left within their reach. In almost every room of a person's home, there are substances that can poison a child. Your local **Poison Control Center** provides information about what household substances are poisonous and can tell you what to do in the event of poisoning. Figure 25-4 indicates some safety guidelines you can follow to prevent accidental poisoning.

Poisonous gases are another hazard. All gas, wood, coal, and oil stoves and heating equipment should be checked regularly to make sure they are working properly. Never leave a motor vehicle running in a closed garage. When using products that produce harmful fumes, work outdoors or in a well-ventilated area.

Preventing Accidental Poisoning

- Do not leave any medications or poisonous substances such as household cleansers, cosmetics, alcohol, or gasoline products within a child's reach.
- Make sure that all poisonous substances are clearly labeled.
- Never place poisonous substances in food containers.
- Keep hazardous substances in a cabinet that is locked or has a childproof latch.
- Always carefully follow the directions for taking or giving medications.
- Post the phone number of the Poison Control Center next to your telephone.
- Keep a remedy for accidental poisoning (such as syrup of ipecac) in your medicine cabinet, but do NOT use it until you have consulted with the Poison Control Center.

▲
Figure 25-4. What is the telephone number of the Poison Control Center in your area?

SUFFOCATION AND DROWNING When a person's breathing is blocked, it is called **suffocation.** Suffocation may be caused by an object that gets caught in the breathing passages, by smothering, or by being trapped in an enclosed space. To reduce your risk of suffocation, do not run or jump when eating. Chew food slowly and thoroughly. Do not laugh or talk when swallowing food.

If you are caring for small children, remember the following safety rules. Do not let children put small toys or other objects in their mouths. Cut food into small pieces. Never prop a bottle in a baby's mouth and then leave the baby alone. Keep plastic bags away from children. Make sure bed pillows, blankets, sheets, and clothing do not interfere with a child's breathing. Teach children not to wind ropes or long scarves around their necks.

To prevent drowning accidents, never leave young children alone in the bathroom or near a pool. Never allow anyone who has been using drugs or alcohol in a home pool.

FIREARMS Each year approximately 1,000 people are accidentally killed by firearms in their homes. Most of the deaths occur among young people between the ages of 15 and 24. To keep this from happening to you or someone you know, keep firearms unloaded and locked in a place where children cannot reach them. Lock ammunition in a separate place. Always point a firearm away from yourself and others when you are cleaning or showing it. Do not handle firearms if you have not been trained in their use.

OTHER HOME HAZARDS Electricity and faulty or misused equipment pose other risks. Make sure that your home is properly wired. Keep all home appliances in good repair and know how to use them safely. Never try to repair an electric appliance when it is plugged in.

Death from exposure to electricity is called **electrocution** (ih lek truh **kyoo** shun). To prevent electrocution, keep young children away from electrical outlets. Place safety covers over unused electrical outlets. Never use appliances when you are wet or near water.

It is possible to be injured inside your home during an electrical storm. To prevent injury, stay off the telephone and avoid using water and electrical appliances until the storm has passed.

Hazards to Your Community

Hurricanes, tornadoes, blizzards, floods, earthquakes, nuclear accidents, hazardous chemical spills, and forest fires are all examples of disasters. **Disasters** are sudden, catastrophic events that affect many people. Disasters may be natural or the result of technology or human error.

To reduce your risk of suffocation, do not run or jump while eating, and avoid laughing or talking while swallowing food.

▲
Figure 25-5. Make sure you follow the safety instructions when using an electrical appliance.

What can you do to prepare for disasters or lessen the effects of disasters on you and your family? Figure 25-6 lists seven steps you and your family can take. When a disaster occurs, emergency instructions are broadcast on television and radio. Listen to the instructions and do as they direct.

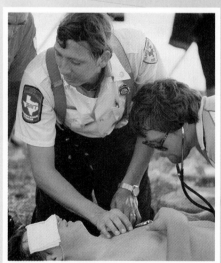

To prepare for a hurricane, tape and board up windows and bring outdoor furniture inside.

HURRICANES Powerful storms characterized by winds over 75 miles per hour and heavy rains are called **hurricanes.** If you hear that a hurricane is coming, place tape across the glass panes, and then board up the windows. Anchor or bring inside any furniture or other items outside your home. Hurricane-force winds can knock down power lines. Avoid contact with downed power lines.

TORNADOES Another kind of natural disaster is the **tornado,** which is a rapidly rotating column of air. Tornadoes are frequent occurrences in central and southern United States. If you are caught outdoors during a tornado, move away from the tornado at right angles to its path. If the tornado is too close for you to escape, find shelter or lie flat in the nearest ditch or low place in the earth. If you are at home, go to the lowest floor of your home. Keep some windows open to equalize pressure, but stay away from them. If you live in a mobile home, go to a tornado shelter.

Health careers

Whenever an ambulance responds to a medical emergency call, an **emergency medical technician (EMT)** is inside, ready to take action.

EMTs are trained to provide immediate care to ill or injured persons at the site of an accident and on the way to a hospital. They can perform lifesaving techniques, such as cardiopulmonary resuscitation (CPR).

To become an emergency medical technician, a high-school graduate must complete a basic EMT training course. This course usually is given by local hospitals, police or fire departments, or community colleges. Most EMTs who complete this course work on either a part-time or volunteer basis for an emergency rescue squad.

An EMT who wants to work full-time often goes on to become an EMT **paramedic.** Paramedics take additional courses to learn to use medical equipment, such as a defibrillator (to regulate heartbeat). Paramedics also are trained to administer special medications.

An EMT is trained in first aid and rescue techniques.

BLIZZARDS A heavy snowstorm with strong winds is called a **blizzard.** Generally, the safest place to be during a blizzard is inside your home or other warm shelter. If you have a problem requiring special treatment, alert local emergency management authorities so that you can be evacuated safely from your home. Do not try to go out on your own.

FLOODS Most floods can be predicted, but **flash floods** can occur without warning after a heavy rainfall or snow melt. Check the history of your area to find out if there is a risk of flooding. If your area is at risk, find out where you should go if evacuation is ordered. In the event of a flood, turn off the water, gas, and electricity and move your belongings to the highest floor before leaving home. When you are able to return home, discard any liquids or foods touched by flood waters. Drink bottled water until local authorities tell you that the tap water is safe.

EARTHQUAKES An **earthquake** is a sudden shaking of the ground caused by a shift in the plates that make up the earth's crust. So far, scientists have had little success in predicting major earthquakes. If you are indoors during an earthquake, stand under the frame of an interior door or crawl under a table or desk. Stay away from windows, glass doors, heavy hanging objects, or furniture that might tip over. If you are outside, stay in the open, away from buildings, walls, and electrical wires. If you are driving, pull over and stop. After a major earthquake, turn off the gas and electricity in your home to prevent a possible gas leak or fire.

HUMAN-CAUSED DISASTERS Nuclear power plant accidents, hazardous material spills, illegal dumping of toxic wastes, and some forest and brush fires are examples of disasters caused by humans. It is the job of emergency management authorities, such as civil defense, to prevent or lessen the effects of disasters and help communities recover. In the event of a disaster, follow the instructions given over the emergency broadcast system on your radio or television.

How to Be Prepared for a Disaster

- Know where your family's first-aid kit is kept.
- Have flashlights and a supply of fresh batteries on hand.
- Keep a battery-powered radio for listening to emergency broadcasts.
- Store a two-week supply of bottled water.
- Maintain a supply of precooked canned foods.
- Find out how to turn off the main switches to the gas, the electricity, and the water in your home.
- Be sure your vehicle's gas tank is kept at least half full at all times.

▲
Figure 25-6. Would your family be prepared if a disaster struck?

Section Review

1. List the four factors that can prevent accidents.
2. Name the leading kinds of home accidents.
3. Why is falling dangerous for older adults?
4. How would you prepare for a major disaster?

What Do You Think?
5. What changes would you make in your home to assure a one-year-old's safety during a visit?

2. SAFETY AT WORK AND PLAY

Many accidents occur either at work or while participating in recreational activities. Although you are not working full time yet, you probably will be someday. In preparation for that time, you should know about the possible hazards of the workplace and what to do about them. You should also be aware of the hazards of any leisure-time activities you are involved in.

Occupational Safety

Each year more than one-and-a-half million workers suffer disabling injuries on the job; another 10,000 are killed, and 250,000 workers develop work-related illnesses.

The **Occupational Health and Safety Administration (OSHA)** is a U.S. government agency that identifies occupational hazards and sets standards for safety. OSHA defines an **occupational injury** as any injury that results from a work accident or from exposure to a hazard in the work environment. OSHA defines an **occupational illness** as any abnormal condition or disorder, excluding injuries, caused by exposure to the workplace environment. Certain cancers, for example, are classified as occupational illnesses.

Which jobs are most hazardous to your health? Figure 25-7 shows the frequency of accidents that result in death or disability in various industries. Overall, however, the rates

Figure 25-7. Which industries have the highest death and injury rates?

Source: National Safety Council, data for 1986

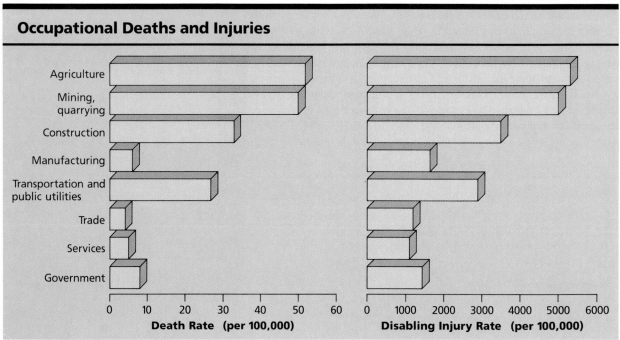

Occupational Deaths and Injuries

Agriculture
Mining, quarrying
Construction
Manufacturing
Transportation and public utilities
Trade
Services
Government

0 10 20 30 40 50 60
Death Rate   (per 100,000)

0 1000 2000 3000 4000 5000 6000
Disabling Injury Rate   (per 100,000)

▲
Figure 25-8. To prevent injury, workers need to know the safety risks of their occupations.

of death, injury, and illness have been declining steadily due to the efforts of employers and employees.

Many occupational injuries and illnesses can be prevented or made less serious by removing potential hazards from the work environment. It is the responsibility of your employer to keep the workplace as healthful as possible and to inform you of any on-the-job hazards. It is your responsibility to be well rested and alert on the job, to wear appropriate clothing, and follow all safety procedures.

When selecting a career, you should be aware of the possible health hazards. Farmers are exposed to many dangerous chemicals in pest-killing agents and fertilizers. Miners are exposed to dust that can lead to lung diseases. These hazards can be reduced by using special equipment and following safety rules. Employers and employees are responsible for following OSHA's guidelines for their industry.

Today, many office workers work on a video display terminal (VDT) that is part of a computer. Some VDT operators have reported health problems, such as eyestrain and muscle and skeletal aches. Another issue is whether VDTs cause harm to the developing babies of pregnant VDT operators. As of now, there is no answer to this question, although scientific studies are under way.

Whatever job you choose, you should know the health risks involved. Be informed about how these risks can be prevented or reduced. You always have the option of changing jobs if a job proves to be hazardous to your health.

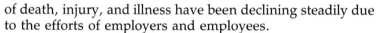

Both employers and employees must follow the safety guidelines set for their industries.

Recreational Safety

Almost everyone in this country enjoys some kind of recreational activity. What leisure-time activities do you like? Swimming? Boating? Basketball? Jogging? Camping?

Whatever activities you enjoy, there are four basic safety guidelines you should follow:

- Learn and apply the proper skills.
- Have appropriate, well-maintained equipment.
- Know the safety rules specific to the activity.
- Prepare adequately for the activity.

As you read about various recreational activities, keep these four guidelines in mind.

WATER SAFETY Drowning is the third leading cause of accidental death in the United States. Most of these drownings are associated with swimming and boating accidents. The highest number of drownings occurs among young people between the ages of 15 and 24.

Most drownings can be prevented if the person can swim 20 yards. The American Red Cross provides programs for swimming and water safety instruction. These programs are offered year-round in many communities. If you do not know how to swim, check with the Red Cross or with your community recreational center for places to learn.

Even if you never learn how to swim, you should know how to protect yourself from drowning. Figure 25-9 shows

Follow the four basic safety guidelines about skills, equipment, rules, and preparation during leisure-time activities.

Figure 25-9. Drownproofing allows nonswimmers to stay afloat until help arrives.
▼

Drownproofing

1. **Rest**—Take a deep breath and sink vertically beneath the surface, relax your arms and legs, keep chin down and allow fingertips to touch knees. Keep neck relaxed and back of head above the surface.

2. **Get set**—Gently raise arms to a crossed position with back of wrists touching forehead. At the same time step forward with one leg and backward with the other.

3. **Lift head, exhale**—Without moving your arms and legs from the *get set* position raise your head quickly but smoothly to the vertical and *exhale through your nose.*

4. **Stroke and kick, inhale**—To support your head above the surface while you *inhale through your mouth*—gently sweep the arms outward and downward and step downward with both feet.

5. **Head down, press**—As you drop beneath the surface put your *head down* and press downward with your arms and hands to stop your fall.

6. **Rest!**—Relax completely as in Step #1 for 6 to 10 seconds. *Always* breathe from choice—*never* from necessity.

drownproofing, a lifesaving water safety technique that allows you to float and breathe without using much energy. You also should be aware of the water safety tips given in Figure 25-10.

Local Coast Guard auxiliaries, community boating facilities, and the American Red Cross offer boating safety classes. Before you go out in a boat, check the weather conditions and make sure the boat is in good repair. Each person on the boat should have an approved flotation device, such as a life preserver or life jacket. Nonswimmers should wear flotation devices at all times. Signal lights should be kept on between dusk and dawn, and you should have a whistle or horn to signal with when visibility is poor. No alcohol or drug use should be allowed on board a boat.

When a boat turns over, it is called **capsizing**. Capsizing is the most frequent cause of death among users of small boats. Usually capsizing results from improper loading and unloading of the boat, but it can also occur when a boat has a motor that is too powerful. If you are in a boat when it capsizes, grab your flotation device and stay with the boat until you are rescued.

If someone falls overboard, immediately toss a flotation device and a tow line to the person. Shut off the motor and help the person into the boat. If the person is injured, have a strong swimmer, wearing a flotation device with a line attached, slip into the water to rescue the injured person.

SPORTS SAFETY Sports injuries usually occur when you do not warm up properly before vigorous activity or cool off properly afterward. Injuries also occur when you have faulty or inappropriate equipment. For example, if you are roller-skating or skateboarding you should wear protective equipment, such as a helmet, wrist guards, elbow and knee pads, and light gloves. Injuries can occur too if you engage in a sport in hazardous situations. Do not roller-skate or skateboard on heavily trafficked roads. Be alert to your surroundings—do not wear headphones. You also should never engage in a sport when you are ill or if you have used alcohol or drugs.

When exercising vigorously, your body uses up fluids rapidly. Whenever you are exercising you should drink lots of water, even in cold weather.

Camping or hunting outdoors presents special safety risks. To avoid hazards, camp or hunt only in approved areas. Always let someone know where you are and when you expect to return. Beforehand, find out the potential dangers, such as bears, ticks, or poisonous snakes or plants. Take along a first-aid kit and know how to treat likely accidents, such as snakebites or skin infections. Check the weather conditions and be prepared. Take plenty of water and stow food and garbage so as not to attract animals. Cook

Water Safety Tips

- Do not swim immediately after eating.
- Always swim in a known, supervised area.
- Know your swimming ability. Make sure that you can return to shore easily.
- Do not use underwater equipment unless you have received proper training and instructions.
- Wear a flotation device when required; do not rely on a float or rubber tube.
- Never dive in an area where the water may not be deep enough for diving or where there may be rocks, swimmers, or other obstacles.
- Never swim or dive after drinking alcoholic beverages or taking drugs.
- Do not walk on the ice over a lake or river or pond unless local recreation authorities state that it is safe.
- If you are on an ice-covered body of water and the ice begins to crack, immediately lie down and crawl to shore.

Figure 25-10. Which of these tips do you already practice?

When camping or hunting, let someone know where you are and when you expect to return.

Figure 25-11. When camping, take ▷ care not to attract animals or start a fire.

 Wear a brightly colored vest or hat when you are hunting.

in a protected area so that sparks will not start a brush or forest fire. Dress appropriately for the weather and follow all posted campsite rules.

If you are hunting, wear a bright-colored vest or hat so that you will not be mistaken for prey by another hunter. While hunting, keep the safety on until you are ready to shoot. Keep your trigger finger outside the trigger guard. Unload your gun as soon as you have finished hunting.

Section Review

1. From what government agency can you obtain information about occupational hazards and safety regulations?
2. What are the responsibilities of the employer and the employee regarding occupational safety?
3. Why should people never engage in a recreational activity when they are ill or when they are using alcohol or drugs?
4. Select one recreational activity and describe what you can do to prevent accidents when you are participating in this activity.

What Do You Think?
5. Suppose a friend of yours tries to persuade you to go diving with him in a water-filled quarry at night. How would you talk your friend into doing something less hazardous than this?

3. VEHICLE SAFETY

The leading cause of accidental death is motor vehicle accidents. Each year about 50,000 deaths and millions of injuries occur as a result of motor vehicle accidents. On average, one out of every two Americans will be involved in a motor vehicle accident during his or her lifetime.

Motor Vehicle Safety

The main factor contributing to motor vehicle accidents is the human factor, especially among young drivers. The human factor includes a driver's attitude and self-control. Although young drivers have better reflexes than older drivers, drivers between the ages of 15 and 24 are involved in more accidents than any other age group. Males have a higher rate of reckless driving than females. Because of their higher accident rate, drivers between the ages of 15 and 24 pay high insurance premiums.

The use of alcohol and drugs is another major factor in motor vehicle accidents and injuries. Over 50 percent of all fatal accidents involving motor vehicles have been linked to alcohol use. As you read in Chapter 20, alcohol inhibits good judgment and self-control, slows reaction time, blurs vision, and reduces coordination. Drivers between the ages of 20 and 24 have more drunk driving convictions and alcohol-related accidents than any other group.

Other factors contributing to motor vehicle accidents are the condition of the vehicle and driving conditions. Defective brakes, lights, tires, and windshield wipers contribute to

Figure 25-12. Seat belts have saved many lives.

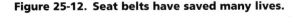

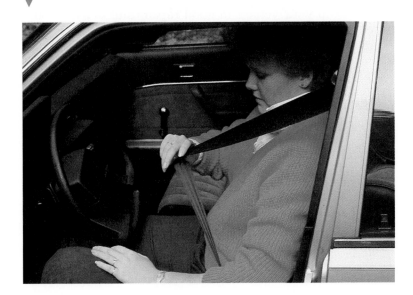

Voice-Activated Controls

Drivers are most unsafe when they are not paying full attention to the road. Sometimes, little things, such as tuning the radio, can cause an accident. To eliminate these types of distractions, car makers are working to develop car controls that are operated by the driver's voice.

Car manufacturers hope that voice-activated door locks, radios, air conditioning, alarm systems, and cruise control will be common by the 1990s. In one cruise control system now being worked on, a driver speaks into a microphone mounted on the steering wheel. Wires lead from the microphone to a box on the car's floor. Inside, an electronic computer chip translates the verbal commands into electronic signals that tell the car to adjust its speed.

Voice-activated control systems do not yet work perfectly but car makers are hopeful they can be improved. Once perfected, voice-activated controls might make the roads a safer place to be.

Will voice-activated controls eliminate distractions?

Figure 25-13. Which of these tips are ▶
especially important for teenagers?

Figure 25-14. Motorcyclists and
moped riders need to take special
safety precautions.

▼

Motorcycle and Moped Safety

- Always wear a helmet. Have an extra helmet for a passenger to wear.
- Learn how to operate your vehicle safely before taking it on the open road.
- Follow the traffic rules that apply to larger vehicles.
- Never ride your vehicle when using alcohol or drugs.
- Avoid carrying anything that will interfere with your ability to drive.
- Only carry an additional passenger if your vehicle has an attached second seat and foot rests.
- Never grab on to another moving vehicle.
- If your vehicle lacks a wind-screen, wear eye protection, such as goggles.
- Make sure your vehicle is equipped with a working headlight, taillight, stoplight, reflectors, and rear-view mirror.
- Signal stops, turns, or changes in direction.
- Watch for possible hazards, such as a car door opening or a rope or wire across your driving path.
- Get your vehicle inspected periodically to make sure it is in good repair.
- Wear bright-colored, sturdy clothing that will not catch on the moving parts of your motorcycle or moped.

Safe Driving Tips

- Never let a driver who is using alcohol or drugs get behind the wheel.
- Always wear a seat belt and insist that others wear their seat belts.
- If young children or babies are in the car, make sure that they are fastened securely into a car safety seat.
- Always drive slightly slower than conditions require.
- Allow enough distance between you and the car in front of you so that you can stop suddenly without hitting it.
- On slippery roads, rather than using the brake, shift to a lower gear and let the engine slow the car.
- Practice defensive driving, which means anticipating the worst from other drivers and being alert to possible road hazards.
- Do not let passengers ride in the back of an open truck.
- Never carry a flammable substance, such as extra gasoline, in the trunk of your car.
- Eliminate distractions, such as loud music, hot liquids that might spill, and animals inside the car.

many motor vehicle accidents. Poor driving conditions, such as defects in the road, bad weather, and low visibility, increase the likelihood of motor vehicle accidents. The risks of serious injury and death are compounded by excessive speed and by not using seat belts. Always wear a seat belt when you are in a motor vehicle.

FOUR-WHEEL MOTOR VEHICLES There are steps you can take to reduce your chances of being in a car, van, or small truck accident or being seriously injured in a motor-vehicle accident. To start with, take a course in driver education, keep your vehicle in good repair, and avoid driving when you are tired, angry, or depressed. Figure 25-13 provides more safe driving tips.

TWO-WHEEL MOTOR VEHICLES Human error is the main contributing factor to most accidents with two-wheel motor vehicles, such as motorcycles and mopeds. It is therefore up to the riders to behave in ways that enhance their safety. Figure 25-14 lists some safety suggestions for motorcycle and moped riders.

Bicycles and Recreational Vehicles

Many people, especially young people, are killed or injured each year in accidents involving bicycles or recreational vehicles, such as snowmobiles or all-terrain vehicles (ATVs). These accidents usually are the result of human behavior, mechanical problems, and ignorance of basic safety rules.

Bicycle Maintenance

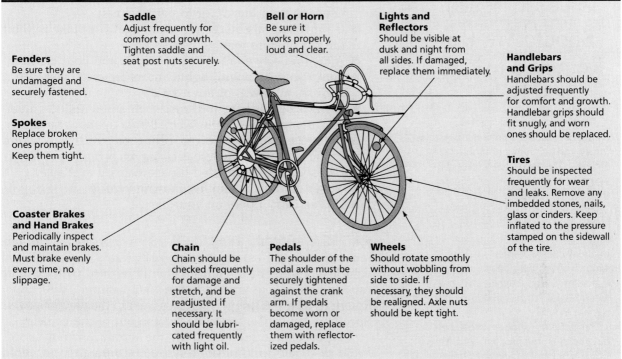

Fenders
Be sure they are undamaged and securely fastened.

Spokes
Replace broken ones promptly. Keep them tight.

Coaster Brakes and Hand Brakes
Periodically inspect and maintain brakes. Must brake evenly every time, no slippage.

Saddle
Adjust frequently for comfort and growth. Tighten saddle and seat post nuts securely.

Bell or Horn
Be sure it works properly, loud and clear.

Lights and Reflectors
Should be visible at dusk and night from all sides. If damaged, replace them immediately.

Handlebars and Grips
Handlebars should be adjusted frequently for comfort and growth. Handlebar grips should fit snugly, and worn ones should be replaced.

Tires
Should be inspected frequently for wear and leaks. Remove any imbedded stones, nails, glass or cinders. Keep inflated to the pressure stamped on the sidewall of the tire.

Chain
Chain should be checked frequently for damage and stretch, and be readjusted if necessary. It should be lubricated frequently with light oil.

Pedals
The shoulder of the pedal axle must be securely tightened against the crank arm. If pedals become worn or damaged, replace them with reflectorized pedals.

Wheels
Should rotate smoothly without wobbling from side to side. If necessary, they should be realigned. Axle nuts should be kept tight.

Source: Bicycle Manufacturers Association

BICYCLES Before you buy or ride a bike, inspect it thoroughly to make sure it is the right size for you and that it is safe and properly equipped. You should be able to touch the ground with the toes of both feet when you are seated on the bicycle. Figure 25-15 shows you how to decide whether or not a bicycle is in good repair and adequately equipped. About one-fifth of all bicycle accidents are the result of mechanical problems with the bicycle.

Before riding your bicycle a long distance, make sure cycling conditions are safe. Check the weather report. Avoid taking a long ride on a hot day. Take along some water to drink. Never ride when you are ill or on medication. Do not ride immediately after eating.

The most dangerous bicycle accidents are collisions with motor vehicles. Fifty percent of all collisions occur at intersections, and 70 percent occur during the daylight hours. In most cases, the bicyclist was disobeying traffic laws at the time of the accident. Here are some rules you should follow to prevent or lessen the severity of bicycle accidents:

- Always wear a safety helmet.
- Ride single file with the flow of traffic on the right.
- Obey all traffic rules and laws.
- Signal your intentions with hand signals, illustrated in Figure 25-16, before turning or stopping.

▲
Figure 25-15. Before riding a bicycle, be sure it is in good repair.

Proper Hand Signals

| Left turn | Right turn | Stop or Slow |

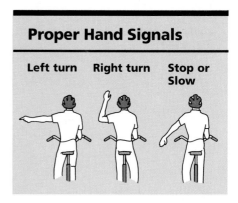

▲
Figure 25-16. Bicyclists should use hand signals to make drivers aware of their intentions.

Should We Be Required to Use Seat Belts?

People in favor of a seat belt law claim that seat belts protect against injury and death in automobile accidents. They say that a properly worn seat belt almost guarantees that injuries will be less severe. They also point out that automobile injuries cost our society millions of dollars each year in medical costs, worker's compensation, welfare, and related expenses. Thus, seat belt laws protect not only the individual, but society as well.

People who oppose a seat belt law feel that it denies our constitutional right to freedom of choice. They also claim that seat belt use actually makes injuries in some cases worse by causing internal bleeding. Seat belts might also prevent a person from escaping from a car if it were to plunge into a body of water or catch fire. For these reasons, they feel that people should be left to decide for themselves whether or not to use seat belts.

Do you feel that seat belt use should be required by law? Why or why not?

- Always use crosswalks to walk your bicycle across busy intersections.
- For riding in traffic, use a rear-view mirror attached either to your bicycle or to your helmet.
- If a mechanical emergency occurs, get your bike well off the road before making repairs.
- Attach reflective tape to your bicycle and your clothing.
- Equip your bike with lights and reflectors if you ride it at dusk, at dawn, or after dark.
- Always be alert for hazards, such as oil spills, gravel, ice, ruts, potholes, railroad tracks, or opening car doors.
- Whenever possible, avoid riding on roadways where traffic is heavy or where cars maintain high speeds.
- Use specially designated bicycle paths if available.
- Never grab on to another moving vehicle.
- Do not carry riders on your bicycle.

RECREATIONAL VEHICLES Snowmobiles and all-terrain vehicles (ATVs) are two popular kinds of recreational vehicles. Both kinds of vehicles should be used with extreme caution and only according to the manufacturer's directions. Rough terrain and uneven surfaces can flip the machine over. Speeding can cause you to be thrown out of the vehicle.

To prevent accidents, know the terrain, do not speed, avoid roadways, and never venture out onto an ice-covered body of water. Do not wear loose scarves or clothing that can become tangled in the machinery. Wear a safety helmet. Always go with a friend when traveling any distance and pack a first-aid kit and a container of drinking water. Take enough emergency food and equipment to enable you to survive and signal for help if you should need it. If you use your vehicle improperly or are not prepared for an emergency, recreational vehicles can be extremely hazardous.

Section Review

1. Name the factor that plays a major role in all kinds of vehicle accidents.

2. What is meant by defensive driving?

3. Describe some safety guidelines for operating a motorcycle or moped and tell how they prevent accidents.

4. Where and when do most bicycle accidents occur?

What Do You Think?

5. A good friend of yours is, in your view, an unsafe driver. He drives at high speeds, disobeys traffic rules, and frequently takes his eyes off the road. What could you do or say to your friend to encourage him to drive more safely?

4. CRIME PREVENTION

If current trends continue, you may be the victim of or the witness to a violent crime, such as murder, rape, or robbery, at some time during your life. Your risks are higher if you live in a major city. How can you reduce your risks?

Self-Protection

An unlawful attempt or threat to harm someone is called an **assault.** You can prevent assault or reduce the likelihood of serious injury by following certain safety guidelines. The most basic guideline is to avoid all risky situations.

AT HOME If you are at home by yourself or babysitting in someone's home, lock all doors and windows. If a stranger knocks at the door, do not allow him or her inside. If the person asks for help, tell him or her to stay outside while you telephone for help. Never let a caller know you are by yourself or give your name, address, or telephone number to a person who has called the wrong number. If you hear someone breaking in, leave immediately and call the police from a neighbor's house or public phone. Do not keep keys to your home in an obvious hiding place, such as under a doormat, in the mailbox, or above the door.

AWAY FROM HOME Avoid deserted places, such as dark streets, parks, and garages. Make sure you are with a friend if you must enter or walk through a deserted or dangerous area. Always walk purposefully and quickly. Stay away from dark doorways and hedges where an attacker might be hiding. If someone starts to follow you, step into a nearby store or restaurant or walk up to the door of a house and ring the bell.

When driving, keep the car doors locked and the windows rolled up far enough so that no one can reach inside. If a menacing person tries to get into your car, honk your horn. Never get out to help a stranger. Do not hitchhike or pick up hitchhikers. If your car breaks down, pull over to the side of the road, put your hood up, and blink your headlights. If a stranger stops to help, do not open your car door, just ask the person to call the police. Park in a well-lit place, close all the windows, and lock all the doors. Before getting back into your car, always check to make sure no one is hiding in the back seat or on the floor.

IF YOU ARE ATTACKED Your possessions are not as important as your survival. If someone tries to rob you, give them what they want. Do not resist, or you may be physically harmed or killed. Report the attack to the police as soon as it is safe to do so.

Never let a stranger into the house when you are babysitting or when you are home alone.

Figure 25-17. When walking through a deserted area, always walk with someone and be aware of your surroundings.

▼

WITNESSING A CRIME If you see a crime in progress, call the police immediately. Do not try to intervene by yourself, especially if weapons could be involved. Give the police as much detailed information as you can: location; license plate and type of car; description of the suspect; your name, address, and telephone number. Do not hang up until you have given all the necessary information and have answered any questions the police may have.

Rape Prevention

One type of assault that is both physically and psychologically painful is rape. **Rape** means that one person forces another to have sexual relations. Figure 25-18 gives some myths and facts about rape.

Contrary to the myths, rapes usually are carried out by someone the victim knows in a place that is familiar to either the victim or the rapist. Date rape occurs when a rape is carried out by someone the victim is dating; acquaintance rape is a rape carried out by someone known to the victim. It is hard to tell if a person is a potential rapist, but there are some warning signs you should know. Stay away from a person who

- acts strangely to you and makes you uncomfortable.
- pays no attention to you when you say "no" or "stop."
- tries to touch you when you do not want to be touched or says suggestive things to you.
- pushes you to do risky things you do not want to do.

Figure 25-18. Which of these myths about rape did you once believe?

▼

It is important to trust your own judgment; if a person makes you uncomfortable and shows little respect for you, do not

---

Myths and Facts About Rape

1. **Myth:** Only young, attractive women are raped.
   Fact: Both males and females of all ages are potential victims of rape.
2. **Myth:** Rapists are always strangers.
   Fact: A rapist can be a date or another person who is known to the rape victim as well as a stranger.
3. **Myth:** Rapists are people who are driven by the urge to have sex.
   Fact: Sex has nothing to do with the act of rape; rapists usually are angry and are trying to humiliate or demonstrate their power over another person.
4. **Myth:** Rape is usually an unplanned assault.
   Fact: Rapists generally select a vulnerable person and then plan their attack.

5. **Myth:** Some victims "ask for it" by the way they dress and act.
   Fact: Studies show that rapists look for people who appear weak and vulnerable, not people who dress or act in a certain way.
6. **Myth:** Rapes usually occur in unfamiliar, deserted places.
   Fact: Rapes are most likely to occur in a familiar place, such as a person's home or apartment building.
7. **Myth:** Most rapists are poor, uneducated, and emotionally disturbed.
   Fact: Most rapists appear to be normal and can come from any kind of background—rich, middle-class, poor, educated, or uneducated.

---

allow yourself to be alone with him. When on a date, baby-sitting, or somewhere else, let someone know where you are and when you will return home.

Most rape victims felt that their lives were at risk when they were attacked. If someone tries to rape you, do whatever you need to do to protect your life. Since each situation is different, use your common sense in deciding what action to take. Escape if you can.

All rape victims should seek medical treatment immediately. Reporting a rape is not an easy thing to do. Recalling the event can be extremely painful. Most police departments, however, have women police officers who specialize in helping rape victims. Many communities also have hotlines and **rape crisis centers,** agencies that provide counseling and support for rape victims.

Crime Prevention Programs

You can help reduce crime in general by taking part in organized crime-prevention programs in your community. In some communities, volunteers have formed **Neighborhood Crime Watch** groups, who report any suspicious activities they see to the police. Some communities also have block parents, who provide a safe place for children who feel threatened on the street.

Operation Identification is a nationwide program to encourage the marking of personal property. Your local police department can provide you with marking materials and a decal to post in your window, which may prevent a burglary. Your local police can give you more information about protecting yourself. Many police departments have special crime prevention officers who can advise you.

Figure 25-19. Neighborhood crime groups work with police to make their communities safer.

Section Review

1. List four things you can do to protect yourself from crime when you are babysitting or when you are home by yourself.
2. How can you reduce your chances of being assaulted when you are away from your home?
3. How can a person reduce the chances of being raped in a dating situation?
4. What should you do if you are assaulted?

What Do You Think?
5. Suppose you had a weekend job working until midnight at a restaurant about a mile from your house. How would you get home each night? What safety precautions would you take?

25 | Chapter Review

Chapter Summary

- Knowledge and awareness, ability, state of mind, and environmental conditions are the four main factors to consider when trying to prevent or lessen the effects of accidents.
- The leading causes of death from home accidents are falls, fire, poisoning, suffocation, firearms, and drowning.
- To prevent falls, remove objects from floors and stairs. Take special precautions for young children or older adults.
- By installing smoke detectors, correcting faulty electrical wiring, and removing flammable materials from your home, you can prevent fires in the home.
- Keep all medications and other poisonous substances out of the reach of children. Store guns unloaded and locked away.
- Every family should have a first-aid kit, flashlights, a battery-powered radio, bottled water, canned food, and a means of escape.
- The Occupational Health and Safety Administration (OSHA) is the U.S. government agency that identifies hazards in the workplace and sets standards for safety.
- The four basic safety guidelines for recreational activities are to learn and apply proper skills; to have appropriate, well-maintained equipment; to know the safety rules; and to prepare adequately.
- The human factor, the use of alcohol and drugs, the condition of the vehicle, and driving conditions are the main elements contributing to motor vehicle accidents.
- When riding a bicycle, always wear a helmet and ride with the flow of traffic.
- To lessen the chances of being assaulted, keep doors and windows locked at home and do not let strangers in. Outside, avoid deserted places and walk with someone.
- To avoid rape, do not allow yourself to be alone with anyone who shows little respect for you. In a rape situation, use your best judgment in deciding what action to take. Do not put your life at risk.

Vocabulary Review

Listed below are some of the important terms in this chapter. Choose the term that best matches the phrase in the exercise that follows.

accident
assault
blizzard
capsizing
disasters
drownproofing

earthquake
electrocution
flammable materials
hurricanes
Neighborhood Crime
   Watch

occupational illness
occupational injury
Poison Control Center
rape
Rape Crisis Center

risk behavior
safe behavior
suffocation
tornado

1. place where a person can obtain information about how to treat a poisoning victim

2. any abnormal condition or disorder, excluding injuries, caused by exposure to environmental factors in the workplace

3. action that protects a person from danger or lessens the effects of a harmful situation

4. unlawful attempt to harm someone

5. place that helps sexual assault victims

6. lifesaving water safety technique

7. death from exposure to electricity

8. substances that can catch fire easily or burn quickly

9. program of observing and reporting suspicious activities to the police

10. obstruction of a person's breathing

What Have You Learned?

1. What safety behaviors can you practice in your home to prevent falling accidents?
2. Describe what you would do in a fire emergency in your home.
3. How do emergency management authorities notify people during a disaster?
4. Give one example each of occupational injuries and occupational illnesses.
5. Describe with words and diagrams the technique of drownproofing.
6. What safety behaviors should a skateboarder practice to prevent accidents?
7. What safety procedures should you follow to ensure a child's safety in a car?
8. What safety precautions would you take before riding a motorcycle or a moped?
9. Why are all-terrain vehicles dangerous?
10. Where can a rape victim go for help?
11. What should you do if you see a crime?
12. How can you discourage burglars?

What Do You Think?

1. Which safe behaviors are the most important ones to practice when caring for an infant?
2. Explain how alcohol or drug use on board a boat can endanger everyone on the boat and in the surrounding waters.
3. The sale of three-wheel ATVs has been banned in the United States because of the high rates of accidental death and injury associated with their use. Do you think that the three-wheel ATVs already sold should be recalled? Why or why not?
4. Suppose you have just bought a new electric saw. You have used electric saws for years. Should you read the instruction manual before you use it? Why or why not?
5. Why do you think young men drive more recklessly than young women? What measures would make young drivers safer?

What Would You Do?

1. Suppose your grandmother was going to move into your home. What changes would you make to ensure her safety?
2. Imagine your baby sister has eaten some pills from a wastebasket. What would you do?
3. If a friend invited you to go on a day-long bicycle trip, how would you prepare for it?
4. Suppose your class was planning a camping trip. Make a list of the kind of information your class would need to plan a safe trip.
5. Imagine that your parent's car broke down and you were left with the car in a deserted area while your parent went in search of a call-box. How would you protect yourself?

For Further Study

1. Check each room of your home for safety hazards. Make a list of any hazards that you discover and tell how each one could be eliminated or lessened.
2. Cut out articles about accidents from old newspapers. Display them on a poster, explaining how each accident could have been prevented or made less severe.
3. Contact your local fire department and find out how your household can plan a fire escape route. Following these guidelines, plan the escape route with your family and practice it so that all family members understand what to do.

As you read, think about

▶ what actions you should take when a person has been injured.

▶ how to perform first aid in a life-threatening emergency.

▶ how to treat common injuries.

▶ what common outdoor emergencies are and how they should be treated.

First Aid

The rain is over, and you're riding your bike. The storm blew many of the fallen leaves across your path. After coming up a hill, you're coasting down a long grade. Suddenly, there's a bicycle right in front of you. The rider cuts around you, skids, and tumbles off.

You rush over to help. When you look around, you see no one else. You're in charge. How seriously is she hurt? How can you tell? What should you do first?

This chapter will help prepare you for emergency situations like this one. You'll learn about first-aid procedures. You'll also find out how to recognize various kinds of medical problems, from shock and fractures to poisoning and heat exhaustion. Among other skills, you'll learn how to control bleeding and how to treat burns. This knowledge will help you feel more confident—and be more useful—in a medical emergency.

If you know first-aid procedures, you will be prepared to handle an emergency.

Check Your Wellness

If you were in a situation where someone had been injured, would you know what to do? To test your knowledge of emergency procedures, indicate whether the statements below are true or false.

1. If a neck or spinal injury is suspected, you should not move the victim.
2. When trying to stop bleeding, you should apply direct pressure on the wound and elevate it above the heart.
3. In treating a poison victim, call a poison control center immediately.
4. Some early signs of shock are restlessness; pale, clammy skin; unusual thirst; and a rapid heartbeat.
5. For a minor burn, cool the burned area with cold water and cover it with a clean cloth.
6. To treat frostbite, wrap the frostbitten area in a blanket and keep it dry.
7. The emergency telephone number for your community is 911.

1. THE IMPORTANCE OF FIRST AID

In an emergency, you may have only seconds to save a life; you may not even have enough time for a telephone call. The only person you may have to depend on is yourself. Properly administered **first aid,** the immediate care given in an accident or sudden illness before professional medical help arrives, can mean the difference between life and death. Many of the people killed or injured in accidents each year could have been helped by proper first aid.

Guidelines for First Aid

Emergencies come in all sizes and shapes. Two cars collide, and someone is injured; it is an emergency. You are walking down a crowded street, and the person in front of you collapses. This, too, is an emergency. Suppose you were the first person on the scene of an emergency. Would you know what to do?

Whatever the emergency, there are certain procedures you should follow when you react to the situation.

1. Assess the situation and the immediate environment for possible dangers. Do not put your safety at risk when you are trying to rescue a person or perform first aid.
2. Work calmly, quickly, and efficiently. Demonstrate self-confidence and knowledge.
3. Determine whether or not the individual is conscious by tapping him or her on the shoulder and shouting, "Are you OK?" If the individual does not respond, shout "Help!" to get the attention of people nearby.
4. If the individual is unconscious, check whether or not the person is breathing and has a pulse. You will learn these procedures later in this chapter. If there are no signs of breathing or a pulse, or if there is severe bleeding, treat these conditions first because they are life threatening.
5. Call or send someone to call for medical help. In many communities, you can dial 911 for help in any type of emergency. Otherwise, dial 0, the operator, for assistance, and be prepared to follow the steps given below.

- Speak slowly and clearly.
- Give the exact location of the accident. Give the town, street name, and number. If you are calling at night, describe the building.
- Describe what has happened. Give essential details about the victim(s), the situation, and any treatments you have given.
- Identify yourself and the phone number from which you are calling.

▲
Figure 26-1. You should be prepared to deal with all types of accidents.

- Ask for advice. Let the person on the other end ask you questions and tell you what to do until help arrives. Take notes, if necessary.
- Hang up last. The person on the other end may have more questions or advice for you. Let the other person hang up first.

6. Once life-threatening conditions have been cared for, examine the individual's body from head to toe. Do not stop after finding one injury. Look for a Medic Alert tag around the neck or wrist. This tag, which is shown in Figure 26-2, provides information about medical problems.

7. Continue to treat or monitor the individual until medical help arrives. Do not move the person unless there are dangers nearby, such as fire, poisonous gases, or downed power lines. If the person has suffered any type of serious injury, such as heavy bleeding, treat for shock (page 603), even if there are no symptoms.

As the first person on the scene of an accident, you need to identify the injuries, give emergency treatment, contact the proper rescue personnel, and prevent further injury. If the individual is conscious, it is also important to keep him or her calm. You can reassure an individual through your words and your actions. Demonstrate that you are in control of the situation and that you know what you are doing.

▲
Figure 26-2. A Medic Alert tag provides useful medical information about the person wearing it.

Figure 26-3. First-aid classes give you the knowledge and confidence to handle emergency situations. ▶

You can be prepared for any emergency by knowing how to administer first aid.

The Good Samaritan Law

Sometimes, complications occur even when first aid has been administered properly. To protect the rescuer, most states have enacted a **Good Samaritan law.** This law protects people from lawsuits if medical complications arise after they have administered first aid correctly. If someone's life is in danger and you are knowledgeable, you should give first aid. Be sure, however, that your help will not harm the individual. If you are not sure of a procedure, you probably should not attempt it.

First-aid courses and regular refresher classes are the best way to become prepared for any emergency. Contact the local branch of the American Red Cross or the American Heart Association to find out about the first-aid classes offered in your area. Often, local police departments, fire departments, and community colleges, offer various classes in first aid.

Section Review

1. What is first aid?
2. What information should you provide in an emergency phone call?
3. What is the purpose of the Good Samaritan law?

What Do You Think?
4. How would you react if you were the first person on the scene of an accident? What feelings and thoughts would run through your mind?

2. FIRST-AID PRIORITIES

Life-threatening situations—respiratory emergencies, heart failure, stroke, shock, severe bleeding, and poisoning—must be treated before any other injury. After these dangerous problems are under control, you should look for and treat any other injuries.

Respiratory Emergencies

A person's breathing may stop or become blocked for a number of reasons, including exposure to poisonous gas, electrical shock, choking, drug overdose, injury, or drowning. When breathing stops, the body's **cells,** its smallest living units, quickly run out of oxygen and begin to die. This is especially dangerous to the cells of the brain. Permanent brain damage usually takes place four to six minutes after breathing has stopped.

BREATHING FAILURE You can recognize total breathing failure by the absence of breathing movements; a bluish color to the lips, tongue, and fingernails; and dilated, or enlarged, pupils. If a person experiences breathing failure, you should perform rescue breathing immediately. **Rescue breathing,** also known as mouth-to-mouth resuscitation, is a method of inflating a person's lungs with air from your lungs. It is done by blowing air into the individual's mouth or nose or into both, in the case of a child or infant. The steps given in Figure 26-4 outline the procedure you should follow when using rescue breathing.

Figure 26-4. To perform rescue breathing: (A) open the victim's airway by tipping the head backward while lifting the jaw; (B) determine that the victim is not breathing; (C) rest one hand on the victim's forehead and pinch the nose closed; (D) form an airtight seal with your mouth over the victim's mouth and deliver two slow, full breaths; (E) check for a pulse by placing two fingers on the side of the neck and feeling for rhythmic pulsations; and (F) if there is a pulse, deliver one breath every five seconds for adults, or 1 breath every 3 seconds for children.

▼

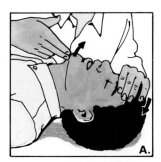
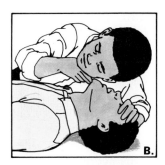

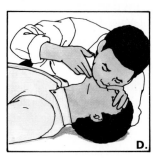
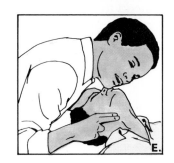
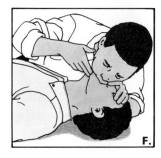

A Chest Vest for CPR

When the heart fails, it is essential to keep blood flowing to a person's vital organs. In CPR, this is done manually, by pushing down on the victim's chest. Now, researchers have developed an inflatable vest that may provide a more efficient way of moving blood through the body.

The inflatable vest developed from a new understanding of how CPR works. It had been thought that manual chest compressions pushed down directly on the heart, thereby squeezing blood out to the rest of the body. Recent studies have shown that this is not the case. In reality, manual compressions increase the overall pressure within the chest cavity. It is this increased pressure that causes blood to flow.

In studies done on animals, the vest pushed two times more blood through the body than did manual compression. The next step is to test the vest on those people who have failed to revive after manual CPR has been attempted.

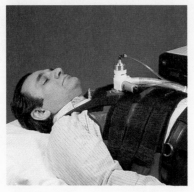

This new CPR vest may help save lives.

CHOKING   When food or some other object becomes lodged in the throat or airway, it can cause choking. The person may gasp for breath, have violent fits of coughing, be unable to talk or breathe, and become pale, then blue, or even unconscious.

If a choking individual can speak or cough loudly, you should allow the person to cough up the foreign object. Do not interfere with the person's attempts to dislodge the object. If the person is coughing weakly, or not coughing at all, and cannot speak, perform the **Heimlich** (**hym** lik) **maneuver.** The Heimlich maneuver is a technique that uses abdominal thrusts to dislodge the object blocking an individual's airway. The Health Skills on page 608 describes how to apply this technique.

Heart Failure and Stroke

Cardiovascular (kar dee oh **vas** kyuh lur) **failure,** the failure of a person's heart or circulatory system to function properly, often causes a life-threatening situation. It can occur as a result of a block or a break in a blood vessel, a breathing failure, a drug overdose, poisoning, or electrical shock. These types of cardiovascular failure require immediate rescue action to prevent brain damage.

CARDIAC ARREST   **Cardiac arrest,** or failure of the heart to beat, can be recognized by the absence of a pulse.

When a person's heart stops beating, breathing automatically ceases. **Cardiopulmonary resuscitation** (kar dee oh **pul** muh nehr ee rih suhs uh **tay** shun) **(CPR)** can keep the individual alive. Cardiopulmonary resuscitation is a procedure that uses both external heart massage and rescue breathing. If CPR is not done properly, it may cause further injuries. For this reason, you should **not** attempt CPR unless you have been properly trained. If you want to learn CPR, check with your local chapters of the American Red Cross and the American Heart Association. They frequently offer courses in this vital life-saving technique.

CPR involves forceful hand pressure applied to the individual's breastbone at regular and rapidly spaced intervals. This action increases the pressure within the chest, forcing blood to flow through the body. As shown in Figure 26-5, a rescuer alternates short periods of rescue breathing with short periods of chest compressions. The rescuer should perform CPR until the individual's heartbeat and breathing are restored or until medical help arrives.

If two rescuers are present, they should take turns giving CPR to avoid fatigue. One rescuer should carry out the procedure until he or she is tired, at which point the second rescuer should take over. If help does not arrive quickly, the first rescuer can replace the second rescuer when needed.

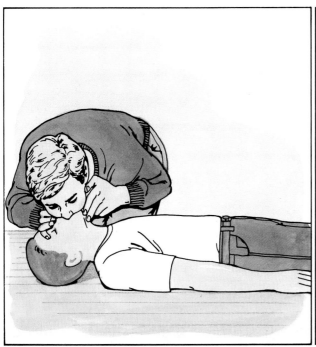
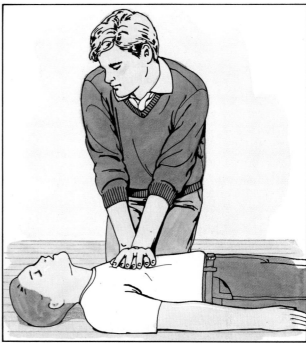

Figure 26-5. In CPR, rescue breathing alternates with chest compressions.

The most common cause of cardiac arrest is a **heart attack,** which results from a block in a coronary artery. Symptoms of a heart attack include chest pain, sweating, shortness of breath, and nausea. In treating a heart attack, you should follow the guidelines given in Figure 26-6.

STROKE A **stroke** occurs when a blood vessel in the brain ruptures, or breaks, or when a blood clot forms and blocks the flow of blood in the brain. A person who has suffered a stroke may show some or all of the following symptoms: paralysis on one side of the body, pupils of unequal size, dizziness, difficulty in breathing, slurred speech, mental confusion, or loss of consciousness.

If a person has had a stroke, gently place the person on one side and cover him or her with a blanket. Monitor the individual's breathing as rescue breathing may be necessary. Get medical help as soon as possible.

Shock

Shock is a condition in which the individual's circulation and breathing progressively slow down. If left untreated, shock results in death.

There are several types of shock. Shock caused by an injury is called **traumatic** (trow **mat** ik) **shock.** The more severe the injury, the more likely that shock will develop. Even if the injury itself is not life-threatening, traumatic shock can lead to death.

Treatment for a Heart Attack

- Have the victim sit or lie down, and prop the head with pillows.
- Call for an ambulance. If possible, contact the victim's doctor.
- If the victim takes heart medication, such as nitroglycerin, help administer it. If in doubt and if possible, consult with the victim's doctor.
- Monitor the victim's breathing and pulse. Rescue breathing or CPR may be necessary.

Figure 26-6. Begin treatment for a heart attack as soon as you notice its symptoms.

Treatment for Shock

1. Keep the victim calm and quiet. Call for medical help.
2. Place the victim on the back and elevate the feet. If the person is unconscious or vomiting, place him or her on the side with the head turned to one side. Do **not** move the victim if you suspect a fracture or a spine or neck injury.
3. Treat the condition that caused the victim to go into shock. Conditions that bring on shock, such as severe bleeding, are life-threatening and must be treated immediately.
4. Maintain the victim's normal body temperature. If necessary, either cover or cool the victim. If the victim is outdoors, put a blanket underneath the person so body heat is not lost to the ground.
5. Do not give the victim any food or drink.

▲
Figure 26-7. With any serious injury, treat for shock before any of its symptoms appear.

⟁—🔑
Bleeding can be controlled almost always with pressure and elevation.

The early signs of shock include restlessness, thirst, pale skin, and a rapid, weak heartbeat. The person going into shock may appear excited or calm and tired. Even though the skin feels cool and clammy to the touch, the individual may be sweating. As shock progresses, the individual begins to breathe in small, fast breaths or gasps, even if the airway is clear. He or she may stare vacantly into space, and the pupils of the eyes may become dilated. Eventually, the individual will become unconscious. You should treat for shock even before any of its symptoms appear. Follow the procedure described in Figure 26-7.

Severe Bleeding

Severe bleeding, or **hemorrhage** (**hem** uh rij), can result in shock and death if not treated promptly. The severity of bleeding depends upon the size of the injured blood vessels. The larger the vessel, the more blood it carries, and the more severe the bleeding will be.

STEPS FOR CONTROLLING BLEEDING The procedure for controlling severe bleeding is the same no matter what kind of blood vessel is affected. It is a good idea, however, to avoid direct contact with the individual's blood when performing the procedure. This will prevent the transmission of any infectious disease the person may carry. You should wear gloves or use many layers of absorbent cloth when following the steps given below.

1. Cover the wound with a **dressing,** a clean and absorbent cloth, usually made of gauze. Apply pressure directly on the wound unless there are signs of a broken bone. If blood begins to soak through a dressing, do not remove it. Apply another dressing on top of it.
2. If the injury involves an arm or leg, raise the arm or leg as you apply pressure. This is shown in Figure 26-8. Most bleeding, even severe bleeding, can be stopped by applying pressure and raising the injured arm or leg.
3. If the bleeding continues, apply pressure to the **pressure point,** the point at which the injured artery lies near the skin surface and passes over a bone above the injury. Figure 26-9 shows the major pressure points. Hold the pressure point tightly for about five minutes or until the bleeding stops, then release slowly. Continue direct pressure on the wound and keep the arm or leg raised.

If all attempts to control severe bleeding have failed, a **tourniquet** (**toor** nih kit) may be applied to an arm or a leg as a last resort. A tourniquet is a band or strip of strong, but flexible, material used to control bleeding. Because most severe bleeding usually can be controlled using the above steps, tourniquets are rarely, if ever, necessary.

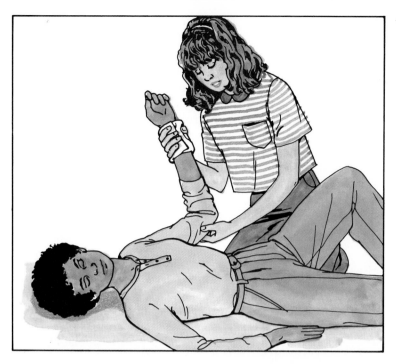

▲ **Figure 26-8.** To control bleeding, apply pressure on the wound and raise the injured arm or leg above the heart.

Figure 26-9. Severe bleeding can be controlled by pushing on the pressure point supplying blood to the wound.

▼

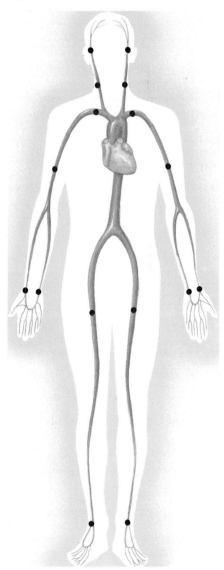

If a tourniquet is necessary, it should be applied between the wound and the point at which the arm or leg is attached to the body and as close to the wound as possible. It should be tightened just enough to stop the bleeding. Once applied, a tourniquet should only be removed by someone with medical training. This must be done soon to prevent tissue death.

CARE FOR INTERNAL BLEEDING Internal bleeding often goes unnoticed if the person is unconscious. It may be the result of an injury or a physical illness, such as a stomach ulcer. Recognizing the early signs of internal bleeding can prevent life-threatening complications. These signs include pain, although there may be no sign of injury, and/or the symptoms of shock—paleness, cold and clammy skin, rapid but weak pulse, dilated pupils, thirst, nausea, and vomiting.

If you suspect internal bleeding, keep the person quiet and lying down. Treat for shock. If the person is unconscious or vomiting blood from the mouth, place him or her on the side with the head turned to one side to prevent choking. Seek medical help.

Poisoning

Poisoning is the effect of one or more harmful substances on the body. Poisons can be swallowed, inhaled, or absorbed through the skin. Once in the body, a poison may damage or destroy the body's cells and tissues, cause severe discomfort or pain, disrupt normal body functions, and in some cases, cause death.

Signs of Oral Poisoning

- Sudden, severe abdominal pain
- Nausea or vomiting
- Chemical burns on the lips and mouth
- Drowsiness followed by unconsciousness
- Dilated or constricted pupils
- Chemical odor on the breath
- Presence nearby of a container of a poisonous substance

Figure 26-10. Do you know the signs of oral poisoning?

Treatment for Inhalation Poisoning

1. Protect your safety first. Take a deep breath of air before entering an area where a poison is present.
2. Hold your breath as you ventilate the area by opening doors and windows. Quickly remove the victim from the area.
3. Get medical help.
4. Keep the victim's airway open by tilting the head. Loosen clothing around the neck and waist.
5. Watch the victim's breathing. If the victim's breathing stops, apply rescue breathing.

Figure 26-11. Protect yourself when rescuing a victim of poisonous fumes.

ORAL POISONING Oral poisoning occurs when a harmful substance, such as a household cleaner, a medication, or a poisonous plant, is swallowed. Some common signs of oral poisoning are listed in Figure 26-10. If a person shows signs of oral poisoning, you must act quickly.

First aid for oral poisoning depends on the substance swallowed. Call a poison control center immediately. If you do not know the number, dial 0 and the operator will help you. Give all the information you have to the poison control expert and follow the instructions that you are given. If the person is unconscious and breathing has stopped, apply rescue breathing through the individual's nose to avoid contact with any poison that may be on the mouth. Get medical help as quickly as possible.

INHALATION POISONING Poisoning by gases or fumes causes over 2,000 deaths each year in the United States. Poisonous gases include carbon monoxide, chlorine, and the fumes from certain glues, paints, and petroleum-based fuels and solvents.

Carbon monoxide, a frequent cause of inhalation poisoning, is a tasteless, colorless, odorless gas, formed when some fuels, for example, gasoline or kerosene, are incompletely burned. Carbon monoxide poisoning can occur whenever there is poor ventilation and a source of carbon monoxide, such as the exhaust from an automobile. The poisoning occurs rapidly. Although the person usually experiences dizziness or a headache before becoming unconscious, he or she often does not realize what is happening. Fresh air is vital to the victim of inhalation poisoning, but you, as the rescuer, must protect yourself. Figure 26-11 describes the procedure for all inhaled poisons.

Figure 26-12. Car exhaust is a source of carbon monoxide.

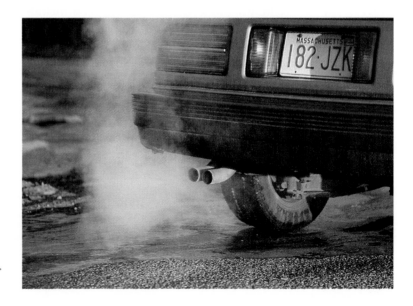

Figure 26-13. It is important to be able to recognize poison ivy, poison oak, and poison sumac, shown here from left to right.

CONTACT POISONING Poisons that come in contact with the skin may affect only the area touched by the poison or the entire body. Solvents, pesticides, and plants, such as poison ivy, poison oak and poison sumac, are common sources of contact poisons. Learning to recognize poisonous plants is the first step in avoiding contact with them. Study Figure 26-13 to become familiar with the characteristics of poison ivy, poison oak, and poison sumac.

Although some people do not react to these poisonous plants, people who are affected develop a severe rash on areas of the skin touched by the plant. Swelling, blisters, burning, and itching are typical symptoms that usually occur a day or two after contact. In severe cases, a person may develop a fever for several days.

The initial steps for treating any type of contact poisoning are the same:

1. Remove contaminated clothing and pour large amounts of water over the skin area touched by the poison.
2. Wash the skin area thoroughly with soap and water.

If the poisoning is from a plant and a rash develops, apply calamine lotion to reduce itching. In cases of severe irritation, inflammation, and pain, contact a doctor. If the poisoning is from a solvent, pesticide, or other chemical, follow the treatment given for chemical burns on page 613.

For contact poisoning, flood the affected skin area with large amounts of water.

Section Review

1. List six life-threatening situations.
2. In a respiratory emergency, how do you open a victim's airway?
3. What is the general procedure for controlling bleeding?
4. What are some signs of oral poisoning?

What Do You Think?

5. How could you convince a friend that it is important to take a course in first aid?

The Heimlich Maneuver

Suppose you were eating lunch with your friends, and someone started to choke on a piece of food. Would you know what was happening? How would you react?

You might be surprised to learn that choking is the sixth leading cause of accidental death in this country. Choking is an emergency situation—there is no time to call an ambulance. A choking person may die or suffer permanent brain damage within four minutes if the object is not dislodged.

In order to prevent a death from choking, you must be prepared to take immediate action. The American Red Cross and the American Heart Association recommend the Heimlich maneuver. The Heimlich maneuver, also known as abdominal thrusts, works by using the air in the lungs to force an obstruction out of the airway. If you master the steps of the Heimlich maneuver below, you may save the life of a choking person.

1. Determine That the Person is Choking

Ask the person, "Are you choking?" If the person is unable to answer, he or she may be choking. In addition, a choking person may
- be unable to cough or breathe or do so weakly.
- turn white or blue.
- make the universal choking signal, shown below.

2. Position Yourself Behind the Person

Stand behind the person, who may be standing or sitting, and wrap your arms around the person's waist.

3. Position Your Hands on the Person's Abdomen

Make a fist with one hand and place the thumb side of the fist against the person's abdomen, slightly above the navel and below the ribcage.

4. Deliver Abdominal Thrusts

Grasp the fist with your other hand and press into the abdomen with a quick upward thrust. Repeat the thrust several times, if necessary, until the object is dislodged.

5. What to Do If the Person Becomes Unconscious

a. Lie the person down on his or her back.
b. Check the throat for an obstruction, using the "finger sweep." With your thumb in the victim's mouth, push down on the tongue and jaw to open the mouth. With the index finger of your other hand, sweep across the mouth from one cheek to the other.
c. Attempt to ventilate (as in rescue breathing, page 601).
d. If the chest does not rise, deliver 6-10 abdominal thrusts.

By learning the Heimlich maneuver you can prevent a choking death.

e. Repeat the finger sweep, ventilations, and thrusts until the object is dislodged.

Special Case: You are alone and choking.

1. Perform the Heimlich maneuver on yourself, following steps 3 and 4 outlined above.
2. If this is not successful, position yourself over the edge of a firm surface, such as the back of a chair. Give thrusts by pushing upward and in against your abdomen.

APPLY THE SKILL

1. Following your teacher's instructions, practice the steps of the Heimlich maneuver with a classmate. DO NOT actually deliver the abdominal thrusts (step 4) as this could result in injury.
2. At home, teach your family members how to perform the Heimlich maneuver. Again, DO NOT deliver the abdominal thrusts when you are demonstrating or practicing the procedure with family members.
3. In addition to the special case presented here, there are variations of the Heimlich maneuver that can be used for pregnant women, obese individuals, and infants. Find out about the recommended procedures in each of these cases and how to apply them. Make a poster describing one of these special cases. Report on your findings to the class.

3. COMMON EMERGENCIES

Suppose you were playing basketball and your friend suddenly fell to the ground, clutching her ankle. What would you do? What if a child you were babysitting began to rub his eye and complain that there was something in it? Would you know what to do?

Injuries like these happen all the time. Although these kinds of injuries are not life-threatening, they still require prompt first aid. Proper treatment can help to ease pain and prevent further injury.

Bone, Joint, and Muscle Injuries

Bone, joint, and muscle injuries, although usually not life-threatening, require proper first aid to prevent further injury and increase the chances for a speedy recovery. As you know, these injuries should be treated only after life-threatening conditions have been handled.

FRACTURES A break or crack in a bone is a **fracture.** There are two types of fractures. In a **closed fracture,** the broken bone does not push through the skin surface. Although the skin's surface is not broken, the tissue beneath the skin may be damaged. If a broken end of a bone pierces the skin surface, the fracture is an **open fracture.** An open fracture may bleed heavily and can become infected.

Fractures may or may not be easy to detect, depending on the type and location of the break. An x-ray, like the one in Figure 26-14, is the only sure way to diagnose a fracture. At the scene of an accident, however, you will not have an x-ray, so you should be able to recognize some of the common symptoms of fractures. These include deformity, such as crookedness; swelling; discoloration (black and blue); a grating sound; exposed bone; loss of movement; and severe pain. Sometimes there is a cracking sound at the time of injury. To treat a possible fracture, you should follow the steps given below.

1. If the fracture is open, stop the bleeding. Using a dressing, apply pressure around the bone end that is piercing the skin. **Do not** put pressure directly on the bone. **Do not** attempt to push the bone back through the skin.
2. In any fracture, **do not** try to put a bone back into place. Do not move the individual unless it is essential in order to get medical attention, or it is necessary to escape further danger. Not moving the victim is especially important if there is any chance the spine has been injured.
3. Immobilize the injured region. If you do not have to move the individual, support the possible fracture between your two hands and caution the individual not to move it. Keep the region immobilized this way until medical help arrives.

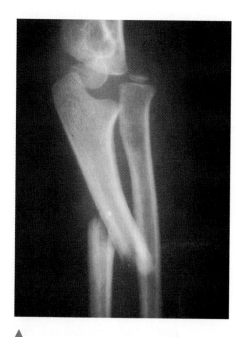

▲
Figure 26-14. X-rays can detect both open and closed fractures.

If you must move the individual, apply a splint. A **splint** is a rigid material that is tied to the injured part of the body to keep the part from moving. You can make splints from boards, rolled newspapers, cardboard, poles, or sticks. Place a splint on each side of the injury. Use padding between the injured part and the splints to prevent pressure and further injury. Attach the splints so that the joints above and below the broken bone cannot move, as shown in Figure 26-15. Tie the limb and splint together firmly at several points above and below the broken bone on the outside of the splint. Be sure the material used as a tie does not limit circulation. To check circulation, leave fingers and toes exposed if they are not involved.

SPRAINS AND STRAINS   **Sprains** occur when ligaments or tendons near a joint are either torn or stretched. **Ligaments** are the fibrous bands of tissue that prevent the bones from popping apart at a joint. **Tendons** are thick strands of tissue that connect muscles to bones. Sprains often result from violently twisting a joint. They frequently affect ankles, wrists, and knees. Sprains present some of the same signs and symptoms as fractures: pain on movement, swelling, and discoloration. If the pain and swelling remain severe after treatment, an x-ray should be taken to rule out the possibility of a fracture.

Overstretching a muscle or tendon often results in a **strain**. Back strains from lifting heavy objects incorrectly are common injuries. The signs and symptoms of a strain can include intense pain, slight swelling, and pain and difficulty in moving the part.

For all strains and sprains, it is important to rest the injured area in order to prevent further injury. For strains and sprains not affecting the back, cold packs usually relieve swelling and pain. Back strains usually require moist heat. Figure 26-16 summarizes the correct procedures to follow when treating sprains and strains.

▲
Figure 26-15. Splints help to immobilize a broken bone and to prevent further injury.

Figure 26-16. In treating a sprain or strain, when would you use a cold pack?

▼

First Aid for Sprains and Strains

Sprains	Strains
1. Apply cold packs to the area for the first 24 hours.	1. Rest the injured part.
2. Elevate the injured part.	2. For a back strain, apply moist heat. For other strains, elevate the injured area and apply cold packs for the first 24 hours.
3. Do not use or walk on the injured part.	
4. See a doctor and have an x-ray taken, if the pain and swelling are severe.	3. Get medical help, especially if back pain persists.

Figure 26-17. A muscle cramp can be eased by gently massaging the muscle.

DISLOCATIONS   A **dislocation** is a separation of the bone from its joint. People who participate in contact sports, such as football, often suffer dislocations. Common signs and symptoms include deformity, pain, and loss of function.

1. Do not try to set the joint. Immobilize and support the affected part, as in the treatment for a fracture.
2. Apply cold packs to the injury to keep swelling down.
3. Seek immediate medical attention.

MUSCLE CRAMPS   One common type of muscle problem that has no apparent cause is the muscle cramp. A **muscle cramp** occurs when a muscle contracts suddenly, causing a muscle spasm, pain, and loss of movement. Muscle cramps occur most frequently in leg and hand muscles. Most muscle cramps can be relieved by gently massaging the muscle with the heel of the hand, as shown in Figure 26-17. This helps to stretch the contracted muscles.

If you are swimming and a muscle cramp occurs, do not panic. Tread water while you massage the muscle. If people are nearby, yell to them for help.

Burns

A burn is an injury caused by exposure to hot liquids, chemicals, electricity, fire, or the sun's rays. Burns are classified according to the degree of damage they cause. **First-degree burns** are surface burns in which the outer layer of the skin is reddened and painful. **Second-degree** burns extend through the outer layer of the skin, causing blisters and reddening. **Third-degree burns** damage all the layers of the skin and the tissues underneath. In these burns, the skin may look gray or charred. The important factors to consider when treating burns are the prevention of shock and infection and the relief of pain.

MINOR BURNS   To treat a first-degree burn, such as a sunburn, apply cold water to the burned area until the pain decreases. For a small burn that is blistered, immerse it in cold water and then cover it with a clean dressing to prevent possible infection. Do not break any blisters.

SEVERE BURNS   Medical attention is needed for severe burns in which the skin is blistered and charred. While waiting for medical help to arrive, you should take steps to prevent contamination and infection.

1. Place a clean dressing over the burned area. A clean sheet may be used if a dressing is not available. If pieces of clothing are stuck to the burn, do not try to remove them. Do not clean the burn in any way or break any blisters. **Do not** put any ointment or medication whatsoever on the burn.

2. If the arms or legs are burned, elevate them above heart level. For burns on the face, hands, or feet, apply cold packs.
3. Monitor the person's breathing and treat for shock.

CHEMICAL BURNS When an irritating chemical comes in contact with the skin, it can burn the skin. Many common household products, such as bleach and ammonia, can cause chemical burns. Chemical burns need immediate treatment.

1. Remove clothing that has had the chemical spilled on it.
2. Flood the skin with water for at least 15 minutes until all the chemical has been removed.
3. Call a poison control center or a doctor for specific instructions on how to treat the burn.

If a chemical has gotten into the eye, flood the eye with water immediately. As Figure 26-18 shows, hold the eyelid open and flood the eye with water from the nose outward for at least 10 minutes. Make sure that the chemical does not wash into the other eye. Cover the eye with a clean dressing (not cotton) and seek medical attention.

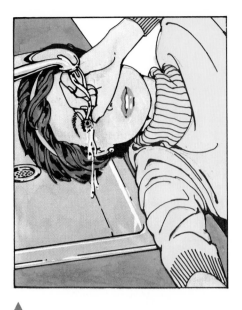

Figure 26-18. When flooding the eye, be careful the chemical does not get into the other eye.

Electrical Shock

When an electrical current passes through the body, **electrical shock** results. Even low-voltage currents, including those found in the home, may cause cardiac or respiratory failure. Electrical shock is not the same as shock (see p. 603), but severe electrical shocks can cause traumatic shock.

Electrical shock can occur indoors or outside. Working or playing outside during an electrical storm can result in a high-voltage electrical shock by lightning. Coming into contact with downed "live" electric power lines will also result in a high-voltage electrical shock. Inside the home, electrical shock may happen when a person does not shut off the electricity before repairing electrical appliances. Using power tools or small appliances in wet areas also may result in electrical shock.

Do not touch a person who is in contact with an electric current. The current, which is passing through the person's body, will be passed on to you.

1. If the main switch is nearby, turn it off. If not, do not waste time searching for it. Use a dry wooden pole or some other object that does not conduct electricity to separate the individual from the wire. This is shown in Figure 26-19.
2. After you have turned off the current or separated the individual from the wire, start rescue breathing or CPR if needed and if you are trained.
3. Treat for shock.
4. Treat any burns according to the degree of the burn.
5. Get medical help.

Figure 26-19. To separate a person from "live" wire, stand on a dry mat and use a dry, wooden pole.

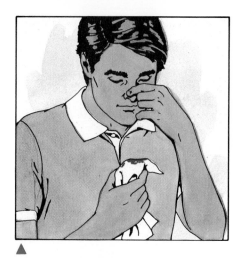

Figure 26-20. Most nosebleeds can be stopped by leaning forward and pinching the nostrils together.

Figure 26-21. Breathing into a paper bag helps to restore carbon dioxide to normal levels in the blood.

Nosebleeds

Nosebleeds can occur as a result of a blow. The nose usually bleeds from one nostril. Minor nosebleeds seldom require medical attention. People who experience frequent nosebleeds without cause should see a doctor. To treat a minor nosebleed, follow the steps given below.

1. As shown in Figure 26-20, have the victim sit in a chair, bend slightly forward, pinch the nostrils together, and breathe through the mouth for about five minutes.
2. If the bleeding does not stop, press the bleeding nostril against the center partition of the nose with a cold, wet towel for five minutes.
3. If these procedures do not stop the bleeding, place gauze (not fluffy cotton) in the bleeding nostril with about one inch hanging out, and seek medical attention.

Hyperventilation

Hyperventilation (hy pur vent l **ay** shun), rapid deep breathing, sometimes accompanied by dizziness, chest pains, and fainting, lowers the level of carbon dioxide in the blood. Anxiety, emotional disturbance, or poor circulation to the brain are frequent causes of hyperventilation. The treatment for hyperventilation attempts to return the level of carbon dioxide in the blood to normal.

1. Keep the individual calm. Have the person sit down and lower the head.
2. As shown in Figure 26-21, have the individual breathe into a paper bag or cupped hands to help the carbon dioxide level in the blood return to normal. If these techniques do not ease the problem, have the individual close the mouth and one nostril, and breathe through the other nostril.
3. If these efforts fail, seek medical attention.

Fainting

Fainting is a temporary loss of consciousness that is usually caused by too little blood flowing to the brain. Paleness, weakness, cold perspiration, and dizziness usually precede unconsciousness. An individual who faints usually regains consciousness within two minutes.

1. If someone complains of weakness and dizziness, have the individual lie down or bend over and lower the head to increase the flow of blood to the brain.
2. If the person does faint keep him or her lying down. Apply cool cloths to the face.

3. If the person does not recover within five minutes, treat for shock and get medical help.

4. While waiting for medical help, watch the victim's breathing in case rescue breathing is necessary.

Convulsions

Convulsions are alternating periods of severe muscular contraction and relaxation. The jerking, twisting, wrenching movements during a convulsion may be accompanied by a loss of bladder or bowel control, chewing on the tongue and inner cheeks, and drooling.

In infants and young children, convulsions sometimes accompany a high fever. Epilepsy, food poisoning, and other diseases, including malnutrition and infection, also can cause convulsions. Follow the steps described in Figure 26-22 in treating a person having convulsions.

Objects in the Eye

An eyelash, dust particle, or other foreign object in the eye can cause pain and irritation. Do not rub the eye because further injury can result.

1. If the object is under the upper eyelid, grasp the eyelashes of the upper lid and pull the lid up and away until tears flow freely. The tears usually wash the object or particle out of the eye.

2. If the particle is not washed out by tears, inspect the eyeball and look under the lower lid. Gently brush the object away with the moist, clean corner of a handkerchief.

3. If the object is not under the lower lid or on the eyeball, inspect the inside of the upper lid. To do this, grasp the eyelashes with the thumb and index finger, and place a small stick or swab over the lid. Pull the lid over the stick, as shown in Figure 26-23. Examine the inside of the lid while the person looks down. Gently remove the particle with the moist, clean corner of a handkerchief. Flood the eye with water.

4. If the pain and irritation continue, seek medical help.

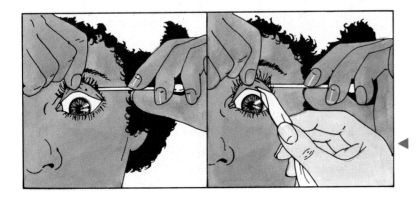

Treatment for Convulsions

1. Protect the victim from further injury by loosening tight clothing and clearing away furniture.
2. Do not restrain the victim. Do not put anything into the victim's mouth.
3. Watch the breathing, as rescue breathing may be necessary.
4. If the victim is unconscious after the convulsions have ended, turn head to one side. Let the victim rest.
5. Seek medical attention.

▲

Figure 26-22. First aid for convulsions is aimed at preventing injury.

◄ **Figure 26-23. If an object is lodged beneath the upper eyelid, pull the lid over a small stick or swab and remove the object with a clean cloth.**

If an object is embedded in the eyeball, **do not** try to remove the object. Protect the injured eye and prevent it from moving by covering *both* with loose bandages. You should cover the uninjured eye as well as the injured eye because a person's eyes automatically move together. If the uninjured eye moves, the injured eye also will move. Seek immediate medical attention.

Head Injuries

Scalp wounds are injuries to the surface of the head. A scalp wound may only affect the blood vessels supplying the scalp. Sometimes, however, scalp wounds are more serious and are accompanied by severe head injuries, such as skull fractures or brain injuries.

Most scalp wounds, even minor ones, bleed heavily because of the large number of blood vessels in the scalp. The first aid you offer should be directed toward stopping the bleeding as quickly as possible.

1. Elevate the victim's head and shoulders. Do not bend the neck in case of a neck injury.
2. Apply a dressing directly to the wound.
3. Get medical help.

If a person has suffered a serious blow to the head, you should suspect a severe head injury. Look for the following signs: loss of consciousness, vomiting, slow breathing, convulsions, slurred speech, pupils of unequal size, memory loss, or blood or other fluid escaping from the nose or ears. If there is paralysis, or if the head or spine is in an unnatural position, the individual may have suffered a neck or spinal injury. If you suspect a neck or spinal injury, do not move the individual unless the person is in immediate danger.

For severe head injuries, treat life-threatening conditions and seek immediate medical attention. If rescue breathing is necessary, keep the head and neck still. Open the airway by pulling the jaw forward, as shown in Figure 26-24.

▲
Figure 26-24. To perform rescue breathing when a spinal injury is suspected, gently pull the jaw forward without tilting the head.

Section Review

1. What is a splint?
2. On what basis are burns classified?
3. How do you stop a nosebleed?
4. If a spinal injury is suspected, what should you *NOT* do to the individual?

What Do You Think?
5. What would you say to calm an anxious burn victim while waiting for medical help to arrive?

4. OUTDOOR EMERGENCIES

In recent years, more and more people have begun to enjoy outdoor activities, such as hiking, camping, bicycle riding, and skiing. If you participate in these exciting and healthful activities, it is important for you to know how to handle any outdoor emergencies that may occur. If you feel confident in your ability to handle these emergencies, you will enjoy your outdoor activities even more.

Snakebites

Coral snakes, rattlesnakes, copperheads, and water moccasins (cottonmouths) are poisonous snakes found in the United States. Coral snakes are members of the cobra family; rattlesnakes, copperheads, and water moccasins belong to the family of pit vipers. These snakes and the difference between poisonous and nonpoisonous snakebites are illustrated in Figure 26-26.

A person who has been bitten by a poisonous snake will experience swelling and pain soon after being bitten. Breathing difficulties, nausea, twitching, convulsions, and unconsciousness may occur shortly thereafter. If a person has been bitten, and you do not know whether or not the snake was poisonous, you should treat the bite as if it were made by a poisonous snake.

1. Keep the individual calm and lying still. If the bite is on an arm or leg, keep the affected area still and below the level of the heart.
2. Wash the wound with soap and water.
3. If the person experiences the symptoms of a poisonous snakebite, apply a band (about ¾ to 1½ inches wide) 2 to 4 inches above the bite. Do not apply the band around a joint, such as the elbow or knee. The band should be loose enough to slip a finger under it.
4. Seek medical attention immediately. Individuals who have suffered poisonous snakebites must receive medical care within four hours.

▲
Figure 26-25. Knowing how to handle outdoor emergencies helps you to enjoy outdoor activities more fully.

Figure 26-26. Top: fang marks of poisonous and nonpoisonous snakes. Bottom, left to right: rattlesnake, copperhead, water moccasin, and coral snake.
▼

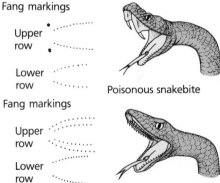

Fang markings

Upper row

Lower row

Poisonous snakebite

Fang markings

Upper row

Lower row

Nonpoisonous snakebite

Other Bites and Stings

Although most other types of bites and stings are minor, some can be deadly. For this reason, it is important to know the correct treatment for them.

INSECT STINGS Some people are allergic to the stings of certain insects, such as bees, hornets, and wasps. These people suffer severe reactions and can die within one hour.

For people who are not allergic to insect stings, there will be some pain, redness, and itching.

1. Examine the sting site. If a stinger is embedded in the skin, scrape it off with your fingernail or a credit card. Do not pull the stinger out as this may force more venom into the individual's body.
2. Place ice on the sting, or apply a paste of baking soda and water. A towel dampened with household ammonia and placed on the sting also will relieve pain and redness.
3. Watch the individual for at least 30 minutes for signs of an allergic reaction.

If you know the individual is allergic to insect stings, or if the person has trouble breathing or experiences dizziness, nausea, stomach pains, or wheezing, seek medical attention immediately. If necessary, begin treatment for shock and perform rescue breathing.

SPIDER BITES AND SCORPION STINGS Although most spiders in the United States are harmless, the bites of the black widow spider and brown recluse spider, as well as the stings of scorpions, can cause severe reactions.

1. Keep the victim calm.
2. Apply ice or a paste of baking soda and water around the region of the sting or bite.
3. Seek immediate medical attention and treat for shock. Monitor the victim's breathing carefully in case rescue breathing becomes necessary.

ANIMAL BITES The major concerns in animal bites are bleeding and infection. The bites of mammals, such as humans, dogs, cats, squirrels, rats, bats, and raccoons, can result in **tetanus,** a bacterial disease that can be fatal. Diseased animals may also carry **rabies,** a serious viral disease that can be passed on to people. If possible, catch the animal so that health authorities can examine it for rabies. Do not risk injury to do this.

1. Wash the bite with soap and water.
2. Cover the wound with a dry, clean dressing.
3. Seek medical attention and notify the health department. Treatment for tetanus or rabies may be needed.

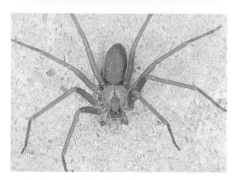

▲
Figure 26-27. The bites or stings of the black widow spider, brown recluse spider, and scorpion (shown here from top to bottom) can be life-threatening.

Frostbite

When a person is exposed to cold temperatures for some period of time, **frostbite,** or the freezing of body tissue, may result. The body parts most easily frostbitten are the cheeks, nose, ears, hands, and feet. Frostbite can involve only the skin or extend deep beneath it.

Frostbitten skin appears pale or grayish-yellow in color. It feels cold and numb. The frozen area feels doughy. In deep frostbite, the area is hard and solid. Blisters will appear on the skin within 24 hours.

1. Cover or wrap the frostbitten area with a blanket or clothing. Keep it dry.
2. Bring the person indoors if possible.
3. Do not massage or rub the area. Immerse in warm water (about 102° F) to heat it gradually, as shown in Figure 26-28. Do not permit the individual to stand or sit near a radiator, stove, or fire.
4. When the area becomes flushed, discontinue warming. As long as the feet are not involved, elevate the part that was frostbitten and have the individual exercise it. If the feet are affected, do not allow the victim to walk.
5. Seek medical attention. This is especially important if deep tissue damage has occurred as infection may result from it.

Figure 26-28. To treat frostbite, immerse the area in warm water until the skin becomes flushed.

Hypothermia

Another hazard associated with exposure to cold is **hypothermia** (hy poh **thur** mee a). Hypothermia is a serious loss of body heat, which causes the body temperature to fall well below normal. It can occur whenever and wherever the temperature is low—outdoors, in a shelter, or in water. Hypothermia is most common when temperatures are between 30° F and 50° F, when it is rainy and windy, and when a person is tired or rundown.

The signs of hypothermia include shivering, slurred speech, muscular weakness, excessive tiredness, slow breathing and pulse, bewilderment, semiconsciousness, and hallucinations. This condition can be fatal.

1. Check the person's breathing and heartbeat. If necessary, begin rescue breathing or CPR if you are trained.
2. Call or send someone for medical help.
3. Bring the individual into a warm room. Remove wet clothing and dry the individual.
4. Warm the person using hot water bottles, warm blankets, warm bodies, or other sources of heat. Give the person hot liquids to drink, but be careful that the liquid does not burn the individual.
5. Continue to monitor the individual's breathing rate and heartbeat carefully.

Figure 26-29. Hypothermia most often occurs in cold, damp weather.

Heat Exhaustion

When a person is exposed to excessive heat over a period of time, a condition known as **heat exhaustion** may result. Heat exhaustion is caused by the loss of water and salt from the body. Symptoms can include headache, heavy sweating, weakness, dizziness, and muscle cramps. The skin becomes pale and clammy. Heat exhaustion can occur either gradually or suddenly.

1. Move the individual into a cool, shaded area and raise the feet about 10 inches.
2. Loosen clothing.
3. Cool the victim with cool, wet cloths and fanning.
4. If the individual is conscious, give a glass of cool water to sip. Should the individual become nauseated or vomit, stop and transport him or her to the nearest medical facility.
5. Advise the victim to rest for a few days and to avoid becoming overheated.

Heatstroke

Heatstroke, also known as sunstroke, is a life-threatening emergency caused by prolonged exposure to high heat. The first sign of heatstroke may be a lack of perspiration. Other signs include high body temperature, reddened skin, and unconsciousness. Unconsciousness may come suddenly

D E C I D E

| **D**efine problem | **E**xplore alternatives | **C**onsider consequences | **I**dentify values | **D**ecide and act | **E**valuate results |

HELP FOR SOMEONE IN DANGER?

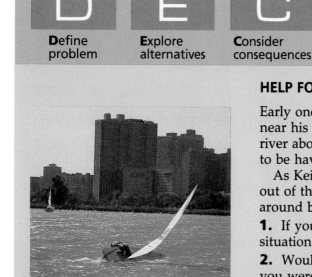

How would you react to a cry for help from a drowning person?

Early one morning, Keith went for a jog along the river near his house. As he ran, he noticed a lone boat on the river about a half a mile ahead of him. The boat seemed to be having difficulties on the rough water.

As Keith got closer to the boat, he saw a person fall out of the boat into the river. Keith quickly glanced around but did not see anybody.

1. If you were Keith, what would you do in this situation? Explain your reasoning.

2. Would the DECIDE process on page 16 be helpful if you were really in a situation like this? Why or why not?

3. Would your decision be different if the drowning person was someone you knew? If there were other people around? Explain

or may be preceded by headache, dizziness, rapid pulse, nausea, vomiting, and mental confusion. A rescuer must take immediate action to cool the person's body.

1. Move the person to shaded area and loosen clothing.
2. If possible, place the individual in a tub of cold water or a cold shower. If this is not possible, place ice packs in the groin, under the arms, and along the sides of the neck.
3. Monitor the person's symptoms. If the skin feels cool and has regained normal color, discontinue cooling.
4. If the individual's temperature begins to go up again, seek immediate medical attention. If you must transport the person to a medical facility, keep him or her cool with cold-water sponges on the way.

Drowning

Each year, about 6,000 people drown in this country for many reasons, including the inability to swim, overestimating their swimming ability, or panicking in the water. Sometimes, a person may drown after suffering a heart attack, muscle cramps, or physical injury in the water. Children can drown in water only a few inches deep.

If a swimmer seems to be having trouble, assess the situation quickly. Then, scream for help and then determine how you can rescue the person without risking your own safety. You need to consider your swimming ability, water conditions, and the availability of help. Speed is essential. Once the rescue has begun, follow the steps given below.

1. If you are not a strong swimmer, use one of the methods shown in Figure 26-30 to move the person to shallow water. Begin rescue breathing as shown in Figure 26-31.
2. Strong swimmers, trained in deep-water rescue, should begin rescue breathing while still in deep water. Give one or two breaths before starting for shore. Ordinary swimmers should not attempt rescue breathing in deep water.
3. Seek immediate medical attention. If necessary and you are trained to do so, perform CPR.

Section Review

1. How should you treat a bee sting?
2. Under what weather conditions is hypothermia most likely to occur?
3. What are some symptoms of heatstroke?

What Do You Think?
4. If you were going on a camping trip, what items would you include in a first-aid kit?

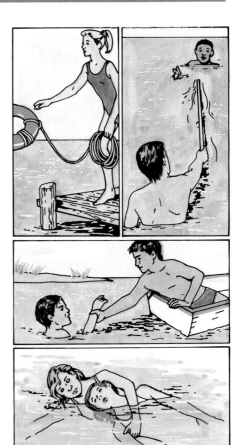

Figure 26-30. Which of these rescue methods would you use to save a person from drowning?

Figure 26-31. In saving a drowning person, begin rescue breathing as soon as you are in shallow water.

26 | Chapter Review

Chapter Summary

- In an emergency, properly applied first aid can mean the difference between life and death. A rescuer must be both knowledgeable and confident in his or her ability to perform first aid.
- A rescuer should treat life-threatening conditions first. These are respiratory emergencies, heart failure, stroke, shock, severe bleeding, and poisoning.
- Respiratory emergencies can lead to brain damage and death in minutes. Rescue breathing and the Heimlich maneuver are two important techniques for respiratory emergencies.
- If a person's heart fails, cardiopulmonary resuscitation (CPR) can save his or her life. Only properly trained rescuers should perform CPR.
- An individual who has suffered any serious injury should be treated for shock. Treatment for shock should begin before any of its symptoms appear.

- Most cases of severe bleeding can be controlled by applying pressure to the wound and elevating it above the heart.
- If oral poisoning occurs, a rescuer should call a poison control center for instructions. In cases of inhalation poisoning, the room should be ventilated and the victim removed. In cases of contact poisoning, the affected area should be flooded with water.
- Injuries to bones, joints, and muscles, although not life-threatening, require first aid to relieve pain and prevent further injury to the area.
- Burns are classified according to the degree of damage they cause. They must be treated properly to prevent infection and shock.
- A rescuer should be prepared for common emergencies such as nosebleeds, fainting, and eye injuries.
- Common outdoor emergencies include animal bites and stings, weather-related emergencies, and drownings.

Vocabulary Review

Listed below are some of the important terms in this chapter. Choose the term that best matches the phrase in the exercise that follows.

convulsions	frostbite	hypothermia	rescue breathing
CPR	heatstroke	ligament	splint
dislocation	Heimlich maneuver	muscle cramp	strain
dressing	hemorrhage	open fracture	third-degree burn
first-degree burn	hyperventilation	pressure point	traumatic shock

1. an injury to a muscle or a tendon
2. a procedure using external heart massage and rescue breathing
3. a condition in which the heart stops beating
4. a point at which an artery lies near the skin surface and passes over a bone
5. an effective technique for forcing a foreign object out of the throat

6. a condition resulting from the separation of bones at a joint
7. a life-threatening condition associated with any injury
8. an injury in which the skin is charred
9. an injury in which the end of a broken bone sticks through the skin
10. a life-threatening condition in which the body's temperature falls well below normal

What Have You Learned?

1. What are the major responsibilities of the first person on the scene of an accident?
2. How can you determine if a person has stopped breathing?
3. What should you do if a person is bleeding severely from the leg? How would the procedure differ if you suspect a leg fracture?
4. What steps should you take if someone has swallowed a poisonous substance?
5. Describe the three types of burns and the proper treatment for each.
6. Why are insect stings sometimes dangerous? What symptoms should you look for in a person who has been bitten?

7. What are some causes of hyperventilation and how should you treat it?
8. Which parts of the body most commonly suffer from frostbite?
9. How can you distinguish between heat exhaustion and heatstroke?
10. What is a splint, and what is the correct way to apply it?
11. What are some of the common symptoms of a heart attack?
12. How can you tell the difference between a poisonous and a nonpoisonous snakebite? What is the recommended procedure for treating a snakebite?

What Do You Think?

1. Which first-aid procedures do you feel are most important for a babysitter to know?
2. Why do you think it is important to treat for shock before there are any symptoms?
3. Why do you think a tourniquet is used only as a last resort to stop severe bleeding?

4. Why do you think that breathing automatically ceases when the heart stops beating?
5. Do you think the Good Samaritan law is a fair law? Why or why not?
6. At what age would you recommend that people take a course in first aid? Explain.

What Would You Do?

1. Suppose you were eating in a restaurant when the person at the table next to yours began coughing loudly and holding his throat. His dinner companion shouted frantically, "Does anyone know the Heimlich maneuver?" What would you do?
2. How would you attempt to calm an anxious accident victim who was bleeding moderately?

3. What would you do if, while jogging near your home, you were bitten by a stray dog?
4. Suppose you were playing tennis on a hot day and your partner started complaining of dizziness and weakness. What would you do?
5. What would you do if you came upon an unconscious accident victim but you were unsure of your ability to perform first aid?

For Further Study

1. Prepare a short skit in which an accident takes place. Have a classmate demonstrate the proper procedure to care for the victim.
2. Find out about various first-aid courses offered in your area. Prepare a poster with your findings. Be sure to include the name of the organization offering the course, the type of course, when and where it meets, the cost, and any specific requirements for it.
3. Research the recommended treatments for common household poisons, such as bleach, laundry detergent, perfume, and kerosene.

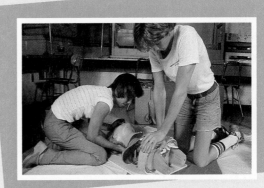

Glossary

abnormal behaving, feeling, or thinking in a way that is unusual or inappropriate (70).

accident an unplanned event that usually results in injury, death, or property damage (576).

acid rain rain that contains nitric acid or sulfuric acid or both (519).

acne (ak nee) a skin problem in which the oil glands become irritated, infected, and swollen (148).

acquaintance (uh kwayn tuns) a person you are familiar with but not close to (96).

acquired immunodeficiency (im myu noh dee **fish** en see) **syndrome (AIDS)** the most deadly of the sexually transmitted diseases. Currently, it has no known cure or vaccine (390, 559).

action what a drug does to your body (439).

active immunity immunity created by your own immune system (382).

active listening focusing your full attention on what the other person is saying while letting that person know you understand and care (102).

acute stage the stage of disease during which signs and symptoms are most severe (379).

addiction (uh dik shun) physical dependence; a condition in which the body becomes adjusted to a drug and requires the drug to function normally (445).

additive a chemical added to food to prevent spoilage, to control or improve color and texture, to replace or add vitamins and minerals, and to improve or give more flavor (197).

additive interaction a condition in which two drugs work together in a positive way (440).

adolescence (ad'l es unz) the period from about age 12 to 19 during which a child changes gradually into an adult (322).

adoption a legal procedure in which a child is taken into a family to be raised in the same way as any child born to the parents (301).

adrenal (uh dree nul) **glands** a pair of glands found above each kidney. They produce a number of hormones that affect kidneys, cellular metabolism, and the response to stress (275).

adrenaline (uh dren uh lin) or epinephrine; a hormone produced by the adrenal glands that causes heartbeat, breathing rate, and blood pressure to increase (51, 275)

aerobic (uh roh bik) **exercise** continuous, vigorous physical activity lasting for at least 10 minutes during which the heart rate increase and the oxygen supplied to the muscles meets the muscles' demand for oxygen (246).

affective disorder a condition in which moods or emotions become extreme and interfere with daily life (75).

afterbirth the placenta (311).

aggressive acting in a forceful, threatening, or disrespectful manner (25, 103).

agoraphobia (ag uh ruh **foh** bee uh) the fear of going out alone (73).

AIDS-related complex (ARC) an HIV infection that is an early form of AIDS (402).

Al-Anon an organization that helps people cope with an alcoholic family member (129, 483).

alarm stage the first stage of the general adaptation syndrome. This stage includes the fight or flight response (51).

Alateen an organization that helps teenagers who live with alcoholics (129, 483).

albino (al by noh) a person or animal lacking the cells that produce melanin (147).

Alcoholics Anonymous (AA) an alcohol rehabilitation group in which alcoholics help each other (483).

alcoholism a progressive, incurable disease in which a person is physically and psychologically dependent on alcohol (474).

algae (al jee) small water plants (524).

allied health workers health-care professionals who work with the primary care physician to care for patients. These include nurses, dietitians, physical therapists, dental hygienists, and psychologists (536).

alveoli (al vee uh ly) the balloonlike air sacs at the end of the bronchioles (232).

Alzheimer's (Ahlts hy murz) **disease** a type of dementia marked by forgetfulness, mental confusion, and helplessness (357).

amalgam (uh mal gum) a silver-colored mixture of several metals used to fill cavities in teeth (163).

amino acids (uh mee noh **as** ids) the 21 different chemical substances that make up proteins (184).

amnesia (am nee zhuh) the sudden loss of memory (79).

amniocentesis a procedure involving the removal of a small amount of fluid from around the fetus at about the sixteenth week of pregnancy. Four weeks later, it is examined for signs of an inherited disorder (307).

amniotic (am nee aht ik) **fluid** the fluid within the amniotic sac in which the embryo floats (304).

amniotic (am nee ahd ik) **sac** a bag of thin tissue that encloses the developing embryo (304).

amphetamines (am fet uh meens) stimulants (450).

amputation the accidental or surgical removal of all or some part of a limb (428).

amylase (am uh lays) an enzyme in saliva that begins the digestion of starchy foods (172).

amyl nitrite (am ul **ny** tryt) an inhaled drug that causes relaxation, light-headedness, and a burst of energy (454).

anabolic steroid (an uh bahl ik **ster** oyd) a drug used to boost muscle size and raise tolerance to pain (454).

anaerobic (an uh roh bik) **exercise** intense physical activity lasting only a few seconds to a few minutes (247).

anesthesia (an is thee zhuh) a painkilling method that is used during surgery (312).

aneurysm (an yuh riz um) a blood-filled weak spot that balloons out from the artery wall (418).

angina pectoris (an jy nuh **pek** tuh ris) the chest pain of coronary heart disease (417).

anorexia nervosa (an uh rek see uh nur **voh** suh) a life-threatening eating disorder in which a person refuses to eat normally or to retain food in the body (76, 204).

anoxia (an ahk see uh) a decreased oxygen level in the body (496).

antagonistic (an tag uh nis tik) **interaction** a condition that occurs when drugs are taken together and their effects are either cancelled out by each other or the action of both drugs is so reduced that neither one has the predicted result (440).

anti-anxiety drug minor tranquilizer; a type of depressant used to relieve tension, reduce anxiety, and cause drowsiness (448).

antibiotics (an tee by aht iks) substances that are able to inhibit or kill bacteria (383).

antibodies (an tee bahd eez) proteins that "tie up" pathogens by attaching to their surfaces, which helps the phagocytes find the invading pathogens (376).

antipsychotic (an tee sy **kaht** ik) major tranquilizer; a depressant used to treat severe mental or emotional illnesses (448).

anxiety (ang zy ih tee) fear that does not have an identifiable source, or fear caused by a danger that no longer exists (73).

anxiety disorder   anxiety that interferes with normal functioning (73).

aorta (ay **or** tuh)   the large artery that carries oxygen-rich blood from the heart (231).

Apgar score   a score that rates a newborn's heart rate, breathing, muscle tone, ability to react to stimulus, and skin color (311).

appendicular (ap un **dik** yuh lur) **skeleton**   the bones of the arms, legs, shoulders, and hips (225).

appropriate death   a death that fulfills a person's expectations and ideals (359).

arrhythmia (uh **rith** mee uh)   an irregularity of the heartbeat (419).

artery   a thick-walled, elastic vessel that carries blood from the heart to the tissues and organs of the body (231).

arteriole (ar **teer** ee ohl)   a small artery within tissues and organs (231).

arteriosclerosis (ar teer ee oh skluh **roh** sis)   "hardening of the arteries"; a condition in which arteries become hard and stiff (415).

arthritis (ar **thry** tis)   a disease that is marked by painful swelling of the joints (355).

artificial pacemaker   a small, surgically implanted, battery-operated unit that produces the electrical impulses needed to make the heart pump rhythmically (231, 419).

artificial sources (of radiation)   technological uses of radiation, such as x-rays (529).

asbestos (as **bes** tus)   a mineral in the form of fibers. It damages the lungs when inhaled (520).

asbestosis (as bes **toh** sis)   a disease marked by damage to the lungs. It is caused by inhaling asbestos (521).

assault   an unlawful attempt or threat to harm someone (591).

assertive (uh **sur** tiv)   able to stand up for yourself and to express your feelings in a way that does not threaten other people or make you anxious (25, 103).

asthma (**az** muh)   a breathing disorder that causes wheezing, coughing, and difficulty in breathing (55, 234).

astigmatism (uh **stig** muh tiz um)   blurred vision caused by the uneven curvature of the cornea (155).

atherosclerosis (ath uh roh skluh **roh** sis)   a disease in which fatty deposits narrow or block arteries (416, 498).

atrioventricular (ay tree oh ven **trik** you lur) **node (AV node)**   a group of cells in the heart that regulates heartbeat when it is less than 60 beats per minute (231).

atrium (**ay** tree um)   the smaller of the two chambers of the heart (230).

auditory (**aw** duh tor ee) **nerve**   a nerve that transmits sound from the cochlea to the brain (159).

auricle (**or** ih kul)   the outer part of the ear. It acts as a collecting funnel for sound waves (158).

autonomic nervous system   the part of the peripheral nervous system that regulates actions you do not usually control, such as heartbeat, breathing, and digestion (222).

autonomy (aw **tahn** uh mee)   independence (336).

axial (ak **see** ul) **skeleton**   the skull, vertebral column, ribs, and breastbone (225).

axon (**ak** sahn)   a long, thin fiber in a neuron that carries messages from the cell body (218).

B cells   B lymphocytes; the memory part of the immune system that produces antibodies quickly for specific pathogens (376).

background radiation   natural radiation from the sun, cosmic rays from space, and other substances in the air, water, and soil (529).

bacterium (bak **teer** ee um) plural: **bacteria** (bak **teer** ee uh) germ; single-celled microorganism (148, 372, 559).

basal metabolic (**bay** sul met uh **bahl** ik) **rate (BMR)**   the rate at which you use energy when you are completely at rest (181).

benign (bih **nyn**) **tumor**   a mass of tissue formed from noncancerous cells that grow more rapidly than normal cells (422).

benzopyrene (ben zoh **py** reen)   a chemical found in cigarette smoke that causes cancer (493).

benzoyl peroxide (**ben** zo ihl pur **ox** ide)   a chemical that dries out pimples and kills bacteria. It can help mild cases of acne (148).

bile   the digestive juice produced by the liver (174).

biodegradable (by oh dih **gray** duh bul) **wastes**   wastes that can be broken down in the environment (517).

biofeedback   a method of stress management in which you learn to control some physical functions by recognizing your body's signals (62).

biopsy (**by** ahp see)   a surgical procedure in which a small piece of tissue is removed to be examined for signs of cancer (425).

birthing room   a hospital room that looks just like a bedroom. It is used for childbirth (309).

blackouts   periods of time that a person who has been drinking cannot remember (475).

bladder   a muscular sac that stores urine (178).

blastocyst (**blast** toh sist)   the stage of an embryo's development when it begins to attach itself to the wall of the uterus (302).

blended family   a family consisting of a biological parent, a stepparent, and the children of one or both parents (126).

blizzard   a heavy snowstorm with strong winds (581).

blood alcohol concentration (BAC)   a way to express the amount of alcohol in a person's body (467).

blood pressure   the force of blood against the walls of arteries and veins (415).

body image   the way you think you look (333).

body language   a way of communicating information, mood, or attitude through body movement, posture, and facial expression (100).

brain   the control center of the central nervous system. It is made up of 10 billion neurons that control everything you do and everything you sense (219).

brain stem   an area of the brain below the cerebellum that acts as the body's life support system. It controls heartbeat, breathing, and blood pressure (221).

bronchi   bronchial tubes; two cartilage-ringed tubes that branch off the trachea to each lung (232).

bronchioles (**brahng** kee ohlz)   narrower branches off the bronchi (232).

bulimia (boo **lim** ee uh)   an eating disorder in which a person goes on eating binges followed by purging, or getting rid of food (76, 204).

butyl nitrite (**byoot** l ny tryt)   an inhaled drug that causes relaxation, light-headedness, and a burst of energy (454).

calculus (**kal** kyuh lus)   tartar; hardened plaque (164).

calories (**kal** ur eez)   units that measure the amount of heat energy released when nutrients are burned (180).

cancer   a disease marked by the uncontrolled growth of cells and destruction of tissue (54, 149, 280, 422, 499).

candidiasis (kan dih **dy** uh sis)   a yeast infection of the vagina, caused by the fungus *Candida* (397).

canines (**kay** nyns)   the single-pointed teeth on either side of the incisors used for tearing food (162).

capillaries (**kap** uh lehr ees)   tiny blood vessels (174).

capsizing   a boat turning over (585).

carbohydrate (kar boh **hy** drayt)   a class of nutrients that includes sugars and starches (181).

carbohydrate loading   an attempt to store extra carbohydrates in the muscles and liver for an endurance event (257).

carbon dioxide   a naturally occurring, nonpoisonous gas that makes up air. It is also produced during burning (518).

carbon monoxide   a dangerous, poisonous, odorless gas produced when fuels are burned (495, 518).

carcinogens (kar **sin** uh juns)   cancer-causing agents (422, 495, 527).

cardiac arrest   complete stopping of the heartbeat (415, 602).

cardiac muscle   involuntary muscle found only in the walls of the heart (227).

cardiac stress test   a test for heart disease, taken when a patient is exercising (420).

cardiopulmonary resuscitation (kar dee oh **pul** muh ner ee rih sus uh **ta** shun) **(CPR)**   a combination of chest compression and rescue breathing to maintain the flow of oxygen-rich blood to the brain while the heart is not working (415, 602).

cardiorespiratory endurance   the ability of your heart, blood vessels, and lungs to deliver nutrients and oxygen to your muscles and to remove wastes (236).

cardiovascular (kar dee oh **vas** kyuh lur) **diseases**   diseases of the heart and blood vessels (415, 497).

cardiovascular (kar dee oh **vas** kyuh lur) **failure**   the failure of a person's heart or circulatory system to function properly (602).

cartilage (**kar** tuh lij)   a tough, supportive tissue similar to bone but softer and more flexible (224).

case history   a brief description of someone who suffers from a disorder (73).

cataplexy (**kat** a plex ee)   usually associated with narcolepsy, a sudden loss of muscle tone that may result in falling and weak muscles around the eyes and mouth (262).

cataract (**kat** uh rakt)   the clouding of the eye's lens (156).

cataract (**kat** uh rakt) **surgery**   surgery to remove a cloudy lens from the eye (538).

cell   the smallest living unit in the body (146, 601).

cell body   the part of a neuron that controls the growth of the nerve cell (218).

cementum (si **men** tum)   the outer tissue of a tooth's roots that covers the root dentin (162).

central nervous system (CNS)   the brain and the spinal cord (219).

cerebellum (sehr ah **bel** um)   an area of the brain beneath the back part of the cerebrum. It coordinates muscles for movement (220).

cerebral hemorrhage (suh **ree** brul **hem** uh rij)   a stroke caused by bleeding from an artery in the cerebrum (418).

cerebral palsy (suh **ree** brul **paul** zee)   any of several disorders of the nervous system that occur early in life and result in a lack of full control of physical movement (222, 428).

cerebrospinal (suh ree broh **spy** nul) **fluid**   a fluid that helps to cushion the brain and spinal cord (219).

cerebrum (suh **ree** brum)   the large upper region of the brain (219).

cervix   the base and opening of the uterus (283, 397).

cesarean (sih **zair** ee un) **section**   a surgical method of birth (312, 397).

chancre (**shang** ker)   a small, painless sore that appears in the first stage of syphilis (396).

chancroid (**shang** kroyd)   a bacterial sexually transmitted disease with symptoms similar to the first stage of syphilis (397).

chemotherapy (kee moh **thehr** uh pee)   the use of drugs to treat cancers (425).

chewing tobacco   a smokeless tobacco product that is placed between the cheek and gum and then chewed (496).

chlamydia (klam **id** ee uh)   a common sexually transmitted disease, which, if untreated, can cause serious, painful infections of the urinary tract in men and infections of the reproductive organs in women (394).

cholera (**kahl** uh ruh)   a disease that causes severe diarrhea, muscle cramps, and vomiting (556).

cholesterol (kuh **les** tuh rawl)   a waxy, fatlike substance found in the cells of all animals (182).

chorion (**kor** ee ahn)   a part of the developing placenta (307).

chorionic villus (**vil** us) **sampling**   a procedure that can be performed during pregnancy in which a small piece of the chorion is examined for signs of inherited disorders (307).

choroid (**kor** oyd)   a dark membrane that makes up most of the middle layer of the eye (154).

chromosomes (**kroh** muh sohmz)   tiny structures, found in almost every cell, that carry information about inherited characteristics (289).

chronic bronchitis (brahng **ky** tis)   a condition in which the bronchial tubes are swollen and clogged with mucus (498).

chyme (kym)   a thick, liquid mix of foods and gastric juices (173).

cilia (**sil** ee uh)   tiny, hairlike structures in the respiratory tract that move mucus up toward the mouth and sweep foreign particles away from the lungs (374, 495, 520).

ciliary (**sil** ee ehr ee) **body**   a structure that produces a watery fluid that fills the front chamber of the eye between the cornea and the lens. Muscles in this structure change the shape of the lens (154).

circadian (sur **kay** dee un) **rhythm**   any 24-hour cycle (260).

circumcision (sur kum **siz** un)   a surgical procedure in which the foreskin is removed from the penis (278).

cirrhosis (sih **roh** sis)   a disease in which scar tissue replaces normal liver tissue and interferes with the liver's ability to function (476).

claustrophobia (klaw struh **foh** bee uh)   the fear of small, enclosed places (74).

climacteric (kly **mak** tur ik)   the gradual reduction of certain hormones that takes place over a period of three to eight years during middle adulthood (351).

clinic   a facility where primary health care is provided by one or more doctors and other allied health workers (538).

clinical depression   a condition in which a person is overwhelmed by sad feelings for months and stops being able to carry out everyday activities (75).

clinical psychologist   a mental health professional who specializes in recognizing and treating abnormal behavior (87).

closed fracture   a broken bone that does not push through the skin (610).

cluster suicide   a situation in which several people in a group try to kill or kill themselves within a short period of time (83).

cocaine   a highly addictive stimulant drug (450).

cochlea (**kahk** lee uh)   a hollow, fluid-filled, coiled tube found in the inner ear (159).

codeine (**koh** deen)   a natural narcotic that is made from the opium poppy (449).

color blindness   the inability to distinguish clearly one or more colors (156, 292).

commitment   the determination to develop a fulfilling relationship (120).

common cold   one of the most common infectious diseases. It is caused by a variety of viruses (380).

communication   the process of sharing information, thoughts, ideas, or feelings (49).

compatibility   the ability to exist in harmony with someone (106).

compensation   making up for weakness in one area by excelling in another area (40).

compromise (**kahm** pruh myz)   giving up something in order to reach agreement (121).

compulsion (kum **puhl** shun)   an unreasonable need to behave in a certain way (74).

compulsive personality disorder   a condition marked by the compulsion to do things in a set way over and over again (78).

conditioning being rewarded for desirable behavior and punished for undesirable behavior (27).

condoms latex sheaths that cover the penis (406).

congenital (kun **jen** uh tul) **disease** a genetic disease that is present at birth (412).

congenital (kun **jen** uh tul) **heart defect** a structural deformity of the heart caused by abnormal development before birth (419).

congenital (kun **jen** ih tl) **syphilis** syphilis passed on to a baby by its mother during pregnancy (396).

conjunctiva (kahn jungk **ty** vuh) a thin, moist membrane that covers the front part of the sclera and the inside of the eyelid (153).

conjunctivitis (kun jungk tuh **vy** tis) pinkeye; an inflammation of the conjunctiva (156).

conscious (**kahn** shus) **thoughts** those thoughts of which a person is aware (30).

constipation infrequent or difficult elimination of feces (175).

consumer anyone who buys goods and services (536).

contagious (kun **tay** jes) capable of spreading disease (370).

continuum (kun **tin** yoo um) a progression that moves from one stage to another (9).

contraception (kahn trah **sep** shun) birth control; any method of preventing pregnancy (301).

controlled substance a drug that is limited by law because its use can cause dependence (445).

convalescence (kahn vuh **les** ens) the stage of disease between infection and feeling completely well (379).

convalescent (kahn vuh **les** unt) **center** rehabilitation center; a facility that provides care for people who are recovering from surgery, illness, or injury (540).

convulsions alternating periods of severe muscular contraction and relaxation (615).

cool-down a 10-to-15 minute period of mild exercise after a workout. It allows the body and heart to return to resting rate slowly (255).

copayment the portion of a medical bill that the patient must pay after the deductible and after the insurance company has paid a specified percentage (546).

coping strategy a way of dealing with a feeling or situation that is unbearable to you (38).

cornea (**kor** nee uh) the transparent front of the sclera (153).

coronary angiography (an jee **ahg** ruh fee) an x-ray technique that detects blood flow through the coronary arteries (420).

coronary bypass surgery surgery in which a vein or an artificial vessel is used to construct a detour around a blocked coronary artery (420).

coronary heart disease blocking of the arteries that supply blood to the heart tissue (233, 416).

courtship a period that may lead to engagement and marriage. It may include going steady (111).

Cowper's (**Kow** purz) **glands** paired male sex glands located at the base of the penis (279).

crack "rock"; a concentrated, smokable form of cocaine (450).

creative visualization (vizh oo ul y **zay** shun) a way of using your imagination to cope with the stressors in your life (61).

culture the ideas, customs, and ways of living that characterize a group of people (7, 71).

cystic fibrosis (**sis** tik fy **broh** sis) a recessive genetic disorder affecting the lungs (292).

daydreaming creating made-up situations and indulging in periods of fantasy (40).

decibels units of intensity of loudness of sound (161, 531).

decomposers organisms that break down, or decompose, wastes (517).

deductible the portion of the year's medical expenses that the insured patient must pay before the insurance begins paying (546).

deep breathing a relaxation technique in which you take in as much air as you can and make sure your abdomen, as well as your chest, expands (60).

defense mechanisms coping strategies; the ways people defend themselves against negative emotions (38).

dehydration (de hy **dray** shun) a severe loss of water from the tissues of the body (175, 471).

delirium tremens (dih **leer** ee um **tree** munz) **(DTs)** a reaction of the central nervous system to the absence of alcohol in cases of advanced alcoholism. They are marked by uncontrollable shaking, hallucinations, and insomnia (474).

delivery the actual birth of the baby during which the baby is pushed through the cervix and vagina (310).

dementia (dih **men** shuh) mental confusion and loss of brain function that can be caused by disease or old age (71, 357).

dendrites (**den** drytz) the short, branched fibers of a neuron that carry nerve messages toward the neuron cell body (218).

denial refusing to recognize an emotion or problem (38).

dental hygienist (hy **jen** ist) a technician trained to clean and x-ray teeth and to assist a dentist (538).

dental specialist a dentist with extra training and certification in a particular branch of dentistry (538).

dentin (**den** tin) a yellow, dense, bonelike tissue that makes up most of a tooth (162).

dentist a health professional who has completed three to four years of training and earned the degree of Doctor of Dentistry (D.D.). He or she examines mouth, teeth, and gums and fills cavities (537).

deoxyribonucleic (dee akh see ry boh noo **klee** ik) **acid (DNA)** the chemical substance that makes up chromosomes (289).

dependence a state in which a person becomes incapable of controlling drug use (444).

depressants (dih **pres** unts) drugs used to slow down the body's functions (448).

depression an emotional state in which you feel hopeless and worthless (37).

dermatitis (dur muh **ty** tis) a skin disorder in which an area of skin may become red, swollen, hot, and itchy (149).

dermatologist a doctor who specializes in skin disorders (149).

dermis (**dur** mis) the tough, elastic inner layer of the skin that contains muscle fibers, blood vessels, and nerves (147).

designer drugs synthetic drugs that are chemically similar to some illegal drugs (455).

detoxification (dee tahk suh fih **kay** shun) **program** a treatment program that involves a gradual but complete withdrawal from an abused drug (456).

diabetes mellitus (dy uh **bee** tis muh **ly** tus) a disorder in which the body does not produce or properly use insulin (55, 275).

diagnosis (dy ug **noh** sis) a doctor's opinion of the nature or cause of a medical condition (536).

diaphragm (**dy** uh fram) a dome-shaped sheet of muscle just below the lungs (233).

diarrhea loose, watery, frequent bowel movements (174).

diastolic (dy uh **stahl** ik) **pressure** the second, and lower, reading when blood pressure is taken. It is the amount of force recorded when the ventricles relax between beats (231).

dietitian (dy uh **tish** un) a health professional who has completed a degree program in foods and nutrition (537).

digestion (dy **jes** chun) the process of changing foods into a form your body can use (172).

disasters sudden, catastrophic events that affect many people (579).

dislocation a separation of the bone from its joint (612).

displacement transferring emotions from the source to another person or object (40).

dissociative disorder a mental disorder in which a person becomes disconnected from, or dissociated from, his or her former identity (79).

distillation (dis tuh **lay** shun) the process by which fermented liquid is heated to a vapor and then cooled back to a liquid with a higher level of alcohol (466).

distress negative stress (49).

disulfiram (dy **sul** fur am) a drug used to treat alcoholism. It causes severe nausea and vomiting if the person taking it drinks alcohol (483).

diuretic (dy uh **ret** ik) a medication that promotes the excretion of excess body fluids and salt in the urine (415).

diuretic (dy uh **ret** ik) **effect** a condition in which alcohol or another diuretic causes the body to lose more water than usual (471).

divorce a legal agreement to end a marriage (126).

dominant genes genes that will show up in the child whenever they are present (290).

dosage (**doh** sij) the proper amount of a drug (439).

Down's syndrome a genetic disorder that occurs when a child receives an extra chromosome. The disorder is marked by mental retardation and a distinctive physical appearance (293).

dressing a clean absorbent cloth, usually made of gauze, which is applied to a wound (604).

drug any substance that alters the way cells or tissues function (438).

drug abuse intentional misuse of drugs for nonmedical purposes (441).

drug allergies side effects of a drug that occur because your body tries to reject the drug (439).

drug misuse improper use of drugs (440).

drug therapy the use of medications to relieve the symptoms of a mental disorder (76).

drug use taking a drug exactly as it is prescribed or according to its directions (440).

Duchenne muscular dystrophy (**dis** truh fee) a sex-linked genetic disorder in which a child's muscle tissue breaks down (292).

duodenum (doo uh **dee** num) the first 10 inches of small intestine, where most of the remaining digestion takes place (174).

ear canal a narrow cavity that leads from the auricle to the middle ear (158).

eardrum a thin membrane at the end of the ear canal that vibrates when sound waves strike it (159).

early bloomer adolescents who develop at an early age (327).

earthquake a sudden shaking of the ground caused by a shift in the plates that make up the earth's crust (581).

ectopic (ek **tahp** ik) **pregnancy** a condition in which the blastocyst becomes implanted, not in the uterus, but in the fallopian tube or elsewhere in the abdomen (311).

effect the physical and mental response the body has to the action of a drug (439).

ego according to Freud, the thoughtful, decision-making part of the personality (30).

ejaculation (ih jak yuh **lay** shun) the forceful ejection of sperm from the penis (278).

ejaculatory (ih **jak** yuh luh tor ee) **ducts** tubes lined with muscles that contract to force semen out of the body during ejaculation (279).

elasticity (ih la **stis** ih tee) with skin, how well it fits your body or snaps back into place when pulled (354).

electrical shock a shock that occurs when an electrical current passes through the body (613).

electrocardiogram (ih lek troh **kar** dee uh gram) **(ECG)** a graph of the heart's electrical activity. It can show any abnormalities in heart function (419).

electroconvulsive therapy (ECT) the passing of an electric current through the brain for a fraction of a second. It is sometimes used as treatment for severe depression (89).

electrocution (ih lek truh **kyoo** shun) death resulting from exposure to electricity (579).

elimination the process of releasing wastes from the body (174).

embryo (**em** bree oh) the blastocyst after it has attached itself to the wall of the uterus (302).

emotion feeling; a reaction to a situation that involves the mind, body, and behavior (35).

emotional intimacy the sharing of intimate feelings with someone else (113, 349).

emotional neglect a situation in which parents fail to give their child love and emotional support (131).

empathy (**em** puh thee) the ability to understand how another person feels (106).

emphysema (em fuh **see** muh) a breathing disorder in which the small air sacs in the lungs lose their elasticity (233, 498).

emulsifier (ih **muhl** suh fy ur) an additive used to keep the ingredients in a food from separating (197).

enamel (ee **nam** ul) the hard outer layer that covers the crown of a tooth (162).

endocrine glands organs that release chemicals directly into the bloodstream (272).

endocrine (**en** duh crin) **system** the body's communications system. It controls many of the body's daily activities as well as its overall development (272).

endometriosis (en doh mee tree **oh** sis) a condition in which the endometrium grows somewhere other than the uterus (285).

endometrium (en doh **mee** tree um) the lining of the uterus (283).

endorphins (en **dor** funs) substances produced in the brain that help give a sense of satisfaction when a person exercises (245).

enriched having nutrients, usually vitamins and minerals, added to a food to replace those lost during processing (197).

environment (en **vy** run munt) all of the physical and social conditions surrounding a person and the influences they have on the person (6, 26, 516).

environmental factors the experiences and events that a person undergoes (71).

environmental risk factor a risk factor that originates in the environment (413).

environmental tobacco smoke the smoke in the air from other people's cigars, pipes, or cigarettes (500).

enzyme (**en** zym) a substance that speeds up the chemical reactions in digestion (172).

epidemic (ep ih **dem** ik) an outbreak of a disease that strikes many people within a short period of time (556).

epidemiologist (ep uh dee mee **ahl** uh jist) a scientist who studies unusual outbreaks of disease (558).

epidermis (ep uh **dur** mis) the outermost layer of skin (146).

epididymis (ep ih **did** uh mis) a J-shaped tube located on the back of each testicle that stores sperm for two to four days after they have been produced (278).

epiglottis (ep ih **glaht** is) a small flap of tissue that covers the opening to the windpipe (172).

epilepsy (**ep** uh lep see) a disorder in which the brain's electrical impulses become disturbed and cause seizures (223, 448).

epinephrine (ep uh **nef** rin) adrenaline; a hormone produced by the adrenal glands that causes heartbeat, breathing rate, and blood pressure to increase (275).

erection a condition in which the penis becomes larger and stiffer due to an increased flow of blood through it (278).

esophagus (ih **sahf** uh gus) a muscular tube about 12 inches (30 cm) long, leading to the stomach (172).

essential amino acids the nine amino acids the body cannot manufacture and that must be supplied by food (185).

estrogen (**ehs** truh jun) a female sex hormone (276).

ethanol (**eth** uh nawl) ethyl alcohol; the alcohol used in alcoholic beverages (466).

eustachian (yoo **stay** shun) **tube** a narrow tube that connects the middle ear to the back of the throat (159).

eustress (**yoo** stres) stress that produces positive effects (48).

eutrophication (yoo trohf uh **kay** shun) the process of overproduction of algae followed by decay and lack of oxygen that occurs when some pollutants are washed into streams, rivers, and lakes (524).

excretion (ek **skree** shun) the process by which the body collects and removes waste produced by its cells (177).

exhaustion stage the third stage of the general adaptation syndrome. It occurs when stress is prolonged and beyond a person's control (53).

expiration (ek spuh **ray** shun) **date** a date after which a drug may not be effective (441).

extended family a network of close relatives that might include aunts, cousins, and grandparents (125).

extrovert (**ek** struh vurt) a friendly and outgoing person (25).

eye contact meeting someone's gaze (101).

fad diet a currently popular diet that may help a person lose weight temporarily (202).

fainting a temporary loss of consciousness, usually caused by too little blood flowing to the brain (614).

fallopian (fah **loh** pee un) **tubes** oviducts; small tubes that carry the eggs released from the ovaries (283).

fallout radioactivity that is carried to earth by rain or snow (530).

familial disease tendency the tendency of one or more diseases to run in a family (412).

famine a widespread lack of food (566).

farsightedness a vision problem marked by the inability to see nearby objects (155).

fasting refraining from eating all or certain foods (202).

fats nutrients with the highest energy content (183).

feces (**fee** seez) solid waste materials eliminated through the digestive system (174).

fermentation (fur men **tay** shun) the process by which yeast produces ethanol (alcohol) from sugar (466).

fertilization conception; the joining of a sperm cell with an egg cell (277, 302).

fetal alcohol syndrome a condition in which the alcohol that an expectant mother has consumed changes fetal development. It may include mental retardation, heart defects, malformed face, or delayed growth (306, 477).

fetus (**fee** tuhs) the stage by the end of the second month of pregnancy at which the developing baby is about 1.2 inches (3 cm) long and has a recognizably human form (304).

fiber the undigestible material found in plant cells. It is necessary for the proper functioning of the digestive system (182).

fibrillation (fib ruh **lay** shun) a life-threatening arrhythmia (419).

fight or flight response the body's reaction to stress in which it becomes physically ready to fight the danger or stress or to take flight from it (51).

first aid the immediate care given in an accident or sudden illness before professional medical help arrives (598).

first-degree burn surface burns in which the outer layer of the skin is reddened and painful (612).

flammable material anything that catches fire easily and/or burns quickly (577).

flashback an unexpected return to a bad drug trip that may occur long after the drug was taken (451).

flash floods floods that occur without warning after a heavy rainfall or snow melt (581).

flexibility the ability to use a muscle throughout its entire range of motion (237).

fluorocarbon (floor oh **kar** bun) a chemical containing fluorine and carbon that contributes to air pollution; also known as freon (520).

follicle-stimulating hormone (FSH) a hormone produced by the pituitary gland in both males and females. It is important in reproduction (276).

food allergy a condition in which the body's cells respond to a food by releasing substances that cause fluid to leak into the surrounding tissues (209).

formaldehyde (for **mal** duh hyd) a chemical found in cigarette smoke that causes cancer (493).

fortified having vitamins, minerals, and proteins added to a food that does not contain them (197).

foster parents parents who take care of children whose biological parents are unable to do so (125, 301).

fracture a break or crack in a bone (228, 610).

fraternal twins twins who develop from two eggs fertilized by two sperms (313).

freon common name for some fluorocarbons (520).

friendship a give-and-take relationship based on mutual trust, acceptance, and common interests or values (104).

frostbite the freezing of body tissue caused by exposure to cold temperatures for some period of time (619).

functional (fung **shuh** nul) **disorders** mental disorders that may be caused by personal experiences or stressful events (71).

fungi (**fuhn** jy) small, simple organisms that grow either as parasites in living organisms or on the remains of dead organisms (373).

gallbladder a membranous sac, attached to the liver, where bile is stored (174).

gene a part of a chromosome that determines a single trait, such as eye color (289, 412).

general adaption syndrome the process of adapting to stress, which occurs in three stages—the alarm stage, the resistance stage, and the exhaustion stage (51).

general anxiety disorder a condition in which a person is anxious without a specific cause (74).

general hospital a hospital that treats all sorts of patients with various types of illnesses and injuries (539).

generativity (jen ur a **tiv** ih tee) the central task of middle adulthood; the process by which people shift their concern from themselves to the welfare of others in the future (352).

generic (jih **nehr** ik) a standard name under which a medicine may be sold (549).

genetic counseling counseling in which a genetic counselor explains to a couple what the chances are that they will pass a disease on to a child (300).

genetic disorder any abnormal condition inherited through genes (291).

genetic risk factor an inherited risk factor that increases the likelihood of a disease (412).

genital herpes (jen ih tl **hur** peez)   an incurable condition characterized by clusters of painful blisters that appear periodically on or around the genitals (396).

genitals (jen ih tlz)   the external parts of the reproductive system (397).

genital (jen ih tl) **warts**   warts in the genital region that are sexually transmitted (397).

gingiva (jin jy vuh)   the gum, or tissue, that surrounds the teeth and covers the bone around teeth (162).

gingivitis (jin juh vy tis)   a condition in which calculus irritates the gums, causing them to become red and swollen and to bleed easily (164).

gland   a cell, or group of cells, that produces and releases a chemical substance (147, 272).

glans   the tip of the penis that is covered by the foreskin (278).

glaucoma (glau koh muh)   pressure buildup within the eye (156).

glucose (gloo kohs)   a sugar; the major carbohydrate in blood which is used by cells for energy (181).

glue sniffing   a form of drug abuse in which glue fumes are inhaled (454).

glycogen (gly kuh jun)   a type of starch that can be converted to or from glucose (181).

goal   a result you want to achieve (3).

goiter   a swelling of the thyroid gland (275).

gonococcus (gahn uh kahk us)   the bacterium that causes gonorrhea, a sexually transmitted disease (394).

gonorrhea (gahn uh ree uh)   a sexually transmitted disease that infects the urinary tract in both men and women, as well as the reproductive organs of women (394).

Good Samaritan law   a law that protects people from lawsuits if medical complications arise after they have administered first aid correctly at the scene of an accident (600).

greenhouse effect   an increase in the earth's temperature caused by the burning of coal and petroleum (519).

grief   a period of deep sorrow (38).

groin area   the area of the external sexual organs (280).

group therapy   talking with others who share the same problems in a group. The group is led by a therapist (76).

gynecologist (guy nih kahl uh jist)   a doctor specializing in the female reproductive system (288).

habit   a pattern of behavior that has become automatic (14).

hair follicle   a narrow cavity in which an individual hair develops (150).

halitosis (hal uh toh sis)   bad breath (164).

hallucinations (huh loo suh nay shunz)   imaginary sights and sounds. People with hallucinations are out of touch with reality (445).

hallucinogen (huh loo suh nuh jun)   psychedelic; a drug that changes a person's mental state (451).

handicap   a limitation on what you can accomplish (427).

hangover   unpleasant physical symptoms, such as nausea, upset stomach, headache, and sensitivity to noise, that result from drinking too much alcohol (470).

hashish (hash eesh)   "hash"; an illegal psychedelic drug made from the Indian hemp plant (453).

hashish oil   an illegal drug made by boiling hashish (453).

hazardous wastes   substances that are flammable, explosive, corrosive, or toxic to human or other life (526).

health   the well-being of your body, mind, and relationships with other people (3).

health food   food that manufacturers claim has special "health-giving" qualities (198).

health insurance   a health-care payment plan that pays for a major part of an individual's medical expenses (545).

health maintenance organization (HMO)   a group of doctors and allied health workers who provide complete medical services to individuals who are members of the HMO (547).

heart   the strongest and most efficient muscle in the body. It pumps six quarts (5.7 liters) of blood per minute throughout the body (230).

heart attack   an event during which the heart tissue becomes starved of oxygen and dies as a result of a block in a coronary artery. It may lead to cardiac arrest. The signs include shortness of breath, chest pain, sweating, and nausea (416, 603).

heart disease   any of several cardiac, or heart, problems, including malformation (233).

heart valve disease   a disease that prevents the heart valves from working properly (419).

heat exhaustion   a condition caused by the loss of water and salt. It occurs when a person is exposed to excessive heat over time. Its signs include headache, heavy sweating, weakness, dizziness, and muscle cramps (620).

heat stroke   sunstroke; a life-threatening emergency caused by prolonged exposure to high heat. The signs include high body temperature, reddened skin, and unconsciousness (620).

Heimlich (hym lik) **maneuver**   a technique that uses abdominal thrusts to dislodge an object blocking a person's airway (602).

hemoglobin (hee muh gloh bun)   a substance in red blood cells that carries oxygen to all parts of the body (211, 495, 518).

hemophilia (hee muh fil ee uh)   a sex-linked genetic disorder in which blood cannot clot (292).

hemophiliacs (hee muh fil ee aks)   people with a blood-clotting disorder (403).

hemorrhage (hem uh rij)   severe bleeding (604).

hemorrhoids (hem uh roids)   enlarged veins in the anal area (176, 544).

hepatitis (hep uh ty tis)   inflammation of the liver. It can be caused by a virus (476).

hepatitis A   the milder form of hepatitis, transmitted in human wastes and contaminated food and water (381).

hepatitis B   the more severe form of hepatitis, transmitted by blood and sexual contact (381).

heredity   the traits that are passed on biologically from parent to child (5, 26, 289).

hernia (hur nee ah)   the condition in which an organ pushes outward through a weakened area in the body wall that normally holds the organ in place (280).

heroin   a natural narcotic made from the opium poppy plant (449).

herpes (hur peez) **simplex I**   a virus that causes clusters of watery blisters, or cold sores, around the mouth (149).

herpes simplex II   a virus that causes genital herpes (396).

heterosexuality (het uh roh sek shoo al ih tee)   being sexually attracted to people of the opposite sex (109).

high blood pressure   hypertension; a condition in which there is higher than normal pressure on the walls of the blood vessels (55, 210, 415).

histamine (his tuh meen)   a substance released in toxic amounts when you eat food to which you are allergic (209).

Hodgkin's disease   cancer of the lymph nodes (424).

holistic (hoh lis tik)   whole; viewing wellness as a combination of physical, mental, and social well-being (3).

homeostasis (home ee o stay sis)   a normal, balanced state (53).

homosexual (hoh moh sek shoo ul)   a person who has sexual relations with someone of the same sex (399).

homosexuality (hoh mo sek shoo al ih tee)   being sexually attracted to people of the same sex (109).

hormones   chemical substances, produced by the endocrine glands, that act as chemical messengers in the body (272).

hospice (**hahs** pis)   a program or live-in facility that provides physical, emotional, and spiritual care for dying people and support for their families (359, 540).

human chorionic gonadotropin (kor ee **ahn** ik   goh nad uh **troh** pin) **(HCG) hormone**   a hormone produced by a pregnant mother at the time of implantation (302).

human immunodeficiency virus (HIV)   the virus that causes AIDS by attacking and disabling T-lymphocytes. It is spread through contact with body fluids (400).

hurricane   a powerful storm characterized by winds over 75 miles per hour and heavy rains (580).

hydrocarbons (hy druh kar bunz)   substances, made up of hydrogen and carbon, that help to form smog (519).

hypertension (hy pur **ten** shun)   high blood pressure (415).

hyperventilation (hy pur vent l **ay** shun)   rapid, deep breathing, which lowers the level of carbon dioxide in the blood and may be accompanied by dizziness, chest pains, and fainting (614).

hypochondria (hy puh **kahn** dree uh)   a somatoform disorder in which a person is convinced that he or she is, or is about to become, ill (770).

hypoglycemia (hy poh gly **see** mee uh)   low blood sugar; a condition in which the body produces too much insulin (210, 275).

hypothalamus (hy poh **thal** uh mus)   a bundle of nerve fibers in the brain that regulates body temperature, use of water, blood pressure, and release of hormones (221, 274).

hypothermia (hy poh **thur** mee a)   a serious loss of body heat that causes the body temperature to fall well below normal (619).

id   according to Freud, one part of the personality that consists of biological urges, such as hunger, thirst, and the seeking of physical pleasure (30).

ideal weight   the healthiest weight for your body (201).

identical twins   same-sex twins who develop from the same fertilized egg and have identical inherited traits (313).

identification   assuming the qualities of a person you admire (40).

identity   who a person is (32, 333).

illegal drugs   "street drugs"; drugs sold for a purpose that is against the law (438).

Illness-Wellness continuum   a continuum, or progression, that illustrates your overall wellness. As you move in one direction, you move toward illness; as you move the other way, you approach wellness (9).

"I" message   a statement of your feelings and expectations that does not blame or judge the other person (102).

immune (ih **myoon**) **system**   an internal system that protects the body from disease. It recognizes and destroys pathogens in the body (54, 375, 529).

immunity   the ability of the immune system to "remember" and kill pathogens that have previously invaded the body (375).

immunization   vaccination; an injection of small amounts of dead or altered pathogens that protects you from an infectious disease (382).

immunotherapy (ih myuh noh **thehr** uh pee)   a cancer treatment in which the body's own disease-fighting system is stimulated to control cancer (425).

implantation (im plan **tay** shun)   the process of attachment of the embryo to the wall of the uterus (302).

incest   sexual activity between any family members other than husband and wife (131).

incisors (in **sy** zurz)   teeth with sharp edges at the front of the mouth used to cut food (162).

incubation (in kyoo **bay** shun) **period**   the stage of disease between entry of a pathogen and the development of signs and symptoms (378).

incubator   a special chamber that protects a premature baby until it is more developed (313).

indigestion   difficulty in digesting food (175).

infatuation   crush; a feeling of intense or overwhelming interest in another person (109).

infectious (in **fek** shus) **disease**   communicable disease; a disease caused by organisms that live in or on human body (370, 556).

infectious mononucleosis (**mahn** oh noo klee **oh** sis)   "mono"; "the kissing disease"; a viral infection that causes the lymph nodes, tonsils, and spleen to become swollen and tender (380).

infertile (in **fur** til)   unable to have biological children (301).

inflamed   red, swollen, and sore due to inflammation (375).

inflammation (in fluh **may** shun)   the body's response to injury. It is marked by increased blood flow that brings phagocytes and chemicals to heal injured tissues (375).

influenza (in floo **en** zuh)   respiratory flu (378).

inguinal hernia (**in** gwuh nul   **hur** nee ah)   a common hernia that occurs when a part of the intestine pushes into the scrotum through a weak spot in the wall near the scrotum (280).

inhalants (in **hay** lunts)   drugs that are inhaled (453).

inhibitions (in huh **bish** unz)   the controls people put on their emotions (469).

inpatient   a patient who must stay in a hospital overnight or longer (539).

insertion   the attachment of a muscle to a movable bone (228).

insomnia   difficulty in falling asleep or staying asleep (262).

insulin (**in** suh lun)   a substance produced by the body. It allows glucose to enter the cells (209).

integrity (in **teg** rih tee)   according to Erikson, the life stage of feeling complete. At this stage, you have reviewed your life and accepted the good and bad without regrets (356).

interferon (in tur **feer** ahn)   a substance produced by T lymphocytes that warns healthy cells that pathogens are near (377).

interneurons   nerve cells in the brain and spinal cord that receive sensory messages and send responses to motor neurons, which tell the muscles or glands to act (218).

intoxication (in tahk sih **kay** shun)   the effects alcohol has on the body, ranging from a mild loss of judgment to a loss of consciousness (468).

introvert (**in** truh vurt)   someone who is not outgoing and whose thoughts are directed inward (25).

iris   a colored disk at the front of the eye with an opening in its center, which allows light to enter the eye (154).

isokinetic (eye suh kih **net** ik) **exercise**   exercise that makes use of weight-training machines to move muscles at a constant rate of speed through their full range of movement (248).

isometric (eye suh **met** rik) **exercise**   exercise in which a muscle contracts but does not shorten. This type of exercise increases strength but only at the joint angle at which the exercise is performed (248).

isotonic (eye suh **tahn** ik) **exercise**   the contraction and relaxation of muscles through their full range of motion. This type of exercise develops muscle strength (248).

jaundice (**jawn** dis)   yellowing of the skin (381).

jet lag   the fatigue and disorientation often suffered by air travelers whose circadian rhythms are interrupted (262).

joint   the point at which two bones come together (226).

joint custody   an arrangement in which divorced parents share equal responsibility for all aspects of their children's lives (126).

Kaposi's sarcoma (Kuh **poh** sheez sar **koh** muh) **(KS)**   a rare, deadly cancer characterized by reddish-purple blotches on the skin (402).

kidney   fist-sized organ on either side of the spine at elbow height that filters waste products from the bloodstream (177).

kidney dialysis (dy **al** uh sis)   a process in which a machine is used in place of the kidneys to filter wastes (178).

kidney stones   painful, pebblelike masses that form in the kidneys or urinary tract (178).

kinesics (kih **nee** siks)   the science of body language (100).

labor   the work of pushing the fetus out of the mother during birth (309).

landfill   an area where wastes are left and covered with soil (526).

large intestine   a five-foot long (1.5 meter) tube into which undigested food with water passes from the small intestine (174).

larynx (**la** ringks)   the voice box, located at the base of the tongue (232).

late bloomer   adolescents who develop at a late age (327).

Legionnaires' (lee juh **nairz**) **disease**   a serious respiratory infection thought to be spread by air in buildings with contaminated air conditioning systems (371).

legumes (**leg** yoomz)   plants that bear seeds in pods, such as beans, peas, and peanuts (188).

lens   a transparent structure just behind the iris that focuses light on the inner back side of the eye (154).

leukemia (loo **kee** mee uh)   a form of cancer affecting the tissues in which blood is formed, mostly bone marrow (424).

leukoplakia (lu koh **play** kee uh)   hard, white patches or sores that form on the inside of the mouth and may develop into cancer. They are often the result of the use of tobacco products (499).

licensed practical nurse (L.P.N.)   a health-care professional who has had one or two years of training in a practical nursing program and passed a state licensing test. An L.P.N. has less training and fewer responsibilities than an R.N. (537).

life style   the way you choose to live your life (5).

life-style risk factor   a harmful behavior or habit that can be avoided or reduced (414).

ligaments   touch, fibrous bands of tissue that prevent bones from popping out of joints (226, 611).

liquor (**lik** ur)   the cooled vapor that is produced by distilling fermented liquid (466).

liver   a large organ that secretes digestive juices and removes harmful substances from the blood (174).

look-alike drug   a drug that is sold on the street and made to look like a commonly abused drug (455).

lungs   two large, elastic organs that consist of tubes, blood vessels, and spongy tissue (232).

luteinizing (**loo** tee in y zing) **hormone (LH)**   a hormone produced by the pituitary gland in both males and females. It is important for reproduction (276).

lymph (limf)   lymphatic fluid (376).

lymphatic (lim **fat** ik) **system**   a network of vessels that collects fluid and cells from tissues and then delivers the fluid and cells to the bloodstream (375).

lymph nodes (limf nohdz)   lymph glands; small stations in the lymphatic system that filter lymphatic fluid (376).

lymphocytes (**lim** fuh syts)   the immune system's weapons; a class of white blood cells in the blood, tissues, and lymph nodes that attack pathogens (375).

lysergic (ly **sur** jik) **acid diethylamide** (dy eth ul **am** id) **(LSD)**   the strongest of the psychedelic drugs. It may either stimulate or depress the body (451).

major tranquilizers   antipsychotics; depressants used to treat severe mental or emotional illnesses (448).

malignant (mah **lig** nunt) **tumor**   cancer cells that form a mass of tissue in the body (422).

malnutrition   any condition of poor nutrition (200).

malocclusion (mal uh **kloo** zhun)   improper bite; a condition in which the upper and lower teeth do not meet properly (163).

mammogram (**mam** uh gram)   an x-ray of the breasts that can detect cancer (288, 423).

manic-depressive disorder   a condition marked by extreme mood swings (76).

marijuana   an illegal psychedelic drug made from the flowers and leaves of the Indian hemp plant (452).

marital (**ma** rih tul) **roles**   the responsibilities each spouse accepts in marriage (122).

marrow (**ma** roh)   a soft tissue in bones that produces blood cells (224).

Maslow's hierarchy of needs   a pyramid, described by Abraham Maslow, showing the needs of people, from the physical needs of the body to the need for self-actualization (33).

maturity (muh **tyoor** ih tee)   the state of being fully grown and developed (346).

maximum heart rate   your heart's top speed (251).

Medicaid   a state and federal assistance program that pays for the health care of anyone with an income below an established level (547).

medical doctor   a health professional who has spent four years in a medical school and has earned the degree of Doctor of Medicine (M.D.) or Doctor of Osteopathy (D.O.) (536).

medical history   a record of a person's present and past health as well as the health of family members (543).

medical specialist   a doctor with years of additional training in a particular branch of medicine and who is certified to practice in this specialty (536).

Medicare   the federally financed insurance program for elderly people (546).

medicine   any substance used to treat a disease, disorder, or injury (438, 549).

medulla (muh **duhl** uh)   a part of the brain stem that controls breathing, heart rate, and swallowing (221).

melanin (**mel** uh nin)   a brown substance in the epidermis that is produced by special cells (147).

melanoma (mel uh **noh** muh)   the most serious of the various types of skin cancer (423).

meninges (muh **nin** jeez)   the three layers of skinlike membranes that cover and protect the brain (219).

meningitis (men in **jy** tis)   an inflammation of the meninges of the brain or spinal cord, caused by a bacterial infection or a virus (223).

menopause (**men** uh pawz)   the time of life, around the age of 45 to 55, when the ovaries slow down hormone production and stop producing mature eggs (285).

menstrual (**men** stroo ul) **cycle**   the process in which women produce and release egg cells (283).

menstruation (men stroo **ay** shun)   the menstrual period; a discharge of blood and tissue that marks the end of the menstrual cycle (283).

mental disorder   an illness that affects the mind and prevents a person from being productive, adjusting to life, or getting along with other people (70).

mental health   the state of being comfortable with yourself, with others, and with your surroundings (25).

meperidine (muh **pehr** ih deen)   a synthetic narcotic (449).

mescaline (**mes** kuh leen)   a psychedelic drug made from the peyote cactus (451).

metabolism (muh **tab** uh liz um)   the chemical reactions that change a substance, such as food, so that it can be used or removed from the body (181, 272, 468).

metastasis (muh **tas** tuh sis)   the spread of cancer from where it first developed to other parts of the body (422).

methadone (**meth** uh dohn)   an addictive drug sometimes substituted for heroin in treatment programs for heroin addiction (449).

methadone maintenance   a type of treatment for heroin addicts that involves substituting methadone for heroin to prevent withdrawal symptoms and to block the effects of heroin (457).

methaqualone (meth uh **kway** lohn)   a tranquilizer similar to a barbiturate (448).

microorganisms   organisms that can only be seen through a microscope (370).

midbrain   a part of the brain stem that controls eye movement and pupil size (221).

migraine (**my** grayn)   a severe headache that occurs when the blood vessels around the brain dilate, or swell (222).

minerals   nutrients required by the body in small amounts (187).

minor tranquilizer (**tran** kwuh lyz ur)   anti-anxiety drug; a depressant used to relieve tension, reduce anxiety, and cause drowsiness (448).

miscarriage   the expulsion of a dead zygote, blastocyst, embryo, or fetus from the uterus (311).

mixed message   a situation in which one part of a message contradicts another (102).

modeling   copying the behavior of others (27).

molars (**moh** lurz)   teeth with large, flat surfaces for grinding food (162).

morning sickness   attacks of nausea and vomiting that can occur in morning or at any time of day during pregnancy, usually in the first trimester (305).

morphine (**mor** feen)   a natural narcotic made from the opium poppy plant (449).

motor neurons   nerve cells that send instructions to your muscles or glands to act (218).

mucous (**myoo** kus) **membranes**   moist linings of the entrances to the body, such as the mouth, eyes, and nose (374).

multiple birth   the delivery of more than one fetus. This includes twins, triplets, quadruplets, quintuplets, or sextuplets (313).

multiple personality disorder   a rare condition in which a person has two or more separate personalities (79).

muscle cramp   a common type of muscle problem that occurs when a muscle contracts suddenly, causing a muscle spasm, pain, and loss of movement (612).

muscular endurance   the ability of a muscle or a group of muscles to apply force over a period of time (237).

muscular strength   the ability of a muscle to exert or to resist a force (237).

mutagen (**myoo** tuh jun)   a chemical that changes a cell's genetic material (528).

myoclonic (my oh **klawn** ik) **jerk**   a sudden jerk of the muscles that may occur during the first stage of NREM sleep (260).

narcolepsy (**nahr** kuh lep see)   a disorder of REM sleep in which a person falls asleep suddenly and inappropriately for short periods (262).

narcotic   any depressant that is made from or is chemically similar to opium (449).

natural food   a food that contains no additives (198).

nearsightedness   a vision problem marked by the inability to see objects that are far away clearly (155).

Neighborhood Crime Watch   community volunteers who report suspicious activities to the police (593).

nephritis (nuh **fry** tis)   an inflammation of the nephrons of the kidneys (178).

nephrons (**nehf** rahns)   the working units of the kidneys (178).

nerves   bundles of nerve fibers (axons) bound together by connective tissue (218).

neurologist (nu **rahl** uh jist)   a physician who specializes in detecting and treating organic disorders of the brain and nervous system (87).

neuron (**noor** ahn)   the basic cell of the nervous system (218).

nicotine   an addictive substance found in tobacco (493).

nicotine withdrawal   a reaction to the lack of nicotine in the body. Its symptoms may include headache, irritability, restlessness, and a feeling of illness (494).

night blindness   the inability to see well in dim light. It is caused by a lack of the light-sensitive substance that is produced by rod and cone cells (156).

nitric (**ny** trik) **acid**   a waste gas, formed when fuels are burned (516).

nitrous oxide   "laughing gas"; an inhalant, sometimes used by dentists as a painkiller (454).

nocturnal emission   "wet dream"; ejaculation during sleep. It is not unusual during adolescence (278).

noninfectious diseases   diseases, such as cancer and heart disease, that are not caused by pathogens and cannot be transmitted by contact with a person, object, or substance (412, 557).

nonrapid eye movement (NREM) sleep   sleep in which your eyes are relaxed (260).

nuclear (**noo** klee ur) **family**   a family that consists only of parents and their child or children (125).

nurse   a licensed health-care professional who, in collaboration with a doctor, provides direct care to patients (537).

nurse-midwife   a person trained to assist in the birth process (309).

nurse practitioner (N.P.)   a registered nurse with additional training that enables him or her to do many of the tasks that only doctors used to perform, such as taking medical histories, performing physical exams, and treating routine medical problems (537).

nursing home   a facility that provides long-term care for the elderly or the chronically ill who cannot care for themselves (540).

nutrient (**noo** tree unt)   a substance found in food that the body needs to regulate body functions, promote growth, repair body tissues, and obtain energy (180).

nutrient density   the proportion of nutrients in a food compared to the number of calories (190).

nutrition   the process by which the body takes in and uses the nutrients from food (180).

obesity (oh **bee** sut ee)   the condition of being 20 percent or more above your most comfortable weight (200).

obsession (uhb **sesh** un)   an idea or thought that takes over the mind and cannot be forgotten (74).

obsessive-compulsive disorder   a disorder characterized by the unreasonable need to behave in a certain way (74).

obstetrician (ahb stih **trish** un)   a doctor who specializes in caring for pregnant women and assisting at births (301).

Occupational Health and Safety Administration (OSHA)   a U.S. government agency that identifies occupational hazards and sets standards for safety (582).

occupational illness   any abnormal condition or disorder, excluding injuries, caused by exposure to the work environment (582).

occupational injury   any injury that results from a work accident or from exposure to a hazard in the work environment (582).

occupational therapists   therapists who help the mentally ill become productive members of society by teaching them practical skills (87).

oncogenes (**ahn** koh jeenz)   genes that cause cancer when stimulated by carcinogens (422).

open fracture   a broken bone that pierces the skin surface (610).

Operation Identification   a nationwide program to encourage the marking of personal property (593).

opium (**oh** pee um)   a depressant drug obtained from the opium poppy plant (449).

opportunistic (op ur too **nis** tik) **diseases**   diseases that attack a person whose immune system is weakened (402).

oppositional (ahp uh **zish** uh nul) **disorder**   a condition marked by behavior that causes constant conflict with others (79).

optic nerve   the nerve that transmits visual information from the eye to the brain (153).

optimum (**ahp** tuh mum) **health**   the highest level of wellness possible for an individual (5).

oral rehydration therapy   the gradual reintroduction of fluids to someone who has suffered severe fluid loss from diarrhea or other causes (566).

organ   a body structure that performs one or more specific functions within the body (146).

organic disorder   a mental disorder with a physical cause (71).

organic food   food grown in soil fertilized only with manure or humus rather than chemical fertilizers (198).

orgasm (**or** gaz um)   the climax of sexual excitement (325).

origin   the attachment of one end of a muscle to a bone that is stationary (228).

orthodontist (or thuh **dahn** tist)   a dentist who specializes in correcting the position of teeth (163, 538).

ossification (ahs uh fih **kay** shun)   the process by which cartilage changes to bone (224).

osteopathy (ahz tee **ahp** uh thee)   a branch of medicine that emphasizes the relationship of the body's muscular and skeletal systems to general health (536).

osteoporosis (ahs tee oh puh **roh** sis)   a condition in which bones become thin and brittle due to the loss of bone calcium (224, 355).

outpatient   a patient admitted to a hospital or clinic for tests or treatments that do not require an overnight stay (538).

ova (singular **ovum**)   mature egg cells; the female sex cells (276).

oval window   a small membrane separating the middle ear from the inner ear (159).

ovarian cyst (sist)   a growth on the outside of an ovary (286).

ovaries (**oh** vuh reez)   female reproductive glands (276).

overdose   a serious reaction to a drug that can be fatal (440).

over-the-counter (OTC) drugs or medicines   drugs or medicines that do not require a doctor's prescription (438, 549).

overweight   more than 10 percent over the weight that best suits your height and body frame (200).

ovulation (oh vyuh **lay** shun)   a process during which the ovaries produce and release a ripened egg (283).

oxytocin (ox ih **toh** sin)   a hormone that causes the uterus to get smaller after childbirth and helps breast tissue to eject milk when the baby suckles (313).

ozone   a form of oxygen found in the upper atmosphere. This layer absorbs most of the sun's ultraviolet light (520).

ozone layer   a thin layer of the upper atmosphere made up of ozone (520).

pancreas (**pang** kree us)   an elongated gland behind the stomach that secretes digestive juices and controls blood-sugar levels (174, 275).

panic disorder   a condition marked by attacks of extreme anxiety without apparent cause (74).

Pap test   a medical procedure in which a doctor takes a sample of cells from the cervix and checks them for signs of cancer (287, 424).

paranoid (**par** uh noyd) **schizophrenic disorder**   schizophrenic disorder marked by the false belief that others are trying to harm or influence a person (80).

parasite (**pa** ruh syt)   an organism that lives on or inside another living thing (372).

parathyroid glands   four tiny glands attached to the back of the thyroid gland that regulate calcium and phosphorus levels (275).

Parkinson's disease   a serious illness marked by progressive loss of normal muscle function. Over time, the muscles become stiff, causing shaky movements (355).

particulates (pur **tik** yuh litz)   particles of dust, soot, mold spores, metals, and minerals (520).

passive   holding back your thoughts and feelings and yielding to others (25, 103).

passive-aggressive personality disorders   a condition in which a person depends on others for direction but resents being told what to do and is unable to express anger openly (78).

passive immunity   temporary immunity acquired by receiving antibodies from another immune system (382).

passive smokers   involuntary smokers; people who inhale smoke in the air from other people's cigars, pipes, or cigarettes (500).

pastoral counselors   members of the religious community who have been trained to counsel people with mental and social problems (87).

pathogens (**path** uh junz)   organisms that cause disease in plants or animals (370).

pediatrician (peed ee uh **trish** un)   a doctor who specializes in caring for babies and children (315).

peer group   friends who are about the same age and share similar interests (28).

peer pressure   the need to conform to the expectations of friends and classmates (324).

pelvic inflammatory disease (PID)   a serious infection of the female reproductive organs (394).

penis (**pee** nis)   the external male sexual organ through which sperm are delivered into the female's body (278).

peptic ulcer   an open sore in the lining of the stomach or nearby part of the digestive system (500).

periodontist (per ee oh **dahn** tist)   a dentist who specializes in treating gum diseases (538).

periodontitis (pehr ee oh dahn **ty** tis)   an advanced stage of gum disease in which the buildup of plaque and calculus causes gums to pull away from teeth (164).

periosteum (pehr ee **ahs** tee um)   a tough membrane covering a bone and containing cells that produce new bone for growth and repair (224).

peripheral (puh **rif** ur ul) **nervous system (PNS)**   all the parts of the nervous system except the brain and spinal cord. The PNS is made up of the cranial nerves and the spinal nerves (222).

peripheral (puh **rif** ur ul) **vision**   the ability to see things off to the side of what you are looking at (155).

personality   traits that make each individual different from everyone else (24).

personality disorder   a condition marked by inflexible behavior that interferes with the person's pursuit of a happy, healthy life (78).

perspiration (pur spuh **ray** shun)   sweating; a method by which the body cools itself. Water containing mineral salts travels from the sweat glands in the skin tissue to the surface of the skin (177).

peyote (pay **oh** tee)   a psychedelic drug that is made from the peyote cactus (451).

phagocytes (fag uh syts)   eater cells; white blood cells that "eat up" pathogens and give off substances that cause healing to begin (375).

pharmacist   a person licensed to dispense medicines prescribed by doctors (536).

phenocyclidine (fen noh **sy** kluh deen) **(PCP)**   "angel dust"; a psychedelic drug with unpredictable effects (451).

phenylketonuria (fen ul kee tah **nyoor** ee uh) **(PKU)**   a recessive genetic disorder characterized by the inability to break down phenylalanine, a chemical commonly found in food. It can cause severe retardation in infants (292).

phobia (foh bee uh)   anxiety or fear brought about by a specific situation or object (73).

phonocardiography (foh nuh kar dee **ahg** ruh fee)   a method of transforming heart sounds into graphic displays that can show defects in the heart (420).

physical abuse   punishment that leaves a mark that can be seen the next day (129).

physical dependence   a condition in which the body becomes adjusted to a drug and requires the drug to function normally (444).

physical disability   a condition that prevents normal physical functioning (427).

physical environment   physical surroundings, such as climate, air, and water (6).

physical examination   a head-to-toe check of the body to identify medical problems (543).

physical fitness   the ability of the heart, blood vessels, lungs, and muscles to work together to meet the body's needs (236).

physical peak   the state of having body weight at a healthy level and physical abilities at maximum levels (346).

physical therapist (fiz ih kul **thehr** uh pist)   an allied health professional who rehabilitates patients disabled by problems such as back pain, burns, strokes, and injuries (537).

physician's assistant   a health professional who can perform some tasks previously done by doctors, such as taking medical histories and performing physical examinations, but only under the close supervision of a doctor (537).

pituitary (pi **too** uh tehr ee) **gland**   the "master gland"; a small gland at the base of the brain that controls other endocrine glands and many activities, including growth, cellular metabolism, and reproduction (273).

placenta (pluh **sen** tuh)   the attachment that holds the embryo to the wall of the uterus (303).

plaque (plak)   a sticky, colorless film of bacteria that covers the surface of teeth (163).

pneumonia (noo **mohn** yuh)   a serious infection of the lungs caused by viruses, bacteria, or fungi (380).

pneumocystis carinii (noo moh **sis** tis   koh **reen** ee)   a rare form of pneumonia; an opportunistic disease that afflicts people with HIV (402).

Poison Control Center   an agency that provides information about which household substances are poisonous and can tell you what to do in the event of poisoning (578).

poisoning   the effect that one or more harmful substances may have on the body (605).

polio   a disease that causes inflammation of the spinal cord and can result in paralysis (559).

pollutants   wastes that enter the environment (516).

pollution   the condition that occurs when wastes have entered the environment (516).

pons   a part of the brain stem that regulates breathing and helps control eye movement (221).

pore   the opening of the narrow channel, also known as a duct, that leads to a gland (147).

postpartum   a period of adjustment for parents as well as newborns that begins with delivery and lasts about six weeks (313).

premature birth   the delivery of a live fetus before it is ready to be born, usually during the third trimester (313).

premenstrual syndrome (PMS)   a condition that may occur some time before menstruation. It is marked by severe discomfort, nervous tension, mood swings, headaches, bloating, and irritability (286).

premium   the annual fee paid to the insurance company for insurance coverage (545).

premolars (pree moh lurz)   teeth that have flat surfaces with two rounded ridges for crushing food (162).

prenatal (pre **nay** tul) **care**   medical care during pregnancy (301).

prescription   a request from a doctor to a pharmacist specifying the medicine to be given to a patient (536).

prescription (prih **skrip** shun) **drugs or medicines**   drugs or medicines that are safe to use only under the direction of a doctor (438, 549).

preservatives   additives used to prevent spoilage or to keep foods from losing their natural color or texture (197).

pressure point   the point at which an injured artery lies near the skin surface and passes over a bone above the injury (604).

primary-care physician   the doctor who takes care of most of your routine medical needs (536).

private self   the real you or the way you are when you are alone (29).

problem drinking   drinking behavior that becomes too frequent or involves excessive amounts of alcohol (473).

prodromal (proh **drohm** ul) **period**   the second stage of an infectious disease when the immune system discovers the pathogen (379).

progesterone (proh **jes** tuh rohn)   a female sex hormone (276).

progressive relaxation   a technique in which you relax each group of muscles in your body, one at a time (60).

projection   putting your own faults onto another person (40).

prolactin (proh **lak** tin)   a hormone that causes milk to form in the breasts after childbirth (313).

proof   a measure of the percent of a given volume of a beverage that is made up of alcohol (466).

propoxyphene (proh **pahks** uh feen)   a synthetic narcotic (449).

prostate gland   a male sex gland near the bladder (279).

proteins   nutrients that contain nitrogen, carbon, hydrogen, and oxygen. Proteins are found in every cell, are a source of energy, and play a role in the growth and repair of body tissues (184).

psilocybin (sil uh **sy** bin)   a psychedelic drug made from a Mexican mushroom. Its effects are similar to LSD but milder (452).

psychedelic (sy kih **del** ik)   hallucinogen; a drug that changes a person's mental state (451).

psychiatric nurse   a nurse who specializes in the care and treatment of the mentally ill (87).

psychiatric social worker   a social worker who specializes in helping the mentally ill and their families (87).

psychiatrist (sy **ky** uh trist)   a medical doctor who specializes in the treatment of mental disorders (86, 538).

psychoanalysis (sy koh uh **nal** uh sis)   a form of therapy that involves bringing unconscious thoughts into the conscious mind to resolve inner conflicts (30).

psychological (sy kuh **lahj** ih kul) **dependence**   a strong desire or need to continue using a drug (445).

psychologist (sy **kahl** uh jist)   a health professional with two to six years of training beyond college in evaluating and helping people with emotional problems. A psychologist studies the human mind and behavior (25, 538).

psychosomatic (sy kuh so **mat** ik) **symptoms**   physical symptoms that can be caused by stress (54).

psychotherapy (sy koh **thehr** uh pee)   conversation with a trained therapist who helps a person understand and overcome a mental problem (74).

puberty   a period of sexual development during which males and females become able to produce children (277).

pubic (pyu bik) **lice**   lice that infest the hair in the genital area (398).

public health   the health of people as a group or as a community (556).

public health system   all the government agencies and private organizations that work to prevent disease and to promote the general health of the public (556).

public self   the way you want others to see you (29).

pulmonary circulation   the pathway blood follows from the heart to the lungs (231).

pulp   a soft tissue that fills the center of each tooth and contains nerves and blood vessels (162).

pupil   the opening in the center of the iris through which light enters the eye (154).

pyrogens (py ruh junz)   chemicals that signal the brain to raise body temperature (379).

quacks   people who are involved in the selling of useless medical treatments or products (550).

quackery (kwak ur ee)   the selling of useless medical treatments or products (550).

quality of life   a holistic concept of wellness referring to how satisfying and rewarding your life is (4).

quarantine (kwor un teen)   isolating people who have an infectious disease to prevent spread of the disease (556).

rabies   a serious viral disease that can be passed from diseased animals to people (618).

radiation   a form of high energy, including ultraviolet light, x-rays, cosmic rays, and energy given off by certain substances, such as uranium, that can damage living things (529).

radiation sickness   a disease caused by exposure to higher-than-background levels of radiation (529).

radiation therapy   the use of radiation to kill cancer cells (425).

radioactive   giving off radiation (529).

rape   an assault in which one person forces another to have sexual relations (592).

rape crisis center   an agency that provides counseling and support for rape victims (593).

rapid eye movement (REM) sleep   sleep during which the eyes flicker back and forth behind closed eyelids (260).

rationalization   making excuses for actions or feelings (40).

reaction formation   behaving in a way opposite to the way you are feeling (40).

recessive genes   genes that will show up in the child only when dominant genes are not present (290).

recovery stage   stage of disease between acute illness and convalescence, when a person starts to feel better (379).

rectum   the last few inches of the large intestine, which holds the feces until they are eliminated from the body (174).

registered nurse (R.N.)   a nurse who has completed a two-to-four year nursing program and passed a state licensing examination. R.N.s observe and assess patient symptoms, plan the best approach to promoting recovery, and evaluate progress (537).

regression   showing the emotional behavior characteristic of young children (40).

rehabilitation (ree huh bil ih **tay** shun)   the process of long-term improvement and recovery from disease or injury (483).

relapse   the return of a disease during or soon after the period of convalescence (379).

relationship   an association between people who share interests or goals and who exchange information, feelings, and ideas (96).

relaxation   a state in which your body and mind are resting (60).

releasing hormone   a chemical produced by the hypothalamus that causes the pituitary gland to release a hormone (275).

remission   the absence of any signs and/or symptoms of a previous disease (425).

reproduction   the producing of offspring (273).

reproductive maturity   the ability to produce children. It is signaled by ovulation in girls and sperm production in boys (325).

rescue breathing   mouth-to-mouth resuscitation; a method of inflating a person's lungs with air from your lungs (601).

resident microorganisms   harmless microorganisms present in the body at all times (372).

resistance stage   the second stage of the general adaption syndrome; the body returns to homeostasis, its normal state (53).

retina (ret un uh)   a thin, delicate membrane that makes up the innermost layer of the eye. It is the light-sensing part of the eye (154).

reverse tolerance   a condition in which less and less of a drug is needed to experience its effects (444).

rheumatic (roo **mat** ik) **heart disease**   an inflammatory disease in which the body's own immune system damages the heart valves (419).

Rh factor   a substance present in the blood of some people (312).

Rh incompatibility   a condition in which a pregnant woman is Rh negative and the fetus is Rh positive (312).

Rh negative   the lack of the Rh factor in blood (312).

Rh positive   the presence of the Rh factor in blood (312).

right to choose   your first and foremost right as a consumer (551).

right to complain   the consumer's right to express dissatisfaction with a service or product (551).

right to information   the consumer's right to learn enough about a service or product to make a judgment about it (551).

right to safety   the consumer's right to expect that any service or product is reasonably safe (551).

risk behavior   a behavior that increases the chances of a harmful outcome (10, 576).

risk factor   a factor that increases a person's chances of getting a disease (412).

root canal   a channel through which nerves and blood vessels from the tooth pass to connect with blood vessels and nerves in the jawbone (162).

rubella (roo **bel** uh)   German measles; a disease caused by a virus that can cause birth defects in babies whose mothers have been exposed during the first few months of pregnancy (380).

safe behavior   behavior that protects a person from danger and lessens the effects of a harmful situation (576).

saliva (suh **ly** vuh)   a tasteless liquid made by the salivary glands inside your mouth (172).

saturated (sach uh ray tid) **fats**   fats that contain as much hydrogen in their structure as chemically possible (183).

scabies (scay beez)   an itchy rash that is caused by a tiny animal called a mite (398).

schizoid (skit soyd) **personality disorder**   a condition in which a person is totally withdrawn and shows no warm feelings toward other people (79).

schizophrenia (skit suh **free** nee uh)   a disorder in which the mind is "split off" from reality (79).

sclera (skleer uh)   the white outer layer of the eye (153).

scoliosis (skoh lee **oh** sis)   an abnormal curvature of the spine. It may be either mild or severe (228, 544).

screening test   a method for the early detection of disease (425).

scrotum (**skroh** tum)   the sac of skin outside the body in which the testes hang (278).

secondary sex characteristics   physical changes occurring during puberty that are not directly related to reproduction (326).

second-degree burn   a burn that extends through the outer layer of the skin, causing blisters and reddening (612).

second opinion   the diagnosis and advice of a second doctor (542).

sedative-hypnotic   a type of depressant used to relax a person and induce sleep (448).

seizures   attacks during which a person may lose consciousness and experience convulsions (223, 445).

self-actualization   according to Abraham Maslow, the process by which each person strives to be all that she or he can be (33).

self-concept   the physical and mental picture you have of yourself (28, 333, 347).

self-disclosure   the process of expressing personal feelings and revealing information about yourself (99).

self-esteem   how much one likes oneself and feels good about oneself (33, 98).

semen (**see** mun)   the mixture of sperm and fluids from the male sex glands (279, 400).

semicircular canals   a set of three hollow tubes in the inner ear that detect changes in body position (159).

seminal vesicles (**ves** i kulz)   paired male sex glands located near the bladder (279).

senility (sih **nil** ih tee)   dementia; a disorder characterized by the loss of mental abilities (357).

sensory neurons   nerve cells that pick up information about the body and carry it to interneurons in the brain or spinal cord (218).

separation   an arrangement in which spouses live apart and try to work out their problems (128).

sex roles   behaviors and attitudes that are socially accepted as either masculine or feminine (105).

sex-linked disorder   a recessive genetic disorder in which the gene for the disorder is found on the X chromosome (290).

sexual abstinence (**ab** stuh nuns)   not having any kind of sexual contact with another person (390).

sexual abuse   a criminal offense in which a child or an adolescent is used for sexual activity (130).

sexual fidelity   having a caring relationship, such as marriage, with only one other person (393).

sexually transmitted diseases (STDs)   venereal diseases; a group of diseases usually spread through sexual contact (390).

shock   a condition in which an individual's circulation and breathing progressively slow down (603).

sickle cell anemia   a recessive genetic blood disorder characterized by abnormally shaped red blood cells (292).

side effects   effects that are in addition to the desired effects of a drug (439, 550).

sign   the visible or measurable evidence of disease (378).

single-parent family   a family in which only one parent lives with the child or children (126).

sinoatrial node (SA node)   a group of cells in the heart that regulate the heartbeat when it is 60 or more beats per minute (231).

sinusitis   a swelling and reddening of the sinuses (500).

skeletal muscle   voluntary muscle (227).

skin test   a test for a food allergy in which a small portion of the food is injected under the surface of the skin (209).

sleep   deep relaxation of body and mind during which eyes are closed and there is little conscious thought or movement (260).

sleep apnea   a sleeping disorder in which a person stop breathing for short periods during sleep (261).

small intestine   a long, coiled organ in the digestive system, about 1 inch (2.5 cm) in diameter and 20 feet (6 meters) long, into which chyme passes from the stomach (174).

small talk   casual or trivial conversation (99).

smog   a brownish haze produced when hydrocarbons react to nitric oxide in the presence of light (519).

smooth muscle   involuntary muscle that works automatically to control movement such as breathing, digestion, and blood circulation (227).

snuff   finely ground tobacco that is either inhaled through the nose or held between the cheek and gums (496).

social drinking   drinking occasionally with others in relaxed, pleasant circumstances to enhance or complement the enjoyment of a social occasion (473).

social environment   your family, friends, and other people you spend time with (6).

socialization (soh shul ih **zay** shun)   the process by which children learn from people close to them about feelings, attitudes, and appropriate ways of behaving (27, 127).

social worker   health-care professional with a master's degree from a school of social work, trained to resolve emotional problems with the entire family as well as the individual (538).

somatic nervous system   the part of the peripheral nervous system that is responsible for actions that you control (222).

somatoform (soh **mat** uh form) **disorder**   a mental disorder in which a person complains of physical symptoms but shows no underlying physical cause for the symptoms (77).

specialty hospital   a hospital that specializes in treating one age group or one type of disorder (539).

sperm   the male sex cell (276).

spermatogenesis (spur mat uh **jen** i sis)   process by which sperm are produced (279).

spinal cord   a rod of brain tissue inside the spinal column; a part of the central nervous system (221).

spirochete (**spy** ruh keet)   a bacterium that causes syphilis (396).

splint   a rigid material that is tied to an injured part of the body to keep the part from moving (611).

sprain   stretched or torn ligaments or stretched or torn tendons near a joint (611).

stabilizer   an additive that keeps solid ingredients from separating out of liquids (197).

statistician (stat ih **stish** un)   a person who collects, analyzes, and interprets numerical data (559).

stereoscopic vision (stehr ee uh **skahp** ik) **vision**   the ability to see things three dimensionally (155).

sterility   the inability to reproduce (280, 394).

stethoscope (**steth** uh skohp)   an instrument used to listen to sounds produced within the body (544).

stillbirth   the birth of a dead, full-term fetus (311).

stimulants   drugs that speed up the body's activity (450).

stomach   a muscular, saclike organ in the digestive system that stores, churns, mixes, and breaks up food (173).

strain   overstretching a muscle or a tendon (611).

stress   a reaction of the body and mind to the demands of everyday life (48).

stressors   the causes of stress (48).

stroke   a clot or break in a blood vessel in the brain that disrupts blood flow to the brain (233, 417, 603).

sty   a red, painful swelling caused when the pore of an eyelash oil gland becomes infected (156).

style   your delivery, or the attitude you express as you speak, listen, and respond (100).

sublimation   channelling energy into an acceptable goal rather than an unacceptable one (40).

suffocation   a condition that results from a person's breathing being blocked by an object, by smothering, or by being trapped in an enclosed space (579).

sulfuric (suhl **fyoor** ik) **acid**   a waste gas formed when fuels are burned (519).

superego   according to Freud, the part of the personality that has knowledge of right and wrong; conscience (30).

sympathetic pregnancy   a condition in which fathers share some of the mothers' discomfort during pregnancy, such as morning sickness and frequent urination (306).

symptom   a sensation, such as pain, which is caused by disease or stress and which cannot be measured (54, 378).

synergistic (sin ur **jis** tik) **reaction**   effects produced when two or more drugs are taken together that are many times greater than either drug would produce by itself (440).

synovial (suh **noh** vee ul) **fluid**   the secretion that flows over bones at the joint to prevent wear on bones (226).

syphilis (sif uh lis)   a serious, many-staged sexually transmitted disease, caused by a spirochete bacterium (396).

systemic (si **stem** ik) **circulation**   the pathway oxygen-rich blood follows from the heart to the rest of the body (231).

systolic (sis **tahl** ik) **pressure**   the first, and higher reading, when blood pressure is taken. It is the amount of force recorded when the ventricles of the heart contract and your heart beats (231).

T cells   T lymphocytes; cells of the immune system that produce interferon and other substances that regulate the functions of the immune system (377).

tar   a dark, sticky mixture of chemicals formed when tobacco burns (495).

target heart rate   the heart rate you need to maintain during a workout to improve your cardiorespiratory fitness (251).

Tay-Sachs disease   a recessive genetic disorder characterized by the lack of an important chemical in the brain. It is found primarily among people of eastern European descent (292).

teaching hospitals   hospitals in large cities near medical schools whose faculty members are on the hospital staff (539).

tear glands   glands located above each eye that produce fluids to protect the eyes and keep them moist (153).

temperature inversion   a situation in which a layer of cool air near the ground is trapped under a layer of warm air (521).

tendons   thick strands of connective tissue that attach muscles to bones (227, 611).

terminal illness   an illness resulting in death (360).

testes (tes teez)   testicles; male reproductive glands that produce testosterone and sperm (276).

testicles (tes ti kuhls)   testes; male reproductive glands that produce testosterone and sperm (278).

testicular cancer   cancer of the testicles. It can occur in men between the ages of 15 and 34 (280).

testosterone (tes tahs tuh rohn)   male sex hormone (276, 454).

tetanus   a bacterial disease that can be fatal (618).

tetanus toxin (tet un us **tahk** sin)   a poison, produced by the tetanus bacteria. It damages the nervous system, causing uncontrollable muscle contractions and paralysis (372).

tetracycline (tet ruh **sy** kleen)   an antibiotic drug (440).

thalamus (thal uh mus)   a relay station for the senses in the brain; it processes sensory information and helps control muscle activity (221).

THC   the active chemical in hashish and marijuana (453).

theory (thee uh ree)   an organized set of ideas used to explain something (30).

therapeutic (ther uh **pyoo** tik) **community**   residential treatment center where drug abusers can live and learn to adjust to drug-free lives (457).

therapist   a mental health professional (73).

therapy   treatment technique for a mental disorder (73).

thermal pollution   a condition of elevated temperature in a body of water resulting from industries using water from rivers, lakes, or streams to cool their machinery (524).

thickener   an additive used to give a thicker consistency to food (197).

third-degree burn   a burn that damages all layers of skin and the tissues underneath, sometimes causing the skin to take on a gray or charred appearance (612).

thrombus (thrahm bus)   a blood clot (417).

thymus   a gland located in the upper chest that helps to develop the body's defenses against infection (275).

thyroid (thy royd) **gland**   a large gland, shaped like a bowtie and located at the front of the neck. It regulates the rate of metabolism (275).

thyroxine (thy rahk sin)   a hormone, containing iodine, produced by the thyroid gland (275).

tissue   cells of the same type that are connected and function together in the body (146).

tolerance (tahl ur uns)   resistance to a drug (444).

tone of voice   the way something is said (101).

tornado   a rapidly rotating column of air (580).

tourniquet (toor nih kit)   a brand or strip of strong, flexible material applied to an arm or leg to control bleeding (604).

toxemia (tahk see mee uh)   a serious condition during pregnancy characterized by high blood pressure, protein in the urine, and swelling of the body tissues (311).

toxic shock syndrome (TSS)   a rare bacterial disease usually found in menstruating women who are using tampons (286).

toxins (tahk sins)   poisons (372).

trachea (tray kee uh)   the windpipe (232).

trauma (trow muh)   a painful physical or emotional experience (79).

traumatic (trow **mat** ik) **shock**   shock caused by an injury (603).

Trichomonas (trik oh **moh** nis)   single-celled pathogen that causes a type of vaginitis (397).

trimester (try mes tur)   one of the three periods into which the nine months of pregnancy are divided (305).

type A personality   people who tend to be competitive and driven to succeed. They may be likely to develop stress-related illnesses (56).

type B personality   people who tend to be calm and noncompetitive. They are not likely to develop stress-related illness (57).

ulcer (uhl sur)   an open sore in the lining of the stomach or small intestine, caused by too much acid (54, 176).

ulcerative colitis (ul suh **ray** tiv koh **lyt** us)   a chronic inflammation of the lining of the lower part of the large intestine (176).

ultrasound   high-frequency sound waves that may be used to make a "picture" of a fetus, bones, muscles, and internal organs (308).

umbilical cord (uhm **bil** ih kul) **cord**   the embryo's lifeline; a cord between the embryo and the placenta (303).

unconscious (un **kahn** shus) **thoughts**   thoughts of which a person is not aware (30).

undescended (uhn dih **send** ed) **testes**   a condition in which one of the testes does not descend into the scrotum at birth (280).

unit price the cost per ounce of a product (199).

United States Recommended Daily Allowances (U.S. RDA) a nutritional guide that specifies the amount of calories, protein, vitamins, and minerals needed daily, based on allowances set by the Food and Nutrition Board of the National Academy of Sciences (190).

unsaturated (uh **sach** uh ray tid) **fats** fats that have less than the maximum possible amount of hydrogen in their structure (183).

urea (yoo **ree** uh) one of two waste products produced by the body (177).

uremia (yoo **ree** mee uh) poisoning of the body caused by the failure of the kidneys to remove waste products (178).

ureter (yoo **rih** tur) a long tube that leads from each kidney to the bladder (178).

urethra (yoo **ree** thruh) a short tube in the urinary tract that carries urine out of the body (178, 279).

uric (**yoor** ik) **acid** one of two waste products produced by the body (177).

urinary tract the system through which urine passes from the kidneys. It is made up of the ureters, bladder, and urethra (178).

urine (**yoor** in) waste products from the kidneys. It includes urea, uric acid, and excess water (178).

uterus (**yoo** tur uhs) the womb; a hollow, muscular, pear-shaped organ in the female reproductive tract. It is located between the two ovaries. A fertilized egg may develop and grow into a baby in the uterus (283, 397).

vaccination (**vak** suh **nay** shun) immunization; injection of small amounts of dead or altered pathogens that protect you from an infectious disease (382).

vaccine (**vak seen**) a substance containing small amounts of dead or altered pathogens or their toxins. It is used in vaccination (382).

vagina (vuh **jy** nuh) birth canal; a hollow tube leading from the uterus to the outside of the body (283, 397).

vaginitis (vaj uh **ny** tis) a vaginal infectioin or irritation (285, 397).

validation (val ih **day** shun) the reassurance a person receives from friends and others that his or her feelings, ideas, or decisions are reasonable (348).

values beliefs that are important to people and help them to clarify what they believe is right and wrong (13, 333).

varicose (**va** rih kohs) **veins** veins that become inflated from the pressure of blood (418).

vas deferens (vas **def** ur unz) an 18-inch (45 cm) tube that conveys sperm from the epididymis to the ejaculatory ducts (278).

vegetarian a person who eats no meat (207).

veins (vaynz) the thin-walled, slightly elastic blood vessels that return blood from the body tissues to the heart (231).

veneral (vuh **neer** ee ul) **disease (VD)** sexually transmitted disease; a type of disease usually spread through sexual contact (390).

ventricle (**ven** trih kul) the larger of the two chambers that make up the heart (230).

venules (**ven** yules) tiny blood vessels through which blood passes on the way from the capillaries to the veins (231).

vertebrae (**vur** tuh bree) the more than 24 ring-shaped bones that make up the spinal column (222).

vestibule (**ves** tuh byool) a fluid-filled chamber in the inner ear that helps to maintain balance (159).

villi (**vil** eye) tiny, fingerlike projections covering the inner wall of the small intestine that aid in absorbing food substances into the bloodstream (174).

viruses microscopic germs that cause disease; the simplest type of parasite (303, 372).

vital statistics the number of births and deaths in a community (561).

vitamins nutrients that assist many of the chemical reactions in the body (185).

vitreous (vit **ree** us) **humor** a clear, jellylike substance that fills the large central chamber of the eye and gives the eye its shape (154).

warm-up a 5-to-10 minute period during which you prepare your body for vigorous exercise (254).

wastes things that we no longer need, want, or can use (516).

wellness a concept of health that includes physical health, mental health, and social health (3).

withdrawal symptoms the body's reaction to not having a drug it depends upon (445, 483).

womb (**woom**) the uterus; the hollow, muscular, pear-shaped organ located between the two ovaries. A fertilized egg may develop and grow into a baby in the womb (283).

zygote (**zy** goht) the united egg and sperm, which begins to divide shortly after fertilization (302).

Index

Acknowledgments

Text, continued

9 "Illness-Wellness Continuum," adapted from Travis and Ryan, *Wellness Workbook.* Berkeley: Ten Speed Press, 1988.

16–17 "DECIDE," adapted from "The Stanford University DECIDE Drug Education Curriculum." Project Pegasus, CA.

49 "Ranking of Stressors by High School Students," reprinted with permission from *Journal of Psychosomatic Research,* 16 (1972). Pergammon Journals, Ltd.

103 "Assertive, Passive, and Aggressive Communication," reprinted with permission from *Self Discovery* (1984).

106 "Making New Friends," reprinted with permission from *Self Discovery* (1984).

473 "A Problem Drinker's Self-Test," reprinted and adapted with permission from *A Message to Teenagers* . . . A.A. World Services, Inc., P.O. Box 459, Grand Central Station, 1980.

482 "Contract for Life," courtesy of S.A.D.D., Students Against Driving Drunk, © 1987. Marlboro, MA.

490 Centers for Disease Control. *Morbidity and Mortality Weekly Report.* 11 September 1987, p. 582.

541 Jeffrey R. M. Kunz, M.D. *AMA Family Medical Guide.* NY: Random House, Inc., 1982.

558 "Causes of Death," adapted with permission from Green and Anderson, *Community Health,* 5th ed. St. Louis: C. V. Mosby Co., 1986, p. 118.

Illustrations

Leon Bishop: 52 (with Michael Granger), 146, 148, 153, 155, 158, 162, 164, 173, 174, 177, 219, 220, 221, 224, 225, 226 (with Michael Granger), 227, 230, 232, 273, 277, 282, 284, 375, 416, 418, 419, 605B, 617
Boston Graphics, Incorporated: 3, 9, 33, 161, 180, 181, 184, 191, 196, 198, 199, 200, 203, 207, 234, 255, 258, 260, 261, 290, 326, 376, 377, 379, 399, 413, 439, 467, 490, 494, 495, 499, 519, 521, 526, 558, 565, 577, 582
Lane Gregory: 61, 165, 264, 265, 288, 578, 584, 589, 601, 603, 605T, 608, 609, 611, 612, 613, 614, 615, 616, 619, 621
Edwin Huff: 303, 304, 307, 310, 471

Photographs

Larry Lawfer: i, ii, iii, xvi, 1, 16, 17, 20, 21, 22, 23, 42, 43, 46, 47, 62, 63, 64L, 65, 68, 69, 82, 83, 92, 93, 94, 95, 114, 115, 118, 119, 134, 135, 138, 139, 142, 143, 144, 145, 166, 167, 170, 171, 182, 183, 194, 195, 212, 213, 216, 217, 237, 238, 239, 242, 243, 264, 265, 268, 269, 270, 271, 286, 287, 296, 297, 320, 321, 340, 341, 344, 345, 356, 357B, 362, 363, 366, 367, 368, 369, 388, 389, 402, 403, 410, 411, 430, 431T, 434, 435, 436, 437, 460, 461, 464, 465, 474, 475, 484, 485, 488, 489, 501, 508, 509, 512, 513, 514, 515, 534, 535, 542, 543, 554, 555, 568, 569, 572, 573, 574, 575, 596, 597, 608, 609

Photos above styled by Deborah Bassette. Sculpture on p. 69 created by Amanda Annis. The publisher gratefully acknowledges the assistance of Beaver Country Day School, Chestnut Hill, MA; Braintree High School, Braintree, MA; Cypress Lakes High School, Fort Myers, FL; Estero High School, Estero, FL; Banana Republic, Inc., Boston, MA; and Eddie Bauer, Inc., Boston, MA.

vii Coco McCoy/Rainbow; **viii T** James Whitmer; **viii B** Bob Daemmrich; **ix** Walter Modges/Click/Chicago; **x** Ted Cordingley; **xi** Frank Siteman/The Picture Cube; **xii** Charles Gupton/Stock Boston; **xiii** Dennis Stock/Magnum Photos; **3** James Whitmer; **5** William Thompson; **6** James Whitmer; **7 R** R. Rowan/Photo Researchers; **7 L** Benny Tillman/The Image Bank; **8** Richard Hutchings/Photo Researchers; **10 R** Chris Luneski/Photo Researchers; **10 L** Brian Parker/Tom Stack & Associates; **11** Digiacom/The Image Bank; **13** Erika Stone; **14** Ziggy Kaluzny/Gamma-Liaison; **15** Nancy Sheehan; **19** Erika Stone; **25** Nancy Sheehan; **26** Donald Smetzer/Click/Chicago; **27** Erika Stone; **28** Leslie Powell; **29** Coco McCoy/Rainbow; **30** Erika Stone; **32** Burk Uzzie/Archive; **34** Francis Miller, Life Magazine © 1963/Time, Inc.; **35** Suzanne Murphy/Click/Chicago; **36 T** Barbara Burnes/Photo Researchers; **36 B** Robert Frerck/Odyssey Productions; **37 T** James Whitmer; **37 B** James Whitmer; **38** Erik Hill/Anchorage Daily News; **40** Focus on Sports; **41** Donald Smetzer/Click/Chicago; **45** Richard H. Thom/Tom Stack & Associates; **50 R** David M. Grossman; **50 L** Richard Hutchings/Photo Researchers; **51** Frank Siteman/Stock Boston; **53** Bob Daemmrich/Stock Boston; **54** Phil Huber/Black Star; **55** Jeff March/Tom Stack & Associates; **56 R** Donald Smetzer/Click/Chicago; **56 L** Charles Gupton/Stock Boston; **58** Donald Smetzer/Click/Chicago; **59** Terry Farmer/Click/Chicago; **60** David Dempster/Photosynthesis; **64 R** Ann Duncan/Tom Stack & Associates; **67** James Whitmer; **71 T** Sund/The Image Bank; **71 B** Alan Mercer/Stock Boston; **72** Elyse Lewin/The Image Bank; **74** Steve Dunwell/The Image Bank; **76** March of Dimes; **77 R** William Thompson; **77 L** William Thompson; **78** Nancy Sheehan; **79** The Memory Shop; **80 L & R** Evelyn Raske; **84** Frank Siteman/The Picture Cube; **86 R** Lester Sloan/Woodfin Camp & Associates; **86 M** © Andrew Brilliant; **86 L** Mieke Maas/The Image Bank; **89** Bob Daemmrich; **91** Arthur Grace/SYGMA; **97 T** Donald Smetzer/Click/Chicago; **97 M** Sobel/Klonsky/The Image Bank; **97 B** Richard Hutchings/Photo Researchers; **98 R** Donald Smetzer/Click/Chicago; **98 L** James Whitmer; **100** Blair Seitz/Photo Researchers; **101** Courtesy of Children's Hospital, Boston, photo by Maria Iacobo; **102** James Whitmer; **104** Richard Hutchings/Photo Researchers; **105** Richard Hutchings/Photo Researchers; **107** Richard Hutchings/Photo Researchers; **108** Donald Smetzer/Click/Chicago; **109** Bob Daemmrich; **110** Bob Daemmrich; **111** Bob Daemmrich; **112** Nancy Sheehan; **117** Bob Daemmrich; **121** Daryl Jacobson/FourByFive; **122 R** © Carol Palmer; **122 L** Cary Wolinski/Stock Boston; **123** Jose Carrillo; **124** Nancy Sheehan; **125 R** Blair Seitz/Photo Researchers; **125 L** Michael Heron; **128** Blair Seitz/Photo Researchers; **129** Bob Daemmrich; **130** Bob Daemmrich; **131** Erika Stone; **132 T** Bob Daemmrich; **132** Face Software/Nancy Burson; **133** Michael Heron; **137** Erika Stone; **141** Richard Hutchings/Photo Researchers; **147** Bob Daemmrich; **149** Bob Daemmrich; **150** Barbara Alper/Stock Boston; **151** Bob Daemmrich; **152** Bob Daemmrich; **154** E. R. Lewis/Tom Stack & Associates; **157 TR** Robert Semeniuk/The Stock Market of New York; **157 TL** Mark Bray/Unicorn Stock Photos; **157 B** Bob Daemmrich; **159 T** Gabe Palmer/The Stock Market of New York; **159 B** MacDonald Photography/The Picture Cube; **161** Peter Miller/The Image Bank; **163** Bob Daemmrich; **164** Arnold Kaplan/Berg & Associates; **169** Bob Daemmrich; **176** Robert Frerck/Odyssey Productions; **178** Courtesy Candela Laser Corporation; **179** Roy Morsch/The Stock Market of New York; **185** Roy Morsch/The Stock Market of New York; **187** Bob Daemmrich; **188 T** Gordon E. Smith Photography; **188 B** John Curtis Studio; **189 T** Stock Imagery; **189 B** David Dempster/Photosynthesis; **190** David Dempster/Photosynthesis; **193** Bob Daemmrich; **197** Dave Schaefer; **201** Craig Hammell/The Stock Market of New York; **202** David Dempster/Photosynthesis; **203** Gia Barto/The Image Bank; **204** Raycroft/McCormick; **205** Dan McCoy/Rainbow; **207 R** David Dempster/Photosynthesis; **207 L** David Dempster/Photosynthesis; **208** Dan McCoy/Rainbow; **211** David Dempster/Photosynthesis; **215** David Dempster/Photosynthesis; **221** Bob

Daemmrich/Stock Boston; **222** The Bettmann Archive; **223 T** Addison Geary/Stock Boston; **223 M** Dennis Stock/Magnum Photos; **223 B** Bob Daemmrich; **224** Bob Daemmrich; **227** Stanley Rowin/The Picture Cube; **228** Ted Cordingley; **229** Dan McCoy/Rainbow; **231** Bob Daemmrich; **233 R** Biophoto Associates/Science Source/Photo Researchers; **233 L** Science Source/Photo Researchers; **235** Bob Daemmrich; **236** Bob Daemmrich; **241** Joe McNally/Wheeler Pictures; **245 R** Peter Menzel/Stock Boston; **245 L** Lou Jones; **246** Bob Daemmrich; **248** Lewis Portnoy/The Stock Market of New York; **249 T** Gabe Palmer/The Stock Market of New York; **249 B** Ted Cordingley; **251** Steve Hansen/Stock Boston; **254** Sarah Putnam/The Picture Cube; **256 R** Bob Daemmrich; **256 L** Melchior DiGiacomo/The Image Bank; **256 B** Courtesy of Powercise International Corporation; **257** David M. Grossman; **259** Ted Cordingley; **262** Ted Cordingley; **263** Miguel/The Image Bank; **267** Bill Bachman/Photo Researchers; **275** James Whitmer; **276** Janeart Ltd./The Image Bank; **279** Lester V. Bergman Associates; **281** Bob McKeever/Tom Stack & Associates; **285** SIU/Science Source/Photo Researchers; **289** Janet S. Mendes/The Picture Cube; **291 T** Omnikron/Science Source/Photo Researchers; **291 M** Bill Lonacone/Photo Researchers; **291 B** Bill Lonacone/Photo Researchers; **292** Russ Kinne/Comstock; **293** Frank Varney; **295** Ted Cordingley; **298** David N. Hamilton/The Image Bank; **299** Michael Heron; **300** Julie Houck/Stock Boston; **302** David Phillips/Visuals Unlimited; **305** Petit Format/Nestle/Science Source/Photo Researchers; **306 T** Jose Carrillo; **306 B** Edward Lenau/Photo Researchers; **308** Bill Gallery/Stock Boston; **309** William Thompson; **311** Erika Stone; **312** Herb Snitzer/Stock Boston; **313 T** Bill Bachman/Photo Researchers; **313 B** Erika Stone; **314** M. W. Peterson/The Image Bank; **315** Gabor Demjen/Stock Boston; **316 T** Michael Heron; **316 B** Gregory K. Scott/Photo Researchers; **317** Bob Daemmrich/Stock Boston; **319** Jose Carrillo; **322** Mieke Maas/The Image Bank; **323** Mieke Mass/The Image Bank; **327** Walter Bibikow/The Image Bank; **328** Sobel/Klonsky/The Image Bank; **329** Deon Klumpp/The Image Bank; **332** Billy E. Barnes/Stock Boston; **333 T** Bob Daemmrich/Stock Boston; **333 M** Ellis Herwig/The Picture Cube; **333 B** Gio Barto/The Image Bank; **334** Janeart Ltd./The Image Bank; **335** Bob Daemmrich; **336** Janeart Ltd./The Image Bank; **337** Joe Devenney/The Image Bank; **338** Gobel Klonsky/The Image Bank; **339** Michael Heron; **343** Herb Snitzer/Stock Boston; **347** Scott Goldsmith/Black Star; **348** Bob Daemmrich; **349 T** Bill Bachman/Photo Researchers; **349 B** Jose Carrillo; **350** Diane Graham-Henry/Click/Chicago; **351** Ted Cordingley; **352** Heg Robinson/Stock Boston; **353** Suzanne L. Murphy/Click/Chicago; **355** William Thompson; **357 T** Ray Ellis/Photo Researchers; **358** Walter Hodges/Click/Chicago; **360** William Thompson; **361** James Whitmer; **365** Richard Hutchings/Photo Researchers; **371 T** Cheryl McNee/Click/Chicago; **371 B** Don & Pat Valenti/Tom Stack & Associates; **372 T** CNRI/Science Photo Library/Photo Researchers; **372 M** CNRI/Science Photo Library/Photo Researchers; **372 B** CNRI/Science Photo Library/Photo Researchers; **372 BR** K.G. Murti/Visuals Unlimited; **378** David Dempster/Photosynthesis; **380** Martin M. Rotker/Taurus Photos; **381** William Thompson; **382** Jacques Jangoux/Peter Arnold, Inc.; **384** Stacy Pick/Stock Boston; **385** Jose Carrillo; **387** Bob Daemmrich; **392** Susan Van Etten; **393** Peter Pearson/Click/Chicago; **394** William Thompson; **395 T** CNRI/Science Source/Photo Researchers; **395 TM** CDC/Science Source/Photo Researchers; **395 BM** CNRI/Science Source/Photo Researchers; **395 B** M. Abbey Photos/Science Source/Photo Researchers; **396 R** Center for Prevention Services; **396 L** Custom Medical Stock Photos; **397** St. Bartholomew's Hospital/Science Source/Photo Researchers; **398** Science Source/Photo Researchers; **400 R** Bob Daemmrich/Stock Boston; **400 L** Lennart Nilsson/Boehringer Ingelheim International, GmbH; **404** Jan Halaska/Photo Researchers; **405** Glenn Kulbako/The Picture Cube; **407** Ted Cordingley; **409** Bob Daemmrich; **414** Don Smetzer/Click/Chicago; **416** Bob Daemmrich; **417** Custom Medical Stock Photo; **420 T** R. Rossman/Custom Medical Stock Photo; **420 B** Stock Imagery; **421** James Whitmer; **422** Bob Hahn/Taurus Photos; **424** Jon Riley/Click/Chicago; **427** Lynn Johnson/Black Star; **429** Dick Traum, Achilles Track Club, Photo by Leszek Sibilski; **431 B** Ted Cordingley; **433** Bob Daemmrich; **438** John Anderson/Click/Chicago; **440** Mary L. Baer/Tom Stack & Associates; **441** Williams Mears/Click/Chicago; **442** G. L. Chryslin/The Image Bank; **443** Bob Daemmrich; **444** Courtesy of Psychemedic Corp.; **445** Erika Stone/Photo Researchers; **446** Peter LeGrand/Click/Chicago; **447** Mieke Maas/The Image Bank; **448** Ted Cordingley/Courtesy Frahers Apothecary; **449** Charles Marden Fitch/Taurus Photos; **450** Ted Cordingley/Courtesy Frahers Apothecary; **451** Dailey & Associates Advertising; **452** Dennis Stock/Magnum Photos; **453** Schleikorn/Custom Medical Stock Photo; **454 T** Jim Pickerell/Click/Chicago; **454 B** Jeff Jacobson/Archive; **457** Herman Kokojan/Black Star; **458** Bob Daemmrich; **459** Loren Santow/Click/Chicago; **463** Bob Daemmrich; **467** Michael Stuckey/Comstock; **469** Ted Cordingley; **470** Ted Cordingley; **472** Ted Cordingley; **476** A. Guberman/Photo Researchers; **477** Dan McCoy/Rainbow; **478** Guardian Technologies, Inc.; **479** Bob Daemmrich; **480** James Whitmer; **481** Bob Daemmrich; **483** Bob Daemmrich/Stock Boston; **487** Ted Cordingley; **491** Billy E. Barnes/Click/Chicago; **492** Courtesy of American Cancer Society; **495** Michael Gabridge/Visuals Unlimited; **497 T** Bob Daemmrich; **497 B** Ted Cordingley; **498** Bob Daemmrich; **500** Courtesy of American Cancer Society; **502** Ted Cordingley; **504** Ted Cordingley; **506** Susan Van Etten/The Picture Cube; **507** Nancy Sheehan/The Picture Cube; **511** Ted Cordingley; **516** Charles Gupton/Stock Boston; **517** Bob Daemmrich; **518** David M. Doody/Tom Stack & Associates; **519** Judy Canty/Stock Boston; **520** Stan Ries/The Picture Cube; **522** Bob Daemmrich; **523 T** David Dempster/Photosynthesis; **523 BR** Owen Franken/Stock Boston; **523 BL** Peter Menzel/Stock Boston; **524 T** Daniel Brody/Stock Boston; **524 B** Bob Daemmrich; **525** Bob Daemmerich/Stock Boston; **526** Bob Daemmrich; **527 T** Gary Milburn/Tom Stack & Associates; **527 B** William Patterson/Tom Stack & Associates; **528** Steve Elmore/Tom Stack & Associates; **529** Dagmar Fabricious/Stock Boston; **530 T** David M. Doody/Tom Stack & Associates; **530 B1** David Conklin/The Picture Cube; **530 B2** J. D. Sloan/The Picture Cube; **530 B3** John Coletti/The Picture Cube; **530 B4** Greg Vaughn/Tom Stack & Associates; **531** Nancy Sheehan; **533** Peter Menzel/Stock Boston; **539** William Thompson; **540** Richard Pasley/Stock Boston; **544** Peter Bates/The Picture Cube; **545** Stacy Pick/Stock Boston; **549** Ted Cordingley; **551** North Wind Picture Archives; **553** Bob Daemmrich; **557 T** The Bettmann Archive; **557 B** R. B. Sanchez/The Stock Market of New York; **558** Bob Daemmrich; **559** Ulrike Welsch; **560** Blair Seitz/Photo Researchers; **561** Bob Daemmrich; **562** Bob Daemmrich; **563** Bob Daemmrich; **564** Center for Disease Control; **566** United Nations/Photo Distribution; **567** Carolyn Watson/Peace Corps; **571** Bob Daemmrich; **574** Tom Stack/Tom Stack & Associates; **575** Tom Stack/Tom Stack & Associates; **579** Ted Cordingley; **580** Bob Daemmrich; **583 R** Richard Hutchings/Photo Researchers; **583 L** Hank Morgan/Rainbow; **586** David Lissy/Click/Chicago; **587 R** Ted Cordingley; **587 L** Coco McCoy/Rainbow; **591** Ted Cordingley; **593** Jim Pickerell/Click/Chicago; **595** Ted Cordingley; **599 T** Bob Daemmrich; **599 B** Bob Daemmrich; **600** Bob Daemmrich; **602** Zuhair Kareem/Johns Hopkins Clayton Heart Center; **606** Ted Cordingley; **607 TR** Perry D. Slocum/Earth Scenes; **607 TM** Spencer Grant/The Picture Cube; **607 TL** Gil Fahey/The Picture Cube; **610** Tom Stack & Associates; **617 T** David Stoecklein/The Stock Market of New York; **617 B1, B2, B4** Z. Leszczynski/Animals Animals; **617 B3** Joe McDonald/Animals Animals; **618 T** Raymond A. Mendez/Animals Animals; **618 M** Ann Moreton; **618 B** John Cancalosi/Tom Stack & Associates; **619** William Means/Click/Chicago; **620** Robert Frerck/Odyssey Productions; **623** Frank Siteman/The Picture Cube.